D1154269

INTERSCIENCE MONOGRAPHS ON CHEMISTRY

Interscience Monographs on Chemistry

INORGANIC CHEMISTRY SECTION

Edited by F. Albert Cotton and G. Wilkinson

GOODENOUGH	Magnetism and the Chemical Bond
COLTON	The Chemistry of Rhenium and Technetium
GRIFFITH	The Chemistry of the Rarer Platinum Metals

Other Volumes to follow

The Chemistry of THE RARER PLATINUM METALS (Os, Ru, Ir and Rh)

W. P. GRIFFITH
Imperial College, London

1967
INTERSCIENCE PUBLISHERS
a division of John Wiley & Sons
London New York Sydney

Library of Congress catalog card number: 67-25431

Made and printed in Great Britain by
William Clowes and Sons, Limited, London and Beccles

PREFACE

Over the past decade there has been a considerable and growing interest in the coordination chemistry of the four platinum group metals discussed in this book, particularly in respect of the molecular structures and the physical, chemical and catalytic properties of their complexes. Since there has been no other recent treatise on this topic it is hoped that this volume may stimulate further interest in a field in which there remains great scope for systematic investigation.

In order to keep the book to a reasonable size and for ease of reference, much material is presented in tabular form. Complexes are normally mentioned only when they have been isolated, and for their preparations reference is given to the simplest or most direct method. While it is not claimed that all known complexes of the metals are given in these pages it is hoped that there are few serious omissions. For coverage of the earlier literature considerable use has been made of the two standard texts on the subject, Gmelin's *Handbuch der Anorganischen Chemie* (8 Auflage, Vols. 63, 64, 66 and 67; Verlag Chemie, Berlin, 1939) and the less comprehensive *Nouveau Traité de Chemie Mineralé* (Ed. P. Pascal, Masson et Cie, Paris, 1958); all accessible references taken from these sources have been checked and an independent survey of the earlier literature has been carried out. Citation of the literature is selective in that where an earlier reference appears to have been superseded by a more recent one, only the latter is quoted. Literature coverage extends to the end of 1966 for most journals with a few later references; the patent literature has not been covered.

Classification of material in a book of this type is a difficult matter and any scheme is likely to meet with a number of objections. Here the metal oxidation state and ligand donor atom have been used as a basis (see p. 27) and the sequence osmium–ruthenium, iridium–rhodium follows from this, the greater diversity of oxidation states arising with the third row elements.

I would like to thank Dr. J. A. Osborn, Dr. A. J. Pöe and Professor G. Wilkinson for reading parts of the manuscript and for their constructive criticism and advice, and Miss M. Longden for her help in arranging the references. In particular I wish to express my sincere gratitude to Dr. D. F. Evans and Dr. L. Pratt who have given generously of their time to read the manuscripts and proofs; their help, advice and encouragement have been of the utmost value and have saved me from much error and inconsistency. For the remaining deficiencies I alone am responsible.

W. P. Griffith

ABBREVIATIONS

LIGANDS

Apart from those explained in the relevant parts of the text, the following common abbreviations of ligand names are used both in the text and for tabulated material.

acac	acetylacetone	en	ethylenediamine
bipy	2,2′-bipyridyl	OAc	acetate
Cp	π-cyclopentadienyl	ox	oxalate
diars	*o*-phenylenebisdimethylarsine	phen	*o*-phenanthroline
dien	diethylenetriamine	py	pyridine
diphos	diphosphine*		
DMG	dimethylglyoximate	terpy	2,2′,2″-terpyridyl
EDTA	ethylenediamine tetraacetate		

PHYSICAL MEASUREMENTS

In the tables summarizing the preparation of certain of the complexes the following letters are used to indicate the more important physical measurements made on them.

D	dipole moment
el.	electronic absorption spectra
e.s.r.	electron spin resonance
i.r.	infra-red spectra
kin.	kinetics
mag.	magnetism
pol.	polarography
pot.	potentiometry
R	Raman spectra

* Normally $C_2H_4(PPh_2)_2$ unless otherwise stated

CONTENTS

1 THE METALS

DISCOVERY, NATURAL OCCURRENCE AND EXTRACTION

All four metals were discovered in the first half of the nineteenth century, as was palladium (platinum, however, has a much longer history).

Osmium

It was so named by its discoverer, Smithson Tennant (1761–1815), from the characteristic odour of its tetroxide (Greek *osme*—smell, odour). Tennant, who was for a short time Professor of Chemistry at the University of Cambridge, discovered the new element in 1803 and announced it in 1804. He had heated to red heat with soda the insoluble black residues which were left after the digestion of native platinum by aqua regia, and dissolved the resulting mass in water. The yellow filtrate, which the celebrated French chemist Vauquelin had previously suggested contained chromates, was acidified and the tetroxide distilled off. Tennant remarks that[24] '. . . the oxide . . . stains the skin of a dark colour, which cannot be effaced' and goes on to suggest that '. . . as the smell is one of its most distinguishing characters, I should on that account incline to call the metal *Osmium*'. In this latter connection it is of interest to note that Tennant had earlier proposed to call the element *ptène* (from *ptenos*—volatile) but was fortunately persuaded to abandon this idea.

Osmium is a rare and consequently expensive element, the current market price (1966) being about £145 an ounce. Its abundance in the upper part of the earth's crust has been estimated at 0·0004 p.p.m.[12], and it has also been detected (often in far larger proportions) in certain meteorites. In the terrestrial sources of the element it is always found in the presence of one or more of the other five platinum metals, and sometimes with gold. The most important single source is probably osmiridium, which is basically an alloy of osmium and iridium together with varying proportions of the other platinum metals: this is found chiefly in the Goodnews Bay area of Alaska and on the Witwatersrand gold reef. The elemental osmium content of the mineral varies widely—it may be as little as 1% in some Russian ores, 2% from Colombian sources, while one sample from California was reported to have an osmium content of 30%. Another important but very rare source is laurite, (Os, Ru)S_2, found principally in parts of Borneo and the Transvaal—the content of osmium here is normally of the order of 3%. Other low-grade sources include the platinum deposits found in the Urals, in Colombia and Ethiopia.

The modern method for extracting the element does not differ greatly from Tennant's original procedure. Platinum-bearing concentrates are extracted with aqua regia and the insoluble portion heated in an oxidizing flux such as sodium peroxide (osmiridium and laurite are treated directly with peroxide, the aqua regia step being omitted). The resulting mass is extracted with water; the insoluble fraction is treated for iridium and rhodium while the soluble portion contains perosmate and ruthenate ions, $[OsO_4(OH)_2]^{2-}$ and $[RuO_4]^{2-}$. The osmium may at this stage be removed by distillation with nitric acid which gives the tetroxide, or alcohol may be added to the alkaline solution, which precipitates the ruthenium as the hydrated dioxide and reduces the perosmate to the soluble violet potassium osmate, $K_2[OsO_2(OH)_4]$. The latter can then be precipitated by addition of concentrated potassium hydroxide solution (and then acidified to give the tetroxide), or treated with an alcohol–hydrochloric acid–ammonium chloride mixture to give ammonium hexachloroosmate (IV). The latter may be heated in an inert atmosphere in a graphite vessel to give the pure metal, which can also be got by reducing the tetroxide in hydrogen.

A simplified flow-sheet for the industrial separation of the four metals from platinum metal concentrates is given in Figure 1.1.

Ruthenium

This was the last of the six platinum elements to be discovered. In 1826 Gottfried Wilhelm Osann (1796–1866) examined with the help of Berzelius a sample of the residues remaining from the treatment of crude platinum from the Urals with aqua regia, and announced the discovery of three new elements which he called Pluranium, Ruthenium and Polinium[18] although Berzelius, the most powerful chemical critic of the time, did not associate himself with this announcement and would not accept the existence of the new elements. Osann's work was later taken up by Karl Karlovitch Klaus (1796–1864) who, like Osann, was at one time Professor of Chemistry at the University of Dorpat. As a result of his work he isolated, in 1844, the last new element of the platinum group, naming it Ruthenium, both in honour of his native Russia and of the pioneering work of Osann; this time Berzelius accepted the discovery. Klaus's procedure was to take the insoluble residues from the aqua regia treatment of platinum concentrates and ignite them with a potassium nitrate–potash mixture in a silver crucible. The melt was dissolved in water and then distilled with aqua regia to remove osmium as the tetroxide; on mixing the residue with ammonium chloride and heating the resulting ammonium hexachlororuthenate (IV) in an inert atmosphere the metal was isolated[13].

Ruthenium is as rare as osmium—its abundance in the earth's crust is probably near 0·0004 p.p.m.[12], and the main sources of the element are the same as for osmium—laurite (essentially ruthenium disulphide with some osmium disulphide), osmiridium and platinum

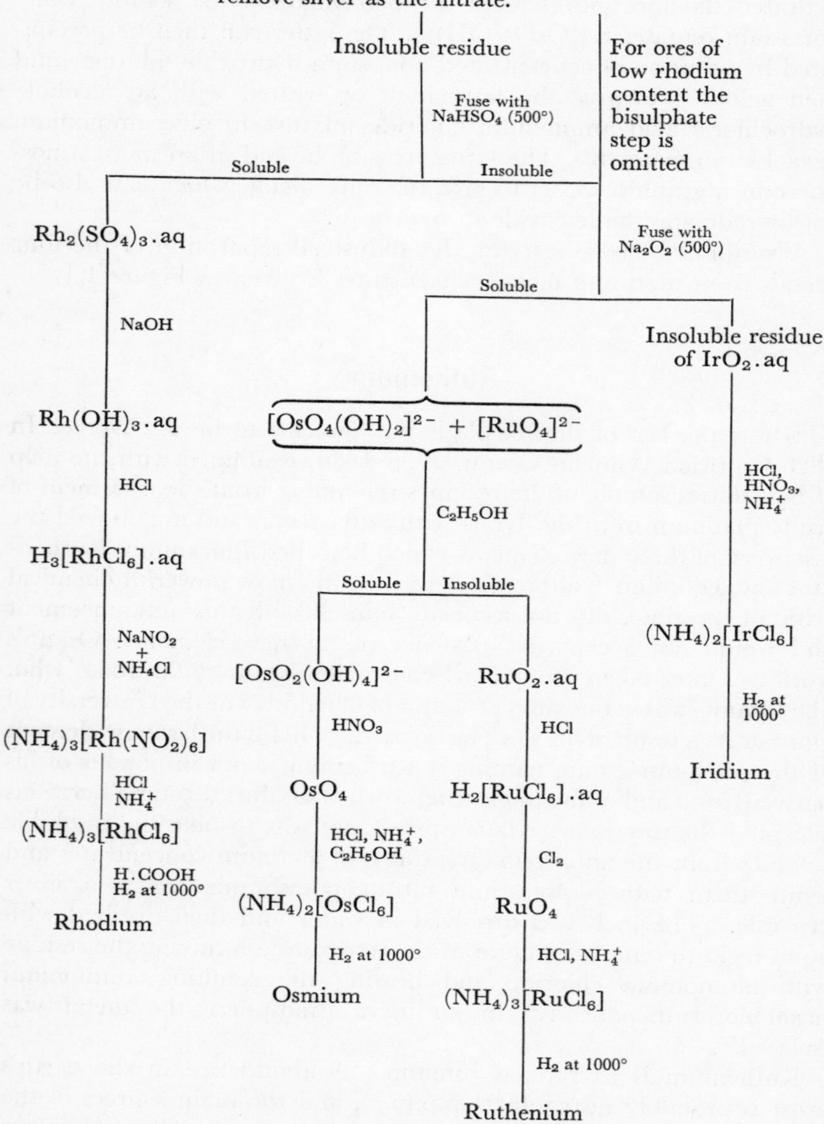

Figure 1.1 Extraction of the four metals from platinum ore concentrates: simplified overall scheme

concentrates; the proportion of ruthenium in the minerals is highly variable. The current cost of the metal is £22 per ounce.

Extraction follows exactly the same course as that described above for osmium. After extraction of the peroxide melt, alcohol is added to the soluble portion to precipitate hydrated ruthenium dioxide (osmium remains in solution as the osmate). The ruthenium dioxide may, however, carry down small amounts of osmium, so it is normal to dissolve it in hydrochloric acid, evaporate and boil with nitric acid to remove osmium tetroxide. The residue is then treated with chlorine to give the volatile ruthenium tetroxide (in some cases, particularly when the osmium content of the minerals is low, the alcohol precipitation stage may be omitted and the extract from peroxide fusion oxidized by chlorine directly). The ruthenium tetroxide is condensed into hydrochloric acid to give $(NH_4)_3[RuCl_6]$.aq which, when isolated, may be heated in an inert atmosphere to give the metal. For osmium-rich ores a final treatment with nitric acid may be required to remove trace quantities of osmium, in which case the product is $H_2[RuCl_5(NO)]$.aq, which on heating in an inert atmosphere also yields the metal.

Iridium

This was isolated by Smithson Tennant in 1803 and the discovery was announced together with that of osmium[24]. It was named after the Greek word *iris*—rainbow; in his original paper Tennant says that 'I should incline to call this metal *Iridium*, from the striking variety of colours which it gives, while dissolving in marine acid'. He made iridium by heating the black powder remaining from the aqua regia treatment of platinum concentrates with soda to a red heat, dissolving the mass in water and then treating the black residue with hydrochloric acid (marine acid). This gave a blue solution which became red on heating and deposited red crystals, and these on heating in an inert atmosphere gave the new metal.

Iridium has an abundance in the earth's crust of about 0·0004 p.p.m.[12]. The chief ore is native osmiridium which, as already mentioned, is found in Alaska and parts of South Africa (content varying from 25 to 75% of iridium). It is also found as an alloy with platinum in parts of Brazil and Burma (up to 75% iridium), and iridium-bearing ores have been exploited in the Caucasus, Tasmania and Siberia. The extraction process from platinum concentrates proceeds as for the other platinum metals: after aqua regia treatment the insoluble portion (which contains rhodium, iridium, some ruthenium and osmium and often a little silver) is smelted with lead carbonate and treated with nitric acid, which removes the silver as the nitrate. The insoluble residue is fused with sodium bisulphate (osmiridium ores may be directly treated with bisulphate) to remove rhodium as a water-soluble sulphate, and the residue fused with sodium peroxide. The resulting mass is extracted with water and the solution treated to extract osmium and ruthenium, as already described, while the residue, consisting mainly of hydrated iridium dioxide, is treated with aqua regia and ammonium chloride to give ammonium hexachloroiridate (IV). This, after recrystallization, can be reduced to the metal. The current price of the metal is £70 per ounce.

Rhodium

This was discovered by William Hyde Wollaston (1766–1828) (probably the most colourful character in the long history of platinum metal chemistry) at almost the same time (1803) as Tennant's discovery of osmium and iridium. He named the new element rhodium (Greek *rhodos*—a rose) 'from the rose colour of a dilute solution of the salts containing it'[26]. Crude platinum concentrates were dissolved in aqua regia, neutralized with sodium hydroxide and treated with ammonium chloride and mercuric cyanide to remove platinum and palladium. Acidification of the filtrate after evaporation and alcohol washing gave the rose-red salt $Na_3[RhCl_6]$, which Wollaston reduced with hydrogen. He subsequently succeeded in making a button of the pure metal.

The abundance of rhodium in the earth's crust has been assessed at 0·0004 p.p.m.[12]. It is usually found together with other platinum metals and often with nickel and copper (an important source is the copper–nickel deposits at Sudbury, Ontario, the rhodium content being about 0·1%). Other sources include the gold-bearing ores of Brazil and Colombia (1 to 3%), some osmiridium ores from Ceylon (up to 11%), and there are small quantities in the platinum deposits from the Urals, Borneo, Australia and the Transvaal. The cost per ounce of the metal is at present £72.

The extraction procedure follows that detailed above for iridium. After bisulphate fusion of the fraction of the platinum concentrates insoluble in aqua regia, the resulting mass is extracted with water and the solution, which contains rhodium sulphate, is treated with sodium hydroxide to precipitate hydrated rhodium sesquioxide. This, after purification, is then dissolved in an ammonium chloride–hydrochloric acid mixture to give ammonium hexachlororhodate (III) which can be directly reduced to the metal.

PHYSICAL PROPERTIES

These are summarized in Table 1.1, and the isotopic properties in Appendix I. The specific gravities of osmium and iridium are worth special mention here; it was for a long time believed that osmium was the densest of all the elements, but the most accurate data available (Table 1.1) indicate that iridium is very slightly denser: these values are based on x-ray determinations of the lattice parameters for the metals and are thus likely to be more accurate than values obtained by bulk specific-gravity determinations. All the metals are silvery white in colour, although osmium has a slightly blue tinge.

CHEMICAL PROPERTIES

Osmium

The ease of attack by oxygen depends very much on the state of the metal: in powder form it is stated to be oxidizable at room temperatures, and indeed finely divided osmium does carry a very faint but unmistakable odour of the tetroxide; in bulk form, however, it does not oxidize in air below 400°. The product of oxidation is the tetroxide although there is some evidence for formation of the dioxide as a surface film. The powdered metal will also absorb substantial quantities of hydrogen. It is attacked by fluorine at about 100° to give a mixture of fluorides and is also attacked by chlorine at this temperature. It is barely affected by aqua regia, oxidizing acids or hydrochloric and sulphuric acids, but is dissolved by molten alkalis and oxidizing fluxes.

Ruthenium

This is more resistant to oxygen than is osmium, but less so than iridium and rhodium, and a rapid reaction does not set in below 600°; there is evidence for the formation of a protective film of the dioxide. The metal is insoluble in all acids including aqua regia (but if potassium chlorate is added to the latter it will explosively oxidize the metal). It is attacked by chlorine and also by fluorine above 300° to give mixtures of the halides. It does not react directly with sulphur but will do so with arsenic, silicon, phosphorus and boron at high temperatures. Like osmium, it is dissolved by molten alkalis and by oxidizing fluxes.

Iridium

It is attacked by oxygen at red heat to give the dioxide, although this forms a surface film which protects the metal in the massive state from further oxidation until much higher temperatures are reached. It is also attacked by the four halogens, although not below red heat. It is unaffected by all acids (including aqua regia) and is only slightly attacked by non-oxidizing molten alkalis, and for this reason it has sometimes been used in place of platinum for making crucibles and other apparatus.

Rhodium

This is somewhat more resistant to aerial oxidation at red heat than iridium, and under similar conditions its reactions with the halogens are slower (it is particularly resistant to fluorine). It is insoluble in all acids, including aqua regia, but differs from iridium in that it may be dissolved in a potassium bisulphate melt, a property utilized in its commercial extraction. A curious property of rhodium–zinc alloys (also for zinc alloys with iridium and platinum but not for those with osmium or palladium) is that the powder remaining after acid extraction of the zinc from the alloy is explosive (a fact first noted by Bunsen); this is possibly due to the presence of occluded hydrogen [7].

CATALYTIC PROPERTIES[5]

In general the price of these four platinum metals limits their commercial application as heterogeneous catalysts, and furthermore there is little evidence that they are more effective in this respect than platinum or palladium. Osmium is on the whole a rather more powerful catalyst than ruthenium for the oxidation of alcohols and aldehydes to carboxylic acids, and for the hydrogenation of acetylenes, olefins, ketones and heterocyclic systems. Iridium and rhodium have similar catalytic powers—in particular rhodium has been used in hydrogenation reactions such as the conversion of benzene to cyclohexane and also for the dehydrogenation of alcohols to aldehydes. The homogeneous catalyses by compounds of these metals is dealt with in Chapters 4 and 6.

INDUSTRIAL APPLICATIONS OF THE METALS[16] AND THEIR COMPOUNDS

Osmium and ruthenium metals are little used industrially owing chiefly to their expense and also to the very considerable difficulty of working the metals, although it has become easier to do so with the use of modern techniques of rolling and forging. Iridium and rhodium are less costlythan osmium; now that modern electrodeposition processes are available they are often used for plating jewellery. The great hardness of osmium and iridium has led to their use (usually as osmiridium) for the tips of pen nibs and, occasionally, for gramophone record styli and the bearings of clocks and watches. Iridium and ruthenium are sometimes used in alloy with platinum for porcelain dental restorations. The extreme resistance to chemical attack has led to iridium being preferred over platinum for certain specialized pieces of scientific apparatus, and rhodium has recently found application for furnace windings, anodes for electrochemical processes and especially for thermocouples.

In the past osmium has been used in alloy in electric light filaments (hence the trade-name 'Osram') and for the detection of speeds of explosion limits in gelignite. Iridium was used as its platinum alloy (with an iridium content of up to 20%) for coinage in Russia from 1828 until its withdrawal from this purpose in 1845; and both iridium and rhodium have been used to provide a durable black colour for porcelain designs.

The compounds of these metals are little used in industry, although it is quite possible that they have a considerable future for catalytic purposes. Osmium tetroxide solution is extensively used (as 'Osmic acid') as a staining reagent for microscopic examination of tissues, and both osmium and ruthenium tetroxides are used for organic oxidations (see pp. 66 and 147).

The modern industrial applications of ruthenium have been reviewed[4], and there are papers on the applications of all four metals[16]. Processes and applications for electrodeposition of ruthenium, iridium and rhodium have been listed in a recent paper[20].

ANALYTICAL CHEMISTRY

There are a number of reviews of the analytical chemistry of the platinum metals[3,6].

Osmium

It is usually determined by colorimetric procedures, the most common of which makes use of the osmium (III) hexathiourea complex; ruthenium interferes and should not be present to an extent greater than 10% of the osmium concentration[22]. If ruthenium is present in higher concentrations the osmium may be estimated colorimetrically as $(Ph_4As)_2[OsCl_6]$[17], but in general it is preferable to separate the two elements first by acid distillation. For the determination of very small quantities of osmium (down to 0·01γ) the catalysis by the tetroxide of the cerium (IV)–arsenic (III) reaction may be used[23]. Gravimetric methods include estimation as the metal after ignition of the hydrated dioxide in hydrogen[11], as the sulphide[14] and as the 1,2,3-benzotriazole complex, $Os(OH)_3(C_6H_4NHN_2)_3$[3,25]. Polarographic methods are not in general well developed for this element, but have been used for the higher oxidation states[8,15].

Ruthenium

This can also be colorimetrically estimated as a thiourea complex (osmium and palladium interfere, but none of the other platinum metals do so)[2]. Provided that osmium is not present in more than a ten-fold excess, ruthenium can be colorimetrically determined (5–15γ) as a 2,4-diphenylthiosemicarbazide complex[10]. In very small amounts (0·002 to 0·1γ) it can be determined by its catalytic effect as the tetroxide on the cerium (IV)–arsenic (III) reaction[14]. Gravimetric methods include estimation as the sulphide[14] or as the thionalide complex followed by reduction to the metal[3,21]. Polarographic methods are not highly developed for ruthenium—a method has recently been given for determination of the element after conversion to $[RuCl_6]^{2-}$. There is a book on the analytical chemistry of ruthenium[1].

Iridium

The most common colorimetric method uses the stannous chloride–hydrobromic acid procedure, but cannot be applied in the presence of rhodium, platinum or palladium[14]. Iridium may be determined gravimetrically by precipitation as the sulphide or the hydrated oxide[3], which are then reduced to the metal, and there is a volumetric procedure based on oxidation to the tetravalent state[14]. Spectrophotometric estimation as the hexachloroiridate (IV) ion has also been used[14].

Rhodium

The best colorimetric method is probably that with stannous chloride[14]. Gravimetric methods include sulphide and oxide precipitations with subsequent reduction to the metal[3,14].

Table 1.1 Physical properties of the metals[19]

Physical property	Osmium	Ruthenium	Iridium	Rhodium
Atomic number	76	44	77	45
Atomic weight	190·2	101·07	192·2	102·905
Melting point (°C)	3050 ± 30	2310 ± 20	2443	1960
Boiling point (°C)	5020 ± 100	4080 ± 100	4500	3700
Specific gravity (20°C)	22·61	12·45	22·65	12·41
Specific heat (cal/g °C at 0°C)	0·0309	0·0551	0·0307	0·0589
Lattice structure[a]	c.p.h.	c.p.h.	f.c.c.	f.c.c.
Lattice constants (Å at 20°C):				
a	2·7341	2·7056	3·8394	3·8031
c/a	1·5800	1·5820		
Vapour pressure (3000°C, mm, est.)	0·0195	4·1	0·541	5·17
Mass susceptibility χ_g (c.g.s. units) × 10^{-6}	+0·052	+0·427	+0·133	+0·9903
Thermal conductivity (0–100°C; J/cm sec °C)	0·87	1·05	1·48	1·50
Resistivity (microohm/cm, at 0°C)	8·12	6·71	4·71	4·33
Temperature coefficient of resistance (0–100°C)	0·0042	0·0042	0·0043	0·0046
Thermionic function A (A/cm °K)			170	100
Work function ϕ (V)			5·40	4·90
First ionization potential (eV)[9]	8·7	7·36	9·6	7·46
Second ionization potential (eV)	17	16·8		18·07

[a] c.p.h. = close-packed hexagonal, f.c.c. = face-centered cubic.

REFERENCES

1. Avtokratova, T. D., *Analytical Chemistry of Ruthenium*, Israel programme for Scientific Translators, Jerusalem (Oldbourne Press, London) (1963).
2. Ayres, G. H., and F. Young, *Z. Anal. Chem.*, **22**, 1277 (1950).
3. Beamish, F. E., *Talanta*, **12**, 789 (1965); **13**, 773 (1966); *Analytical Chemistry of the Noble Metals*, Pergamon Press, Oxford, 1966.
4. Betteridge, W., and D. W. Rees, *Metal Ind.* (*London*), (1960).
5. Bond, G. C., and P. B. Wells, *Adv. Catalysis*, **15**, 91 (1964).
6. Busev, A. I., and V. K. Akimov, *Talanta*, **11**, 1657 (1964).
7. Cohen, E., and T. Strengers, *Z. Physik. Chem.*, **61**, 698 (1907).
8. Crowell, W. R., J. Heyrovsky and D. W. Engelkmeier, *J. Am. Chem. Soc.*, **63**, 2888 (1941).
9. Dillard, J. G., and R. W. Kiser, *J. Phys. Chem.*, **69**, 3893 (1965).
10. Geilmann, W., and R. Neeb, *Z. Anal. Chem.*, **152**, 96 (1956).
11. Gilchrist, R., *Bur. Stand. J. Res.*, **6**, 421 (1931).
12. Goldschmidt, V. M., *Geochemistry*, Oxford University Press, Oxford (1954).
13. Klaus, K. K., *J. Pharm. Chim.*, **8** (3), 381 (1845).
14. Kolthoff, I. M., and P. J. Elving, *Treatise on Analytical Chemistry*, **8** (II), Interscience, New York (1963).
15. Meites, L., *J. Am. Chem. Soc.*, **79**, 4931 (1957); **83**, 4706 (1961) (with R. E. Cover).
16. Mond Nickel Co. publications on Ruthenium, Iridium and Rhodium and Refining of Platinum metals.
17. Neeb, R., *Z. Anal. Chem.*, **54**, 23 (1957).
18. Osann, G. W., *Phil. Mag.*, **2**, 391 (1827).
19. *Platinum Metals Rev.*, **8**, 60 (1964); *Tech. Bull.* (Engelhard Industries Ltd.), **1965**, 61.
20. Reid, F. H., *Metal Finishing J.* (*London*) (1963).
21. Rogers, W. J., F. E. Beamish and D. S. Russell, *Ind. Eng. Chem.*, **12**, 561 (1940).
22. Sandell, E. B., *Colorimetric Methods for Traces of Metals*, Interscience, New York (1963).
23. Sauerbrann, R. D., and E. B. Sandell, *Microchim. Acta*, (**1953**), 22.
24. Smithson Tennant, *Phil. Trans.*, **94**, 411 (1804); *Nicholson's Journal of the Arts and Natural Philosophy*, **10**, 24 (1805).
25. Wilson, R. F., and L. J. Baye, *Talanta*, **1**, 351 (1958).
26. Wollaston, W. H., *Phil. Trans.*, **94**, 419 (1804); *Nicholson's Journal of the Arts and Natural Philosophy*, **10**, 34 (1805).

2 GENERAL SURVEY

In this chapter the distinctive features of the chemistry of the four metals will be outlined. Firstly, the range of oxidation states and stereochemistries encountered in the metal complexes is considered, and also the reactivities of the complexes as indicated by the rather sparse kinetic data available. This is followed by a survey of the physical measurements which have been carried out, with some indication of the chemical information which can be derived from them, and finally there is a brief review of the principal ligands found to coordinate with the metals.

OXIDATION STATES

Osmium and ruthenium resemble each other in the wide range of oxidation states represented in their compounds (from (VIII) to (O) inclusive). For iridium and rhodium all the oxidation states from (VI) to (O) are found, and iridium also forms nitrosyl phosphine complexes in which the formal oxidation states are (−I) and (−II). The 'normal' oxidation state for each metal (i.e. that for which the greatest diversity of complexes is found) is (IV) for osmium and (III) for ruthenium, iridium and rhodium. The least common states are (VII), (I) and (O) for osmium and ruthenium and (VI), (V) and (II) for iridium and rhodium.

The role of certain ligands in stabilizing high or low oxidation states is well exemplified by these four metals. Small and electronegative ligands such as fluoride and oxide stabilize complexes of osmium and ruthenium (VIII) to (IV) and of iridium and rhodium (VI) to (IV); in the case of the oxide ligand, at least, this may be associated with its strong π-donor properties. The highest oxidation states of osmium and ruthenium (i.e. (VIII) and (VII)) are found only in oxy complexes, either with or without fluoride or hydroxide ligands, whereas unsubstituted fluoro complexes are found only for oxidation states of (VI) or lower (hexafluoro complexes are known for the (V) and (IV) states of all four elements and for ruthenium (III)). Conversely, efficient π-acceptor ligands such as cyanide, carbon monoxide and phosphines will stabilize low oxidation states such as osmium and ruthenium (II), (I) and (O) and iridium and rhodium (I) and (O). Finally, ligands which are good σ donors, but which have no marked π-donor or π-acceptor properties (such as water, ammonia and ethylenediamine), are often associated with the 'normal' oxidation states of (IV) for osmium and (III) for ruthenium, iridium and rhodium.

The tendency of third-row elements to exhibit oxidation states higher than their second-row analogues is shown by these metals: thus, osmium (VIII) complexes are more common than those of ruthenium (VIII), osmium (VI) than ruthenium (VI) and ruthenium (III) than osmium (III); similarly there are a number of iridium (IV) complexes, but far fewer of rhodium (IV). These differences are not so marked between the lower oxidation states.

Osmium (VI) and (IV), and to a lesser extent ruthenium (VI) and (IV), form bi- or trinuclear complexes involving linearly bound oxygen or nitrogen bridges. This is a special characteristic of these two elements which is not shared by iridium or rhodium (although a few trinuclear iridium species are known). It is probable that this difference of behaviour is associated with the ability of osmium and ruthenium to form high oxidation state complexes; since these metal atoms have few *d* electrons, they can accept electrons from the strong π-donor bridging ligands. A similar reason may be put forward for the formation of stable nitrido complexes by osmium (VIII), (VI) and (IV): the nitride group is a strong π donor and has so far been found only in complexes of a few metals in high oxidation states such as these. It is therefore likely that ruthenium will form nitrido complexes.

STEREOCHEMISTRIES

The great majority of the complexes of all four metals have octahedral, or approximately octahedral, coordination about the metal atom. The principal exceptions are stated in the following four sections.

Tetrahedral species

The only established examples are the tetroxides of osmium and ruthenium and the osmiamate, perruthenate and ruthenate ions. The tendency for unsubstituted oxy complexes to adopt four rather than six coordination may be partly due to a reluctance of the metal atom to accept an excessive negative charge from the π-donating ligands. Osmium tetroxide has a much greater tendency than ruthenium tetroxide to expand its coordination number to six by bonding two more ligands, as in $[OsO_4(OH)_2]^{2-}$ and $[OsO_4F_2]^{2-}$: this is in line with the general tendency of third-row elements to have coordination numbers higher than those of the second (it may be noted that there are no osmium analogues of $[RuO_4]^-$ or of $[RuO_4]^{2-}$).

'Square planar' species

These are found only amongst the d^8 complexes of iridium and rhodium, while few have yet been found for osmium or ruthenium, due presumably to the relative instability of the zero oxidation states of these elements*. All the complexes of iridium (I) and rhodium (I) are planar or (occasionally) pentacoordinated, there being no substantial evidence for octahedral coordination in the solid state. In solution, however, there is likely to be weak association between the metal and the solvent in the axial coordination positions, and such association is probably of importance in the catalytic reactions of these compounds. All the planar complexes of iridium and rhodium involve good π-acceptor ligands such as phosphines and arsines.

* It is probable that the recently reported bisthiobenzil complexes of osmium(II) and ruthenium(II) are square planar, and also the maleonitriledithiolate rhodium(II) anion.

Five-coordinate species

These are of more common occurrence than is often supposed, and there are a number of examples for all four metals. With the higher oxidation states they are rare, probably the only examples are the 1:1 adducts of osmium and ruthenium tetroxides with ammonia, pyridine, etc., and there is no definite evidence that these are truly pentacoordinate rather than polymeric (though the infrared spectrum of $OsO_4.NH_3$ indicates that this has a square pyramidal configuration). With the lower oxidation states, however, there are a number of authenticated examples with confirmatory x-ray data available in a few cases. In general it appears that d^6 and d^8 configurations favour the formation of five-coordinate species, this being particularly so with iridium and rhodium. X-ray measurements and dipole moment data suggest that the trigonal bipyramidal rather than the square pyramidal shape is favoured. In some instances at least the reason for formation of a five- rather than a six-coordinate complex seems to be steric; in $RuCl_2(PPh_3)_3$, one of the few established examples of a square pyramid with these metals, the sixth-coordination position is blocked by one of the phenyl groups.

Seven- and eight-coordinate species

The only established example for these metals is OsF_7, although it has been suggested that $[OsOCl_6]^{2-}$ and some of the deprotonated osmium ethylenediamine complexes are of this type. There is little doubt that seven- and perhaps eight-coordinate intermediates are involved during reactions catalysed by d^6 complexes of these metals, and during S_N2 substitution reactions.

REACTIVITIES OF THE COMPLEXES

The qualitative conclusion to be drawn from the rather limited kinetic data reviewed below is that complexes show an increased inertness to substitution in the order: third row > second row > first row. This is borne out particularly by recent studies of the aquation of chloro and of trisoxalato complexes of these metals. Activation energies for comparable substitution reactions are generally higher for third- than for second-row metals. For example for the aquation of $[MCl_6]^{3-}$ to $[MCl_5(H_2O)]^{2-}$ the activation energy is some 10 kcal/mole higher for iridium than for rhodium; part of this at least must be due to the higher ligand-field stabilization energy in the case of iridium.

KINETICS AND MECHANISM

Electron-transfer reactions

These may be classified as either involving an outer sphere activated complex in which there is little or no dislocation of the first coordination spheres of the reactants, or those involving a bridged activated complex. For these metals very few examples of the latter type have been studied.

Outer-sphere reactions

A number of fast electron-transfer reactions involving platinum metal complexes have been studied, notably those involving the tris-*o*-phenanthroline and bipyridyl complexes of trivalent and divalent osmium (p. 89) and ruthenium (p. 173), and also of hexahaloiridates (IV) (p. 273) and hexachlororhodates (IV) (p. 318). All the complex ions in these reactions undergo substitution much less rapidly than electron transfer, which is thought to take place across the intact first coordination shells. The rates of electron transfer can be very high when, as with these complexes, the electron 'conductivity' of the first coordination shells of both reactants is good. Recent technical advances have made it possible to determine the rates of these reactions or at least the lower limits of the rates. For example the temperature-jump relaxation method has been used to study the $[Os\,bipy_3]^{2+}$–$[Mo(CN)_8]^{3-}$ reaction and the reactions of $[IrX_6]^{2-}$ (X = Cl, Br) with substituted iron (II) trisphenanthroline species. In these cases the observed rates are close to the diffusion controlled limits (i.e. the limits imposed simply by the size, charge and mobility of the ions). In general these results are in agreement with the predictions of the Marcus[31] theory.

The subject of such electron-transfer reactions has recently been reviewed[25,31,35].

Bridged activated complex mechanisms

It has been shown that the reaction of hexaaquo chromium (II) ion with $[M(NH_3)_5X]^{2+}$ (M = Ir, Rh; X = Cl, Br, I) probably proceeds via the formation of a bridged intermediate $[(NH_3)_5M^{III}XCr^{II}]$ followed by an electron transfer to give $[(NH_3)_5M^{II}XCr^{III}]$ which then dissociates.

Ligand-replacement reactions

These reactions are of two main types. Firstly there is substitution by the same ligand, as studied in isotope-exchange reactions—these are the simplest as no net free-energy change is involved. The second type involves substitution by a different ligand; studies of this type on the four metals have been mainly confined to aquation and water-replacement reactions.

Isotope-exchange reactions

A number of halide–halo complex exchange reactions have been studied in aqueous solutions: chloride exchange with $[OsCl_6]^{2-}$ (p. 55), $[IrCl_6]^{2-}$ and $[IrCl_6]^{3-}$ (p. 233) and $[RhCl_6]^{3-}$ (p. 322), and bromide exchange with $[OsBr_6]^{2-}$ (p. 55) and $[IrBr_6]^{2-}$ (p. 235). It has been shown that the exchanges with $[OsCl_6]^{2-}$ and $[RhCl_6]^{3-}$ proceed by a preliminary aquation rather than by direct bimolecular exchange, which is not surprising since there is a large excess of water over uncomplexed chloride ion; it is likely that this is also the case for the other exchange reactions. The exchange of bromide ion with $[M(NH_3)_5Br]^{2+}$ has also been studied (M = Ir, p. 259, and M = Rh, p. 348).

The exchange between ^{18}O labelled water and $[Rh(H_2O)_6]^{3+}$ is discussed in detail on p. 333: the rate of exchange is some hundreds of times slower than the corresponding exchange with $[Cr(H_2O)_6]^{3+}$. The rate of exchange of free oxalate ion with trivalent trisoxalato complexes decreases in the order:

$$\text{Mn} \sim \text{V} \sim \text{Fe} > \text{Ru} \sim \text{Cr} > \text{Co} > \text{Rh} > \text{Ir}$$

as expected from the ligand-field stabilization energies involved (p. 158).

Aquation reactions

The aquation reactions of $[OsCl_6]^{2-}$ (p. 54), $[IrCl_6]^{2-}$ (p. 233), $[IrCl_6]^{3-}$ (p. 242), $[RuCl_6]^{3-}$ (p. 140) and $[RhCl_6]^{3-}$ (p. 322) have been studied, as have the reverse water-replacement ('anation') reactions. For the aquo–chloro systems of trivalent ruthenium, iridium and rhodium it has been observed that the lability of coordinated chloride to substitution increases sharply as the number of coordinated chloride groups increases; it has been suggested that this may be a ligand-field effect (chloride has a smaller ligand-field splitting than water) or a polarizability effect (p. 140). For these three systems the rate of ligand substitution decreases in the sequence: ruthenium > rhodium >

iridium. The aquation of $[OsCl_6]^{2-}$ is 20 times slower than that for $[IrCl_6]^{2-}$ and 4,000 times slower than that for $[IrCl_6]^{3-}$ under comparable conditions.

The aquation of $[Rh\,ox_3]^{3-}$ has been studied and the results compared with those obtained for the corresponding chromium (III) complex (p. 338).

The *trans* effect

So far, *trans*- effect studies in this group have been made only on octahedral rhodium (III) complexes. For the *trans*-dihalogeno bis-ethylenediamine complexes thermodynamic studies suggest that the weakening effect of the halides on the bonds *trans* to them decreases in the series: I > Br > Cl, a conclusion which is supported by parallel kinetic studies (p. 357).

Catalysis of homogeneous hydrogenations

These important reactions are considered separately at the end of Chapters 4 and 6.

PHYSICAL MEASUREMENTS ON COMPLEXES OF THE METALS

Magnetic properties

The magnetic properties of second- and third-row transition-metal complexes have not been investigated as extensively as those of the first-row elements. As Table 2.1 shows, the observed magnetic moments for the complexes of these four elements are not a reliable guide to their oxidation states and the moments are often less than the 'spin only' values calculated from the number of unpaired electrons per metal atom. The main factors responsible for the magnetic behaviour of these elements are:

(a) Ligand-field splittings are larger than those for first-row elements (some 50% greater, in comparable compounds, for 4*d* and 70% greater for 5*d* than for 3*d*). As a result all the complexes of these metals are of the low-spin type—a possible exception is the group of ruthenium (III)–(II) binuclear carboxylates (p. 157).

(b) Spin–orbit coupling constants are very large since they are a function of the fourth power of the effective nuclear charge of the metal ion (cf. Table 2.2). The Russell–Saunders coupling scheme breaks down and it becomes necessary to use intermediate coupling schemes. When the spin–orbit coupling constant is substantially greater than kT (which is about 200 cm^{-1} at room temperatures) the magnetic moment may drop well below the 'spin-only' values.

(c) There is a decrease in interelectronic (Coulombic) repulsions in the second and third rows due to the greater extension of d orbitals.

(d) Antiferromagnetic exchange effects, effects arising from lowering of symmetry, and the delocalization of 'metal' electrons on to the ligands are more important for second- and third-row than for first-row elements.

The references for magnetic measurements on octahedral complexes of these metals are summarized in Table 2.8 at the end of this chapter; all of the measurements quoted were made over a temperature range, normally 80–300°K (the only studies so far reported of measurements at lower temperatures are for salts of $[IrCl_6]^{2-}$ and for ruthenium trichloride). Theoretical interpretations of results or predictions of magnetic behaviour for second- and third-row elements have been given for t_{2g}^1 and t_{2g}^5 [16], t_{2g}^2 and t_{2g}^4 [14,22] and t_{2g}^3 [15]. Comprehensive reviews on transition-metal magnetochemistry are available[16].

Electron spin resonance (e.s.r.) spectra

Complexes which have been studied include salts of $[IrCl_6]^{2-}$, $[IrBr_6]^{2-}$ and $[Ru(NH_3)_6]Cl_3$. For the iridium complexes resolved hyperfine splittings were observed which were ascribed to interactions between the unpaired electron and the magnetic nuclei of the ligands. In these complexes it appears that the unpaired 'iridium' electron spends some 30% of its time on the six ligands.

E.s.r. spectra have been used to estimate the extent and occurrence of antiferromagnetic exchange in salts of $[IrCl_6]^{2-}$ (p. 236).

Nuclear magnetic resonance (n.m.r.) spectra[14a,29a]

Although some of the isotopic nuclei listed in Table 2.3 have been detected by n.m.r. techniques, comparative chemical shifts of the nuclei in complexes of the metals have not yet been studied. One reason for this is that a number of them have very small nuclear magnetic moments (in particular ^{103}Rh), and consequently even when their abundance is high their n.m.r. signals are weak. In addition some of the nuclei have large electric quadrupole moments which will often lead to broadening of the lines.

In the case of the ^{103}Rh nucleus, which is 100% abundant and has a spin of $\frac{1}{2}$, it has been possible to observe the doublet splitting produced by this nucleus in the n.m.r. lines of magnetic nuclei (particularly protons) in the ligands in rhodium complexes. Apart from ^{187}Os the other nuclei listed in Table 2.3 would not generally be expected to give rise to such splittings, since they also have electric quadrupole moments which lead to an averaging out of the splittings through the mechanism of quadrupole relaxation.

Valuable structural information has, however, been derived from the proton and (to a lesser extent) the fluorine magnetic resonance spectra of platinum metal complexes. In particular the presence of diamagnetic hydrido complexes, which are fairly common in this group of metals, has often been detected or confirmed by the observation of the characteristic highly shielded proton signal. It has recently been shown that in phosphine hydride complexes the splitting of the hydride proton resonance by the ^{31}P nucleus is about 10–20 c/s when the phosphine is *cis* to the hydride and about 100–150 c/s when it is *trans*[10]. The n.m.r. technique has also been valuable for the study of organometallic complexes.

Nuclear quadrupole resonance (n.q.r) spectra[26c]

Although n.q.r. spectra of halide nuclei have been observed in diamagnetic halides of several metals, few measurements have been made on the present group of complexes. However, n.q.r. signals of chlorine in $K_2[PtCl_6]$ (diamagnetic) and also on the paramagnetic salts $K_2[OsCl_6]$ and $K_2[IrCl_6]$ have been made at liquid-nitrogen temperatures. From the large differences observed in the resonances of the three complexes it was deduced that π bonding in the metal–chlorine bonds decreases in the order: Os > Ir > Pt, although this conclusion depended on a number of assumptions concerning the *s* and *p* character of the orbitals involved (p. 54).

Some of the metal nuclei (Table 2.3) have large electric quadrupole moments but their n.q.r. absorptions have not yet been observed;

however, this may become an important application of the technique since the n.q.r. of the ^{59}Co nucleus has recently been observed in the $[Co\ en_2Cl_2]^+$ ion.

The Mössbauer effect[18]

Although this was first observed for ^{191}Ir nuclei with ^{191}Os as the radiation source, no chemical applications of the effect with the four metals have yet been reported. The Mössbauer effect, which is concerned with the resonance fluorescence of recoilless γ radiation of the atomic nucleus, gives a measure of the energy difference between the ground and the first-excited states of the nucleus, and is capable in some cases of giving information on the nature of chemical bonding in the complexes.

Electronic spectra

These may be broadly classified into charge-transfer and ligand-field (*d–d*) spectra. For the platinum group complexes most of the transitions observed are the intense charge-transfer bands which often obscure the much weaker ligand-field transitions. When the latter are observed and assigned, however, it is possible to derive information on the magnitude of the ligand-field splitting in the complexes, the spin–orbit coupling constants and the Racah parameters, the latter providing a measure of interelectronic repulsions.

For this group of metals the most detailed studies have been on the hexahalide complexes, particularly of osmium and iridium, and on a number of ammines and amines of iridium and rhodium. A summary of the data available is given in Table 2.8.

Infrared and Raman spectra

These techniques provide a valuable means of obtaining information on the structures of species in the solid state and in solution, and may also give some idea of the strength of the metal–ligand bonds. Few Raman spectra of platinum group complexes have been measured because most of them have deep colours, which renders them unsuitable for study with conventional mercury arc sources. The advent of laser sources will, it is hoped, stimulate further research into this promising field.

The few reasonably comprehensive studies are summarized in Table 2.8 at the end of this chapter.

Dipole moments

Dipole moment determinations have proved to be of considerable value in platinum metal chemistry, although most of the work so far reported for these four metals relates to the phosphine, arsine or stibine complexes. Most of the dipole moment data on these complexes has been obtained by Chatt and coworkers, and their work on rhenium and platinum phosphine complexes is also relevant to this field[11]. The dipole moment data given in Table 2.4 demonstrate that it should normally be possible to distinguish between the geometrical isomers of the octahedral $MX_2(LR_3)_4$ and $MX_3(LR_3)_3$ type and between *cis* and *trans* square planar complexes; fortunately, in the systems listed in Table 2.4, there is little variation of the dipole moment with M, L or R.

It should in principle be possible to obtain data on the geometrical configuration of five-coordinate complexes from their dipole moments. This has apparently been demonstrated only once with these metals: it was suggested that $Rh(diphosphine)_2H$ is trigonal bipyramidal rather than square pyramidal on the basis of its low dipole moment of 4 D (p. 414).

Polarography

Because their reductions at the dropping electrode are almost always irreversible the polarographic technique has been little used for complexes of these metals. Nevertheless, the technique is a useful one because it affords a means of establishing which oxidation states of the metals are stabilized in various media. This has been particularly valuable in the case of osmium, where the existence of a number of unstable species in aqueous solutions of different pH has been demonstrated polarographically (p. 65), and there have been similar, rather more limited, studies with ruthenium (p. 151). There has been little systematic work on iridium, but there is a large and somewhat unreliable literature on the polarographic reduction of rhodium (III) complexes, where there has been considerable confusion as to whether the reduction process involves one, two or three electrons. Most of the difficulty, as has recently been pointed out (p. 322), is due to the fact that the solutions studied contained mixtures of species; since the reductions are irreversible, wrong values were assigned to the diffusion coefficients (D) and erroneous values obtained for n, the number of electrons involved per metal atom in the reduction process. Recent work on a range of solutions containing single well-characterized rhodium (III) species suggests that the cathodic process involves two electrons in most if not all such reductions. It is likely that in most cases the reduction products are rhodium (III) hydridic species rather than monovalent complexes, but this is a point which cannot easily be settled by conventional polarographic techniques. There is a recent review on the applications of the technique to the chemistry of transition metal complexes[36].

There has been little use of the associated techniques either of coulometry, which is particularly valuable for establishing the number of electrons involved in reductions of complexes for which the diffusion coefficients are not easily obtainable, or of chronopotentiometry, though the latter has been used in studies on osmocene and ruthenocene (cf. p. 97).

Bond-length data

Table 2.9 gives a summary of 'significant' bond lengths which have been obtained for complexes of the four metals. All data where the reported accuracy of bond lengths is better than $\pm 0{\cdot}02$ Å have been included; some other less accurate data are included where better information is not available. In each case fuller information on the results of the various structure analyses is given in the main text.

Two determinations deserve special comment. Firstly, the x-ray results on $RhH(CO)(PPh_3)_3$ (p. 389) give a value of $1{\cdot}60 \pm 0{\cdot}12$ Å for the rhodium–hydrogen bond length; this is significant because until recently it has not been possible to establish metal–hydrogen bond lengths in hydrides by x-ray methods, and other techniques such as broad-line proton magnetic resonance had suggested that such distances were abnormally short. This value, however, is that expected for a normal covalent bond (cf. also p. 389). Secondly, the neutron diffraction determination on $Na_2[Ru(NO)(OH)(NO_2)_4]$ (p. 175) has given very accurate bond lengths for the metal–nitrosyl (Ru—N = $1{\cdot}748 \pm 0{\cdot}003$ Å) and metal–nitro (Ru—N = $2{\cdot}079 \pm 0{\cdot}003$ Å) groups. These values demonstrate clearly the shortening of the metal–ligand bond due to the presence of back bonding to the nitrosyl group, for which good evidence has hitherto been lacking. Some difference in bond lengths is to be expected since the hybrid orbitals on nitrogen used in forming the σ bond will approximate to sp for the nitrosyl and sp^2 for the nitro groups, but this difference would not be of the magnitude observed here.

THE LIGANDS IN THE COMPLEXES

The groups of ligands are listed in this section in the order in which they are considered for each oxidation state in the text. The references given after the name of each ligand refer to the most comprehensive review available on the ligand—for the most part these are general reviews which do not deal solely with platinum metal complexes.

Classification

The ligands are arranged throughout this book according to the Periodic Group to which the *donor* atom belongs, and within each group the lighter atoms are listed first. In the few cases where a chelate ligand contains donor atoms from different groups it is classified under the highest group number.

Complexes containing donor ligand atoms from two or more groups are normally listed under the highest group number—e.g. oxyhalides under Group VII. There are a few exceptions, however—thus substituted ammines are listed under Group V irrespective of the substituting donor ligand, carbonyl halides under Group IV, nitrosyl halides under Group V, etc. This latter treatment has been adopted partly for brevity and because it is largely the presence of the ammine, carbonyl, nitrosyl, etc., ligands which dictate the properties of such complexes. Where ambiguities may arise cross references have been given.

Group VII donors

Halides; oxy, hydroxy and aquo halides[4,12,33,37]

These are summarized in Table 2.5a. The tendency of ruthenium (III) and rhodium (III) to form polynuclear halo complexes is remarkable and is not shared, apparently, by osmium or iridium. Aquo halo complexes are well established for tetravalent iridium and trivalent ruthenium, iridium and rhodium, but few hydroxy halo complexes are known. It is possible that the trihalides of these metals form 'clusters' of the type recently shown to exist for other transition metal halides.

There is no substantial evidence for the existence of di- or mono-halides of these metals in the solid state.

Group VI donors

Oxides and oxy complexes[8]

These are summarized in Table 2.5b. The tetroxides and dioxides of osmium and ruthenium have long been known, but the trioxides appear to exist only in the vapour phase. Both iridium and rhodium dioxides and sesquioxides exist; chemically iridium dioxide is more stable than the sesquioxide, the reverse holding for the rhodium compounds. There are unconvincing claims for other solid oxides of all four metals.

Layer lattice oxide complexes of osmium (VII), (VI) and (V), of tetravalent ruthenium, iridium and rhodium and of rhodium (III) have recently been investigated: in each case the metals are octahedrally coordinated. The only unsubstituted charged oxy complexes existing as discrete ions under normal conditions are $[RuO_4]^-$ and $[RuO_4]^{2-}$.

Aquo and hydroxy complexes; hydroxides

The established aquo complexes are $[Ru(H_2O)_6]^{4+}$, $[Ru(H_2O)_6]^{3+}$, $[Ru(H_2O)_6]^{2+}$ and $[Rh(H_2O)_6]^{3+}$, and there are no definite reports of any hexahydroxy species. There are a large number of aquo and hydroxy complexes substituted with halide or ammine groups.

The few hydroxides which have been reported are probably best regarded as hydrated oxides.

Acetylacetone complexes[13,14b]

In addition to neutral tris species which are known for all four metals there are a number of mixed ligand species with osmium and ruthenium (IV) and (III).

Carboxylic acid complexes

These are listed alphabetically in the text; there is a review available on oxalates only[26]. The only osmium carboxylates so far made all involve the 'osmyl' grouping—the absence of $[Os\,ox_3]^{3-}$ is particularly surprising, trisoxalates being known for the other three metals in the trivalent state. Ruthenium (III) acetates and formates are trimers, probably similar in structure to $[Cr_3O(OAc)_6]^+$, and a series of dimeric carboxylates $Ru_2(OCOR)_4Cl$ with anomalous magnetic properties have been made (p. 157). Rhodium acetates and formates are unusual in that they are binuclear and formally contain rhodium (II) with a metal–metal bond.

Nitrates, nitrato and nitrito complexes

The 'nitrates' of ruthenium (IV) and of trivalent iridium and rhodium may possibly contain some coordinated nitrate groups or simply the hexaaquo cations. Both nitrato and nitrito pentammines of iridium (III) and rhodium (III) have been studied; there is a series of nitrato nitrosyl ruthenium (II) complexes (p. 210).

Phosphates and sulphates

Iridium seems to form these more readily than rhodium. In no case has any compound been fully characterized.

Dimethyl sulphoxide complexes

These complexes are known for iridium and rhodium (III).

Sulphides, selenides and tellurides[29]

Disulphides are known for all four elements, and diselenides and ditellurides of osmium, ruthenium and iridium. Sesquisulphides of iridium and rhodium are known.

Sulphito[28] and sulphur dioxide complexes[28]

The former are numerous for these metals, but no structures have been determined. It has been particularly difficult to establish the oxidation state of the metal: claims have been made for complexes containing osmium (IV) and tri- and divalent osmium, ruthenium, iridium and rhodium, but with the latter two elements it is very unlikely that the divalent state is involved. Unfortunately, although infrared spectra of a number of the compounds have been obtained, it has so far been impossible to distinguish between the bewildering variety of bonding possibilities.

Complexes of **sulphur dioxide** are known for ruthenium (II), iridium (I) and rhodium (I).

Thiourea, selenourea and dithiocarbamato complexes[28]

Thiourea complexes are known for trivalent iridium and rhodium and for tetravalent osmium and ruthenium, although with the latter two the complexes are not fully characterized. Selenourea complexes of osmium (IV) and ruthenium (IV) probably exist in solution. The only dithiocarbamates so far reported are the tris species of trivalent ruthenium and rhodium, some nitrosyl dithiocarbamates of ruthenium and carbonyl dithiocarbamates of ruthenium and rhodium.

Thiocyanato complexes[28]

Hexathiocyanato species of iridium (III) and rhodium (III) contain metal–sulphur rather than metal–nitrogen bonds, whereas $[Ru(NO)(NCS)_5]^{2-}$ contains metal–nitrogen bonds. Besides this nitrosyl complex there are no other ruthenium thiocyanates, and there is no osmium complex.

Alkyl sulphide complexes[28]

These have been reported for trivalent ruthenium, iridium and rhodium.

Group V donors

Nitrido[24] and nitrogeno complexes

Nitrido complexes are known for osmium (VIII), (VI) and (IV) and are very stable, yet none has yet been reported for ruthenium; ruthenium (II) nitrogeno ammines have recently been made. For iridium apart from $[Ir_3N(SO_4)_9]^{10-}$ (in which it is believed that the metal atoms surround the nitrogen in a plane) there are some trivalent nitrogeno species.

Ammines and substituted ammines[24]

They are numerous for all four metals in the trivalent state; in addition there is $[Ru^{II}(NH_3)_6]Cl_2$ and a number of substituted ruthenium (II) ammines. There is some evidence for the transient existence of iridium (II) and rhodium (II) ammines during reduction of the trivalent species, and zerovalent osmium and iridium ammines have been claimed, though the latter might well be hydrides.

Saturated organic amine complexes[24]

Trisethylenediamine (en) complexes are known for trivalent osmium, iridium and rhodium and for divalent ruthenium; the absence of $[Ru\ en_3]^{3+}$ is surprising. There is no evidence for the existence of monodentate en groups in platinum group complexes. It has been claimed that certain complexes of osmium (VI), (V) and (IV) and also of trivalent iridium and rhodium contain bidentate ethylenediamine groups from which one or two amine protons have been removed. Crystal-structure analyses of these would be highly desirable.

Heterocyclic amines

The complexes reported are mainly those of pyridine, *o*-phenanthroline (phen)[7], 2,2′-bipyridyl[7] (bipy) and a few ter- and tetrapyridyl complexes. Trisphen and bipy complexes are known for all four metals in their trivalent states, and a wide range of mono- and bisphen and bipy complexes have recently been synthesized with osmium (IV), (III) and (II), ruthenium (III) and (II) and trivalent iridium and rhodium.

Nitro complexes

These complexes have long been known for trivalent iridium and rhodium: as well as substituted species, there are hexanitro compounds $[M(NO_2)_6]^{3-}$. Attempts to prepare the corresponding hexanitro complexes of osmium and ruthenium always lead to the nitrosyls $[M(NO)(OH)(NO_2)_4]^{2-}$ (in fact all ruthenium nitro complexes also contain the nitrosyl group with the exception of $Ru(CO)_2(NO_2)_2$).

Nitrosyl complexes[2,24,25a]

These are more numerous for ruthenium (II) than for any other element, and by comparison osmium (II) forms very few of these complexes; iridium forms phosphine nitrosyl species with a wide range of *formal* oxidation states and there are some rhodium (I) species. In all the complexes of this group so far prepared it is thought that the nitric oxide ligand functions as a three-electron donor; some of the iridium species may involve bridging nitrosyl groups. Dinitrosyls are not found with these metals and are in general rare due probably to the fact that the nitrosyl group is a very powerful π acceptor so that two groups might remove an excessive amount of charge from the metal atom.

Hydrazine complexes[3,24]

These complexes have been claimed for ruthenium and rhodium, but in no case was the complex properly characterized. Monodentate hydrazinium ($N_2H_5^+$) groups are present in $[Ir(N_2H_5)Cl_5]^-$ and $[Rh(N_2H_5)Cl_5]^-$.

Alkyl cyanide and dimethylglyoxime complexes

They are known only for trivalent iridium and rhodium.

Biguanide[34] and phthalocyanine[27] complexes

These are reported for osmium (VI) and for trivalent ruthenium, iridium and rhodium.

Phosphines, arsines and stibines[6,32]

These complexes and the hydrides derived from them[19,21] are of considerable importance for these four metals; they are summarized in Table 2.6. Although many more phosphines are known than arsines or stibines, this may be due in part to the availability of the ligands. There is no doubt that a number of similar hydrides are important as intermediates in catalysed homogeneous hydrogenation, hydroformylation and isomerization reactions.

Nitrosyl phosphines

They have so far been reported for ruthenium(II) and for iridium and rhodium in a variety of low oxidation states.

Phosphorus trihalide complexes

Phosphorus trichloride complexes are formed by iridium (III) only, but phosphorus trifluoride forms complexes with all four elements[26b].

Group IV donors

Cyanides and cyano complexes[9,23]

Tricyanides of ruthenium, iridium, and rhodium and a dicyanide of ruthenium are the only 'simple' cyanides. Hexacyano complexes of divalent osmium and ruthenium and of trivalent iridium and rhodium were made by Martius in 1861, and there is also evidence for the existence in solution of the powerfully oxidizing species $[M(CN)_6]^{3-}$ (M = Os, Ru).

The cyanide hydride $K_2[RhH(CN)_5H_2O]$ was recently isolated, and there is evidence for the existence of $[MH(CN)_5]^{3-}$ (M = Ir, Rh). The cyanide group is not as efficient a π acceptor as the isoelectronic carbonyl group, due probably to its negative charge, and very low oxidation state cyano complexes of these metals are rare.

The nitrosyl pentacyanide $[Ru(CN)_5NO]^{2-}$ is known, but not the osmium analogue.

Isocyanides [30]

These are known for ruthenium (II) and rhodium (I) only.

Carbonyl complexes [1]

These are known for all four elements in their zero oxidation states: $M(CO)_5$ and $M_3(CO)_{12}$ (M = Os, Ru), $[Ru(CO)]_n$, $[M(CO)_4]_2$ and $[M(CO)_3]_n$ (M = Ir, Rh) and $Rh_6(CO)_{16}$. Apart from $M_3(CO)_{12}$ and $Rh_6(CO)_{16}$ the structures of these complexes are unknown. An osmium(II)hexacarbonyl complex, $[Os(CO)_6]Cl_2$, has also been claimed. **Thiocarbonyls** of rhodium and ruthenium have recently been obtained. Few **carbonyl hydrides** have been isolated but there is some evidence for $Os(CO)_4H_2$, $Ir(CO)_4H$ and $Rh(CO)_4H$. **Carbonyl halides** are numerous for all four elements, and tables of them are given in the text.

Carbonyl phosphines, arsines and stibines [6,30a]

These complexes and their hydrides [19,21] are numerous and are listed in Table 2.7. Similar species are likely to be active as catalytic intermediates in homogeneous hydrogenation and hydroformylation reactions.

Alkyls and aryls [26a]

They have been made from osmium (II) and ruthenium (II) diphosphine complexes and are also known for tri- and monovalent iridium and rhodium; for the latter elements they may be intermediates in homogeneous hydrogenation and hydroformylation reactions. A vinyl complex of rhodium (III) has been made and also acyl and aroyl rhodium (III) complexes.

'Sandwich' and delocalized π systems [5a,17,38]

Many studies have been made on osmocene and ruthenocene, Cp_2M. Trivalent iridium and rhodium form biscyclopentadienyls, $[Cp_2M]^+$, and mesitylene complexes are known of rhodium (II) and rhodium (I).

Olefin complexes [5,17a]

There are few for osmium, although the stability of $OsCl_2(C_8H_{12})(PPh_3)_2$ suggests that a number of others could be made. Ruthenium

(II) forms complexes of the form $RuCl_2(diene)(PPh_3)_2$; diene complexes are numerous for iridium (I) and rhodium (I), and a few are known for the trivalent metals. It is noteworthy that almost all the olefin complexes of these metals involve chelating diolefins which seem to impart a special stability; however, $[Rh(C_2H_4)_2Cl]_2$ is also stable. **Fluoro olefin** complexes of iridium and rhodium have been made.

Acetylene complexes[5]

They have so far been reported only for rhodium (I), but there seems no reason why the other metals should not form them.

Allylic complexes[20]

These complexes are so far reported only for trivalent ruthenium and rhodium, and rhodium (I), but they may be involved as intermediates in the catalytic isomerization of olefins by iridium (III) and rhodium (III) species.

Stannous chloride complexes

For many years the colours which develop on addition of acidic solutions of stannous chloride to platinum metal chlorides have been used for the estimation of the metals. Recently it has been shown that these coloured compounds contain the coordinated $(SnCl_3)^-$ group in which tin is the donor atom; such complexes have now been isolated for ruthenium (II), iridium (III) and rhodium (I).

Hydride complexes[19,20]

These are dealt with in the text under the following headings; hydrido phosphine, arsine and stibine complexes (Group V) and hydrido carbonyl phosphine, arsine and stibine complexes (Group IV); examples of these are numerous for the four elements. In addition there exists a wide range of rhodium (III) monohydridic species with a variety of other ligands such as ammonia, ethylenediamine and pyridine, and these are discussed under the latter headings. Although carbonyl hydrides of the metals (not substituted by other ligands) probably exist, only those of ruthenium and osmium have been characterized.

Table 2.1 Magnetic moments at room temperatures of octahedral platinum metal complexes (BM) [a]

Configuration	Pt	Os	Ru	Ir	Rh
t_{2g}^1		1·4			
t_{2g}^2		0^b–1·5(a)	$2·9^b$		
t_{2g}^3		3·2–3·4(a)	3·5–3·6(a)	2·9(a)	
t_{2g}^4	$2·0^b$	1·3–1·7^c(c)	2·8–3·0(c)	1·3(c)	$2·9^b$(b)
t_{2g}^5	1·7	1·6^b–2·2(b)	1·6^b–2·2(b)	1·4–2·0^c(b)	1·7–2·0^c(b)
$t_{2g}^6e_g^1$				$1·3^b$	$1·3^b$

[a] Behaviour over temperature range 70–300°K:
(a) Susceptibility proportional to $1/T$: moment constant with temperature.
(b) Susceptibility increases as T decreases: moment drops substantially with temperature.
(c) Susceptibility approximately independent of temperature over this range.
[b] Distortion from octahedral symmetry likely for some of these complexes.
[c] Exchange effects likely to be operative.

Table 2.2 Free-ion single-electron spin–orbit coupling constants ζ_{nd} (cm^{-1}) [16]

Metal	Metal oxidation state						
	O	I	II	III	IV	V	VI
Fe	255[a]	345[a]	400[a]	460	515[a]	555[a]	665[a]
Ru	745[a]	900[a]	1000[a]	1180	1350	1500	1700
Os				3500	4000	4300	5000
Co	390[a]	455[a]	515[a]	580	650	715[a]	790[a]
Rh	940[a]	1060[a]	1220[a]	1360	1570	1730	1950
Ir					5000	5500	6000
Ni		605[a]	630[a]	715	790	865	950[a]
Pd		1420[a]	1460[a]	1640	1830	2000	2230

[a] From extrapolation of known values.

Table 2.3 Magnetic properties of platinum group nuclei [a]

Isotope	Natural abundance (%)	μ (magnetic moment in multiples of $eh/4\pi Mc$)	Spin I (in multiples of $h/2\pi$)	Electric quadrupole moment Q (in multiples of $e \times 10^{-24}$ cm^2)
^{99}Ru	12·72	−0·63	5/2	Not known
^{101}Ru	17·07	−0·69	5/2	Not known
^{103}Rh	100	−0·0879	1/2	—
^{187}Os	1·64	~0·12	1/2	—
^{189}Os	16·1	0·6506	3/2	2·0
^{191}Ir	37·3	0·16	3/2	~1·2
^{193}Ir	62·7	0·17	3/2	~1·0

[a] Only stable nuclei possessing magnetic moments are included.

Table 2.4 Selected values of dipole moments[11]

Complex[a]	Os	Ru	Ir	Rh	Mean dipoles (D)
1,2,6-$MX_3(LR_3)_3$ (X = Cl)		PEt_2Ph 6·9	PEt_3 6·85; PEt_2Ph 7·0; $AsEt_3$ 6·7	PEt_3 7·0; PEt_2Ph 7·3; $AsMe_2Ph$ 7·25	7·0
(X = Br)				(PPr^n_3): 7·6	
1,2,3-$MCl_3(LR_3)_3$	—	—	—	—	13·0[b]
trans-$MCl_3(LR_3)_3$		$(AsMe_2Ph)$: 1·15			1·1
cis-$M(CO)_2X_2(LR_3)_2$		PEt_3 4·4; PEt_2Ph 4·5; $AsEt_2Ph$ 4·0			4·0
trans-$M(CO)_2X_2(LR_3)_2$		PEt_3 0·6; PEt_2Ph 1·1			1
cis-MX_2D_2	8·3	9·8			10
trans-MX_2D_2		0·9			1
cis-$M(CO)Cl(LR_3)_2$	—	—	—	—	11[b]
trans-$M(CO)Cl(LR_3)_2$			PPh_3 3·9	PPh_3 3·1; $AsPh_3$ 3·2	3

[a] D = $C_2H_4(PPh_2)_2$, L = P or As.
[b] Value estimated or obtained from comparable compounds.

Table 2.5a Halide complexes and oxyhalides

Halide complexes and halides	Os	Ru	Ir	Rh
$M^{VIII}O_3X_2$; $[MO_3X_3]^-$	F			
$M^{VII}OX_5$; MX_7	F			
$M^{VI}X_6$	F	F	F	F
$[M^{VI}OX_4]_n$	F, Cl	F		
trans-$[M^{VI}O_2X_4]^{2-}$	Cl, Br	Cl		
$[M^VX_5]_n$, $[MX_6]^-$	F	F	F	F
$[M^{IV}X_4]_n$	F, Cl, Br	F, Cl	?Cl, Br, I?	
$[M^{IV}X_6]^{2-}$	F, Cl, Br, I	F, Cl, Br, I	F, Cl, Br, I	F, Cl
$[M^{IV}(OH)X_3]_n$	Cl, Br	Cl		
$[M^{III}X_3]_n$	Cl, Br, I	F, Cl, Br, I	F, Cl, Br, I	F, Cl, Br, I
$[M^{III}X_6]^{3-}$	Cl, Br, I	Cl, Br	Cl, Br	F, Cl, Br

Table 2.5b Oxides[a]

Oxides	Os	Ru	Ir	Rh
$M^{VIII}O_4$	s, g	s, g	—	—
$M^{VI}O_3$	s[b]	g	g	g
$M_2^VO_5$	s[b]	s[b]	—	—
$M^{IV}O_2$	s, g	s, g	s, g	s, g
$M_2^{III}O_3$	s[b]	s[b]	s	s
$M^{II}O$	s[b]	s[b]	g	g

[a] s means that the oxide is known in the solid state and g that it has been detected in the gas phase.
[b] Existence is doubtful.

Table 2.6 Phosphine, arsine and stibine complexes and derived hydrides[a]

Complex	Os	Ru	Ir	Rh
$M^{IV}X_4(LR_3)_2$	As			
$[M(LL)_2X_2]^{2+}$	diars			
$M^{III}X_3(LR_3)_3$	P, As, Sb	P, As	P, As, Sb	P, As
$MX_3(LR_3)_2$			P, Sb	
$[MX_4(LR_3)_2]^-$		P	As	
$M_2X_6(LR_3)_4$			P	As
$M_2X_6(LR_3)_3$				As
$[MX_2(LL)_2]^+$	diars	diars		
$MH_3(LR_3)_3$			P, As	
$MH_3(LR_3)_2$			P, As	
$MH_2X(LR_3)_3$			P, As	P, As
$[MH_2(LR_3)_4]^+$			As	
$MHX_2(LR_3)_3$			P, As, Sb	P, As
$M^{II}X_2(LR_3)_4$	P, As, Sb	P, As		
$MX_2(LR_3)_3$	P, As	P, As, Sb		
$[M_2X_3(LR_3)_6]X$	P	P		
$MX_2(LL)_2$	diars, diphos	diars, diphos		
$MXH(LL)_2$	diphos	diphos		
$MH_2(LL)_2$	diphos	diphos		
$M^{I}X(LR_3)_3$			P	P, As, Sb
$[M(LL)_2]^+$				diphos
$MH(LL)_2$				diphos
$M^0(LL)_2$		diphos		

[a] L = P, As or Sb; LL = chelating diphosphine or -arsine; diphos = chelating diphosphine; X = halide; R = alkyl or aryl; diars = chelating diarsine.

Table 2.7 Carbonyl phosphine, arsine and stibine complexes and derived hydrides

Complex[a]	Os	Ru	Ir	Rh
$M^{III}(CO)X_3(LR_3)_2$		P	P, As, Sb	P, As, Sb
$M(CO)_2X_3(LR_3)$			P, As	
$MH_3(CO)(LR_3)_2$			P	
$[MH_2(CO)(LR_3)_2]^+$			P	
$MH(CO)X_2(LR_3)_2$			P, As	
$[MH(CO)X_2(LR_3)]_2$			P	
$MH_2(CO)X(LR_3)_2$			P	
$M^{II}HX(CO)(LR_3)_3$	P, As	P		
$M(CO)_2X_2(LR_3)_2$		P, As, Sb		
$M(CO)X_2(LR_3)_3$	P	P		
$M^{I}(CO)(LR_3)_2X$			P, As, Sb	P, As, Sb
$M(CO)X(LR_3)_3$			P	
$MH(CO)(LR_3)_2$			P	
$MH(CO)(LR_3)_3$			P	P
$M^0(CO)_3(LR_3)_2$	P	P		

[a] L = P, As or Sb; X = halide; R = alkyl or aryl.

Table 2.8 Summary of magnetic and spectroscopic data on complexes of the metals

Configuration	Magnetic properties: Complex	Page ref.	Electronic spectra: Complex	Page ref.	Infrared and Raman spectra: Complex	Page ref.
t_{2g}^0	(Diamagnetic)		OsO_4	65	OsO_4[b]	65
					$[OsO_3N]^-$[b]	79
			RuO_4	146	RuO_4[c]	65
t_{2g}^1			$[RuO_4]^-$	150		
t_{2g}^2	OsF_6	47	OsF_6	48	OsF_6[b]	47, 101
			$[RuO_4]^{2-}$	152	RuF_6[c]	101
t_{2g}^3	$[OsF_6]^-$; $[OsF_5]_n$	51	$[OsF_6]^-$, $[RuF_6]^-$	51	IrF_6[b]	101
	$[RuF_6]^-$; $[RuF_5]_4$	131			RhF_6[b]	101
	IrF_6	230	IrF_6	230		
t_{2g}^4	$[OsX_6]^{2-}$ (F, Cl, Br, I)	58	$[OsX_6]^{2-}$ (F[a], Cl, Br, I)	60	$[OsCl_6]^{2-}$[b]	54, 103
	$[RuX_6]^{2-}$ (F, Cl, Br)	133	$[RuX_6]^{2-}$ (F[a], Cl, I)	132	$[RuCl_6]^{2-}$[c]	103
	$[IrF_6]^-$	231	$[IrF_6]^-$[a]	231		
t_{2g}^5	$[RuCl_6]^{3-}$; $[Ru(NH_3)_6]^{3+}$	214	$[OsX_6]^{3-}$ (Cl, Br, I)	63		
	$[IrX_6]^{2-}$ (F, Cl, Br)	236	$[RuX_6]^{3-}$ (Cl, Br)	138	$[IrCl_6]^{2-}$[c]	103
	$[RhCl_6]^{2-}$	317	$[RhCl_6]^{2-}$[a]	317	$[M(NH_3)_6]^{3+}$ (Os, Ru)[b]	106
t_{2g}^6	(Diamagnetic)		$[M\ ox_3]^{3-}$, $[M\ en_3]^{3+}$ (M = Ir, Rh)	253, 337, 350	$[M(CN)_6]^{4-}$ (Os, Ru)[b]	113
			$[RhX_6]^{n-}$ (X = F, CN, NO_2, SCN, NH_3, thiourea)		$[M(CN)_6]^{3-}$ (Ir, Rh)[b]	113
					$[MCl_6]^{3-}$ (Ir, Rh)[b]	103
					$[M(NH_3)_6]^{3+}$ (Ir, Rh)[b]	106
					Cp_2M(Os, Ru)[b]	116

[a] Solid-state spectra; all others in solution.
[b] Infrared and Raman spectra.
[c] Infrared spectra.

Table 2.9 Selected bond lengths

Osmium complexes	Bond length (Å) [a]	Method [b]	Page in text
Os—Br in $OsH(CO)Br(PPh_3)_3$	2·60	(a)	95
in $K_2[OsBr_6]$	2·51	(a)	55
Os—C in $Os_3(CO)_{12}$	1·95 ± 0·06	(a)	99
Os—Cl in $K_2[OsCl_6]$	2·36	(a)	54
Os—F in OsF_6	1·831	(b)	47
in $K[OsF_6]$	1·82	(a)	51
Os—N in $K[OsO_3N]$	1·56	(a)	78
in $K_2[OsNCl_5]$	1·61	(a)	80
Os—O in OsO_4	1·717 ± 0·003	(b)	64
in *trans*-$K_2[OsO_2Cl_4]$	1·75 ± 0·02	(a)	49
in *trans*-$K_2[OsO_2(OH)_4]$	2·03 (Os—OH dist.)	(a)	73
Os—Os in metal	2·675	(a)	
in $C_6H_8Os_2(CO)_6$	2·74	(a)	98
Os—P in $OsH(CO)Br(PPh_3)_3$	2·34	(a)	95
Ruthenium complexes			
Ru—As in $Ru(QAS)Br_2$	2·4 ± 0·1	(a)	180
Ru—Br in $Ru(QAS)Br_2$	2·615 ± 0·005	(a)	180
Ru—C in *cis*-$Ru(CO)_4I_2$	2·01 ± 0·01	(a)	184
Ru—Cl in $K_2[Ru_2OCl_{10}]$	2·32	(a)	134
in $[Ru(NH_3)_5Cl]Cl_2$	2·34 ± 0·05	(a)	167
in *trans*-$[Ru(NH_3)_4(SO_2)Cl]Cl$	2·415 ± 0·003	(a)	163
in $RuCl_2(PPh_3)_3$	2·387 ± 0·007	(a)	177
Ru—F in $[RuF_5]_4$	1·78 ± 0·03 (terminal)	(a)	130
	2·07 ± 0·1 (bridging)		
Ru—I in *cis*-$Ru(CO)_4I_2$	2·72 ± 0·01	(a)	184
Ru—N in $[Ru(NH_3)_4(SO_2)Cl]Cl$	2·127 ± 0·006	(a)	163
in $Na_2[Ru(NO)(OH)(NO_2)_4]$	2·079 ± 0·003 ($Ru—NO_2$)	(c)	175
	1·748 ± 0·003 (Ru—NO)	(c)	175
Ru—O in $Na_2[Ru(NO)(OH)(NO_2)_4]$	1·950 ± 0·005	(c)	175
Ru—P in $RuCl_2(PPh_3)_3$	2·38 ± 0·05	(a)	177
Ru—Ru in metal	2·650	(a)	
Ru—S in $[Ru(NH_3)_4(SO_2)Cl]Cl$	2·072 ± 0·003	(a)	163
Iridium complexes			
Ir—Cl in $K_2[IrCl_6]$	2·47	(a)	233
in $Ir(SO_2)Cl(CO)(PPh_3)_2$	2·37 ± 0·01	(a)	280
in $IrCl_3$	2·35 (mean)	(a)	239
Ir—P in $IrO_2Cl(CO)(PPh_3)_2$	2·07 ± 0·03	(a)	272

Table 2.9 (*continued*)

Rhodium Complexes				
Rh—C	in $Rh_6(CO)_{16}$	1·864 ± 0·015 (terminal); 2·168 ± 0·012 (bridging)	(a)	401
	in $CpRh(CO)(C_2F_5)I$	2·09 ± 0·03 (Rh—alkyl)	(a)	377
	in $RhH(CO)(PPh_3)_3$	1·81 ± 0·02	(a)	389
Rh—Cl	in $[Rh(NH_3)_5Cl]Cl_2$	2·40	(a)	348
	in $[Rh(CO)_2Cl]_2$	2·38 ± 0·05 (bridging)	(a)	384
	in $[Rh(C_8H_{12})Cl]_2$	2·38 ± 0·01 (bridging)	(a)	397
Rh—H	in $RhH(CO)(PPh_3)_3$	1·60 ± 0·12	(a)	389
Rh—I	in $RhCp(CO)(C_2F_5)I$	2·653	(a)	377
Rh—N	in $[Rh(NH_3)_5Cl]Cl_2$	2·23	(a)	348
Rh—P	in $RhH(CO)(PPh_3)_3$	2·32 ± 0·01	(a)	389
Rh—Rh	in $Rh_2(OAc)_4(H_2O)_2$	2·45	(a)	345
	in metal	2·690	(a)	
	in $Rh_6(CO)_{16}$	2·776 ± 0·001	(a)	401
	in $[Rh(CO)_2Cl]_2$	3·31	(a)	384

[a] Error limits are quoted only when given by the authors.
[b] The methods of determination are indicated by (a), (b) or (c) which are as follows:
(a) x-rays diffraction on crystals
(b) electron diffraction (on gases)
(c) neutron diffraction on crystals

REFERENCES

1. Abel, E. W., *Quart. Rev.* (*London*), **17**, 133 (1963).
2. Addison, C. C., and J. Lewis, *Quart. Rev.* (*London*), **9**, 115 (1955).
3. Audrieth, L. F., and B. Ogg, *Chemistry of Hydrazine*, John Wiley and Sons, New York (1951).
4. Bartlett, N., *Preparative Inorganic Reactions*, **2**, 301 (1965).
5. Bennett, M. A., *Chem. Rev.*, **62**, 611 (1962).

5a. Birmingham, J., *Advan. Organometal. Chem.*, **2**, 365 (1964).

6. Booth, G., *Advan. Inorg. Chem. Nucl. Chem.*, **6**, 1 (1964).
7. Brandt, W. W., F. P. Dwyer and R. C. Gyarfas, *Chem. Rev.*, **54**, 959 (1954).
8. Brewer, L., and G. M. Rosenblatt, *Chem. Rev.*, **61**, 257 (1961).
9. Chadwick, B. M., and A. G. Sharpe, *Advan. Inorg. Chem. Radiochem*, **8**, 84 (1966).
10. Chatt, J., R. S. Coffey and B. L. Shaw, *J. Chem. Soc.*, **1965**, 7391.
11. Chatt, J., and R. G. Wilkins, *J. Chem. Soc.*, **1952**, 4300; J. Chatt and R. G. Hayter, *J. Chem. Soc.*, **1963**, 6017; **1961**, 896; J. Chatt, N. P. Johnson and B. L. Shaw, *J. Chem. Soc.*, **1964**, 1625, 2508; J. Chatt, A. E. Field and B. L. Shaw, *J. Chem. Soc.*, **1964**, 3466; **1963**, 3371.
12. Clarke, R. J., *Advances in Halogen Chemistry*, *in press*.

13. Collmann, J. P., *Advan. Chem. Ser.*, **37**, 8 (1963).
14. Earnshaw, A., B. N. Figgis, J. Lewis and R. D. Peacock, *J. Chem. Soc.*, **1961**, 3132.
14a. Emsley, J. W., J. Feeney and L. H. Sutcliffe, *High Resolution Nuclear Magnetic Resonance Spectroscopy*, Pergamon, Oxford, 1966.
14b. Fackler, J. P., *Progr. inorg. Chem.*, **7**, 362 (1966).
15. Figgis, B. N., J. Lewis and F. E. Mabbs, *J. Chem. Soc.*, **1961**, 3138.
16. Figgis, B. N., and J. Lewis, *Progr. Inorg. Chem.*, **6**, 37 (1964); Figgis, B. N., and J. Lewis, *Modern Co-ordination Chemistry*, Interscience Publishers, London, 1960, p. 400.
17. Fischer, E. O., and H. P. Fritz, *Advan. Inorg. Chem. Radiochem.*, **1**, 55 (1959).
17a. Fischer, E. O., and H. Werner, *Metal pi-complexes*, Harper, London, 1966, Vol. I.
18. Fluck, E., *Advan. Inorg. Chem. Radiochem.*, **6**, 433 (1964).
19. Ginsberg, A. P., *Advan. Trans. Metal Chem.*, **1**, 111 (1965).
20. Green, M. L. H., and P. L. I. Nagy, *Advan. Organometal. Chem.*, **2**, 325 (1964).
21. Green, M. L. H., and D. J. Jones, *Advan. Inorg. Chem. Radiochem.*, **7**, 115 (1965).
22. Griffith, J. S., *Theory of Transition Metal Ions*, Cambridge University Press, Cambridge, 1961; *Trans. Faraday Soc.*, **54**, 1109 (1958).
23. Griffith, W. P., *Quart. Rev. (London)*, **16**, 188 (1962).
24. Griffith, W. P., *Developments in Inorganic Nitrogen Chemistry*, Elsevier, Vienna, (1966), p. 245.
25. Halpern, J., *Quart. Rev. (London)*, **15**, 207 (1961).
25a. Johnson, B. F. G., and J. A. McCleverty, *Progr. Inorg. Chem.* **7**, 277 (1966).
26. Krishnamurty, K. V., and G. M. Harris, *Chem. Rev.*, **61**, 213 (1961).
26a. Kritskaya, I. I., *Russ. Chem. Revs., Engl. Transl.*, **35**, 167 (1966).
26b. Kruck, Th., *Angew. Chem.*, **6**, 53 (1967).
26c. Kubo, M., and D. Nakamura, *Advan. Inorg. Chem. Radiochem*, **8**, 257 (1966).
27. Lever, A. B. P., *Advan. Inorg. Chem. Radiochem.*, **7**, 28 (1965).
28. Livingstone, S. E., *Quart. Rev. (London)*, **19**, 386 (1965).
29. McDonald, J. E., and J. W. Cobble, *J. Phys. Chem.*, **66**, 791 (1962).
29a. Maddox, M. L., S. L. Stafford and H. D. Kaesz, *Advan. Org. Chem.* **3**, 1 (1965).
30. Malatesta, L., *Progr. Inorg. Chem.*, **1**, 283 (1959).
31. Marcus, R. A., *J. Phys. Chem.*, **67**, 583 (1963).
32. Meier, L., *Progr. Inorg. Chem.*, **5**, 27 (1959).
33. Peacock, R. D., *Progr. Inorg. Chem.*, **2**, 455 (1961).
34. Rây, P., *Chem. Rev.*, **61**, 313 (1961).
35. Sutin, N., *Ann. Rev. Nucl. Sci.*, **13**, 285 (1962).
36. Vlček, A., *Progr. Inorg. Chem.*, **5**, 211 (1965).
37. Weinstock, B., *Advan. Chem. Phys.*, **9**, 169 (1965).
38. Wilkinson, G., and F. A. Cotton, *Progr. Inorg. Chem.*, **1**, 1 (1959).

3 OSMIUM

GENERAL CHEMISTRY

Like ruthenium and rhenium, both of which elements it resembles in a number of respects, osmium assumes a wide range of oxidation states, from (VIII) to (O) inclusive. At the moment less is known of its chemistry than of any other platinum metal—in particular there are many gaps in our knowledge of the high oxidation state chemistry, the kinetics of reaction of its complexes and of the detailed magneto-chemistry of the compounds.

Osmium tends to resemble rhenium in its higher oxidation states and ruthenium in its intermediate and low oxidation states, and like the latter element it forms a number of polynuclear complexes with oxygen or nitrogen donor bridging ligands. Fewer parallels may be drawn between it and iridium and rhodium, except perhaps in the low oxidation state chemistry.

Osmium (VIII), (VII) and (VI)

With the exception of the hepta- and hexafluoride, all the established osmium complexes of these states contain the oxide or nitride ligand. The octavalent species are all easily reduced to the hexavalent or lower states; the osmiamates are the most resistant to reduction but even they react with hydrochloric acid to give $[Os^{VI}NCl_5]^{2-}$. Nevertheless, the complexes of this state are less powerful oxidizing agents than those of ruthenium (VIII).

Heptavalent osmium is rare, being represented only by OsF_7, $OsOF_5$ and a number of oxide complexes mostly of the layer lattice type. A wide range of hexavalent species are, however, known, almost all involving the linear (O=Os=O) grouping.

Osmium (V) and (IV)

The pentavalent state is represented only by the pentafluoride and by salts of $[OsF_6]^-$. The tetravalent is the commonest oxidation state for the element, and many Group VII and Group VI ligands form complexes involving it as do a number of nitrogen donor ligands, but there are few carbon donor complexes.

Osmium (III) and (II)

Most trivalent osmium complexes are easily oxidized to the tetravalent state but if the ligands have strong π-acceptor properties, there may be reduction to the divalent state; thus $[OsCl_6]^{3-}$ is easily oxidized to $[OsCl_6]^{2-}$ but $[Os(CN)_6]^{3-}$ is easily reduced to $[Os(CN)_6]^{4-}$. There are few if any binary compounds of osmium (II), but there exists a wide range of complexes with Group V and Group IV π-acceptor ligands (such as phosphines, nitrosyl and carbonyl). Probably more complexes are known for osmium (II) than osmium (IV), but a greater diversity of ligands will coordinate with the latter and it is in this sense that it is a commoner oxidation state.

Osmium (I) and (O)

These are both rare oxidation states for the element: some monovalent carbonyl halides are known, and the only zerovalent species so far reported are the carbonyls.

GROUP VII DONORS

Osmium resembles ruthenium in its halogen chemistry, this being particularly true for the fluorides (cf. Table 2.5a, p. 36); here the analogy with rhenium is less marked than for the oxygen chemistry. The hexafluoride and the hexahaloosmate (IV) ions have been the subject of fairly extensive spectroscopic and magnetic study, but there is little information on kinetics for the halides apart from exchange and aquation work on $[OsCl_6]^{2-}$ and exchange experiments on $[OsBr_6]^{2-}$.

Osmium (VIII)

The supposed osmium octafluoride, OsF_8, was claimed in 1913 to be one of the products of the reaction of the metal with flourine[204], and an early electron-diffraction study on the substance was interpreted in terms of an Archimidaean antiprismatic structure with osmium–fluorine bond lengths varying between 2·47 and 2·52 Å[16]. However, it has now been shown conclusively that the octafluoride of Ruff and Tchirch is in fact the hexafluoride (see below)[111,245]. It is also very likely that the **$Na[OsF_9]$** reported by the same workers is $Na_2[OsF_6]$[113]. Although it now seems that there are no unsubstituted fluorides of osmium (VIII)*, there are a few oxy fluoro species.

$[OsO_3F_2]_n$ can be made by the action of bromine trifluoride on osmium tetroxide with potassium bromide. The orange compound (m.p. 170°) is also formed in small quantities when a mixture of osmium tetrabromide and bromine trifluoride react in the presence

* Recent experiments on the reaction of fluorine at high pressures and temperatures with osmium suggest, however, that under such conditions some octafluoride may be formed; the main product is the heptafluoride[93a].

of a little water[114]. The structure of the substance is not known, but its high melting point and the comparative rarity of five-coordinate complexes of osmium suggest a dimeric formulation, probably with fluorine rather than oxygen bridges, to give the more usual octahedral coordination.

$K[OsO_3F_3]$ is made in a similar manner to $[OsO_3F_2]_n$. It forms orange crystals; caesium and silver salts have also been prepared[114]. Very few octahedral complexes containing three oxide groups as ligands have been reported and it would be of some interest to establish whether the oxide groups occupy the 1,2,3- or the 1,2,6-positions of the octahedron. The former structure, in which all three oxygen atoms would be *cis* to each other, is probably the more likely since this is the configuration found in $K_3[NO_3F_3]$[101].

$Cs_2[OsO_4F_2]$ can be made as yellow crystals from an aqueous solution of osmium tetroxide and caesium fluoride; a rubidium salt was also made[148]. These salts are thermally unstable and very slightly soluble in water (the sodium salt is much more soluble) but there is no evidence that such solutions contain substantial amounts of $[OsO_4F_2]^{2-}$ ions. No infrared data are yet available on them, but presumably the oxide ligands are in a plane as in $K_2[OsO_4(OH)_2]$.

There is no substantial evidence for the existence of any other halides or oxy halides of osmium (VIII). Osmium octachloride, $OsCl_8$, was claimed in the early literature as a by-product of the reaction of hydrogen with the trichloride, but no analyses were presented.

The $[OsO_4(H_2O)I]^-$ ion has been proposed as being one of the products of reaction between osmium tetroxide and hydriodic acid[112], but later studies suggest that this is an osmium (IV) complex $[OsI_5H_2O]^-$[77] or $[Os_2OI_{10}]^{4-}$[135].

Osmium (VII)

This is represented in the halogen chemistry of the element by the heptafluoride and the oxypentafluoride alone.

Osmium heptafluoride, OsF_7, has recently been made as a yellow solid by the action of fluorine on osmium metal at 600° and 400 atmospheres. Its mass spectrum, electron spin resonance spectrum and infrared spectrum were measured, and the latter suggests that it is pentagonal bipyramidal (D_{5h}). The magnetic susceptibility was measured at 90 and 195°K; the magnetic moment is approximately independent of temperature (μ_{eff} = 1·08 BM)[93a].

$OsOF_5$ can be made by fluorination of osmium dioxide at 200°C. It forms green crystals (m.p. 59·8°) and is paramagnetic[8]. Electron spin resonance spectra of the substance in solution in tungsten hexafluoride show a single peak with no fine structure, and fluorine magnetic resonance measurements in the same solvent show a broad, low intensity peak which is ascribed (from its low intensity and contact shift) to the unresolved quintet arising from the axial fluorine group in an AX_4 structure (i.e. the fluorine atom *trans* to the oxygen). No signal is observed which would correspond to the doublet expected to arise from the four equatorial fluorine atoms, and it has been suggested that the presence of the single unpaired spin in the 'non-bonding' $5d_{xy}$ orbital (the O═Os—F lying on the z axis) accounts for the disappearance of the signal[9].

Osmium (VI)

Osmium hexafluoride, OsF_6, is the only known hexahalide of osmium: as already mentioned, it was once thought to be an octafluoride. It can be got by fluorination of the metal at 250°, and is a yellow solid (m.p. 32·1°, b.p. 45·9°)[111,245]. Infrared and Raman measurements (Table 3.1) indicate that the complex has the expected octahedral symmetry[247], and x-ray measurements show that the lattice is of the body-centered cubic type (a_0 = 6·23 Å) with an approximate osmium–fluorine distance of 2·0 Å[245], and there are brief reports of an electron-diffraction determination on the vapour which gives a value of 1·831 Å for this distance[246,247]. Thermodynamic data for the vapour have been derived by statistical methods from the spectroscopic and electron-diffraction measurements[247]. Such data have also been determined directly for the compound, including vapour-pressure equations and the heats and entropies of fusion, transition and vaporization: the heats are, respectively, 1·76, 1·97 and 6·72 kcal/mole and the entropies 5·72, 7·20 and 21·0 cal/mole deg[29].

The magnetic properties of osmium hexafluoride have been studied by two sets of workers (quoted in the same paper)[111]. Over the range 81·5–297°K, the moment follows the Curie–Weiss relationship $\chi_a \propto \frac{1}{(T+\theta)}$ to a fair degree of approximation ($\theta \sim 66°$); with μ_{eff} = 1·50 BM at 297°K (Table 3.16 and Figure 3.2, p. 59). This is a low value for two unpaired spins but is consistent with the moment expected for octahedral osmium (VI) complexes, although there has been a suggestion that the compound is not magnetically dilute[73]. Excellent agreement between the observed susceptibility values and those calculated on the basis of a ligand-field model is found if it is assumed that there is delocalization of the two 'metal' 5*d* electrons on to the six fluoride ligands, to the extent that the electrons have about an equal probability of being on the osmium atom and on the ligands[73]. Electronic spectra for the compound in tungsten hexafluoride solution were obtained from 2,500–40,000 cm^{-1} and a theoretical interpretation of the results given[134,177]. Later calculations by Eisenstein led to the assignment of tentative values for the Coulomb integrals and spin–orbit coupling parameters[73]. The fluorine magnetic resonance spectra and spin-lattice relaxation times of the hexafluoride have been studied as a function of temperature and magnetic field. The chemical shift is large and allows an unambiguous determination of tetragonal distortions in the low-temperature orthorhombic form[15].

There is some evidence for the existence of $(\mathbf{NO})^+[\mathbf{OsF_7}]^-$[10a].

The platinum metal hexafluorides and the Jahn–Teller effect

The platinum metal hexafluorides are of particular interest because of the possibility of observing Jahn–Teller effects from their vibrational spectra. The Jahn–Teller theorem states that, for non-linear polyatomic molecules, orbital electronic degeneracy leads to a certain structural instability which may result in the molecule undergoing distortion in such a way as to counteract this degeneracy[130,235]. In all the hexafluorides under consideration the electrons involved are of the t_{2g} type and for these the Jahn–Teller effect will be small (since the occupied orbitals point between the ligands rather than directly at them), but may appear as a form of vibronic coupling, giving a 'dynamic' Jahn–Teller effect.

If such a dynamic effect were to operate, anomalies would be expected in the vibrational spectra of the molecules: in particular the ν_2 (E_g) and ν_5 (F_{2g}) modes of the octahedron (cf. Table 3.1) should be affected[39,157,223,249]. These changes should be particularly noticeable for t_{2g}^1 and t_{2g}^2 complexes; for the t_{2g}^3 configuration it has been shown that, since only spin degeneracy is involved, the effect on the vibrational spectra is likely to be too small to be observed[38].

The observed infrared spectra of the gaseous hexafluorides and Raman spectra of the liquids are summarized in Table 3.1. For the rhenium (t_{2g}^1) and osmium (t_{2g}^2) compounds the Raman-active mode ν_2 is abnormally weak and the infrared combination band ($\nu_2 + \nu_3$) is much broader than with other hexafluorides; for ruthenium hexafluoride, although the Raman spectrum could not be measured, the ($\nu_2 + \nu_3$) combination is exceptionally broad. These results are consistent with the existence of a dynamic Jahn–Teller effect in these molecules[248,249]. Somewhat similar results have been obtained with the $[OsCl_6]^{2-}$ ion (see p. 54). Since there is no static distortion in the hexafluorides, the molecules have full octahedral (O_h) symmetry, and this is confirmed by these spectra.

Other osmium (VI) compounds

$[OsOF_4]_n$ is often formed as golden-yellow crystals during the preparation of the hexafluoride (sublimes at 90°). It is diamagnetic and may have a polymeric structure probably with bridging fluorine atoms[110].

No other neutral hexahalides of osmium are known; the only unsubstituted osmium (VI) chloro complex reported is the highly dubious species **$Na_6[OsCl_{12}]$**, which was claimed to be formed when hydrochloric acid was added to a solution of osmium tetroxide in sulphite; the product is copper coloured and slightly water soluble[43], and is probably a chlorosulphito complex of osmium (IV). There are, however, some well established oxyhalo species.

$[OsOCl_4]_n$ forms dark brown crystals (m.p. 32°, b.p. 200° giving a deep yellow vapour) and is made by the reaction of metallic osmium with a chlorine–oxygen mixture at 400°; like the oxyfluoride, it is diamagnetic[114] and probably contains chlorine bridges.

$K_2[OsO_2Cl_4]$ is one of the series of 'osmyl' complexes, which are dealt with in more detail below (p. 72). It can be made by gentle treatment of the tetroxide with hydrochloric acid in the presence of potassium chloride, and is obtained as red crystals very soluble in water; ammonium and caesium salts are also known[257]. An x-ray crystal structure study shows that the oxygen atoms are *trans* to each other (Os—O = 1·75 ± 0·02 Å and Os—Cl = 2·38 ± 0·005 Å)[152]. Infrared and far infrared spectra have been reported and the skeletal modes assigned[102]. The complex is diamagnetic like all other 'osmyl' salts.

$Cs_2[OsOCl_6]$ appears to be one of the products of the reaction at low temperatures between caesium chloride and osmium oxytetrachloride. The dark green compound was not obtained pure[114] but was contaminated with $Cs_2[OsO_2Cl_4]$, and its formulation as a seven coordinate species seems somewhat dubious.

$K_2[OsO_2Br_4]$ can be made in the same way as the chloro analogue[257]. It forms deep red crystals which are very soluble in water and are diamagnetic.

$(NH_4)_2[OsO_2(OH)_2Cl_2]$ and **$(NH_4)_2[OsO_2(OH)_2Br_2]$** are likely to be the correct formulae of the products obtained by the treatment of osmium tetroxide with limited amounts of the appropriate halogen acids and ammonium halides. They were first made by Wintrebert[257] who formulated them as containing the apparently five-coordinated 'oxyosmyl' anions $[OsO_3Cl_2]^{2-}$ and $[OsO_3Br_2]^{2-}$, but infrared studies on species similar to these support the six-coordinate structures above[102].

The **nitrido halides** $[OsNCl_5]^{2-}$, $[OsNBr_5]^{2-}$, $[OsN(H_2O)Br_4]^-$, $[OsN(H_2O)(OH)_2F_2]^-$, Os_2NCl_7 and Os_2NCl_5 are considered below (see pp. 80–84).

Osmium (V)

This is a very rare oxidation state for the element and only the fluoride complexes are well established.

Osmium pentafluoride, OsF_5, can be made by reduction of the hexafluoride with tungsten hexacarbonyl, a procedure which gives a mixture of the penta- and tetrafluorides which can then be separated by vacuum distillation at 120°[110]. The pentafluoride forms blue crystals which melt at 70° to give a green liquid and boil at 225·9° to form a colourless vapour[30]. These colour changes suggest that the compound has a polymeric structure in the solid and liquid phases, probably tetrameric like $[RuF_5]_4$, and is monomeric and five coordinate in the vapour state. The heat and entropy of vaporization have been measured: the values are 15·68 kcal/mole and 31·4 cal/mole deg[30], respectively. It is probable, from the properties of the compound, that it is identical to the 'OsF_6' reported by Ruff and Tchirch in 1913[204].

Magnetic measurements on the solid over the range 101·5–297°K show that the moment is 1·73 BM at 101·5°K and 2·06 BM at 297°K, values less than those expected for the three unpaired spins of osmium (v)[110]. This suggests that either the solid is not magnetically dilute or that there is considerable metal–metal interaction; the latter is perhaps the more likely, since $[OsF_6]^-$ salts have moments near 3·3 BM, which is much closer to the expected value[110].

$OsIF_4$, an involatile black solid, results from the reaction of the hexafluoride with iodine[110].

$K[OsF_6]$ can be made as a white crystalline solid from the reaction between osmium tetrabromide, potassium bromide and bromine trifluoride (the other alkali metal salts and a silver salt were also prepared)[113]. The salt is decomposed by water (to the tetroxide and $K_2[OsF_6]$), but more slowly than is $K[RuF_6]$. The potassium salt has a rhombohedral structure (a = 4·99 Å, α = 97·2°) and is isomorphous with $K[RuF_6]$ and $K[IrF_6]$. The x-ray crystal structure shows the lattice to be of the distorted caesium chloride type made up of K^+ and $[OsF_6]^-$ ions. The anions themselves consist of distorted octahedra, flattened along the three-fold axes such that the metal–fluorine distance is 1·82 Å, while the distance between each fluorine atom and its two closest fluorine neighbours is 2·66 Å with two at 2·48 Å[116]. The rubidium and caesium salts of $[OsF_6]^-$ also have the rhombohedral $K[OsF_6]$ lattice but the lithium and sodium salts have a slightly distorted sodium chloride type structure (the so-called rhombohedral $Li[SbF_6]$ lattice), while $Ag[OsF_6]$ has the tetragonal $K[NbF_6]$ structure[144].

Magnetic susceptibility measurements on the potassium and caesium salts were made from 80 to 300°K, over which range the Curie–Weiss relationship is obeyed (see Table 3.16 and Figure 3.2, p. 59). A symmetrical fluorine nuclear magnetic resonance signal was observed in a powdered sample of the potassium salt[74]. The electronic spectrum of solid $Cs[OsF_6]$ has been measured from 10,000 to 40,000 cm^{-1} and assignments proposed on the basis of Tanabe–Sugano diagrams[21]. The infrared spectrum was also measured (Table 3.2)[188].

The oxidation potential of the $[OsF_6]^-/[OsF_6]^{2-}$ couple has been estimated as 0·6 v[187]. Other compounds which have been reported as containing the hexafluoroosmate (v) anion include **$NO^+[OsF_6]^-$**, made from nitric oxide and osmium hexafluoride (the compound is cubic, with a = 10·126 Å)[10], and **$SeOsF_9$**, made by reaction of the hexafluoride with selenium tetrafluoride (this may be $SeF_3^+[OsF_6]^-$[115]). Decomposition of this yields a material $(OsF_5)_2SeF_4$[115].

$OsCl_5$ has not been isolated, but experiments on the formation of $OsCl_4$ give some evidence for the existence of a higher chloride[146].

The compound **Os_2OCl_8** has been claimed; it was made by passing a chlorine–oxygen mixture over osmium metal heated to 700°. The infrared spectrum has a band at 993 cm^{-1} [210]. This seems too high for a bridging oxygen group but would be consistent with the presence of a terminal osmium–oxygen double bond, in which case bridging is likely to occur through chlorine (another and perhaps more likely explanation is that the compound is $[OsOCl_4]_n$).

Osmium (IV)

Osmium tetrafluoride, OsF_4, can be made in the same way as the pentafluoride. It is a yellow solid (m.p. 230°) which gives a clear yellow solution in water[110]. The high melting point suggests a polymeric structure for the solid.

$[OsOF_2]_n$(?) is a black oxyfluoride of unknown composition formed when hydrofluoric acid reacts with hydrated osmium dioxide[178].

Osmium tetrachloride, $OsCl_4$, can be made as red crystals (b.p. 450°) by the direct chlorination of the metal at 600° under 7 atmospheres pressure of chlorine[146]. It is soluble in water and in alcohol to give unstable solutions which decompose to give the hydrated dioxide, but it is insoluble in non-polar organic solvents, in concentrated sulphuric acid and in concentrated nitric acid[146]. A water insoluble red form has also been reported[228]. Thermal dissociation of the compound between 384 and 557° has been studied and thermodynamic data derived (the product of thermal decomposition is the trichloride, which is formed above 350°[146]). The standard enthalpy of formation of the solid from the elements, ΔH^0_{298}, is $-60{\cdot}9 \pm 2{\cdot}8$ kcal/mole[146].

Os_2Cl_7 was reported by Moraht and Wischin[178] to be formed by the action of hydrochloric acid on hydrated osmium trioxide; it is possible that the product is identical with $[Os(OH)Cl_3]_n$ (see p. 53) or is a basic mixed chloride.

Osmium tetrabromide, $OsBr_4$, has recently been made in the anhydrous form by heating the metal with bromine under pressure; it exists as black crystals, which decompose *in vacuo* at 350°[217]. The compound is insoluble in water and in concentrated acids but is very slowly hydrolysed by alkalis. Thermal decomposition yields the tribromide. X-ray powder patterns indicated cubic symmetry[217]. A water-soluble form of the tetrabromide has also been made[113].

Os_2Br_9 (as a hexahydrate) results from the prolonged action of hydrobromic acid with alcohol on hydrated osmium trioxide[178]. The Russian workers who first made anhydrous osmium tetrabromide reported that an involatile compound, whose analysis was close to **Os_2Br_7**, was left as a residue from sublimation of the tetrabromide[217]. The supposed **osmium tetraiodide** was reported to be formed as violet water-soluble crystals by the prolonged action of hydriodic acid on the tetroxide[178], but recent work shows that the product of this reaction is $(H_3O)_2[OsI_6]$, and no tetraiodide could be made[78]. An oxyiodide of unknown composition has been reported[178].

$[Os(OH)Cl_3]_n$ can be made by the action of hydrogen chloride gas on a solution of osmium tetroxide in hydrochloric acid[149] and is variously reported as being reddish-brown[149] or black[146]. It is very hygroscopic; with alkali metal chlorides it is said to give salts M^I_2-$[Os(OH)Cl_5]$[149] (see p. 61).

$[Os(OH)Br_3]_n$ can be made as dark red crystals by the action of hydrobromic acid on the tetroxide; it is very soluble in water and alcohol[149]. Like the chloride it gives salts said to contain $[Os(OH)B_5]^{2-}$ with alkali metal bromides[149].

The hexahaloosmates (IV), $[OsX_6]^{2-}$ (X = F, Cl, Br, I)

These, particularly the chloro complex, are amongst the most important of osmium complexes. In particular there has been extensive work on the magnetic properties and electronic absorption spectra of the complexes as a group; these data are considered in a separate section below (see p. 58).

$K_2[OsF_6]$ can be made as pale yellow crystals by dissolving $K[OsF_6]$ together with an equivalent of potassium hydroxide in water[113], or from the tetrafluoride and potassium fluoride[204]. It has a hexagonal structure (a = 5·80, c = 4·62 Å)[117]; the sodium salt exists in a hexagonal form (a = 9·36, c = 5·11 Å) and an orthorhombic form (a = 5·80, b = 4·50, c = 10·14 Å)[21a]. The solubility of the potassium salt (g/100 ml) is 1·2 and that of the caesium salt 0·7 at 20°. The free acid $H_2[OsF_6]$aq has been obtained in aqueous solution by ion-exchange methods but could not be isolated[117]. The caesium salt has also been prepared. The electronic[21] and infrared[188] spectra have been measured.

$K_2[OsCl_6]$ may be best prepared by reducing, with alcohol or with ferrous ion, a solution of osmium tetroxide in hydrochloric acid. (Hydrochloric acid alone on the tetroxide yields mainly $[OsO_2Cl_4]^{2-}$, from which the hexachloro complex can be made only by prolonged acid treatment unless a reducing agent is also present[226,257].) Sodium, ammonium[69], rubidium, caesium, silver and barium salts are known as well as the free acid (isolated as a hexahydrate)[92]. The ammonium salt has been used to determine the atomic weight of osmium.

The x-ray crystal structure of the potassium salt shows that the lattice is cubic ($a = 9{\cdot}82 \pm 0{\cdot}02$ Å[226], the same dimension as the isomorphous $K_2[PtCl_6]$) with an osmium–chlorine bond length of 2·36 Å[161]. No electron spin resonance signal was observed from a powdered sample of the ammonium salt either alone or diluted with $(NH_4)_2[PtCl_6]$ in contrast to similar experiments with $K_2[RuCl_6]$ where such resonance was observed[106]. Pure chlorine nuclear quadrupole resonance measurements from 90–290°K show that, as expected, all the chlorine atoms are in equivalent environments, and comparisons with $K_2[IrCl_6]$ and $K_2[PtCl_6]$ were said to show that the π character in the metal–ligand bond decreased along the series $K_2[PtCl_6] > K_2[IrCl_6] > K_2[OsCl_6]$ while the 'ionic character' of the bonds remained roughly constant[108a,128].

Infrared and Raman studies on $[OsCl_6]^{2-}$ have led to an almost complete assignment of the fundamental vibrations and are listed in Table 3.3 together with results for other hexachloro species for comparison. It is particularly noticeable that, as for OsF_6, the ν_2 frequency is very weak (too weak to be observed in this case) and its position had to be calculated from the combination mode $(\nu_2 + \nu_3)$; a similar effect was found for $[ReCl_6]^{2-}$[259]. These two have t_{2g}^4 and t_{2g}^3 configurations, respectively, and it was suggested that in these cases a dynamic Jahn–Teller effect might be introduced by the mixing in of a low-lying excited electronic state with the lowest electronic state to give a ground state possessing orbital degeneracy[259]. Although this would have only a very small effect on the spectrum of IrF_6 (t_{2g}^3) it might well be larger for $[OsCl_6]^{2-}$, since the charge on the central metal atom is lower and since delocalization of t_{2g} electrons by π bonding, which would accentuate Jahn–Teller effects, is more likely with chloride than with fluoride ligands[38,259]. This does not, however, explain the fact that whereas the combination modes $(\nu_2 + \nu_3)$ in OsF_6 and ReF_6 are anomalously broad they are of normal breadth in $[OsCl_6]^{2-}$ and $[ReCl_6]^{2-}$ (although the infrared spectra of the latter were run only in mulls)[259].

The kinetics of the reversible reaction

$$[OsCl_6]^{2-} + H_2O \underset{k_{-1}}{\overset{k_1}{\rightleftharpoons}} [OsCl_5(H_2O)]^- + Cl^-$$

were studied in hydrochloric acid media at 80° (perchloric acid could not be used since it oxidizes osmium (IV) at this temperature, while at lower temperatures the aquation reaction is too slow) and in nitric acid from 70–89°. In the latter medium the aquation products and secondary reaction products are rapidly oxidized to the tetroxide and chloride ion. The primary product of aquation is $[OsCl_5(H_2O)]^-$, and some evidence was also obtained for the existence of $OsCl_4(H_2O)_2$ or some other osmium (IV) tetrachloro species. A value of $k_1 = 3{\cdot}5 \times 10^{-6}$ sec^{-1} ($t_{1/2}$ = 55 hours) was found for the aquation of $[OsCl_6]^{2-}$ in nitric or hydrochloric acid up to pH 5, at 80° in the dark; the rate coefficient was essentially independent of ionic strength from 0·5 to 1·32 μ. The activation energy for the aquation process was found to be 33·1 kcal/mole. Studies were also made of the replacement of water by chloride in $[OsCl_5(H_2O)]^-$ and an approximate value of $k_{-1} = 2 \times 10^5$ M^{-1} sec^{-1} in 3·3–3·8 M hydrochloric acid at 80° obtained[176].

The rate of exchange of chloride ion with $[OsCl_6]^{2-}$ labelled with radioactive chlorine has been measured at 80–100° in 8·8 M hydrochloric acid[59]. The exchange rate constant ($k = 3{\cdot}1 \times 10^{-6}$ sec^{-1}) is so close to the rate constant for aquation of $[OsCl_6]^{2-}$ under equivalent conditions as to suggest that direct bimolecular exchange of chloride with $[OsCl_6]^{2-}$ is of negligible importance. The activation energy for the exchange, 30 kcal/mole, is also very close to that found for the aquation[176].

The rate of the electron-transfer reaction between $[OsCl_6]^{2-}$ and $[Fe(CN)_6]^{4-}$ is slow (the second-order rate coefficient is $1{\cdot}79 \times 10^{-1}$ M^{-1} sec^{-1} at 25° in aqueous solution); although this is likely to be a reaction of the outer-sphere type, it has been suggested that the reorganization energy of $[OsCl_6]^{2-}$ is high[96].

The chemical reactions of $K_2[OsCl_6]$ are summarized in the reaction scheme (Figure 3.1).

$K_2[OsBr_6]$ can be made by a method similar to that used for the hexachloro complex, but the addition of alcohol is not necessary as $[OsO_2Br_4]^{2-}$ is easily reduced by an excess of hydrobromic acid[52,226]. The solid salt forms black crystals which are isomorphous with $K_2[OsCl_6]$ and $K_2[PtCl_6]$, and it has a cubic lattice ($a = 10{\cdot}37 \pm 0{\cdot}02$ Å)[226]; the Os—Br bond length is 2·51 Å[161]. Sodium, ammonium[69], rubidium, caesium and silver salts are also known; all are sparingly soluble in water with the exception of the sodium salt. Studies on mixed crystals of $K_2[OsBr_6]$ and $K_2[SnCl_6]$ have been reported[180b].

The exchange reaction between $[OsBr_6]^{2-}$ and labelled bromide

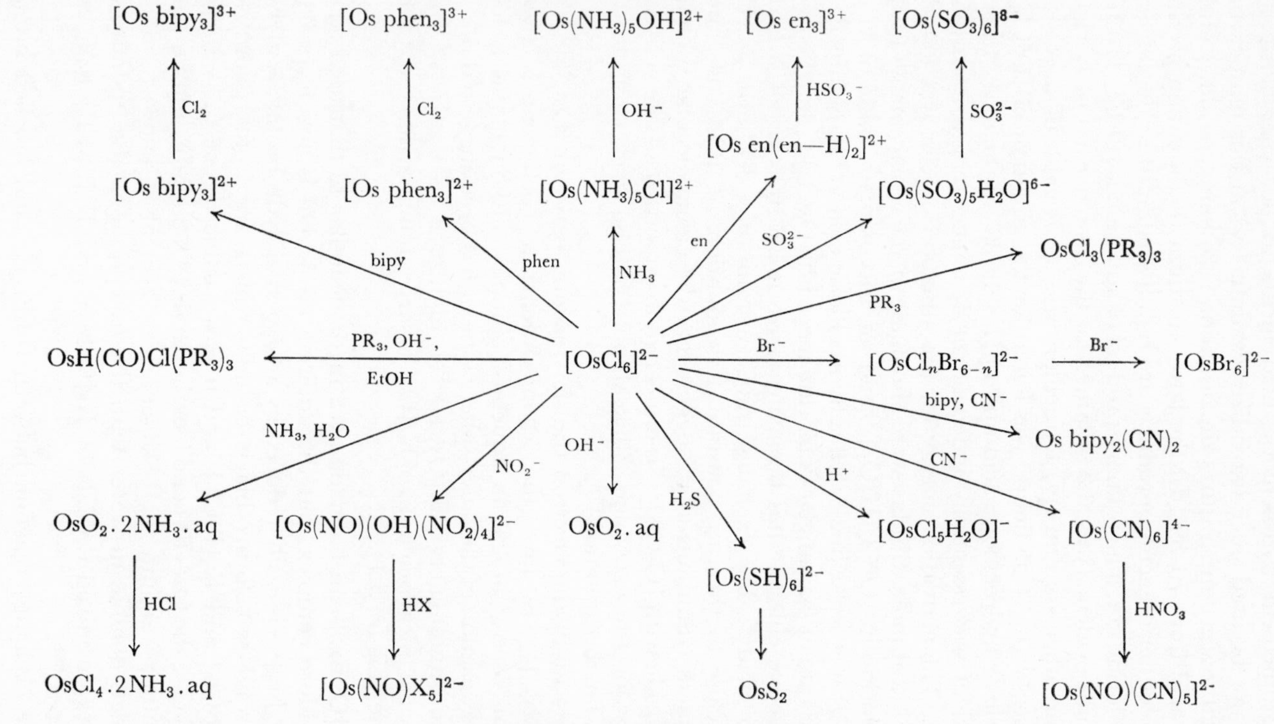

Figure 3.1 Reactions of $[OsCl_6]^{2-}$

ion has been studied at 75° in 1·5–7·5 M hydrobromic acid, and the rate law

$$R = k_1[OsBr_6^{2-}] + k_2[OsBr_6^{2-}][HBr]$$

established (at 75° in 1·5–7·5 M hydrobromic acid, $k_1 = 6{\cdot}6 \times 10^{-3}$ min^{-1} and $k_2 = 7{\cdot}9 \times 10^{-4}$ mole^{-1} min^{-1}) (similar studies were also carried out on $[ReBr_6]^{2-}$, $[IrBr_6]^{2-}$ and $[PtBr_6]^{2-}$). The activation energy of ^{82}Br transfer is 29·4 kcal/mole for the rhenium, osmium and iridium complexes and 12·6 kcal/mole for the platinum complex[213].

$K_2[OsI_6]$ is normally prepared by the action of hydriodic acid on $K_2[OsO_2(OH)_2(NO_2)_2]$ or $K_2[OsO_2ox_2]$[257]. It forms black crystals giving a purple solution in water; it is more soluble in water and the solution is less resistant to hydrolysis than those of the chloro or bromo complexes.

Mixed hexahaloosmate (IV) complexes

$[OsCl_nBr_{6-n}]^{2-}$ (n = 1 to 5) complexes have been isolated by means of high-voltage paper electrophoresis on mixed solutions of the hexachloro and hexabromo complexes. The ionic migration velocities and absorption maxima of the electronic spectra followed a consistent pattern as the chlorine atoms in $[OsCl_6]^{2-}$ were progressively replaced by bromine[14]. Some evidence for the formation of geometrical isomers of $[OsCl_nBr_{6-n}]^{2-}$ (n = 2, 3, 4) has been presented[192].

All the mixed species $[^{191}OsCl_nBr_{6-n}]^{2-}$ ($6 \geqslant n \geqslant 0$) were made in mixed crystals $K_2[OsBr_6]$–$K_2[SnCl_6]$ by the nuclear process[180c]:

$$^{190}Os(n, \gamma)^{191}Os$$

Salts containing $[OsCl_5Br]^{2-}$ and $[OsCl_3Br_3]^{2-}$ have long been known [149].

$[OsCl_nI_{6-n}]^{2-}$ systems have also been investigated but with less definite results. Electrophoretic experiments on hydrochloric acid solutions of osmium tetroxide in the presence of iodide ion indicated the presence of three species[193]: $[OsI_6]^{2-}$ (violet), a blue-green mixed complex $[OsCl_nI_{6-n}]^{2-}$ (n = 3 or 4, though Jorgensen believes that n = 5[135]) and a green hydrolysis product which may be $[Os_2OI_{10}]^{4-}$[135], $[OsI_5H_2O]^{-}$[77] or perhaps another mixed chloro–iodo complex[193]. The electronic absorption spectrum of the blue-green product has been recorded and assignments proposed; the osmium (IV) mixed species can be reduced to an osmium (III) complex which, on reoxidation, regenerates the original osmium (IV) compound[135].

Magnetic and spectral properties of the hexahaloosmates (IV)

The most extensive survey of the magnetic properties was made by Earnshaw and coworkers on the potassium and caesium salts of the four complex anions. For $K_2[OsF_6]$, $K_2[OsCl_6]$ and $K_2[OsBr_6]$ the susceptibility remained virtually constant over the range 80–290°K (i.e. the magnetic moment decreases with decreasing temperature), but a slight drop in χ_m with increasing temperature over the same range was observed for $K_2[OsI_6]$ and for all four caesium salts; this decrease, it was suggested, probably arose from the presence of slight traces of an impurity which was also paramagnetic (cf. Figure 3.2) [71]. Later work suggested that there was magnetic superexchange in salts of $[OsCl_6]^{2-}$ and $[OsBr_6]^{2-}$ since the susceptibilities of these increased considerably when they were dispersed in an isomorphous diamagnetic host lattice (see Table 3.4) [132,253,254]. These effects, which have also been found to occur with $[ReCl_6]^{2-}$ and $[IrCl_6]^{2-}$, (cf. p. 236) probably involve π interaction of the paramagnetic centres through adjacent ligands, the path between two adjacent metal atoms A and B being [254]

$$\text{Metal}_A(d_\pi)\text{—Ligand}_A(p_\pi)\text{—Ligand}_B(p_\pi)\text{—Metal}_B(d_\pi)$$

Thus when the $[OsX_6]^{2-}$ groups are separated from neighbouring paramagnetic centres by large diamagnetic cations or by diamagnetic $[PtX_6]^{2-}$ groups they are able to show their full paramagnetism. The effect is very marked and is illustrated by the results in Table 3.4. By extrapolation of the measurements made on solid solutions of $[OsX_6]^{2-}$ in the diamagnetic $[PtX_6]^{2-}$ lattice, values were found for the susceptibilities at 'infinite dilution' [132,254].

Johannesen and Candela [132] suggest that an intermediate coupling scheme is necessary to explain the experimental results for the $5d^4$ configuration, and that the normal Kotani theory [147] cannot in this case be applied without amendment because spin–orbit coupling is of considerable importance for this configuration. Using the intermediate coupling scheme calculated by Kamimura and coworkers [141] together with the susceptibility expression for low-spin d^4 complexes derived by Griffith [98,99], good agreement is obtained between theory and experiment for χ_∞ values and also for the ligand-field absorption spectrum, giving values of 2100 ± 100 cm^{-1} for the spin–orbit coupling constant, 2800 ± 100 cm^{-1} for the Coulomb interaction coefficient and an orbital reduction factor k of between 0·7 and 0·9 [132]. If exchange did occur through the π orbitals on the metal and halogen atoms, they argue, then the dilution effect should

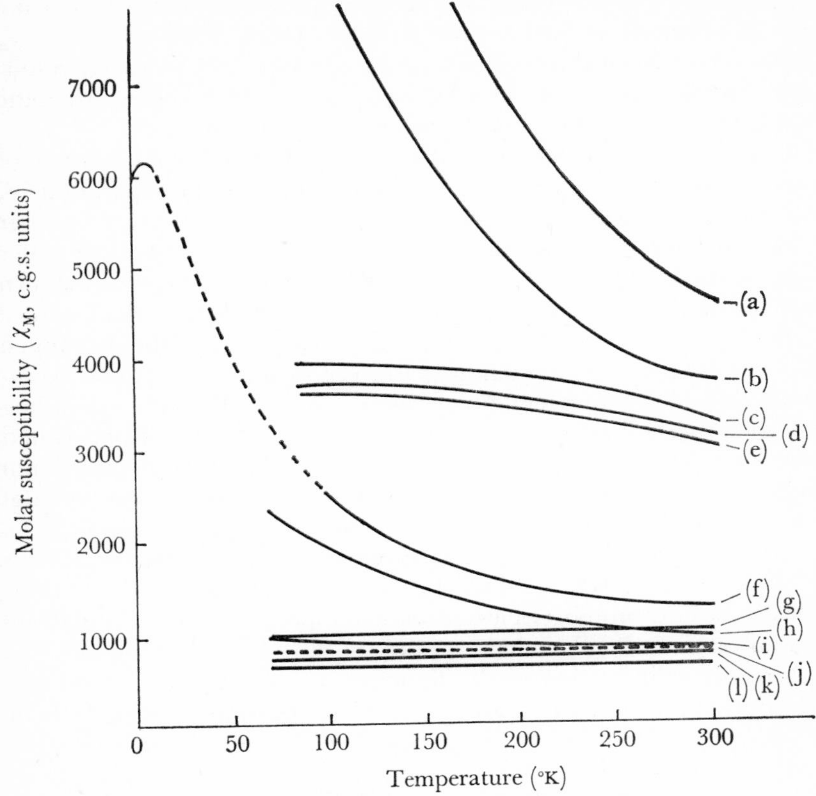

Figure 3.2 Magnetic properties of hexahalo complexes of the four metals: (a) $K[OsF_6]$ (b) IrF_6 (c) $K_2[RuF_6]$ (d) $K_2[RuCl_6]$ (e) $K_2[RuBr_6]$ (f) $K_2[IrCl_6]$ and $Cs_2[RhCl_6]$ (g) $K_2[OsCl_6]$ (h) OsF_6 (i) $K_2[OsI_6]$ (j) $K[IrF_6]$ (k) $K_2[OsF_6]$ (l) $K_2[OsBr_6]$

be dependent on the nature of the halogen as well as on the osmium–osmium distances, whereas in fact the degree of 'exchange' seems to be independent of the halogen (although detailed data are available only for the chloro and bromo complexes). The effect of dilution can be expressed empirically by the equation

$$\chi = \frac{\chi_\infty}{(1 + \lambda d^{-n}\chi_\infty)}$$

where d is the mean distance between adjacent osmium nuclei,

$n \sim 2$, λ is a constant and χ and χ_∞ are the susceptibilities at normal and at infinite dilutions, respectively[132]. Using this expression, χ_m values were calculated and are compared with the observed results in Table 3.4; the extent of agreement does indeed suggest that the dilution effect is independent of the nature of the halogen[132].

It is curious that salts of $[RuCl_6]^{2-}$ do not exhibit an increase of susceptibility with increasing ruthenium–ruthenium separation[252], structurally $K_2[RuCl_6]$ and $K_2[OsCl_6]$ are known to be very similar so that metal–ligand and ligand–ligand distances are likely to differ little between the two compounds. Furthermore, it has been shown that the susceptibility of $Cs_2[OsF_6]$ is some 20% higher than that of $K_2[OsF_6]$, but recent Raman data have shown that there is much less metal–ligand π interaction in transition metal hexafluoro complexes than in the corresponding hexachlorides[262]. Thus if a π-bonding type of superexchange were responsible for these effects one would expect a much smaller susceptibility difference between the potassium and caesium salts for $[OsF_6]^{2-}$ than $[OsCl_6]^{2-}$. More experimental data are clearly needed before any conclusions can be reached: in particular systematic dilution measurements of susceptibilities on salts of $[OsF_6]^{2-}$ and $[OsI_6]^{2-}$ of the type already made for the hexachloro and hexabromo species, and low-temperature measurements on all four osmium (IV) hexahalo species.

A recent examination of the fluorine nuclear magnetic resonance spectrum of powdered $K_2[OsF_6]$ gave a contact shift showing little or no anisotropy, and it was suggested that this result was not compatible with a t_{2g}^4 ground state for osmium (IV) (nor can it be explained in terms of metal–ligand π-bonding effects); however, single-crystal studies are necessary to confirm these conclusions[74].

Absorption spectra of $[OsX_6]^{2-}$ and $[OsX_6]^{3-}$ (X = Cl, Br, I) have been measured over the range 180–1000 mμ, and assignments proposed for the ligand-field bands and for the many charge-transfer transitions[134–138]; the latter have also been studied by Englman[75]. The colours of the osmium (IV) hexahalo salts vary in a remarkable fashion with the nature of the cation; thus while an aqueous solution of $[OsCl_6]^{2-}$ is yellow, the solid potassium and ammonium salts are deep red, the caesium salt orange and the thallous and silver salts are olive-green and brown, respectively. Studies on the reflectance spectra of these and of salts of $[OsBr_6]^{2-}$ suggest that the colour effects arise from shifting and broadening in the charge-transfer bands, brought about by changes in lattice parameters caused by variation in cation size[136]. With the silver and thallium salts a new charge-transfer band appears. Certain of the bands shift towards the red when high pressures are applied to solid solutions of osmium (IV) hexahalides, possibly due to slightly increased spin–orbit coupling at high pressures[4]. It has also been shown that the positions of the bands in solutions of $[OsBr_6]^{2-}$ and $[IrBr_6]^{2-}$ can be correlated with the dielectric constant of the solvent[139].

$(NH_4)_4[Os_2OCl_{10}]$ can be prepared as dark brown crystals by the action of ferrous sulphate on a mixture of ammonium chloride and osmium tetroxide in aqueous solution[60,176]. It was originally formulated as $(NH_4)_2[OsCl_5OH]$[60], but infrared spectra of the complex suggest that it has a binuclear structure with a linear metal–oxygen–metal skeleton as found in $[Ru_2OCl_{10}]^{4-}$[117a]. The electronic absorption spectrum was measured[176]. Magnetic measurements on aqueous solutions of this salt in water are said to indicate the existence of a species with four unpaired spins (whether per metal atom or per two metal atoms is not stated); it was proposed that either $[Os(OH)Cl_5]^{2-}$ or $[Os(OH)_2Cl_4]^{2-}$ was present[131a], but such high spins are unlikely for osmium (IV) complexes.

The same dimeric structure is likely for the compound $K_2[OsCl_5$-$OH]$ made from $[Os(OH)Cl_3]_n$ with potassium chloride[149]. Similarly, it is likely that the compounds **$(CH_3NH_3)_2[OsCl_3Br_2OH]$** and **$(CH_3NH_3)_2[OsBr_5OH]$**, made from methylamine hydrochloride and $[Os(OH)Cl_3]_n$ and $[Os(OH)Br_3]_n$, respectively[149], contain the ions $[Os_2OCl_6Br_4]^{4-}$ and $[Os_2OBr_{10}]^{4-}$, respectively[117a].

$[OsCl_5(H_2O)]^-$ has already been mentioned as being the primary product of aquation of $[OsCl_6]^{2-}$: it was characterized by its electronic absorption spectrum, and the kinetics of the water replacement reaction were studied[176] (see p. 55).

$OsCl_4(H_2O)_2$ may be another of the products of aquation of hexachloroosmate (IV) ion (it was detected in solution only by its absorption spectrum and the osmium:chlorine ratio), but it is possible that the product could be the reduced species $[OsCl_4(H_2O)_2]^-$ or the binuclear $[Os_2OCl_8(H_2O)_2]^{2-}$[176].

$[Os_2OI_{10}]^{4-}$, as already mentioned (p. 46), may be the formula of the product of reaction of osmium tetroxide with iodide ion in acid solution[193]; it is blue-green and soluble in ether.

Osmium (III)

No fluorides of osmium (III) have been reported.

Osmium trichloride, $OsCl_3$, can be made by the thermal decomposition of the tetrachloride at 470° in an atmosphere of chlorine[146]. (Previously reported methods, such as chlorination of the metal at 1000° or heating ammonium hexachloroosmate in a current of chlorine, give different products, cf. p. 84[146].) The trichloride is a dark grey powder, insoluble in water, organic solvents and mineral acids (apart from nitric acid, which oxidizes it to the tetroxide), and the x-ray powder pattern suggests that it is isomorphous with α-$RuCl_3$[146]. It decomposes above 450° to the metal. According to Charonnat another form of the trichloride can be made by heating osmium tetroxide with alcohol and hydrochloric acid, then treating the residue with hydrogen chloride gas at 200°[33], but it seems likely that this is simply an insoluble form of $[Os(OH)Cl_3]_n$[146]; similarly, the alleged trichloride trihydrate made from $OsO_3.aq$ with alcohol and hydrochloric acid[178] is probably also $[Os(OH)Cl_3]_n$ or a mixture of this with the tetrachloride[33]. Thermodynamic data are reported for the trichloride[146]. It will catalyse the polymerization of norbornene in polar solvents, as will other platinum metal trichlorides[176a].

Osmium tribromide, $OsBr_3$, can be made by thermal decomposition of the tetrabromide; it is a dark grey powder insoluble in water, organic solvents and mineral acids; it decomposes at high temperatures to the metal[216]. The compound Os_2Br_9, which behaves as though it were a mixture of the tri- and tetrabromides, has already been considered (see p. 53).

Osmium triiodide, OsI_3, can be made by thermal degradation of $(H_3O)_2[OsI_6]$ or by heating the diiodide with iodine. It is black, and x-ray measurements suggest that it is amorphous. The magnetic moment at room temperatures is 1·8 BM[78].

Hexahaloosmates (III)

These compounds are often given the trivial name of 'osmites' in the earlier literature.

$K_3[OsCl_6]$ exists as such and as a trihydrate. It can be made by heating a mixture of osmium metal and potassium chloride in a current of chlorine or by the prolonged treatment of potassium osmiamate with hydrochloric acid[43]. It forms red crystals, very soluble in water and in alcohol: the solutions are rather unstable and tend to deposit hydrated oxides on standing. They will react with alcohol or with tannic acid to give a violet-blue coloured species which may be $[OsCl_6]^{4-}$ or an aquated form of this[43], or, more likely, a tannic acid complex of osmium (III). The electronic absorption spectrum has been recorded and assignments proposed[138]. The supposed $(NH_4)_2[OsCl_5].1\frac{1}{2}H_2O$, made by addition of ammonium chloride to a solution of osmium tetroxide in hydrochloric acid after reduction by hydrogen sulphide[43], is in fact $(NH_4)_2[OsCl_6]$[101].

$K_3[OsBr_6]$ can be made by electrolytic reduction of a solution of potassium hexabromoosmate (IV) in an atmosphere of carbon dioxide and in the presence of potassium bromide[51]. The compound forms deep brown octahedral crystals, and the electronic absorption spectrum of the aqueous solution has been measured and assignments proposed[138].

$[OsI_6]^{3-}$ has been prepared only in aqueous solution by reduction of hexaiodoosmate (IV) with silver powder. The solution is extremely easily oxidized, but the electronic absorption spectrum was measured and assigned[135].

Osmium (II)

The supposed **osmium dichloride, $OsCl_2$**, was claimed as a product of the thermal decomposition of the trichloride in a stream of chlorine and also as a product of the direct chlorination of osmium[43], and the compound is stated to be paramagnetic ($\chi_A = 83 \times 10^{-6}$ c.g.s. units at 20°)[28]. Recently, however, Kolbin and coworkers have shown that it is unlikely that the compound was obtained by these methods: in particular thermal decomposition of the trichloride gives the metal only[146]. The paramagnetism of Cabrera and Duperier's sample[28] was probably due to the trichloride.

Osmium dibromide does not seem to have been made; thermal decomposition of both the tetra- and tribromide gives the metal[216].

Osmium diiodide, OsI_2, seems to be the only dihalide of osmium. It can be made by the action of heat on hexaiodoosmic (IV) acid, and its magnetic moment at room temperature was reported to be 0·6 BM[78]. It is black and amorphous, but it has been claimed that a yellow sublimable diiodide can be made by heating $(H_3O)_2[OsI_6]$ in a current of hydrogen[43].

$[OsCl_6]^{4-}$ or another anionic osmium (II) chloro complex may be present in the violet-blue solutions obtained by reduction of hexachloroosmate (III)[43].

Osmium (I)

Osmium iodide, OsI, is the only monohalide reported. Like all the other iodides of the metal, it can be made by heating hexaiodoosmic (IV) acid. The x-ray powder pattern was measured, and at room temperature the magnetic moment was found to be 0·5 BM[78].

GROUP VI DONORS

Osmium, like ruthenium, shows in its higher oxidation states a higher affinity for oxygen and for sulphur than for nitrogen while the reverse is true for the lower oxidation states. The existence of a wide range of very stable complexes of osmium (VI) containing the *trans* O=Os=O 'osmyl' unit is striking, particularly since complexes containing only one doubly bonded oxygen atom per osmium are very rare.

Osmium (VIII)

Osmium tetroxide, OsO_4, is the commonest compound of osmium, though certainly among the least pleasant to handle. As already mentioned, it was its very characteristic odour which suggested the name of the element to Smithson Tennant. It may be prepared by oxidizing the metal[15a] or almost any osmium compound with a wide variety of oxidizing agents, of which nitric acid is the most commonly used (osmium and ruthenium tetroxides can be separated by distillation from nitric acid).

Physical properties. Osmium tetroxide is a pale yellow solid (m.p. 40·6°, b.p. 131·2°) which exists in one form only, not two as was once claimed[183]. An x-ray study showed that the solid crystallized in the monoclinic system ($a = 9{\cdot}379$, $b = 4{\cdot}515$, $c = 8{\cdot}632$ Å, $\beta = 116{\cdot}6°$ [227]); the osmium–oxygen bond distance is $1{\cdot}74 \pm 0{\cdot}03$ Å[227]. Two early electron-diffraction determinations on the structure in the vapour phase[17,20] can be discounted as various correction factors were not taken into account in the calculations[57,250]; the latest measurements by this method give an osmium–oxygen distance of 1·717 Å, the molecule being tetrahedral[250] (another recent determination gives $1{\cdot}711_6 \pm 0{\cdot}003$ Å[216a]).

Infrared and Raman spectra also show the molecule to be tetrahedral; the fundamental frequencies (T_d symmetry) for it and for ruthenium tetroxide are

	$\nu_1(A_1)$	$\nu_2(E)$	$\nu_3(F_2)$	$\nu_4(F_2)$	Ref.
OsO_4	965	335	954	335	261
RuO_4	$(880)^a$		913	330	57, 185

^{a} This value is calculated from the $(\nu_1 + \nu_3)$ combination band.

Force constants were calculated for osmium tetroxide from these results[154a, 263]. The electronic spectrum of the vapour has been measured[154] and band assignments proposed[32,164,234]. ^{17}O nuclear magnetic resonance measurements on solutions of this and of other tetroxides and tetrahedral oxy ions have been made, and the chemical shifts correlated with the energy of the lowest electronic transitions in the molecule[81].

For the reaction

$$Os(g) + 2\ O_2 \rightarrow OsO_4(g)$$

a value of $\Delta H^0_{298} = -79{\cdot}9$ kcal/mole was measured[203] (a review on thermodynamic values for this reaction has been given[181a]); the ionization potential of the gaseous tetroxide from electron-impact measurements is $12{\cdot}97 \pm 0{\cdot}1$ ev[56].

The compound is sparingly soluble in water to give a colourless solution; the solubilities, in grams of tetroxide per 100 grams of water, are 5·3 at 0°, 6·47 at 18° and 7·24 at 25°. It is much more soluble in organic solvents, in which it is monomeric; old reports that it was tetrameric in carbon tetrachloride have been disproved[95]. The solubility in this solvent is 250 g per 100 g of tetrachloride at 20°.

Chemical properties. It is a very powerful oxidizing agent, a fact which has been exploited for organic syntheses (see below). It will react with hydrochloric acid to give halo species of the form $[Os^{VI}O_2Cl_4]^{2-}$ and finally $[Os^{IV}Cl_6]^{2-}$, although there is some evidence that solutions of osmium tetroxide in very dilute hydrochloric acid contain osmium (VIII) species. It is more easily reduced by hydrobromic acid to $[OsO_2Br_4]^{2-}$ and $[OsBr_6]^{2-}$. With alkalis the 'perosmate' ion $[Os^{VIII}O_4(OH)_2]^{2-}$ is formed in solution, but this is easily reduced on heating or with alcohol to $[OsO_2(OH)_4]^{2-}$. Osmium tetroxide will react with donor molecules such as ammonia and phosphorus trihalides to give 1:1 or 2:1 adducts[109], and also forms adducts with a number of organic molecules and organic bases[49].

Polarographic and coulometric studies show that in acid solution the tetroxide is reduced at the dropping electrode to the (VI) and (IV) oxidation states, in alkali to the (VI), (V) and (IV) states and in cyanide solutions to the (VI), (III) and (II) states[47,174]. Polarographic studies have also been made with a view to using the OsO_4/$[OsO_2(OH)_4]^{2-}$ couple as a redox system for oxygen transfer[189]. Addition of osmium tetroxide to neutral solutions of hydrogen peroxide causes the peroxide reduction wave to shift from $-0{\cdot}8$ to $-0{\cdot}1$ v (measured against a standard calomel electrode (S.C.E.)) suggesting perhaps that an osmium peroxy complex has been formed; in acidic and buffered solutions of hydrogen peroxide a kinetic wave appears at $+0{\cdot}25$ v due to the repeated oxidation of an electroreduction product of the tetroxide on the electrode surface[91].

Kinetic studies have been reported on the reaction between the tetroxide and hydrobromic acid at 100°, and osmium (VII) and osmium (VI) intermediates were postulated[145].

Osmium tetroxide in organic chemistry. The compound has found extensive use in organic chemistry as an oxidizing agent and as a catalyst for oxidations. An ethereal solution of the compound (benzene, cyclohexane and dioxan have also been used as solvents) will react at room temperature with olefins to give cyclic esters which can be decomposed to *cis* diols. It was shown by Criegee that the course of reaction is likely to be[48]

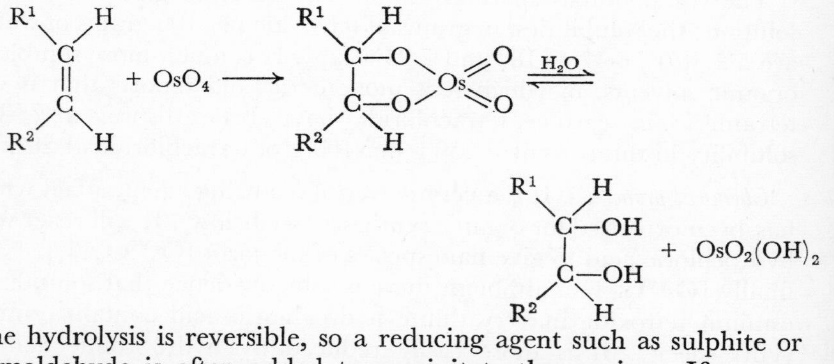

$$R^1HC{=}CHR^2 + OsO_4 \longrightarrow \begin{matrix} R^1HC{-}O \\ | \\ R^2HC{-}O \end{matrix}\!\!>Os(=O)_2 \xrightleftharpoons{H_2O} \begin{matrix} R^1HC{-}OH \\ | \\ R^2HC{-}OH \end{matrix} + OsO_2(OH)_2$$

The hydrolysis is reversible, so a reducing agent such as sulphite or formaldehyde is often added to precipitate the osmium. If a non-hydroxylic solvent is used the intermediate osmium (VI) ester can be isolated and then hydrolysed to the *cis* diol in a separate step. In the presence of tertiary bases such as pyridine the reagent is sufficiently reactive to attack the π systems of aromatic hydrocarbons; thus from anthracene a tetrol is produced

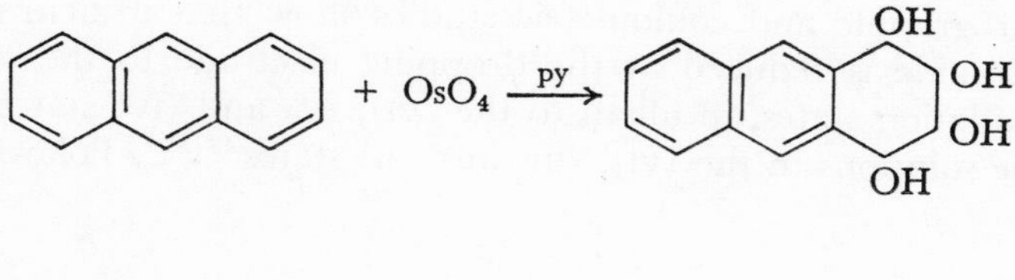

$$\text{anthracene} + OsO_4 \xrightarrow{py} \text{tetrol (OH, OH, OH, OH)}$$

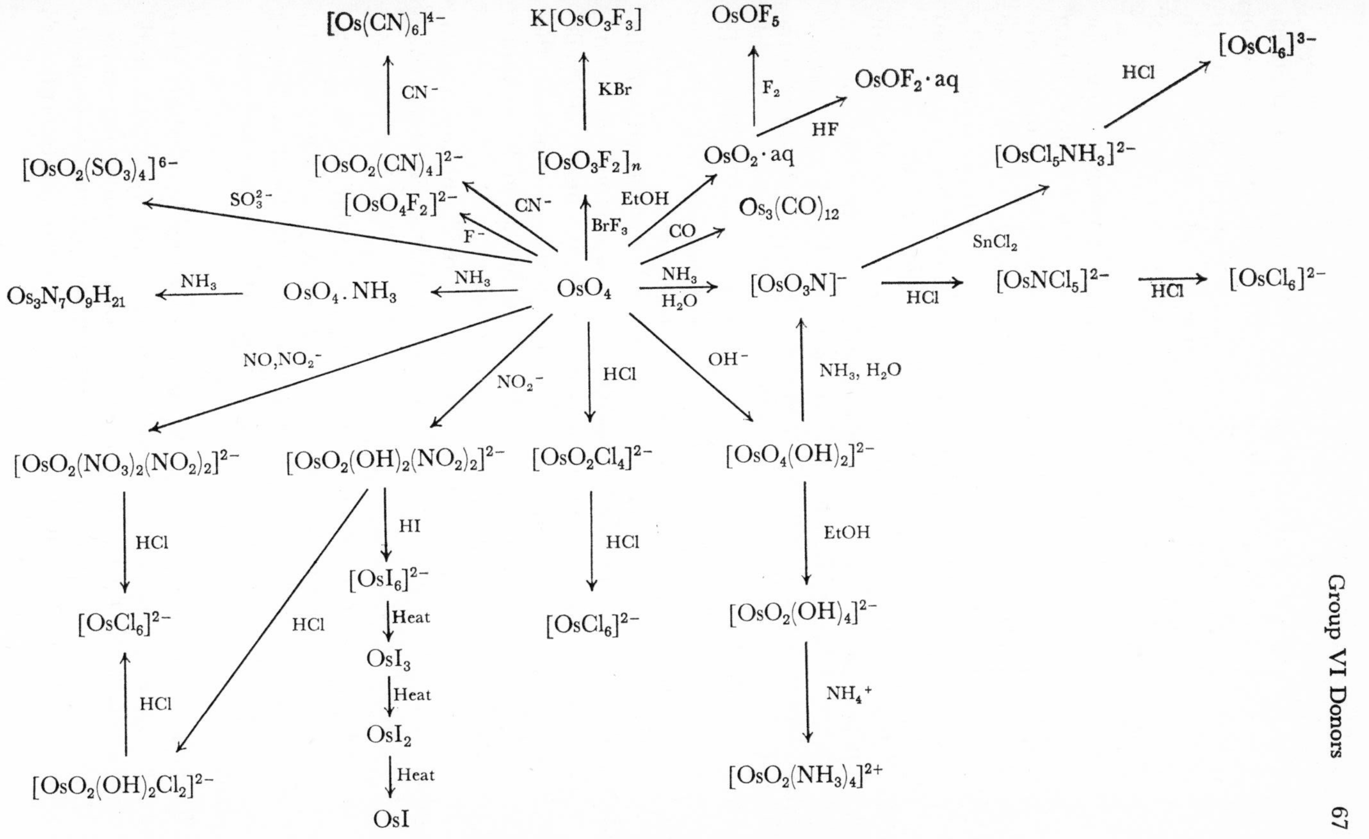

Figure 3.3 Reactions of osmium tetroxide

To some extent osmium tetroxide has been supplanted for these purposes by the Lemieux reagent (periodic acid with a trace of permanganate), which is safer and very much cheaper to use, but it is still used for reactions with substances (such as steroid hormones) which are only available in small quantities when the smoothness of reaction is advantageous.

It can also be used as a catalytic reagent in hydroxylations; for example aqueous solutions of chlorates become strong hydroxylating agents if a little tetroxide is added. Barium and silver chlorates are particularly effective in this respect, and a wide range of organic hydroxylations can be carried out with such a reagent, especially when the compounds involved are soluble in water. The mechanism is obscure; it has been suggested that intermediates such as $OsO_4.ClO_3^-$ are involved[53], that free hypochlorous acid is present and functions as a source of free radicals[238]; or that the reaction proceeds through a cyclic osmium (VI) ester which is then reoxidized by the chlorate to tetroxide[48,49]. Milas's reagent, which consists of a solution of hydrogen peroxide in *t*-butyl alcohol, will not react with olefinic double bonds until a little osmium tetroxide is added. In such cases the hydroxylation can be carried out in non-aqueous solvents. Again the mechanism is not understood, but probably involves a cyclic osmium (VI) ester which is then hydrolysed and the osmium oxidized[48,49,180]. Other solvents such as acetone, ether and benzene can be used. Electron-attracting substituents in alicyclic compounds and stilbenes retard the reactions of these olefins with the tetroxide[112a]. A recent review on olefin hydroxylation by osmium tetroxide and other reagents has been published[108].

Ruthenium tetroxide is a much more violent oxidizing agent than osmium tetroxide, and its applications in organic chemistry so far are few (cf. p. 147).

Biochemical applications. Osmium tetroxide (as 'osmic acid', a 1% aqueous solution) is much used as a microscopic staining reagent, and is particularly useful in staining specimens for electron microscopy. It also has limited uses as a fungicide and as an enzyme inhibitor.

Toxicology. The compound is very toxic, attacking particularly the eyes, nose and throat, but fortunately it has a characteristic and powerful odour. A concentration of 100 microgrammes per cubic metre is sufficient to bring on severe conjunctival irritation (a method for the estimation of osmium tetroxide in industrial atmospheres has been given[165]). There is only one fatality from tetroxide poisoning recorded in the literature, that of a French industrial worker, who died in 1874 from capillary bronchitis and confluent pneumonia brought on by working in an atmosphere containing osmium tetroxide in a platinum metal extraction factory near Paris. The vapour may cause conjunctivitis, corneal ulceration and temporary blindness, and the latter may last for a number of weeks in particularly severe cases. Slight exposure to the vapour may, as the author can attest, cause mistiness of vision for a few days, sufficient to cause haloes to appear around bright lights and to make reading difficult. There is no evidence for cumulative poisoning by the compound. There are a number of reviews on the toxicology of osmium[22,124,165]. Since almost all osmium compounds are very easily oxidized to the tetroxide, great care is necessary in working with them, and a well-ventilated fume cupboard is essential. Because of the high vapour pressure of the solid tetroxide (11 mm at 27°) care must be exercised in handling this too.

Tolerance limits for tetroxide vapour in the atmosphere have been given[220].

Osmium tetrasulphide, OsS_4, has not been definitely established. Claus obtained a product which he believed was this compound from the reaction between the tetroxide in hydrochloric acid and hydrogen sulphide[43] but Juza was unable to prepare a pure sample by this method[140]. Two equally doubtful oxysulphides have been reported:

$Os_3O_5S_7.2H_2O$, made by the action of hydrogen sulphide on a neutral solution of the tetroxide, and **$OsO_3S.1\frac{1}{2}H_2O$,** prepared by dehydrating the above compound; the latter species will react vigorously with ammonia to give a nitrogen-containing species of unknown constitution[175].

Oxy and hydroxy complexes

These are represented by the '*perosmates*' (sometimes called 'osmenates').

Potassium perosmate, $K_2[OsO_4(OH)_2]$, is probably the best established of this rather unstable series of compounds. It can be made by treating osmium tetroxide with cold potassium hydroxide solution, and forms deep red crystals, very soluble in water and very easily reduced to potassium osmate $K_2[OsO_2(OH)_4]$[90a, 148]. The infra-red spectra of the compound and of its deuterated form suggest the above formulation with a *trans* configuration of the two hydroxide groups[102]. Ammonium, caesium and barium salts have been made, and also a caesium and a rubidium salt in which the Cs (or Rb):Os ratio is only 1:1[148]: these probably contain the $[\mathbf{OsO_4(OH)(H_2O)}]^-$ ion. There are frequent references in the literature to 'osmic acid', H_2OsO_5, which is supposed to exist in aqueous solutions of the tetroxide. If such a species exists in which the coordination number of osmium is greater than four it is likely to be $OsO_4(H_2O)_2$ or $[OsO_4(OH)_2]^{2-}$. The Raman spectrum of the tetroxide in aqueous solution suggests that the major species present is the tetrahedral tetroxide[101a].

Reaction of osmium tetroxide with liquid hydrocyanic acid gives, after evaporation of the solution, a white crystalline complex supposed to be $H_2[OsO_4(CN)_2]$[151a]; in view of the known reducing power of cyanide, however, it is more likely that the known hexacyanoosmic acid, $H_4[Os(CN)_6]$, is produced.

Osmium (VII)

Oxy complexes with this oxidation state have recently been reported and form an important addition to the chemistry of the element.

$\mathbf{K_3[OsO_5]}$ was made by Scholder by heating potassium osmate and potassium superoxide together in a stream of nitrogen at 500°. The compound is black, and in water it disproportionates to the tetroxide and potassium osmate. The sodium and barium salts were also made[214].

$\mathbf{Na_5[OsO_6]}$ was obtained by heating osmium with sodium monoxide in an oxygen stream at 550°. The compound is black; lithium and barium salts were also made[214]. The lithium salt has a hexagonal structure[215] and gives $Li_6[OsO_6]$ when heated with lithium oxide[214]. $Ba_2Li[OsO_6]$ was prepared by heating barium oxide, lithium oxide and osmium metal in evacuated silica capsules to 1000°C, and a mixed series $Ba_2Li[Os_xRe_{1-x}O_6]$ was similarly made. X-ray powder photographs showed that all these compounds had the ordered perovskite structure, and for $Ba_2Li[OsO_6]$ a magnetic moment of 1·44 BM at room temperature was reported[218]; the compounds have high electrical conductivities.

Heptavalent oxy complexes have been proposed as intermediates in the osmium tetroxide–hydrobromic acid reaction[145].

Osmium (VI)

The existence of **osmium trioxide, OsO_3,** in the solid state has not been definitely established, although it has been suggested that it is formed when the dioxide is heated to about 650° in osmium tetroxide vapour[205]. It has been reported that the black precipitate obtained by heating potassium osmate with alcohol is $OsO_3.H_2O$[178], but it seems more likely that this is a hydrated form of the dioxide. Decomposition of the cyclic osmium (VI) esters referred to below gives a product which may be $OsO_3.nH_2O$; a pyridine complex $OsO_3.2py$ is known (see p. 82)[48,49]. There is, however, definite evidence for the existence of OsO_3 in the gas phase and mass spectrometric measurements give a value of 12·3 ± 1 ev for its ionization potential[107]; thermodynamic quantities have been estimated for it[181a].

Osmium (VI) esters

These complexes have already been mentioned in connection with the organic applications of the tetroxide. In the course of his classic work on the hydroxylations of olefins Criegee isolated a large number of cyclic esters of the form*

```
  |      O      |               |
 —C—O\   ||   /O—C—            —C—O\
  |    Os         |     and     |     OsO2
 —C—O/      \O—C—              —C—O/
  |             |               |
```

and also some as pyridine adducts[48,49]. These cyclic esters may contain Os=O or $Os(OH)_2$ groups, the metal remaining hexavalent in either case. Recently diesters of osmium (IV) of this type have been claimed[146a] but there seems to be no reason to suppose that these are not in fact osmium (VI) derivatives. The space group of $OsO_5C_4Me_8$ (the osmium (VI) diester of pinacol) is D_4^6; a = 10·15 Å and c = 7·285 Å[181b].

Oxy and hydroxy complexes

$Na_4[OsO_5]$ can be made by heating $Na_5(OsO_6)$ to 800°[214].

$Li_6[OsO_6]$ is prepared by heating $Li_5[OsO_6]$ with an equivalent of lithium monoxide to 800°, and a barium salt was also made[214]. Salts of the form $A_2B[OsO_6]$ (A = Sr, Ca; B = Mg, Ca, Sr, Zn, Cd) were made by heating osmium metal with a mixture of the A and B oxides in oxygen to 800°. The compounds have an ordered perovskite structure, and the magnetic moment of $Ba_2Ca[OsO_6]$ at room temperatures was found to be 2·2 BM [218].

'Osmyl' complexes

These form an important group of compounds for this element. They contain a linear O=Os=O unit, four other ligands in an equatorial plane completing an axially distorted octahedron (cf. Figure 3.5), and they are all diamagnetic. X-ray data for *trans*-$K_2[OsO_2Cl_4]$ (p. 49) [152] and for *trans*-$K_2[OsO_2(OH)_4]$ (see below) [191] show that, in this linear group, the osmium–oxygen bond length is 1·75 Å (similar to that of osmium tetroxide, 1·717 Å) which corresponds to a double rather than to a single bond. Infrared studies on a range of these complexes also suggest that in all of them there is double bonding in the osmyl linkage[102].

Lott and Symons have explained the diamagnetism of these complexes by assuming that the tetragonal distortion of the octahedron ($O_h \rightarrow D_{4h}$) brought about by the strongly π-donating oxide groups is sufficient to cause pairing of the spins of the two *d* electrons in the lower d_{xy} level, assuming the axis of the osmyl group to define the *z* axis [160]; the transitions observed in the electronic spectrum of $[OsO_2(OH)_4]^{2-}$ can then be satisfactorily explained [160]. The bonding in osmyl complexes may be visualized in terms of two three-centre

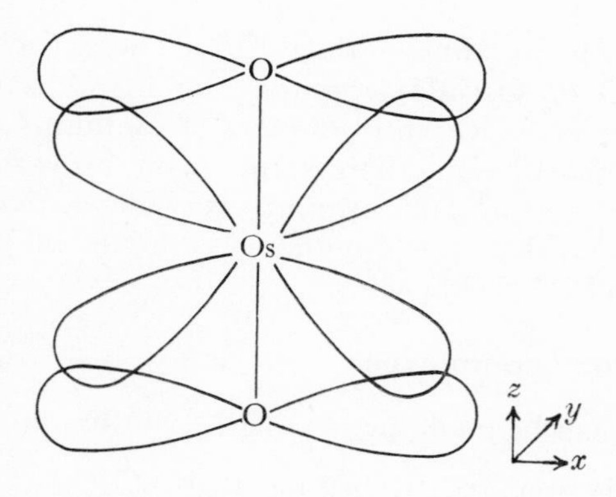

Figure 3.4 Bonding in the 'osmyl' group ($2p_x$–$5d_{xz}$–$2p_x$ overlap): there will be a similar $2p_y$–$5d_{yz}$–$2p_y$ three-centre orbital in the plane perpendicular to the page

molecular orbitals, each of the same energy and containing four electrons, formed by overlap of $p_x - d_{xz} - p_x$ and $p_y - d_{yz} - p_y$ orbitals as shown in Figure 3.4.

The known osmyl complexes are listed in Table 3.5. The following species deserve special comment.

Potassium osmate, $K_2[OsO_2(OH)_4]$, is a useful starting material for other osmium complexes, and is most easily made by reduction of $K_2[OsO_4(OH)_2]$ in solution with ethanol. Barium and sodium salts are also known, all being purple in colour[88,160]. The potassium salt was long thought to be $K_2[OsO_4].2\,H_2O$ and to have a tetrahedral anion as has potassium ruthenate, but its diamagnetism led to the suggestion that it was an osmyl complex[160], and x-ray studies confirmed this[191]. The shorter distances in the osmyl group are clearly shown. Infrared spectra have been measured on the potassium salt[102]. Potassium osmate will react with halogen acids to give $K_2[OsO_2(OH)_2X_2]$ or $K_2[OsO_2X_4]$ (X = Cl, Br) or, on prolonged treatment, $K_2[OsX_6]$ (X = Cl, Br, I). Other chemical reactions of the complex are outlined in Figure 3.3.

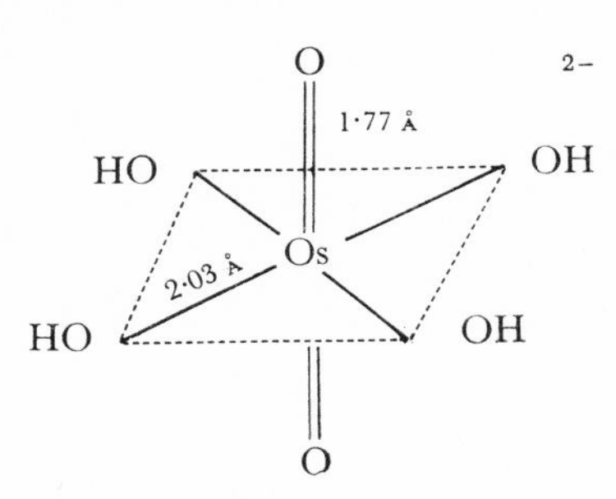

Figure 3.5 The structure of the osmate ion in potassium osmate

$K_2[OsO_2(NO_3)_2(NO_2)_2]$ is made as orange crystals by the action of nitric oxide on a solution of osmium tetroxide in potassium nitrite; it was originally formulated as $K_2[OsO_2(NO_2)_4]$[257] but infrared spectra show that both coordinated nitrate and nitro groups are present[102]. Although **$K[OsO_2(CH_3COO)_3]$**, made from $K_2[OsO_2(OCH_3)_4]$ and acetic acid, is apparently five coordinated[48,49], it is probable that one of the three acetate groups is bidentate or that the complex is polynuclear.

$Na_6[OsO_2(SO_3)_4]$ may involve metal–oxygen or metal–sulphur bonds, probably the latter. The product of the reaction between sulphur dioxide and potassium perosmate[201], whose structure is unknown, may contain $[OsO_2(SO_3)_4]^{6-}$ or $[OsO_2(SO_3)_2]^{2-}$. The 'oxyosmyl' complexes, originally formulated as $[OsO_3X_2]^{2-}$ (X = Cl, Br, NO_2, $\frac{1}{2}$ox)[257] are simply osmyl complexes of the form $[OsO_2(OH)_2X_2]^{2-}$[102,103] and are listed as such in Table 3.5.

The important 'osmyl' complex $K_2[OsO_2(OH)_2(NO_2)_2]$ is considered on p. 83.

Osmium (V)

Os_2O_5 has been claimed as a reduction product of potassium osmate[122], but it is likely that the compound obtained was in fact the hydrated dioxide. There is no evidence for the existence of Os_2O_5 in the vapour phase.

$Sr_2Cr^{III}[OsO_6]$ has been made by the reaction

$$2\ Sr_3[OsO_6] + 3\ CrO_2 + Os \rightarrow 3\ Sr_2Cr[OsO_6]$$

in a sealed silica capsule at 1000°[218]. There is polarographic and coulometric evidence for the transient existence of an osmium (V) oxy or hydroxy species during the reduction of osmium (VI) in 0·5 M sodium hydroxide[47].

It has been claimed that **Os_2S_5** can be made by heating **'OsS_4'** *in vacuo*.

Osmium (IV)

Oxygen complexes of osmium (IV) and of lower oxidation states probably all contain metal–oxygen single bonds.

Osmium dioxide, OsO_2, is normally made by heating osmium metal in a stream of nitric oxide at 650° or by heating the metal to 600° in a stream of nitrogen mixed with osmium tetroxide vapour[205]. The anhydrous oxide appears to exist in both a brown and a black form; the first, which is rather less reactive, has the rutile structure like RuO_2 (a = 4·51, c = 3·19 Å)[94] and can be made by heating the black form to 400°. Both dissolve in hydrochloric acid to give the hexachloroosmate (IV) anion, and will react with oxygen at high temperatures to give the tetroxide. A mono- and a dihydrate are known, the latter being made by alcohol reduction of neutral solutions of the tetroxide and the monohydrate by heating the dihydrate[205]. Both of these are black and have similar properties to the anhydrous compounds; they easily form colloidal 'solutions'.

The ionization potential of the gaseous species has been estimated as 11·2 ev[56] and thermodynamic quantities have been estimated for the solid[181a].

Chemical properties of the dioxide are shown in Figure 3.3.

Osmium (IV) diesters have been claimed[146a] (see footnote p. 71).

Hydroxy complex

A hydroxy complex of osmium (IV) has been detected polarographically by reduction of osmium tetroxide in 0·5 N hydroxide: it can be anodically oxidized to an osmium (V) species[174] and may be $[Os(OH)_6]^{2-}$.

Acetylacetone complexes

A number of such compounds, involving other ligands as well, are known (see Table 3.9). An osmium (IV) acetylacetone complex is probably formed as a by-product during the preparation of Os $acac_3$[64].

Gluconate complexes

These complexes (gluconate:osmium ratio of 2:1) have been reported together with polarographic and spectrophotometric data[209], but none was isolated from solution.

Osmium disulphide, OsS_2, can be made from the elements or by the action of hydrogen sulphide on hexachloroosmate (IV) ion. It is black and has the pyrites structure (a = 5·6075 ± 0·002 Å)[143]. The dissociation pressures at high temperatures have been measured[140] and thermodynamic data obtained[163]. It is probably the only stable sulphide of the metal[140]. The action of hydrogen sulphide on an alkaline solution of $[OsCl_6]^{2-}$ is said to give a red solution which may contain $[Os(SH)_6]^{2-}$; on acidification OsS_2 is precipitated[190a].

$H_2Os_2O_3S_2$ was claimed as the product of reaction between 'osmium trioxide' and hydrogen sulphide[178]. The **diselenide** and **ditelluride, $OsSe_2$** and **$OsTe_2$,** can be made from the elements at about 800°[258a]; they have the pyrites structure with a = 5·933 ± 0·002 for the diselenide and a = 6·369 ± 0·003 Å for the ditelluride[222]. Like the sulphide they are insoluble in alkalis and acids, apart from nitric acid which oxidizes them to the tetroxide.

Sulphito complexes

A substantial number of these have been reported, and are listed in Table 3.6. In most cases the formulae have not been fully authenticated but it is likely that most of them in fact contain osmium (II).

Thiocyanate complexes

The only thiocyanate osmium complexes reported are those obtained by mixing thiocyanate with osmium tetroxide in aqueous solution; the resulting species have been studied spectrophotometrically but not isolated, and it has been suggested that $[Os(SCN)_6]^{2-}$, $[Os(SCN)_4]aq$ and $[Os(SCN)_2]^{2+}$ aq are present[3]. (See also Tables 3.9 and 3.11.)

Dialkyl and diaryl dithiophosphate ($(RO)_2PS_2^-$) complexes

They have been studied spectrophotometrically in connection with the analysis of the element[27], but were not isolated from solution.

Osmium (III)

Os_2O_3 was claimed (as a trihydrate) by Claus who made it by hydrolysis of hexachloroosmate (III), and also as an anhydrous product by reaction of osmium metal with the vapour of the tetroxide[43] (this reaction, according to later workers[205], gives the dioxide). Its existence must be regarded as dubious.

Hydroxy complexes

$[Os(OH)_6]^{3-}$ may be present in the brown solution formed when 'Os_2O_3' is dissolved in alkali[43]. There is also polarographic evidence for the existence of osmium (III) species in reduced solutions of the tetroxide in both acid and alkaline solutions[47,174]

Acetylacetone (acac) complexes

The tris species **Os acac$_3$** can be prepared by reaction of the ligand with $[OsBr_6]^{3-}$ solutions. Purple diamagnetic acetylacetone bromo complexes, probably containing osmium (IV) or (VI), are also formed in the course of the reaction[64] (see also Table 3.9). The magnetic moment at room temperatures is 1·8 BM[64]. The near infrared spectrum of the complex in the solid state and in solution were measured and electronic transitions assigned[56a]. The mass spectrum of the compound was measured[162a].

Thiourea and selenourea complexes

$[Os(CS(NH_2)_2)_6]Cl_3$ can be made by the reaction between sodium hexachloroosmate (IV) and thiourea[208,218a]. It was for a long time thought that this was an osmium (IV) compound $[Os(CS(NH_2)_2)_6]Cl_3(OH)$[221], but work by Sauerbrann and Sandell showed it to have the formula given above. An approximate stability constant was derived for the complex[208]. It is likely, though not certain, that it has metal–sulphur rather than metal–nitrogen bonds.

$\mathbf{[Os(CSe(NH_2)_2)_8]^{3+}}$ has been reported in solution and its stability constant estimated[190]; it seems, however, more likely that the complex is six rather than eight coordinated.

Osmium (III) complexes of 5-chloro-8-mercaptoquinoline have been reported[5a].

Osmium (II)

Osmium monoxide, OsO, is said to be formed as a dark grey, amorphous powder when $K_6[Os(SO_3)_5H_2O]$ is heated, or in hydrated form when osmium sulphite, $OsSO_3$, is heated with concentrated alkali[43,185a]. There is, however, very little evidence that the products are the monoxide. Band spectra of gaseous OsO have been measured[197].

$\mathbf{[Os(CS(NH_2)_2)_6]^{2+}}$ has been made (in solution only) by reduction of the hexathiourea osmate (III) ion with chromous salts[208].

A **bisdithiobenzil** osmium (II) complex has been briefly reported; it is diamagnetic and probably has a square planar structure[215a].

$\mathbf{OsSO_3}$, 'osmium sulphite', is said to be formed as an indigo-blue material when sulphur dioxide reacts with a solution of osmium tetroxide or potassium osmate[43]. Sulphito complexes of osmium (II) are summarized in Table 3.6: it is possible that some 'osmium(IV)' sulphito species do in fact contain divalent osmium.

GROUP V DONORS

Osmium is the only element of the four known to form a number of stable nitrido complexes in which there is a metal–nitrogen triple bond (in view of the existence of these the absence of mono-oxo osmium complexes is remarkable, since formally the ligands in such species are the isoelectronic O^{2-} and N^{3-} ions). Oxidation states of (IV) and (III) are found associated with ligands such as ammonia and ethylenediamine which have no π-acceptor properties, whereas π-acceptor ligands having nitrogen, phosphorus, arsenic and antimony donor atoms coordinate to osmium (III) and (II).

Osmium (VIII)

Nitrido complexes

These are, as already mentioned in the introduction, commoner for osmium than for any other metal. X-ray studies show that in these complexes the metal–nitrogen distance is very short and corresponds to a triple bond; this may be thought of as a σ bond and two π bonds, the latter being formed by overlap of the $2p_x$ and $2p_y$ orbitals of nitrogen with acceptor orbitals on osmium. The bonding is represented diagrammatically for $[OsNCl_5]^{2-}$ in Figure 3.6 (the same type of bonding is envisaged for mono-oxo complexes, e.g. $OsOCl_4$). It seems very likely that the nitride ligand, which is formally N^{3-}, is a very strong π donor, and as such is to be found only with high oxidation state complexes.

$K[OsO_3N]$, potassium osmiamate, can be prepared by adding aqueous ammonia to a solution of potassium perosmate, $K_2[OsO_4(OH)_2]$. It forms pale yellow crystals, only slightly soluble in water[18,44]; salts with the other alkali metals, barium, zinc, silver, thallium, mercury and ammonium have also been made. The sodium salt is very soluble in water, but all the others are only slightly soluble. Werner showed in 1901 that the previously postulated formulation as the nitrosyl derivative $[OsO_2(NO)]^-$ was unlikely, since thermal decomposition of the salts gave pure nitrogen rather than any oxides of nitrogen, while concentrated halogen acids gave oxygen-free salts of the form $M^I_2[OsNX_5]$, suggesting that the nitrogen is directly bonded to the metal. He proposed that the complex anion was $[OsO_3N]^-$, with three oxygen and one nitrogen atoms bonded to the osmium[251].

An x-ray crystal structure study of potassium osmiamate showed this to be the case: the four ligands in $[OsO_3N]^-$ are disposed at the

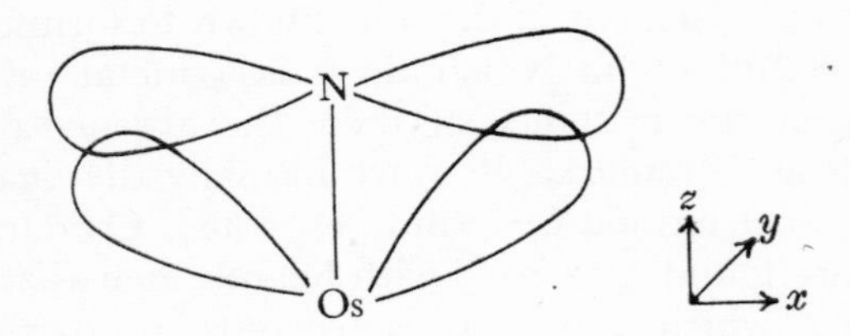

Figure 3.6 $2p_x$–$5d_{xz}$ overlap in $[OsNCl_5]^{2-}$. There will be a similar $2p_y$–$5d_{yz}$ overlap in the yz plane

corners of a tetragonal bisphenoid about the osmium (the structure of potassium ruthenate is similar). The osmium–oxygen and osmium–nitrogen bond lengths were both found to be 1·56 Å, though these are not accurate values[129]. The infrared and Raman spectra of the sodium and potassium salts are fully consistent with this (C_{3v}) structure (see below)[263].

$\nu_1(A_1)$	$\nu_2(A_1)$	$\nu_3(A_1)$	$\nu_4(E)$	$\nu_5(E)$	$\nu_6(E)$	
1021	897	309	871	372	309	cm^{-1}

The osmium–nitrogen stretching frequency at 1021 cm^{-1} shifts to 993 cm^{-1} on ^{15}N substitution[155]. Force constant calculations were made for the anion using the infrared and Raman data[263]; a discussion has recently been given of metal–nitrogen stretching force constants in this and related species[96a].

The free acid, $HOsO_3N$, can be made in solution by the action of sulphuric acid on barium osmiamate, or in the anhydrous state by the action of liquid ammonia on osmium tetroxide[109]. The infrared spectrum of the latter product suggests that the hydrogen atom is attached to one of the oxygen atoms, so the anhydrous compound is best formulated as $Os(OH)O_2N$[104]. The action of ammonia on $Zn[OsO_3N]_2$ is said to yield **$Zn[OsO_3N(NH_3)_2]_2$** as yellow crystals[88a]. There is some confusion as to the nature of $(NH_4)_2[OsO_4(OH)_2]$[148] and $(NH_4)[OsO_3N]$[88a], since both can apparently be made from aqueous ammonia and osmium tetroxide.

Chemical properties of potassium osmiamate are indicated in Figure 3.3.

Imide complexes

Osmium is the only element of the platinum group which has been found to form this type of complex.

$Me_3CN{=}OsO_3$ can be made as a yellow crystalline solid (decomposing at 112°) from *t*-butylamine and osmium tetroxide. The infrared spectrum of the substance has a band at 1184 cm^{-1}, which was assigned to a metal–nitrogen stretch[44]; this, however, seems very high for a metal–nitrogen double bond vibration.

Ammines

The only one reported for this oxidation state is **$OsO_4.NH_3$**, an orange solid which may be sublimed from the reaction mixture of liquid ammonia with osmium tetroxide[109] (other products of the complicated ammonia–OsO_4 reaction are osmiamic acid and the polynuclear species $Os_3N_7H_{21}O_9$ considered below). Infrared spectra of $OsO_4.NH_3$ show that the ammonia group is coordinated to the osmium, and suggest that the overall symmetry is C_{4v}[100]. Solutions of osmium tetroxide in concentrated aqueous ammonia contain the $[OsO_3N]^-$ ion but not $OsO_4.NH_3$, according to studies of the Raman spectrum[101a].

An *amine complex*, $C_6H_{12}N_4{\cdot}2OsO_4$, can be prepared from hexamethylenetetramine and osmium tetroxide. It forms orange needles[221a].

Pyridine complexes

The adducts $\mathbf{2OsO_4.py_4.(C_4H_4Cl_2)}$ and $\mathbf{OsO_4.py.(C_4H_4Cl_2)}$ can be made from 1,4-dichlorobutadiene, pyridine and osmium tetroxide[50], and $\mathbf{OsO_4.py}$ can be made by the action of pyridine on a solution of osmium tetroxide in cyclohexane[49]. The structures are not known.

No osmium (VII) complexes with Group V donors have been reported.

Osmium (VI)

Nitrido complexes

$\mathbf{K_2[OsNCl_5]}$ can be made as reddish-purple crystals by the action of hydrochloric acid on potassium osmiamate (ammonium, caesium and rubidium salts have also been made[44]). The potassium salt is very soluble in water, but the solution rapidly decomposes unless a little hydrochloric acid is added to it. X-ray crystal structure studies on the potassium salt indicate that the anion has a distorted octahedral structure (C_{4v}) with an osmium–nitrogen bond length of 1·61 Å; the four equatorial chlorine atoms are at 2·40 Å and the axial chlorine (*trans* to the nitride group) at 2·16 Å from the metal atom[2,236]. This shortening of the *trans* metal–chlorine bond is unexpected, since the triply bonded nitride group, as expected, exerts some *trans* labilizing effect. In nitrido complexes of this type the axial group is labile to substitution by water; $K_2[OsNBr_5]$ will very easily lose a bromide group to give *trans*-$K[OsN(H_2O)Br_4]$, and attempts to prepare $K_2[OsN(CN)_5]$ give in all cases *trans*-$K[OsN(H_2O)(CN)_4]$[104]. Volkov and Dyatkina have suggested that the observed bond shortening in $K_2[OsNCl_5]$ is due to an osmium–chlorine δ bond[236], but it is difficult to see why the four equatorial chlorine groups should not also form such bonds with the metal. The infrared spectrum of $K_2[OsNCl_5]$ has been measured[104,155] and the value of the metal–nitrogen force constant discussed[96a]. The metal–nitrogen stretching frequency ν_1 is at 1081 cm^{-1}. Examination of the far infrared spectra of $K_2[OsNCl_5]$ showed no bands which could be attributed to the single short metal–chlorine bond[104].

$K_2[OsNBr_5]$ and **$K[OsN(H_2O)Br_4]$** are both formed as ruby-red crystals, very soluble in water to give unstable red solutions, when potassium osmiamate is treated with hydrobromic acid. A brief report of an x-ray crystal structure analysis of the latter complex shows that the anion has a distorted octahedral (C_{4v}) structure with the water molecule *trans* to the nitride group (the osmium–nitrogen distance was 1·61 Å and the osmium–oxygen distance 2·07 Å[2]). Infrared spectra of this salt and its deuterated form have been measured and skeletal modes assigned[104].

$K[OsN(H_2O)X_4]$ (X = CN, $\frac{1}{2}$ox) and **$K[OsN(H_2O)X_2(OH)_2]$** (X = F, $\frac{1}{2}$ox) can be made from potassium osmiamate and the appropriate acids. The infrared spectra indicate that in each case the water group is *trans* to the nitrogen ligand; the frequency of the osmium–nitrogen stretching mode decreases with increasing electronegativity of the X ligands, an effect also observed with transition-metal oxy complexes[104]. All these osmium (VI) complexes are diamagnetic, due no doubt to the axial distortion brought about by the strongly π-donating nitride group (cf. p. 78) (Figure 3.6).

Prolonged action of liquid ammonia on osmium tetroxide yields a trinuclear complex, **$Os_3N_7O_9H_{21}$**, originally formulated as[240,244]

```
H3N       OH   HO        OH   HO       NH3
   \     /       \      /       \     /
  O=Os=N-----------Os-----------N=Os=O
   /     \       /      \       /     \
H3N       OH   H2N       OH   HO       NH3
```

However, infrared studies[101] on the compound fully substituted with ^{15}N suggest the alternative structure

```
HO        OH   H3N       OH   HO       NH3
   \     /       \      /       \     /
 HO—Os=N-----------Os-----------N=Os—OH
   /     \       ///    \       /     \
H3N       OH   N         NH3  HO       OH
```

On heating this another binuclear species $\mathbf{Os_3N_5O_5H_7}$ is formed, and the structure suggested for this is[244]

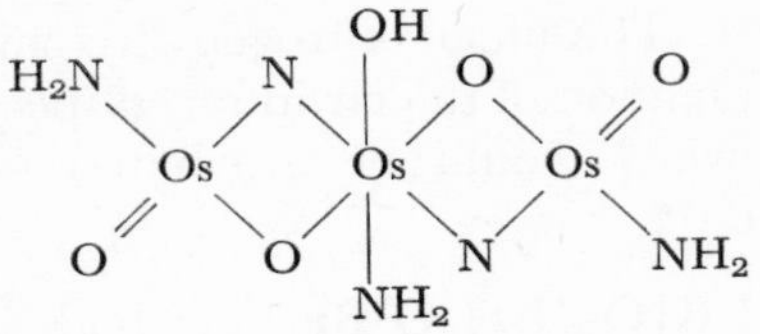

```
                        OH
  H2N          N        |        O             O
     \       /   \      |      /   \         //
       Os              Os              Os
     //  \       /      |      \      /   \
   O        O           |        N          NH2
                       NH2
```

but this seems unlikely, if only because of the known reluctance of the amide group to function as a monodentate ligand.

Ammines

$\mathbf{[OsO_2(NH_3)_4]Cl_2}$ can be made by the reactions[257] in solution

$$K_2[OsO_2(OH)_4] + 4\,NH_4Cl \rightarrow [OsO_2(NH_3)_4]Cl_2 + 2\,KCl + 4\,H_2O$$

By using the appropriate ammonium salts a nitrate, nitrite and oxalate can also be made: all the complexes are yellow and only slightly soluble in water. Infrared studies on the chloride, substituted with deuterium and with ^{15}N, have been made and the vibrational modes assigned[100]. These are 'osmyl' complexes with the oxygen atoms *trans* to each other.

The reaction product of aqueous ammonia and potassium osmate is a stable light brown material supposed to be 'osmiamide', $\mathbf{OsO_2(NH_2)_2}$. With potassium hydroxide this evolves ammonia and regenerates the osmate, and with hydrochloric acid it gives a material, said to be $[OsO_2(NH_3)_2]Cl_2$ which gives crystalline precipitates of unknown constitution with oxalate ion[91b].

Amine complexes

$\mathbf{[Os(en\text{–}H)_4]I_2}$ (the en–H group is ethylenediamine with one proton removed, i.e. $H_2N.(CH_2)_2.NH^-$) can be made by the action of ethylenediamine on $[Os(en\text{–}H)_2en]I_2$ (see below). On the basis of its formula and observed diamagnetism it has been suggested that it has an eight-coordinate structure[63], but more evidence is necessary to confirm this.

$\mathbf{Os\ py_2O_3}$ is formed as olive-green lamellar crystals when alcohol and pyridine are added to a solution of osmium tetroxide in cyclohexane. The structure may be five coordinate[48], although an 'osmyl' formulation as $OsO_2(OH)_2py_2$ is also a possibility. With olefins, the compound will give cyclic esters of the form[48]

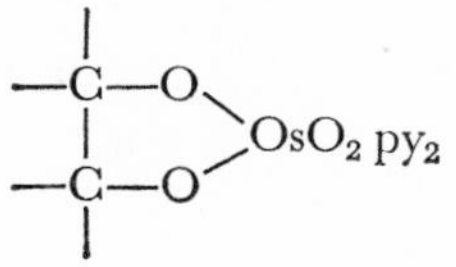

$$\begin{array}{l} \quad | \\ -C-O\diagdown \\ \quad | \qquad\quad OsO_2\,py_2 \\ -C-O\diagup \\ \quad | \end{array}$$

(these could be osmyl complexes with linear O=Os=O groups).

Nitro complexes

$K_2[OsO_2(NO_2)_2(OH)_2]$, an 'osmyl' complex, can be made as beautiful brown needle-shaped crystals, which are slightly soluble in water to give an unstable violet solution, by the action of an aqueous solution of potassium nitrite on potassium osmate or osmium tetroxide[257]. It was originally formulated as $K_2[OsO_3(NO_2)_2]$[257] but later infrared work established the octahedral osmyl structure[102,103]. Like potassium osmate it is a useful starting material for the preparation of osmium halo complexes: gentle action of halogen acids will give $K_2[OsO_2(OH)_2X_2]$ (X = Cl, Br) and $K_2[Os(NO)X_5]$ (X = Cl, Br, I), and more prolonged action gives the hexahaloosmates $K_2[OsX_6]$ (X = Cl, Br, I).

$K_2[OsO_2(NO_2)_4]$ was originally so formulated[257] but has recently been shown to be $K_2[OsO_2(NO_3)_2(NO_2)_2]$ (see p. 73)[103].

Osmium (V)

The two compounds with Group V donors claimed to contain pentavalent osmium have not been fully characterized. The supposed **Os_2NCl_7**, made by heating ammonium hexachloroosmate to 350° in a current of chlorine[146], is probably an osmium (IV) compound, **Os_2NCl_5**[117a]. **$[Os(en\text{–}H)_3en]I_2$**, made by the action of ethylenediamine on $[Os(en\text{–}H)_2en]I_2$, is diamagnetic[63] and so seems unlikely to contain osmium (V). It forms black crystals.

Osmium (IV)

Nitrido complexes

Two of these complexes, both binuclear, have been reported. **$[Os_2N(NH_3)_8X_2]X_3$** (X = Cl, Br) can be made by treatment of ammonium hexachloro- or hexabromoosmate (IV) with ammonia under pressure[12,61,239]. Infrared spectra of the bromo complex and of its deuterated and ^{15}N substituted forms suggest that the structure is

$$[(NH_3)_4BrOs^{IV}—N—Os^{IV}Br(NH_3)_4]Br_3$$

with a linear Os—N—Os skeleton, similar to the complex anion in $K_4[Ru_2OCl_{10}]$ and in $(NH_4)_4[Os_2OCl_{10}]$[117a]. The compounds are diamagnetic.

Os_2NCl_5 appears to be the main product of the reaction between ammonium hexachloroosmate (IV) and chlorine at 300–500°[146]. Infrared spectra and the diamagnetism of the product suggest that there is a linear Os—N—Os skeleton as in the nitrido ammine discussed above[117a].

Reaction of barium nitride with osmium metal at 750° yields **$Ba_9Os_3N_{10}$**, which has a magnetic moment of 1·76 BM at room temperatures (θ = 164·4°). It was suggested that this was a cluster complex containing extensive metal–metal bonding[186a].

Ammines

$OsO_2.2\,NH_3.H_2O$ is said to be formed when osmium tetroxide reacts with aqueous ammonia. With hydrochloric acid **$OsCl_4.2\,NH_3.H_2O$** is formed; both compounds are brown and amorphous[43].

The octammines $[Os_2N(NH_3)_8X_2]X_3$ have already been mentioned (p. 83). No *amide complexes* are known; the supposed $K_2[Os(NH_2)Cl_5]$[18] has been shown to be $K_2[Os(NH_3)Cl_5]$[100] (see p. 86).

Amine complexes

The reaction of ethylenediamine with hexabromoosmates (IV) is complicated. The main product appears to be the pink salt **$[Os(en\text{–}H)_2en]Br_2$** (again en–H represents an ethylenediamine molecule with one proton removed). The complex is diamagnetic and an iodide has also been made[63]. Addition of hydrobromic acid yields another osmium (IV) complex, **$[Os(en\text{–}H)en_2]Br_3$** (this complex is green); an iodide is also known. Addition of ethylenediamine to $[Os(en\text{–}H)_3en]I_2$ gives a mixture of three products containing, respectively, tetravalent, pentavalent and hexavalent osmium: these are **$[Os^{IV}(en\text{–}H)_2en_2]I_2$** (pink), $[Os^{V}(en\text{–}H)_3en]I_2$ (green) and $[Os^{VI}(en\text{–}H)_4]I_2$ (black); it was suggested that these were eight coordinated[63] but clearly more work is needed to confirm the correct formulae and structures of these so-called (en–H) complexes. Recently the infrared spectra of $[Os(en\text{–}H)_2\,en]I_2$ and $[Os(en\text{–}H)en_2]I_3$ were measured[240a].

A few osmium (IV) complexes containing 1,10-phenanthroline and 2,2′-bipyridyl have been prepared[24] (see Table 3.9).

Phthalocyanine complexes

It has been claimed that the dark blue product of the reaction between osmium tetroxide and *o*-dicyanobenzene is $[PcOs^{IV}SO_4]_n$ ($Pc = C_{32}H_{16}N_8^{2-}$)[13], but later work suggests that this is in fact an osmyl compound $OsO_2Pc.C_6H_4(CN)_2$[142]. The magnetic moment of this complex is 1·4 BM at 20°, which is unusual for an 'osmyl' complex (all others are diamagnetic). The infrared and electronic spectra were measured, and a trianilate $PcOsO_2.3C_6H_5NH_2$ made from the complex and aniline[142].

Phosphine, arsine and stibine complexes

Osmium is the only one of these metals to form stable complexes with these ligands in the tetravalent state. Although so far only arsines have been reported there is little reason to doubt that phosphine and stibine complexes could also be made.

$OsBr_4(AsPh_3)_2$ can be made by refluxing ammonium hexabromoosmate (IV) in methanolic solution with the arsine[232]. It is purple, and has a magnetic moment of 1·5 BM at room temperatures[232]. Diarsine complexes of the form **$[Os\ diars_2X_2](ClO_4)_2$** (X = Cl, Br, I) are obtained by oxidation of the trivalent complexes with nitric acid; the magnetic moments of the chloride, bromide and iodide are 1·25, 1·22 and 1·16 BM, respectively, at room temperatures[182].

Osmium (III)

With this and lower oxidation states osmium–nitrogen single bonds are formed; there are no nitrido complexes reported.

Imido complexes

Oxidation of $[OsCl(NH_3)bipy_2]Cl$ with ceric ion yields the dark brown **$[Os_2bipy_4Cl_2(NH)]^{2+}$** ion, which can be precipitated as a perchlorate[24]. Infrared spectra of this and the deuteroimido form confirm that this complex contains an imide group bridging the two osmium atoms[117a].

Ammines

$[Os(NH_3)_6]Br_3$ can be made by treating ammonium hexabromoosmate (IV) with ammonia under pressure at 290°. It is colourless, and from it a trichloride and a triiodide may be prepared[62,241,242]. Magnetic moments of the osmium (III) hexammines $[Os(NH_3)_6]X_3$ are all close to the spin-only values of 1·73 BM at room temperatures. X-ray powder data have also been given[239,241]. A black compound formulated as $\mathbf{[Os^{III}(NH_3)_6].Br.[Os^{IV}Br_6]}$ was obtained from $[Os(NH_3)_6]Cl_3$ and ammonium hexabromoosmate (IV) in the presence of hydrobromic acid[62], and may be identical with $[Os^{III}(NH_3)_6]$-$[Os^{III}Br_6]$, made by the reaction of ammonia and hexabromoosmate (IV) under pressure. The latter product is reported as being amber but under certain conditions of preparation can be very dark in colour[239,241]. Its magnetic moment at room temperature is 1·74 BM per osmium atom[241], and infrared spectra of this and of its deuterated and ^{15}N substituted forms have been measured (see Table 3.7[100]).

The rate of proton exchange between $[Os(NH_3)_6]^{3+}$ and a 0·1 M acetic acid-d_1–acetate buffer at 25° has been determined and compared with the corresponding rates for a number of other metal ammines (M = Co, Cr, Rh, Ir, Ru)[186] (see also Table 5.5, p. 290).

$\mathbf{[Os(NH_3)_5Cl]Cl_2}$ and $\mathbf{[Os(NH_3)_5Br]Br_2}$ were obtained as fawn-coloured solids by reacting ammonium hexachloro- and hexabromo-osmates (IV) with ammonia under pressure at 280° (the yield of pentammine is very low, of the order of 5%, the main product being the hexammine)[61,241,243].

$\mathbf{[Os(NH_3)_5OH]Cl_2}$ was made as fawn-coloured crystals by hydrolysis of the chloropentammine chloride[243].

$\mathbf{K_2[Os(NH_3)Cl_5]}$ can be made by treatment of $K_2[OsNCl_5]$ with stannous chloride in hydrochloric acid[18,19]; it was originally formulated as an amide $K_2[Os(NH_2)Cl_5]$ and a tin salt $Sn[Os(NH_2)Cl_5]$ was also reported, but in fact these two latter salts are identical and have the ammine formulation[100]. The infrared spectra of the normal and deuterated forms have been measured[100]. The potassium salt is sparingly soluble in water to give a yellow solution.

Amine complexes

$\mathbf{[Os\ en_3]I_3}$ was prepared by reduction of $[Os(en\text{–}H)en_2]Br_3$ with sodium hydrogen sulphite followed by treatment with sodium iodide. The salt is yellow but gives a colourless aqueous solution, and is paramagnetic with a magnetic moment of 1·6 BM at room temperature. The chloride was also made[63], and recently a number of mixed halide salts containing $[Os\ en_3]^{3+}$ have been reported[244a].

The reaction of $[Os\ en_3]^{3+}$ with potassium amide yields the diamagnetic products $[Os(en{-}H)en_2]^{2+}$, $[Os(en{-}H)_2en]^+$ and $Os(en{-}H)_3$, all containing trivalent osmium; their infrared spectra and that of $[Os\ en_3]^{3+}$ were measured[240a].

Complexes with heterocyclic bases

A number of complexes containing pyridine, 1,10-phenanthroline and 2,2′-bipyridyl, are known and are listed in Tables 3.8 and 3.9.

$[Os\ bipy_3]Cl_3$ was prepared by oxidation of the divalent complex with chlorine; the enantiomorphic forms of the perchlorate were also made[66a]. Although the oxidation potentials for the $[Os\ bipy_3]^{3+}$/$[Os\ bipy_3]^{2+}$ couple (0·877 V in neutral solution, 0·727 V in 5 N acid) are very close to those for the corresponding phenanthroline complexes, the latter system is preferable for use as an internal redox indicator[65]. Studies have been made on the variation of the III/II potential for the bipyridyl system in the presence of different electrolytes[7,24b].

$[Os\ phen_3](ClO_4)_3$ was made by oxidizing the divalent complex with chlorine; the *d* and *l* forms were made similarly by using the *d* and *l* osmium (II) complexes[66]. The oxidation potential $[Os\ phen_3]^{3+}/[Os\ phen_3]^{2+}$ is 0·859 V in 0·1 N hydrochloric acid[65].

Electron-transfer reactions of $[Os\ bipy_3]^{3+}$ and $[Os\ phen_3]^{3+}$. The interesting and important osmium (III)–osmium (II) bipyridyl and phenanthroline electron-transfer reactions are dealt with below (pp. 89, 110).

Phthalocyanine complexes

$Pc.OsCl.C_6H_4(CN)_2$ ($Pc = C_{32}H_{16}N_8^{2-}$) was made by the action of an excess of 1,2-dicyanobenzene on ammonium hexachloroosmate. The electronic and infrared spectra of the dark blue product were recorded; the magnetic moment is 1·1 BM at room temperatures[142].

Phosphine, arsine and stibine complexes

These are listed in Table 3.11. The main type is $OsX_3(LR_3)_3$ in which the configurations of the phosphines in the octahedron (whether 1,2,3 or 1,2,6) have not been established[70,232]; the bromo complex $OsBr_3(AsMe_2Ph)_3$ exists in two forms, both of which are monomeric[70]. The magnetic susceptibility of $OsCl_3(AsPh_2Me)_3$ has been measured from 80 to 295°K (cf. Table 3.16); at room temperature the magnetic moment is 1·80 BM[80]. Diarsine complexes of the form $[Os\ diars_2X_2]^+$ (X = Cl, Br, I) can be made by oxidation of the corresponding divalent species, and have magnetic moments near 1·90 BM at room temperatures[182]. Measurements of their far infrared spectra suggest that these have the *trans* configuration[156].

Osmium (II)

Ammines

Osmium (II) hexammines have not been isolated, though there is some evidence from potentiometric titrations of $[Os(NH_3)_6]^{3+}$ with a solution of potassium in liquid ammonia of the intermediate existence of $[Os(NH_3)_6]^{2+}$ [242].

The **imido complex** $Os_2(NH)_2$ $bipy_4$ is listed in Table 3.9, p. 109[24]; infrared studies show it to contain bridging imido groups[101].

Complexes with heterocyclic bases

Complexes of osmium (II) containing pyridine, 1,10-phenanthroline and 2,2′-bipyridyl, are listed in Tables 3.8 and 3.9. Studies recently reported on the osmium (III)/(II) oxidation potentials of complexes containing these ligands and pyridine show that changes in the potentials may be correlated with π bonding and the degree of conjugation of the ligands[24b].

$[Os\ bipy_3]Cl_2$ can be made (together with $[Os^{III}bipy_2Cl_2]Cl$) by the action of excess bipyridyl on hexachloroosmates (IV) at 260°*. The complex is dark green, and the iodide, perchlorate, tartrate and hydroxide were also made: the iodide was resolved by the use of silver antimonyl tartrate[26]. The asymmetric synthesis of the compound has been achieved, using osmium tetroxide and the ligand in the presence of optically active tartrates; some 70% of the *l* product was obtained[159].

$[Os\ phen_3]I_2$ was prepared from ammonium hexabromoosmate (IV) with sodium iodide and the ligand at 80°. The complex is greenish-brown; a perchlorate and chloride were also made, and the chloride was resolved by using potassium antimonyl tartrate[67].

$[Os\ terpy_2]Cl_2$ (terpy = 2,2′,2″-terpyridyl) was prepared as green crystals by the reaction between the ligand and potassium hexachloroosmate (IV) at 250°; an iodide was also made similarly.

* A common reaction amongst all these metals is that complex formation often also involves a reduction in the oxidation state of the metal and hence oxidation of the ligand or solvent. The exact nature of these side reactions has seldom been noted or investigated.

Although the solid salts are green the aqueous solutions are red[179]. Other terpyridyl complexes are listed in Table 3.9.

Intramolecular electronic energy transfers in bipyridyl, phenanthroline and terpyridyl osmium (II) complexes have been studied[50a].

Electron-transfer reactions of $[Os\ bipy_3]^{2+}$ *and* $[Os\ phen_3]^{2+}$*. The electron-transfer reactions involving $[Os\ bipy_3]^{3+}$ and $[Os\ bipy_3]^{2+}$ and other oxidants and reductants listed below in Table 3.10 are all very fast, and in most cases it has only been possible to establish lower limits for the second-order rate coefficients. For all these reactions the Marcus electron-transfer theory[166] is likely to be applicable since the reactants involved do not readily undergo substitution and so probably react via outer-sphere activated complexes[96]. The most accurately determined rates are probably those of the equilibrium

$$[Os\ bipy_3]^{2+} + [Mo(CN)_8]^{3-} \underset{k_2}{\overset{k_1}{\rightleftharpoons}} [Os\ bipy_3]^{3+} + [Mo(CN)_8]^{4-}$$

and the values of $2{\cdot}0 \times 10^9$ M^{-1} sec^{-1} and $4{\cdot}0 \times 10^9$ M^{-1} sec^{-1} were found for k_1 and k_2 (at 10° and ionic strength 0·5 μ). The observed rate constants are close to the diffusion-controlled limits, so clearly the energy needed to reorganize the coordination shells of reactants and products cannot be great. Using the data from this reaction, estimates of the rates of other reactions involving the species above can be made after making the necessary corrections, and in this way good agreement was obtained between observed and calculated rate values for the $[Os\ bipy_3]^{3+}/[Os\ bipy_3]^{2+}$ and $[Mo(CN)_8]^{3-}/[Mo(CN)_8]^{4-}$ exchanges; again agreement with the predictions of the Marcus theory was demonstrated[31].

Although it has been reported that the rate of electron exchange between *l*-$[Os\ bipy_3]^{3+}$ and *d*-$[Os\ bipy_3]^{2+}$, as determined by changes in the optical activity, was large but measurable[68], later results suggested that the racemization rate was in fact immeasurably fast[72], a conclusion supported by isotopic tracer[72] and proton magnetic resonance[55] measurements of the exchange rate between the +3 and +2 species.

The rates of oxidation of $[Os\ bipy_3]^{2+}$ and $[Ru\ bipy_3]^{2+}$ by persulphate ion have been studied. In the case of the osmium complex second-order kinetics are followed for about 50% of the reaction, the subsequent departure probably being due to competition for the sulphate radical (SO_4^-) between $[Os\ bipy_3]^{2+}$ and water or traces

* See Table 3.10.

of reducing material; the sulphate radical is probably generated by the primary reaction

$$[Os\,bipy_3]^{2+} + S_2O_8^{2-} \rightarrow [Os\,bipy_3]^{3+} + SO_4^{2-} + SO_4^{\bullet -}$$

The dependence of the reaction rate on temperature, ionic strength and pH was investigated, and also the effect of adding such ions as nitrate, chloride and sulphate[125]. The results were compared with those obtained for the persulphate oxidation of $[Ru\,bipy_3]^{2+}$, $[Fe\,phen_3]^{2+}$ and a number of substituted trisbipyridyl and phenanthroline iron (II) complexes, and the observed differences in rate were correlated with the redox potentials of the transition-metal complexes[126]. Similar studies were made on the rate of reaction between thallium (III) ions and $[Os\,bipy_3]^{2+}$ and it was concluded that both Tl^{3+} and $Tl(OH)^{2+}$ ions were involved; the effects of temperature, hydrogen ion concentration and addition of chloride ion were investigated[127].

Nitro complexes

No unsubstituted nitro complexes are definitely known: the supposed $\mathbf{K_2[Os(NO_2)_5]}$ has been shown to be an osmium (II) nitrosyl complex, $K_2[Os(NO)(OH)(NO_2)_4]$ (see below); $\mathbf{Os(NO_2)_3}$ is claimed as the product of evaporation of an aqueous solution of the free acid derived from this nitrosyl complex[258]. It is dark brown.

Nitrosyl complexes

All the nitrosyl complexes of osmium involve the metal in the divalent state (assuming nitric oxide to function as a three-electron donor) and they are consequently diamagnetic, as indeed are most nitrosyls. In view of the extraordinarily wide range of ruthenium (II) nitrosyl compounds which are known it is likely that many more osmium complexes of this type remain to be prepared.

$\mathbf{K_2[Os(NO)X_5]}$ (X = Cl, Br, I) is best prepared by heating $K_2[Os(NO)(OH)(NO_2)_4]$ with the appropriate halogen acids[257]. The salts form deep red-purple crystals, and the infrared spectra of the chloride and bromide have been recorded from 80 to 4,000 cm^{-1} [91a].

$\mathbf{K_2[Os(NO)(OH)(NO_2)_4]}$ may be prepared as golden-yellow crystals by the prolonged action of potassium nitrite on potassium hexachloroosmate (IV).[258] It was originally incorrectly formulated as $K_2[Os(NO_2)_5]$[258] but infrared spectra show it to contain a nitrosyl group. It is moderately soluble in water to give a yellow, rather unstable solution; the sodium salt is more soluble.

$K_2[Os(NO)(CN)_5]$ has not been isolated, but the 'nitrocyanide' reported in 1861 by Martius[169] to be formed by the reaction of nitric acid with potassium hexacyanoosmate (II) may well be the nitrosyl pentacyanide salt, since this is the method normally used to make the pentacyanonitrosyls of iron and ruthenium.

Phosphine, arsine and stibine complexes*

Tertiary phosphines, arsines and stibines give monomeric complexes of the form $OsX_2(LR_3)_4$[70,232]: these probably have a *trans* structure. Phosphines also give a series of binuclear species of the form $[Os_2Cl_3(PR_3)_6]Cl$ in which it is likely that the metal atoms are bridged by three chloride ligands[34]. The two species reported as $OsBr_2(PPh_3)_3$[232] and $OsI_2(AsPh_3)_3$[70] may be truly pentacoordinated or may have the binuclear structure. Chelating diphosphines such as $C_2H_4(PEt_2)_2$ give both *cis*- and *trans*-OsX_2(diphosphine)$_2$, the configurations having been established by dipole moment measurements[34], while diarsine gives only the *trans*-OsX_2(diars)$_2$ form[182] whose configuration was determined from far infrared measurements[156].

Hydrido phosphines

Hydrido phosphines of osmium (II) (Table 3.11) can be prepared from *cis*- or *trans*-OsX_2(diphosphine)$_2$ and lithium aluminium hydride. Two series are known, *trans*-OsHX(diphosphine)$_2$ and *trans*-OsH_2-(diphosphine)$_2$; the *trans* octahedral structures of the two series were established by proton magnetic resonance and dipole moment measurements[36]. Infrared spectra were also recorded and the osmium–hydrogen stretching modes assigned—these appeared at frequencies about 100 cm^{-1} higher than those in the corresponding ruthenium complexes[36]. The hydridochloro complexes, if crystallized from benzene solutions, were found to be 2:1 complex:benzene adducts, and in these the metal–hydrogen stretching vibration was not observed; it was suggested that the benzene molecule fitted into the cavity above the hydride group and decreased the change in the dipole moment of the metal–hydrogen stretch (benzene adducts of the corresponding ruthenium complexes were also made, but here the metal–hydrogen stretches were observed)[36].

Phosphorus trifluoride complexes of the form **$OsH_2(PF_3)_4$** and **$Os(PF_3)_5$** have recently been reported[151c].

* See Table 3.11.

Osmium (I)

$[Os(NH_3)_6]Br$ can be made by reduction of a solution of $[Os(NH_3)_6]Br_3$ by potassium in liquid ammonia. It is bright yellow and is paramagnetic (μ_{eff} = 1·5 BM at room temperature). X-ray powder data were obtained[242].

$OsX(PPh_3)_3$ (X = Cl, Br) were reported, but these have recently been shown to be octahedral osmium (II) hydride complexes, $OsHX(CO)(PPh_3)_3$ (see p. 95).

Osmium (0)

$Os(NH_3)_6$ can also be made by reduction of $[Os(NH_3)_6]Br_3$ by a solution of potassium in liquid ammonia. It is deep brown and very unstable[242] and could perhaps be a hydrido ammine of osmium (I) or (II). For **$Os(PF_3)_5$** see above, p. 91[151c].

GROUP IV DONORS

The only element of this group so far found to coordinate to osmium is carbon, though $(SnCl_3)^-$ complexes of the element could undoubtedly be made. The carbon complexes are chiefly of osmium (II), most of the ligands being good π acceptors.

The organometallic chemistry of osmium has been little investigated and the field would undoubtedly be worth further study.

Osmium (VIII)

The 1,4-dichlorobutadiene derivatives **$2\,OsO_4 . py_4 . (C_4H_4Cl_2)$** and **$OsO_4 . py(C_4H_4Cl_2)$** were made from pyridine, osmium tetroxide and 1,4-dichlorobutadiene. Their structures are not known[50]. A number of other 'adducts' of organic molecules with osmium tetroxide were isolated by Criegee and coworkers[49].

Osmium (VI)

The only representatives are *trans*-**$K_2[OsO_2(CN)_4]$** (cf. Table 3.5) and *trans*-**$K[OsN(H_2O)(CN)_4]$** (cf. p. 81).

Osmium (IV)

Recently, amine salts of the $[Os(CN)_6]^{2-}$ and $[Ru(CN)_6]^{2-}$ ions have been claimed[255,256], but it has been shown that these are in fact salts of $[Os(CN)_6]^{4-}$ and $[Ru(CN)_6]^{4-}$ [105].

$[Cp_2Os(OH)]^+$ salts can be made by oxidation of osmocene, Cp_2Os, with ferric ammonium sulphate; the hexafluorophosphate is the easiest salt to prepare. With a solution of iodine in sulphuric acid the Cp_2OsI^+ ion is formed from osmocene; these salts are all diamagnetic[84a].

Osmium (III)

Although no osmium (III) cyanide complexes have been isolated, there is polarographic evidence for the existence of the hexacyano species in solution; the $[Os(CN)_6]^{3-}/[Os(CN)_6]^{4-}$ and $[Ru(CN)_6]^{3-}/[Ru(CN)_6]^{4-}$ oxidation potentials are $+0{\cdot}99$[174] and $+0{\cdot}86$ v, respectively[86] (derived from polarographic data).

Osmium (II)

Cyanide complexes

$K_4[Os(CN)_6]$ can be made by the action of excess potassium cyanide on osmium tetroxide or on potassium osmate[151]. It is colourless and fairly soluble in water; barium, nickel and copper salts were also made. With nitric acid it gives an unidentified product[169] which may be $K_2[Os(NO)(CN)_5]$.

Electronic absorption spectra of $K_4[Os(CN)_6]$ and $K_4[Ru(CN)_6]$ have been measured[170] and band assignments proposed on the basis of a molecular-orbital scheme for hexacyano compounds[97]. Infrared and Raman spectra have also been measured[171,171a,181] (see Table 3.12).

Substitution of Fe^{II} in Prussian Blue by Os^{II} or Ru^{II} causes shifts to occur in the low and high frequency electronic bands, the magnitudes of these shifts agreeing with theoretical predictions[198].

The free acid **$H_4[Os(CN)_6]$** can be made in the anhydrous state as white crystals by addition of hydrochloric acid and ether to the potassium salt[11,76,151]. The infrared spectra of the acid and its deuterated form have been measured and give strong evidence for the presence of asymmetric hydrogen bonds in the structure of the solid acid[11,76]. The infrared measurements were also made at low temperatures[93].

Os bipy$_2$(CN)$_2$ can be made by reducing ammonium hexachloroosmate (IV) with bipyridyl and sodium cyanide; the product forms black needles[212]. The absorption spectra of the complex and of the corresponding ruthenium and iron (II) species in acetic acid solution were measured. By observing changes in the spectra with the addition of varying quantities of perchloric acid with a weak base B equilibrium constants for the reaction

$$B.HClO_4 + M\ bipy_2(CN)_2 \rightleftharpoons [M\ bipy_2(CN)_2].HClO_4 + B$$

were determined (B = *o*-chloroaniline; M = Os, Ru, Fe). The proton affinity increases in the sequence: iron $<$ ruthenium $<$ osmium (it was assumed that the nitrogen atoms on the cyanide groups had been protonated[212]). Infrared spectra of the three complexes were interpreted as showing that the degree of metal–carbon π bonding increased in the same sequence as the proton affinities, and it appeared from the spectra that the M bipy$_2$(CN)$_2$ complexes had the *cis* configuration[211], a somewhat surprising result. No isocyanide complexes of osmium have been reported.

Carbonyl complexes

[Os(CO)$_6$]Cl$_2$ has been briefly reported as the product of reaction between Os(CO)$_4$Cl$_2$ and carbon monoxide in the presence of aluminium trichloride, and the analogous iron complex was also made[118].

The oxycarbonyl Os$_4$O$_4$(CO)$_{12}$ has recently been isolated as a product of the reaction of osmium tetroxide with carbon monoxide at 150° and 200 atmospheres pressure. The substance is pale yellow. Its mass spectrum shows that the Os$_4$ cluster breaks up only after the carbonyl groups have been removed; a similar stabilization of the metal cluster was observed for Os$_3$(CO)$_{12}$[132a].

Carbonyl halides

There are four types (see Table 3.13): Os(CO)$_4$X$_2$, [Os(CO)$_3$X$_2$]$_2$ (X = Cl, Br, I); [Os(CO)$_2$X$_2$]$_n$ and [Os(CO)$_4$X]$_2$ (X = Br, I)[119]. (For ruthenium, only Ru(CO)$_4$X$_2$ (X = Cl, I), [Ru(CO)$_2$X$_2$]$_n$ (X = Cl, Br, I) and [Ru(CO)X]$_n$ (X = Br, I) are known.) The structures of the divalent osmium carbonyl halides are not certain but presumably in [Os(CO)$_3$X$_2$]$_2$ the metal has octahedral coordination with bridging halide groups, while [Os(CO)$_2$X$_2$]$_n$

may be highly polymeric, again with bridging halide groups. The bromide and iodide of $Os(CO)_4X_2$ exist in two forms, probably the *cis* and *trans*[119].

Carbonyl phosphine and hydrido carbonyl phosphine complexes*

The reaction of ammonium hexahaloosmates (IV) with triphenylphosphine in 2-methoxyethanol or ethylene glycol solution at 120° yields the hydrido carbonyl **$OsH(CO)X(PPh_3)_3$** (X = Cl, Br), earlier reported as the 'monovalent' $OsX(PPh_3)_3$[231]. Infrared and proton magnetic resonance measurements were made on the complexes, and experiments using ^{14}C labelled ethylene glycol as solvent showed that one carbon atom of the glycol was incorporated into the carbonyl group of the complex[35,229,230].

An x-ray crystal structure determination of $OsH(CO)Br(PPh_3)_3$ shows that the osmium appears to have an octahedral configuration with the bromine atom (Os—Br = 2·60 Å) *trans* to the carbonyl group; the three phosphine groups are in the equatorial position with the fourth position in the plane occupied (presumably) by hydrogen. The osmium–phosphorus distance for the position *trans* to the hydrogen is 2·56 Å while the other two osmium–phosphorus distances are 2·34 Å[184]—the long bond may perhaps be the result of a *trans* weakening effect by the hydride group.

$OsH(CO)Cl(PEt_2Ph)_3$ was made by refluxing $OsCl_3(PEt_2Ph)_3$ with a solution of potassium hydroxide in ethanol (a possible mechanism for this reaction is discussed on p. 186)[35a].

Catalytic activity of $OsHCl(Co)PPh_3)_3$. The complex will catalyse the homogeneous reduction by molecular hydrogen of acetylene to ethylene, and will also react with molecular deuterium to give the monodeutero complex. It has been suggested that eight-coordinate osmium (IV) intermediates are involved[233]:

$$(Ph_3P)_3(CO)ClOsH + D_2 \rightleftharpoons (Ph_3P)_3(CO)ClOsHD_2$$

$$\upharpoonleft\downharpoonright$$

$$(Ph_3P)_3(CO)ClOsD + HD$$

and

$$(Ph_3P)_3(CO)ClOsH_3 + C_2H_4 \rightarrow (Ph_3P)_3(CO)ClOsH + C_2H_6$$

Carbonyl phosphine complexes with metal-metal bonds

The reaction of certain mercuric salts with osmium hydrido carbonyl phosphines gives species which apparently contain mercury–

* See Table 3.13.

osmium bonds, but pure samples could not be isolated[182a]. However, reaction of mercuric halides HgX_2 (X = Cl, Br, I) with $Os(CO)_3(PPh_3)_2$ gives the colourless salts **[Os(HgX)(CO)$_3$(PPh$_3$)$_2$](HgX)$_3$**[44b].

Alkyl and aryl complexes

These complexes have been prepared with chelating diphosphines (see Table 3.11). Some of the osmium complexes crystallize with one molecule of benzene per two molecules of complex, as found also with the hydrido phosphines (see p. 91). It is interesting to note that a change in configuration occurs during preparation of the chloroalkyl complexes: thus triethyl aluminium with *cis*-$OsCl_2$(diphosphine)$_2$ yields *trans*-(OsClEt(disphosphine)$_2$), while with *trans*-$OsCl_2$(diphosphine)$_2$ the *cis*-alkyl isomer is formed. Infrared, proton magnetic resonance and dipole moment measurements were made to establish the configuration of these complexes[37].

Hydrido alkyl complexes

Such complexes as OsHMe(diphosphine)$_2$ can be made by reduction of OsClMe(diphosphine)$_2$ with lithium aluminium hydride (the ethyl complex is also known)[37] (Table 3.11, p. 111).

'Sandwich' complexes*

Osmocene, $(\pi\text{-}C_5H_5)_2Os$ (π-C_5H_5 is abbreviated here as Cp), can be made as colourless crystals (m.p. 229°) by the reaction of sodium cyclopentadienide with osmium trichloride (the yield is somewhat low, about 20%)[84a,194]. The heats of vaporization and fusion have been determined[200]. The x-ray crystal structure of osmocene shows that the osmium–carbon distance is 2·22 Å and that, as in ruthenocene, the two parallel cyclopentadienyl rings are in the eclipsed position; the distance between the rings is 3·71 Å[131].

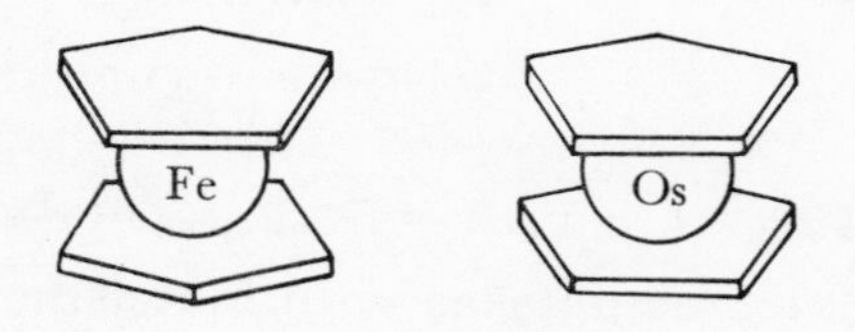

Figure 3.7 Ferrocene and osmocene

* See Table 3.14.

Studies of the infrared spectrum have been made by a number of workers[89,90,194] (see Table 3.15) but there have been no Raman measurements. The electronic absorption spectrum has been measured[200] but no assignments made. Proton magnetic resonance measurements on solutions of osmocene, ruthenocene and ferrocene in carbon tetrachloride show that the τ values decrease from ferrocene (5·96) to osmocene (5·29)[87]. Magnetic anisotropy studies on osmocene have recently been reported[180a], and preliminary x-ray data on monobenzoyl osmocene have been presented[162]. A review of the chemistry of osmocene, ruthenocene and ferrocene has recently been published[200].

Chronopotentiometric studies of the oxidation of osmocene, ruthenocene and ferrocene (and also of substituted osmocenes and ruthenocenes) show that oxidation to osmium (III) ($E_{1/4}$ = 0·633 v against S.C.E.) and then to osmium (IV) ($E_{1/4}$ = 1·50 v against S.C.E.) occurs (for ruthenocene a single step to ruthenium (IV) is found with $E_{1/4}$ = 0·693 v and for ferrocene a single electron step to iron (III) at 0·307 v against S.C.E.)[153]. For osmocene and ruthenocene, D (the diffusion coefficient) is $2{\cdot}2 \times 10^{-5}$ cm^2 sec^{-1}[153]. The osmium (IV) oxidation product is likely to be the orange complex $[Os(OH)Cp_2]^+$, which can also be made by reaction of osmocene with ferric chloride[84a]. Cathodic and anodic oscillographic polarography of osmocene suggest that the electrode processes are reversible, although it is not clear how many electrons per metal atom are involved[224].

The protonation of osmocene, ruthenocene and ferrocene by boron trifluoride hydrate has been studied by proton magnetic resonance; the ease of protonation to $[Cp_2MH]^+$ increases in the order: Fe < Ru < Os. In the protonated species it is likely that the proton is bonded directly to the metal atom[54], and the cyclopentadienyl rings are likely to be tilted with respect to each other as is the case with some other π-cyclopentadienyl metal hydrides[5].

Substituted osmocenes and ruthenocenes

Friedel–Crafts acylation and alkylation have been used to prepare acylosmocenes[83a, 194] and alkylosmocenes[23,25,121], and recently the preparation of trimethylsilyl osmocene has been reported[168]. A number of qualitative and quantitative studies have been made of the reactions of these compounds. Rate constants have been determined for the solvolysis of α-metallocenyl ethyl acetate, π-CpM(π-C_5H_4-(OAc)Me) (M = Os, Ru, Fe): in an 80% acetone–water solvent at 30° these are ($k \times 10^5$, in sec^{-1}) 91·5 for osmocene, 23·2 for ruthenocene and 17·0 for ferrocene, while for trityl acetate the rate constant is only 2·6. This provides convincing evidence for the stability of α-metallocenyl carbonium ions[121]. This order of reactivity (Os > Ru > Fe) is the reverse of that established for the electrophilic reactivity of the parent metallocenes in Friedel–Crafts acylation[194]; the difference may be due to the intramolecular nature of the solvolysis process[199].

Other studies include measurements of the rate of acid cleavage of the cyclopentadienyl–silicon bond in $CpM(\pi\text{-}C_5H_4SiMe_3)$ (M = Os, Ru, Fe)—in aqueous methanol solution with hydrochloric acid the first-order rate coefficients fall in the sequence: Ru > Os > Fe[168]. In the acid-catalysed decomposition of metallocenyl phenylcarbinyl azides a complex reaction occurs, and the nature of the products is found to depend on the metal atom[23].

Proton magnetic resonance spectra of mono- and diacyl derivatives of osmocene, ruthenocene and ferrocene show a gradual deshielding of the ring protons in the sequence: Fe > Ru > Os[195], and a gradual increase in the shielding of methyl protons in the acetyl metallocenes in the same order[167]. Infrared spectral measurements show that some metallocenyl alcohols contain intramolecular hydrogen bonds[121,225].

Olefin complexes

Only a few are known for osmium.

$\mathbf{OsCl_2(C_8H_{12})(PEtPh_2)_2}$ (C_8H_{12} = cycloocta-1,5-diene) can be made by reaction of the olefin with $[Os_2Cl_3(PEtPh_2)_6]Cl$[34].

$\mathbf{C_6H_8Os_2(CO)_6}$ can be made from osmium dodecacarbonyl and 2,3-dimethylbuta-1,3-diene[83]. An x-ray crystal structure analysis

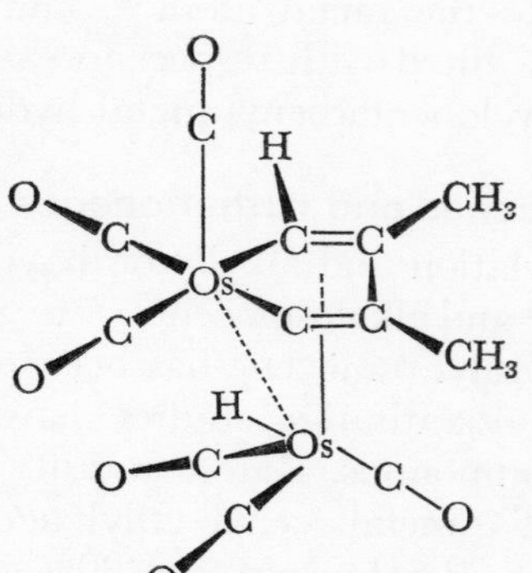

Figure 3.8 Molecular structure of $C_6H_8Os_2(CO)_6$

reveals an extraordinary structure for the complex: two $Os(CO)_3$ units are separated by a metal–metal distance of only 2·74 Å, close enough to indicate substantial bonding between the two. One osmium atom is formally in the (II) state as it forms two σ bonds to the C_4 ring, while the ring itself functions as a diolefinic coordinating ligand to the other osmium atom, which is formally in the zero-valent state. The coordination about each metal atom is approximately octahedral[58]. The species **$[OsLCl]_n$** ($L = C_8H_{12}$, C_6H_6), $[OsL'I_2]_n$ and $[OsL'(PPh_3)]_2]_2$($L' = C_6H_6$) have been isolated[256a] and there is evidence for the existence of $Os(C_8H_{10})(C_8H_{12})$[84].

Osmium (I)

The carbonyl halides **$[Os(CO)_4X]_2$** (see Table 3.13) are very stable[119] and may contain metal–metal bonds as well as halogen bridges. For carbonyl hydrides see below (p. 100).

$[CpOs(CO)_2]_2$ can be made by refluxing dicyclopentadiene with $[Os(CO)_3Cl_2]_2$ for 20 hours. Infrared, dipole moment and proton magnetic resonance data were reported for the complex, which is diamagnetic (it is not isomorphous with the corresponding ruthenium complex)[82,85]. With bromine, **$CpOs(CO)_2Br$** is formed[82].

Osmium (0)

Osmium pentacarbonyl, $Os(CO)_5$, has been made by the action of carbon monoxide under pressure on the triiodide in the presence of silver or copper powder to take up the halogen[120]. It is a colourless, monomeric liquid (m.p. $-15°$) soluble in most organic solvents. Although the molecular structure has not been determined it may well be trigonal bipyramidal like iron pentacarbonyl.

$Os_3(CO)_{12}$ is formed during the above preparation, and can also be made from osmium tetroxide with carbon monoxide under pressure[120]; it forms yellow crystals (m.p. 224°). It was originally formulated as an ennea complex, $Os_2(CO)_9$ and is soluble in most organic solvents, though less so than the pentacarbonyl.

An x-ray crystal structure analysis shows that the correct formula is $Os_3(CO)_{12}$. The molecule has an approximate overall symmetry of D_{3h}, the metal atoms forming an equilateral triangle with four terminal carbonyl groups per metal atom, two approximately in the triangular plane and two perpendicular to it. The three $Os(CO)_4$ units are probably joined by metal–metal bonds only (Os—Os = 2·88 ± 0·01 Å). The mean osmium–carbon and carbon–oxygen

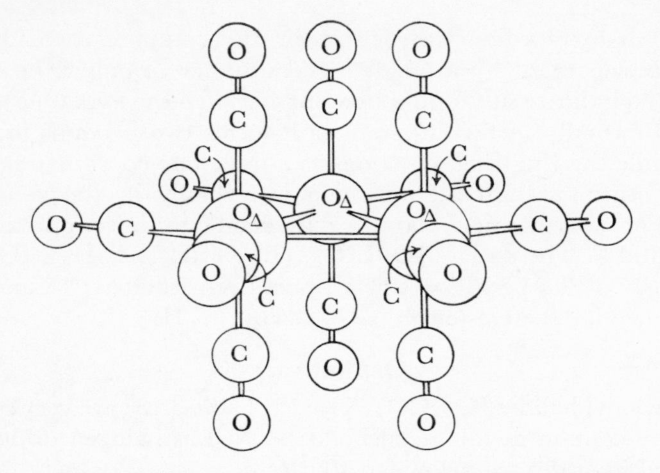

Figure 3.9 Molecular structure of $Os_3(CO)_{12}$ (O_Δ = osmium)

distances are 1·95 and 1·14 Å, respectively[45]. It has been suggested that the bonding in the molecule is best understood in terms of octahedrally disposed metal orbitals not pointing directly at each other to form the metal–metal bonds, i.e. 'bent' bonds are involved[45].

The ruthenium complex originally reported as $Ru_2(CO)_9$ is isomorphous with $Os_3(CO)_{12}$ and so presumably should be reformulated as $Ru_3(CO)_{12}$[46]. The infrared spectrum of $Os_3(CO)_{12}$ has been measured from 290–4000 cm^{-1} and assignments proposed[123].

Mass spectrometric measurements have shown that, in the vapour phase, the carbonyl groups may be successively stripped from Os_3-$(CO)_{12}$ leaving the metal cluster intact[132a].

$Os(CO)_4H_2$, osmium carbonyl hydride, may be the highly volatile substance formed during the preparation of the carbonyls[120]. On treatment of $Os_3(CO)_{12}$ with sodium borohydride, two polynuclear hydrido carbonyls are formed[132a].

Carbonyl phosphine complex

Like ruthenium, osmium forms a five-coordinate zero-valent complex of the form **$Os(CO)_3(PPh_3)_2$**. This is made as yellow crystals by the action of carbon monoxide at 140° and at 4 atmospheres pressure on a mixture of zinc powder and $OsCl_2(CO)_2(PPh_3)_2$. It reacts with hydrogen halides HX to give $OsX_2(CO)_2(PPh_3)_2$ and with halogens X_2 (X = Br, I) $[OsX(CO)_3(PPh_3)_2]^+$; hydride intermediates are probably involved in these reactions[44a].

Arene–olefin complexes

$(\pi\text{-}C_6H_6)Os(C_6H_8)$ (π-benzene cyclohexa-1,3-diene osmium (o)) can be made from osmium trichloride, propyl magnesium bromide and cyclohexadiene. The compound is colourless, and its infrared and proton magnetic resonance spectra were recorded[84].

HOMOGENEOUS CATALYSIS BY OSMIUM COMPLEXES

The only instance so far reported is the catalysis of the reduction by molecular hydrogen of olefins by $OsHCl(CO)(PPh_3)_3$; it has been proposed that there is a homolytic splitting of hydrogen with the formation of an eight-coordinate osmium (IV) trihydride intermediate[233] (p. 95).

Table 3.1 Infrared and Raman spectra of transition metal hexafluorides (O_h)(cm^{-1}) (see p. 48)

Mode	Species	Activity	t_{2g}^0		t_{2g}^1	t_{2g}^2		t_{2g}^3		t_{2g}^4
			MoF_6	WF_6	ReF_6	RuF_6	OsF_6	RhF_6	IrF_6	PtF_6
v_1	(A_{1g})	R, polarized	741	769	755	675	733	634	696	655
v_2	(E_g)	R, depolarized	643	670	596	(573)	632	595	643	601
v_3	(F_{1u})	i.r.	741	712	715	735	720	724	718	705
v_4	(F_{1u})	i.r.	262	256	257	275	268	283	276	273
v_5	(F_{2g})	R, depolarized	(312)	322	246	262	252	269	260	242
v_6	(F_{2u})	Inactive	(122)	216	193		230	192	295	211
Ref.			40	42	41	249	247	249	173	247
f_d (stretch force const., M dyn/Å[a,b])			4·73	5·13	4·79		4·91		4·85	4·48
Bond length[b] (Å)				1·830			1·831		1·833	

[a] Calculated on the basis of a general quadratic potential function.
[b] See reference 42.

Table 3.2 Infrared spectra of transition metal hexafluoro complexes[188]

Metal–fluorine stretching modes, ν_3 (cm^{-1})					
$K[MoF_6]$	$K[WF_6]$	$K[ReF_6]$	$K[RuF_6]$	$K[OsF_6]$	$K[IrF_6]$
623	594	627	640	616	667
		$K_2[ReF_6]$	$K_2[RuF_6]$	$K_2[OsF_6]$[a]	$K_2[RhF_6]$
		541	581	548	589
		$K_3[RuF_6]$		$K_3[RhF_6]$	$K_2[IrF_6]$
		514, 487, 479		530, 512, 500	568

[a] For $K_2[OsF_6]$, ν_4 = 262, 246. See reference 1.

Table 3.4 Magnetic measurements on hexahaloosmates (IV) in solid solutions[132,253]

Complex	% Os	χ_m(obs.)[a]	χ_m(calc.)[a]	d (Å)[b]	μ_{eff}(298°)
$K_2[Os, PtCl_6]$	100	860	936	6·92	1·44
	67·5	930	1035	7·89	
	50·3	950	1103	8·68	
	33·6	1000	1190	9·93	
	18·9	1250	1300	12·15	
	7·9	1570	1410	15·93	
	Infinite dilution	1900			2·13
$K_2[Os, PtBr_6]$	100	990	977	7·30	1·55
	10·4	1590	1402	15·52	

[a] χ values in c.g.s. units × 10^6. χ_m(obs.) values are the *mean* values over the range 90–290°K; χ_m(calc.) values were obtained from reference 132.
[b] d is the mean distance between osmium nuclei.

Table 3.3 Infrared and Raman spectra of transition metal hexachloro complexes[a]

Mode	Species	Activity	$[ReCl_6]^{2-}$	$[RuCl_6]^{2-}$	$[OsCl_6]^{2-}$	$[IrCl_6]^{2-}$	$[PdCl_6]^{2-}$	$[PtCl_6]^{2-}$	$[IrCl_6]^{3-}$ [a]
ν_1	A_{1g}	R, polarized	346		346		317	344	
ν_2	E_g	R, depolarized	275 [b]		274 [b]		292	320	
ν_3	F_{1u}	i.r.	313	346	314	333	356	344	296
ν_4	F_{1u}	i.r.	172	188	177	184		186	200
ν_5	F_{2g}	R, depolarized	159		165		164	162	
ν_6	F_{2u}	Inactive							
Ref.			259	1	259	1	260	260	1

[a] Bands at 316 and 175 cm^{-1} have been observed in the Raman spectra of $[IrC_6l]^{3-}$ solutions (probably ν_1 and ν_5) and at 336 and 298 cm^{-1} in solutions of $[RhCl_6]^{3-}$ (probably ν_1 and ν_2)[151b].

[b] From combination mode.

Table 3.5 'Osmyl' complexes[a]

Oxidation state	Complex	Colour	Physical properties	Preparation	Ref.
VI	$K_2[OsO_2(OH)_4]$	Purple	el.[160] i.r.[102] X[191]	$K_2[OsO_4(OH)_2]$ + EtOH	88, 204a
	$K_2[OsO_2Cl_4]$	Red	i.r.[102] X[152]	$K_2[OsO_2(OH)_4]$ (or OsO_4) + HCl	257
	$K_2[OsO_2Br_4]$	Red		$K_2[OsO(OH)_2(NO_2)_2]$ + HBr	257
	$K_2[OsO_2(OMe)_4]$	Brown	i.r.[102]	OsO_4 + MeOH + KOMe	48
	$K_2[OsO_2(CN)_4]$	Red	i.r.[102]	OsO_4 + KCN	150
	$K_2[OsO_2\ ox_2]$	Brown	i.r.[102]	OsO_4 + KOH; H_2ox	257
	$K_2[OsO_2salicylate_4]$	Red		$K_2[OsO_2(OH)_4]$ + $K_2C_7H_4O_3$	6
	$Na_6[OsO_2(SO_3)_4]$	Brown		OsO_4 + NaOH + SO_2	201
	$[OsO_2(NH_3)_4]Cl_2$	Yellow	i.r.[102]	$K_2[OsO_2(OH)_4]$ + NH_4Cl	257
	OsO_2(phthalocyanine)	Blue		OsO_4 + phthalocyanine	142
	$OsO_2(biguanide)_2$		i.r.[196]	OsO_4 + biguanide	196
	$K_2[OsO_2(OH)_2(NO_2)_2]$	Brown	i.r.[102]	OsO_4 + KNO_2	257
	$K_2[OsO_2(NO_3)_2(NO_2)_2]$	Orange	i.r.[102]	OsO_4 + NO + KNO_2	257
	$K_2[OsO_2(OH)_2X_2]$ (X = Cl, Br)	Brown		$(NH_4)_2[OsO_2(OH)_2(NO_2)_2]$ + HX 209a;	209a, 257
	$K_2[OsO_2(OH)_2\ ox]$	Black	i.r.[102]	OsO_4 + K_2ox	257
	$OsO_2(NH_3)_2Cl_2$	Brown		$K_2[OsO_2(OH)_4]$ + NH_3; HCl	91b

[a] All these complexes are likely to contain the *trans*-(O=Os=O) grouping.

Table 3.6 Sulphito complexes of Osmium

Oxidation state	Complex	Colour	Preparation	Ref.
VI	$Na_6[OsO_2(SO_3)_4]$	Brown	$OsO_4 + NaOH + SO_2$	201
IV	$Na_8[Os(SO_3)_6]$	Brown	$NaHSO_2 + Na_6[OsO_2(SO_3)_4]$	201
	$K_6[Os(SO_3)_5(H_2O)]$	Colourless	$K_2[OsCl_6] + K_2SO_3$	201
	$Na_7[Os(SO_3)_5Cl]$	Violet	$Na_2[OsCl_6] + Na_2SO_3$	201
	$Na_6[Os(SO_3)_4Cl_2]$	Purple	$Na_2[OsCl_6] + Na_2SO_3$	202
	$Na_6[Os(SO_3)_4(OH)_2]$	Violet	$Na_6[Os(SO_3)_6] + Na_2SO_3$	202
	$K_8[Os(SO_3)_4Cl_4]$	Brown	$K_2[OsCl_6] + K_2SO_3$	202, 206
	$K_{11}H_3[Os_2(SO_3)_{11}(H_2O)]$	Rose	$KHSO_3 + OsO_4 + SO_2$	201
II	$Na_4[Os(SO_3)_3]$	Brown	$OsO_3.glycol + Na_2SO_3$	48
	$Na_6Os_4(SO_3)_7.24\,H_2O$	Violet	$Na_2[OsCl_6] + Na_2S_2O_4$	207

Table 3.7 Infrared and Raman spectra of platinum metal ammines[a] [100]

Complex	Ammine vibrations[c]				Skeletal modes for O_h symmetry				
	ν_{N-H}	$\delta^{asym}_{NH_3}$	$\delta^{sym}_{NH_3}$	ρ_{NH_3}	ν_1 A_{1g} R, polarized	ν_2 E_g R, polarized	ν_3 F_{1u} i.r.	ν_4 F_{1u} i.r.	ν_5 F_{2g} R, depolarized
$[Os(NH_3)_6][OsBr_6]$[b]	3125s	1595m	1339s	818s	—	—	452m	256s	—
$[Os(ND_3)_6][OsBr_6]$	2320s	1147m	1027s	621s	—	—	410w		—
$[Ru(NH_3)_6]Cl_3$	3077s	1618m	1368s	788s	500s	475s	463w	283s	248
			1342s					263s	
$[Ru(ND_3)_6]Cl_3$	2424s	1198m	1076w	611s	466s	430m	417w		228
	2342s		1011s						
$[Ir(NH_3)_6]Cl_3$	3155s	1587m	1350s	857s	527m	500w	475m	279s	262w
			1323s					264s	
$[Ir(ND_3)_6]Cl_3$	2398s	1161s	1053m	662s	498m	471w	440m	255s	245w
	2326s		1033s					235s	
$[Rh(NH_3)_6]Cl_3$	3200s	1618m	1353s	845s	514s	483s	472m	302s	240w
			1318s					287s	
$[Rh(ND_3)_6]Cl_3$	2410s	1151m	1035m	658s	489s	455m	433m	278s	220w
	2326s		1018s					256s	

[a] Raman spectra were measured in aqueous or heavy water solutions; infrared spectra as paraffin mulls.
[b] For $[Os(^{15}NH_3)_6][OsBr_6]$, ν_3 = 440 cm^{-1}; all other frequencies are unchanged.
[c] asym. = asymmetric, sym. = symmetric in this and subsequent tables.

Table 3.8 Pyridine complexes of osmium (see also Table 3.9)

Oxidation state	Complex	Colour	Preparation	Ref.
VIII	$OsO_4 . py$	Yellow	OsO_4 + py	49
	$OsO_4py . (C_4H_4Cl_2)$		$C_4H_4Cl_2 + OsO_4$ + py	50
	2 $OsO_4 . py . (C_4H_4Cl_2)$		$C_4H_4Cl_2 + OsO_4$ + py	50
VI	OsO_3py_2	Olive-green	OsO_4 + py + EtOH	48
III	[Os py_4 . bipy]$(ClO_4)_3$	Pink	[Os py_4bipy]$(ClO_4)_2 + Cl_2$	24
	Os py_3Cl_3	Brown	$K_2[OsCl_6]$ + py + EtOH	24
	Os $pyCl_3L$	Brown	$K[OsCl_4L]$ + py	24
	[Os py_3bipy X]$^{2+}$	Yellow	[Os py_3bipy X]$^{+}$ + Ce(IV)	24
	[Os py_2L_2]$(ClO_4)_3$ (L = phen, bipy)	Red	[Os py_2L_2]$(ClO_4)_2 + Cl_2$	24
II	Os py_4X_2 (X = Cl, Br)	Brown	$[OsX_6]^{2-}$ + py	24
	[Os py_3bipy X]X	Brown	$OsCl_4$bipy + py + X^-	24
	[Os py_4bipy]I_2	Green	Os py bipyCl_3 + $H_2PO_2^-$ + I^-	24
	[Os py_2L_2]I_2	Green	$OsCl_2L_2$ + py + I^-	24
	[Os $pyXL_2$]$^+$ (X = Cl, Br, I; L = phen, bipy)	Orange	OsX_2L_2 + py	24
	[Os py_3 terpy]$^{2+}$	Brown	Os terpy Cl_3 + py	24a

Table 3.9 Complexes with bidentate heterocyclic bases (see also Table 3.8)

Oxidation state	Complex[a]	Colour	Physical properties	Preparation	Ref.
IV	Os LX_4 (L = phen, bipy; X = Cl, Br)	Brown		$K(L.H)[OsX_6]$ + Heat	24
IV–III	$[Os_2O\ terpy_2bipy_2](ClO_4)_5$	Red		[Os terpy bipyCl]Cl + ClO_4^- + Ce(IV)	24a
III	Os terpyCl_3	Brown		$K_2[OsCl_6]$ + terpy	24a
	$[Os\ terpy\ bipyX]^{2+}$ (X = Cl, Br, I, NCS, NO_2, MeCN, EtCN)			$[Os\ terpy\ bipyX]^+ + Cl_2$	24a
	$[OsL_3]Cl_3$	Red	kin. (see p. 89)	$[OsL_3]Cl_2 + Cl_2$	65, 66
	$[OsL_2X_2]X$ (X = Cl, Br)	Brown	el.[78a]	$(NH_4)_2[OsX_6]$ + L	24
	$[Os\ bipy\ phen_2](ClO_4)_3$			$[Os\ bipy\ phen_2](ClO_4)_2$ + Ce(IV)	24
	$[Os\ phen\ bipy_2](ClO_4)_3$			$[Os\ phen\ bipy_2](ClO_4)_2$ + Ce(IV)	24
	$K[OsLX_4]$	Brown		$(NH_4)_2[OsCl_6] + L + X^- + H_3PO_2$	24
	Os bipy Cl_2Y	Brown		$K[OsCl_4L]$ + Y	24
	$[Os\ bipy\ Y_2]I$	Brown		$K[OsCl_4\ bipy] + Y + I^-$	24

[a] Y = acac, glycine; L = bipy, phen.

(*Table continued*)

Table 3.9 *(continued)*

Oxidation state	Complex[a]	Colour	Physical properties	Preparation	Ref.
III *(continued)*	$[Os_2bipy_2(NH)Cl_2](ClO_3)_2$	Brown	i.r.[117a]	$[OsCl(NH_3)bipy_2]Cl + Ce(IV)$	24
	$Os_2bipy_2Cl_4(OH)_2$	Brown		$K[OsCl_4\ bipy] + H_2O$	24
	$Os\ bipyCl_3(H_2O)$	Brown		$K[OsCl_4bipy] + H_2SO_4$	24
	$[Os\ terpy\ py_2Cl]^{2+}$			$Cl_2 + [Os\ terpy\ py_2Cl]^+$	24a
	$[Os\ terpy\ bipy\ (pyR)]^{3+}$ (R = Me, Et, $CHMe_2$)			$Cl_2 + [Os\ terpy\ bipy(pyR)]^+$	24a
	$[Os_2O\ bipy_2\ terpy_2](ClO_4)_4$	Blue		$[OsCl\ bipy\ terpy]Cl + ClO_4^-$	24a
II	$[OsL_3]Cl_2$	Green	kin. (p. 89)	$K_2[OsCl_6] + L$	26, 67
	OsL_2ox	Crimson		$OsL_2Cl_2 + ox^{2-}$	24
	$[OsL_2acac]Cl$	Orange		$OsL_2Cl_2 + acac$	24
	$[Os\ bipy_2\ glycine]I$	Brown		$Os\ bipy_2Cl_2 + glycine + I^-$	24
	$[Os\ bipy\ phen_2]I_2$			$Os\ Cl_2phen_2 + bipy + I^-$	24
	$[Os\ phen\ bipy_2]I_2$			$Os\ bipy_2Cl_2 + phen + I^-$	24
	$Os_2bipy_4(NH)_2$	Brown	i.r.[100]	$Os\ bipy_2Cl_2 + NH_3 + I^-$	24
	OsL_2X_2 (X = Cl, Br)	Purple	el.[78a]	$[OsL_2X_2]X + Na_2S_2O_4$	24
	$[Os\ terpy\ py_3](ClO_4)_2$			$Os\ terpyCl_3 + py + ClO_4^-$	24a
	$[Os\ terpy\ bipyX]^+$ (X = Cl, Br, I, NCS, NO_2, MeCN, EtCN)			$OsCl_4bipy + X^- + terpy$	24a
	$[Os\ terpy\ bipy(pyR)]^{2+}$			$[Os\ terpy\ bipyCl]^+ + pyR$	24a
	$[Os_2O\ bipy_2\ terpy_2](ClO_4)_2$	Brown		$[Os_2O\ bipy_2\ terpy_2](ClO_4)_4 + S_2O_4^{2-}$	24a
	$[OsCl(NH_3)bipy_2]Cl$	Red		$OsCl_2\ bipy_2 + NH_3$	24
	$[Os(NH_3)_2bipy_2]I$	Brown		$OsCl_2\ bipy_2 + NH_3 + NaI$	24
	$[Os\ enL_2]I_2$	Brown		$[OsCl_2L_2]^+ + en + EtOH + I^-$	24

[a] L = bipy, phen.

Table 3.10 Second-order rate coefficients for electron exchange reactions of osmium bipyridyl complexes (See also pp. 18, 89 and 90)

Oxidant	Reductant	T(°C)	Medium	k(M^{-1} sec^{-1})	Method[a]	Ref.
$[Os\ bipy_3]^{3+}$	$[Fe(CN)_6]^{4-}$	25	0·5M $HClO_4$	$>10^8$	(a)	96
$[Os\ bipy_3]^{3+}$	$[Os\ bipy_3]^{2+}$	0	3M H_2SO_4	$>10^5$	(b)	237
$[Os\ bipy_3]^{3+}$	$[Os\ bipy_3]^{2+}$	6		$>5 \times 10^4$	(c)	55
$[Ru\ bipy_3]^{3+}$	$[Os\ bipy_3]^{2+}$	25	0·5M $HClO_4$	$>10^8$	(a)	96
$[Ru\ bipy_3]^{3+}$	$[Os\ bipy_3]^{2+}$	0	0·1M H_2SO_4	$>5 \times 10^4$	(b)	72
$[Fe\ bipy_3]^{3+}$	$[Os\ bipy_3]^{2+}$	0	3M H_2SO_4	$>2{\cdot}5 \times 10^6$	(b)	72
$[Fe\ phen_3]^{3+}$	$[Os\ bipy_3]^{2+}$	0	3M H_2SO_4	$>3 \times 10^6$	(b)	72
$[Fe\ phen_3]^{3+}$	$[Os\ bipy_3]^{2+}$	25	0·5M $HClO_4$	$>10^3$[b]	(a)	96
$[Mo(CN)_8]^{3-}$	$[Os\ bipy_3]^{2+}$	10	0·05M HNO_3	2×10^9	(d)	31

[a] The methods of determining the rate coefficients are:
(a) Continuous-flow.
(b) Isotopic-tracer.
(c) Proton magnetic resonance.
(d) Temperature-jump.

[b] May be a misprint in reference 96 for $>10^8$.

Table 3.11 Phosphine, arsine and stibine complexes of osmium

Oxidation state	Complex	Colour	Physical properties	Preparation	Ref.
IV	$Os(AsPh_3)_2Br_4$	Purple		$(NH_4)_2[OsBr_6]$ + $AsPh_3$ + MeOH	232
	[Os $diars_2X_2](ClO_4)_2$	Brown		[Os $diars_2X_2]ClO_4$ + HNO_3	182
III	$Os(LR_3)_3X_3$ (X = Cl, Br; LR_3 = PEt_2Ph, $AsMe_2Ph$, $AsPh_3$, $AsMePh_2$, $SbPh_3$)	Red-purple		$(NH_4)_2[OsX_6]$ + MR_3 + EtOH	70, 232
	[Os $diars_2X_2]^+$ + EtOH		i.r.[156]	[Os $diars_2X_2$] + X_2	182
II	$[Os_2Cl_3(LR_3)_6]Cl$ (LR_2 = PPh_2Et, PPh_2Me, $PPhEt_2$)	Yellow		$(NH_4)_2[OsCl_6]$ + MR_3	34
	[Os $diars_2X_2$]X	Purple	i.r.[156]	Os $diars_2X_2$ + X^- + Cl_2	182
	$OsX_2(AsR_3)_4$ (X = Cl, Br; AsR_3 = $AsMePh_2$, $AsMe_2Ph$)	Yellow		OsX_3AsR_3 + H_3PO_2	70
	$OsBr_2(SbPh_3)_4$	Orange		$(NH_4)_2[OsBr_6]$ + $SbPh_3$ + 2 methoxyethanol	232
	cis- and *trans*-OsX_2(diphosphine)$_2$[a] (X = Cl, I)	Yellow	D[34]	$(NH_4)_2[OsX_6]$ + diphosphine	34
	trans-OsHX(diphosphine)$_2$[a] (X = Cl, I, SCN, H)	Yellow	i.r., n.m.r.[36]	*cis*- or *trans*-$OsX_2diphos_2$ + $LiAlH_4$	36

(*Table continued*)

Table 3.11 *(continued)*

Oxidation state	Complex	Colour	Physical properties[a]	Preparation	Ref.
II (*continued*)	*trans*-$OsHR(diphosphine)_2$[b] (R = Me, Et)		i.r., n.m.r. D[37]	$OsClR(diphosphine)_2 + LiAlH_4$	37
	trans-$OsH_2(diphosphine)_2$[c]		i.r., n.m.r.[36]	$OsHCl(diphosphine)_2 + LiAlH_4$	
	cis- and *trans*-$OsClMe(diphosphine)_2$[b]	Yellow	i.r., n.m.r., D[37]	*cis*- and *trans*-$OsCl_2(diphosphine)_2 + AlMe_3$	37
	trans-$OsClEt(diphosphine)_2$[b]	Yellow	i.r., n.m.r., D[37]	*cis*- and *trans*-$OsCl_2(diphosphine)_2 + AlEt_3$	37
	cis-$OsR_2(diphosphine)_2$[b] (R = Me, Ph)	Yellow	i.r., n.m.r., D[37]	$OsCl_2(diphosphine)_2 + LiR$	37
	$OsClR((C_2H_4)(PPh_2)_2)_2$		i.r.[37]	*trans*-$OsCl_2((C_2H_4)(PPh_2)_2)_2) + AlR_3$	37
	Os $diars_2X_2$ (X = Cl, Br, I, SCN)		i.r.[156]	$(NH_4)_2[OsX_6]$ + diars + X^-	182
	$OsBr_2(PPh_3)_3$	Green		$(NH_3)_2[OsBr_6] + PPh_3 + MeOC_2H_4OH$	232
	$OsI_2(AsR_3)_3$ ($AsR_3 = AsMe_2Ph$ and $AsMePh_2$)	Red		$OsX_3(AsR_3)_3 + HI + Me_2CO$	70

[a] Diphosphine = $C_2H_4(PR_2)_2$ (R = Me, Et, Ph); $CH_2(PPh_2)_2$; o-$C_6H_4(PEt_2)_2$.
[b] Diphosphine = $C_2H_4(PPh_2)_2$.
[c] Diphosphine = o-$C_6H_4(PEt_2)_2$.

Table 3.12 Vibrational spectra of Group VIII hexacyano complexes

Mode[a]	Species	Activity	$K_4[Os(CN)_6]$	$K_4[Ru(CN)_6]$	$K_4[Fe(CN)_6]$	$K_3[Ir(CN)_6]$	$K_3[Rh(CN)_6]$	$K_3[Co(CN)_6]$
ν_1	(A_{1g})	R, polarized	2109	2100	2096	2170	2166	2150
ν_2	(A_{1g})	R, polarized	465			469	445	408
ν_3	(E_g)	R	2062	2067	2063	2146	2147	2137
ν_4	(E_g)	R	450			450	435	(391)[c]
ν_5	(F_{1g})	Inactive	(360)[b]	(340)[b]		(415)[c]	(380)[c]	(358)[c]
ν_6	(F_{1u})	i.r.	2036	2042, 2027	2033, 2021	2131	2133	2129
ν_7	(F_{1u})	i.r.	550	550	585	520	520	564
ν_8	(F_{1u})	i.r.	390	376	414	398	386	416
ν_9	(F_{1u})	i.r.				(82)[b]	(88)[b]	(84)[b]
ν_{10}	(F_{2g})	R	285		(420)	483	(475)[c]	(480)[c]
ν_{11}	(F_{2g})	R	100			95	94	98
ν_{12}	(F_{2u})		(390)[b]			445		(440)[c]
ν_{13}	(F_{2u})					69[b]		72[b]
Ref. i.r.			181, 171a	181	181	133	133	133
R			171a	171	171	172	172	172

[a] Description of modes: C—N stretch ν_1, ν_3, ν_6; M—C stretch ν_2, ν_4, ν_7; M—C—N bend $\nu_5, \nu_8, \nu_{10}, \nu_{12}$; C—M—C deformation $\nu_9, \nu_{11}, \nu_{13}$.
[b] Calculated frequency.
[c] From combination modes.

Table 3.13 Carbonyl complexes of osmium (see also pp. 94 and 99)

Oxidation state	Complex	Colour	Physical properties	Preparation	Ref.
II	$[Os(CO)_6]Cl_2$			$Os(CO)_3Cl_2 + AlCl_3 + CO$(400 atm)	118
	$Os(CO)_4Cl_2$	Colourless	i.r.[12a]	$OsCl_3 + CO$(200 atm, 160°)	119
	$Os(CO)_4Br_2$(2 forms)	Colourless, yellow	i.r.[12a]	$Os_2Br_9 + CO$(200 atm, 160°)	119
	$Os(CO)_4I_2$(2 forms)	Yellow		$H_2[OsI_6] + CO$(200 atm, 120°)	119
	$[Os(CO)_3Cl_2]_2$	Colourless		$OsCl_2 + CO$(pressure)	119
	$[Os(CO)_3Br_2]_2$	Yellow		$Os_2Br_9 + CO$(250°, 1 atm)	119
	$[Os(CO)_3I_2]_2$	Yellow		Heat $Os(CO)_4I_2$ to 140°	119
	$[Os(CO)_2Br_2]_n$	Yellow		Heat $[Os(CO)_3Br_2]_2$ to 120°	119
	$[Os(CO)_2I_2]_n$	Yellow		Heat $Os(CO)_4I_2$ to 300°	119
	$OsCl_2(CO)_2(PR_3)_2$ (PR_3 = OPh, Ph, C_6H_{11})	White		$[Os(CO)_3Cl_2]_2$	120a
	$OsCl(COOR^1)(CO)_2(PR_3)_2$ (R = Ph, C_6H_{11}; R^1 = Me, Et)			$[OsCl(CO)_3(PR_3)_2]^+ + R^1OH + KOH$	120a
	$(OsCl(CO)_3(PR_3)_2)HCl_2$			$OsCl(COOR^1)(CO)_2(PR_3)_2 + HCl$	120a
	$(Os(HgX)(CO)_3(PPh_3)_2)HgX_3$ (X = Cl, Br, I)		i.r.[44b]	$Os(CO)_3(PPh_3)_2 + HgX_2$	44b
	$(Os(CO)_4(PR_3)_2)^+$ (R = OPh, Ph, C_6H_{11})			$OsCl_2(CO)_2(PR_3)_2 + AlCl_3 + CO$	120a

Table 3.13 *(continued)*

Oxidation state	Complex	Colour	Physical properties	Preparation	Ref.
II *(continued)*	? $Os(CO)_4H_2$			$OsI_3 + CO(300\ atm, 300°) + Ag$	120
	$OsHX(CO)(PPh_3)_3$ (X = Cl, Br)		i.r.[229] X^{184}	$(NH_4)_2[OsX_6] + PPh_3$ in 2-methoxyethanol (120°)	230
	$OsHCl(CO)(PEt_2Ph)_3$		i.r.[35a]	$OsCl_3(PEt_2Ph)_3 + KOH + EtOH$	35a
	$OsHX(CO)(AsPh_3)_3$ (X = Cl, Br)			$(NH_4)_2[OsX_6] + AsPh_3$ in 2-methoxyethanol	230
	$OsCl_2(CO)_2(PPh_3)_2$		i.r.[44a]	$OsCl_3 + CO + PPh_3$	44a
	$OsBr_2(CO)_2(PPh_3)_2$		i.r.[44a]	$(NH_4)_2[OsBr_6] + CO + PPh_3$	44a
	$OsI_2(CO)_2(PPh_3)_2$		i.r.[44a]	$Os(CO)_3(PPh_3)_2 + HI$	44a
	$[OsX(CO)_3(PPh_3)_2]^+$ (X = Br, I)		i.r.[44a]	$Os(CO)_3(PPh_3)_2 + X_2$	44a
	$OsCp(CO)_2Br$			$Br_2 + [OsCp(CO)_2]_2$	82
I	$[OsCp(CO)_2]_2$			$[Os(CO)_3Cl_2]_2 + C_{10}H_{10}$	82
	$[Os(CO)_4Br]_2$	Yellow		$Os_2Br_9 + CO(900°)$	120
	$[Os(CO)_4I]_2$	Yellow		$Os(CO)_4I_2 + Ag$	120
O	$Os(CO)_5$	Colourless		$OsI_3 + CO + Ag(300\ atm, 300°)$	120
	$Os_3(CO)_{12}$		X^{45} i.r.[123]	$OsI_3 + CO + Ag(300\ atm, 300°)$	120
	$Os(CO)_3(PPh_3)_2$		i.r.[44a]	$Os(CO)_2Cl_2(PPh_3)_2 + Zn + CO(140°)$	44a

Table 3.14 Physical and thermodynamic properties of the iron group metallocenes[200] (see also p. 97)

Property	Osmocene	Ruthenocene	Ferrocene
Colour	White	Yellow	Orange
M.p.	229°	199·5°	174°
B.p.	311°	278°	249°
Decomposition temp.	540°	610°	540°
Heat of sublimation[a]	18·00	17·64	16·29
Heat of vaporization[a]	10·99	12·89	11·12
Heat of fusion[a]	7·01	4·75	5·17
H^0_{298} for reaction $M(g) + 2\,C_5H_5(g) \rightarrow M(C_5H_5)_2(g)$[a]	−187	−187	−147
Chemical shift (τ)	5·29	5·58	5·96

[a] Values given in kcal/mole.

Table 3.15 Infrared and Raman spectra of metallocenes in solution[a,c]

Mode	Species	Activity	Description	Osmocene[b]	Ruthenocene	Ferrocene
ν_1	A_{1g}	R	C—H stretch (sym.)		3104	3099
ν_3			Ring breathing		1104	1105
ν_4			Ring–metal stretch		330	303
ν_8	A_{2u}	i.r.	C—H stretch (asym.)	3095	3100	3085
ν_{10}		i.r.	Ring breathing		1103	1108
ν_{11}			Ring–metal stretch	353	446	478
ν_{12}	E_{1g}	R	C—H stretch (sym.)		3089	3085
ν_{15}			C—C stretch		1412	1408
ν_{16}			Ring tilt (sym.)		402	388
ν_{17}	E_{1u}	i.r.	C—H stretch (asym.)	2907	3100	3075
ν_{20}			C—C stretch	1400	1413	1411
ν_{21}			Ring tilt (asym.)	428	528	492
ν_{23}	E_{2g}	R	C—H stretch		3089	3085
ν_{26}			C—C stretch		1193	1178
Ref.				89, 90, 194	158	158

[a] Frequencies in cm^{-1}.
[b] No Raman data are available for osmocene.
[c] D_{5h} Symmetry is assumed for the three species in solution.

Table 3.16 Magnetic measurements on osmium complexes (cf. also Table 3.4)

	Complex	χ_a ($\times$ 10^6 c.g.s. units)		μ_{eff} (BM)	Ref.
t_{2g}^1	OsF_7	1,620 (90°)	730 (195°)	1·08 (195°)	93a
t_{2g}^2	OsF_6	1,886 (117°)	943 (297°)	1·50 (297°)	111
t_{2g}^3	$[OsF_5]_4$	3,640 (102°)	1,770 (295°)	2·06 (295°)	110
	$K[OsF_6]$	11,430 (115°)	4,613 (295°)	3·34 (300°)	79
	$Cs[OsF_6]$	10,760 (118°)	4,393 (294°)	3·23 (300°)	79
t_{2g}^4	$K_2[OsF_6]$	713 (89°)	713 (291°)	1·31 (300°)	71
	$Cs_2[OsF_6]$	957 (90°)	937 (279°)	1·50 (300°)	71
	$K_2[OsCl_6]$	941 (90°)	941 (300°)	1·51 (300°)	71
	$Cs_2[OsCl_6]$	1,257 (91°)	1,162 (297°)	1·67 (300°)	71
	$Cs_2[OsCl_6]$	917 (78°)	909 (298°)	1·47 (298°)	132
	$(NH_4)_2[OsCl_6]$	914 (78°)	908 (298°)	1·47 (298°)	132
	$K_2[OsBr_6]$	617 (87°)	603 (295°)	1·21 (300°)	71
	$Cs_2[OsBr_6]$	1,392 (98°)	1,285 (295°)	1·76 (300°)	71
	$Cs_2[OsBr_6]$	994 (78°)	982 (298°)	1·52 (298°)	132
	$(NH_4)_2[OsBr_6]$	988 (78°)	995 (298°)	1·53 (298°)	132
	$K_2[OsI_6]$	877 (88°)	789 (296°)	1·38 (300°)	71
	$Cs_2[OsI_6]$	1,191 (91°)	1,132 (294°)	1·65 (300°)	71
t_{2g}^5	$OsCl_3(AsPh_2Me)_3$			1·80 (80°) 1·95 (295°)	80

Table 3.17 Selected polarographic data for osmium complexes

Complex	Process	$E_{1/2}$ (versus S.C.E.)	Medium	Ref.
OsO_4	VI→IV	−0·61	M NaOH	47, 174
	IV→III	−1·51	M NaOH	47, 174
OsO_4	VI→III	0	M KCN	174
	III→II	−0·81	M KCN	174
OsO_4	VI→IV	0	M HOAc + M OAc^-	174
	IV→III	−0·45	M HOAc + M OAc^-	174
$[OsO_2(OH)_4]^{2-}$	VI→III	0	M HCl or H_2SO_4	47

REFERENCES

1. Adams, D. M., and H. A. Gebbie, *Spectrochim. Acta*, **19**, 925 (1963).
2. Atovyman, L. A., and G. B. Bokii, *J. Struct. Chem. USSR Eng. Transl.*, **1**, 468 (1960).
3. Ayres, G. H., *Anal. Chem.*, **25**, 1622 (1953).
4. Balchan, A. S., and H. G. Drickamer, *J. Chem. Phys.*, **35**, 356 (1961).
5. Ballhausen, C. J., and J. P. Dahl, *Acta Chem. Scand.*, **15**, 1333 (1961).

5a. Bankovskis J., G. Mezarups and A. Levins, *Latvijas PSR Zinatnu Akad. Vestis*, **1962**, 323; **1964**, 135.

6. Barbieri, G. A., *Atti Accad. Nazl. Lincei Mem. Classe Sci. Fis. Mat. Nat. Sez. II*, **25**, 75 (1916).

7. Barnes, G. T., F. P. Dwyer and E. C. Gyarfas, *Trans. Faraday Soc.*, **48**, 269 (1952).
8. Bartlett, N., N. I. Jha and J. Trotter, *Proc. Chem. Soc.*, **1962**, 277.
9. Bartlett, N., S. Beaton, L. W. Reeves and E. J. Wells, *Can. J. Chem.*, **42**, 2531 (1964).
10. Bartlett, N., and D. H. Lohmann, *Proc. Chem. Soc.*, **1962**, 115; *J. Chem. Soc.*, **1962,** 5253.
10a. Bartlett, N., S. P. Beaton and N. K. Jha, *Chem. Commun.*, **1966**, 168.
11. Beck, W., and H. S. Smedal, *Z. Naturforsch.*, **20b**, 109 (1965).
12. Belova, V. I., and Y. K. Syrkin, *Russ. J. Inorg. Chem. Eng. Transl.*, **3**, 33 (1958).
12a. Bennett, M. A., and R. J. H. Clark, *J. Chem. Soc.*, **1964**, 5560.
13. Berezin, B. D., and N. I. Sosnikova, *Dokl. Akad. Nauk. SSSR*, **146**, 831 (1963).
14. Blasius, E., and W. Preetz, *Z. Anorg. Allgem. Chem.*, **335**, 16 (1965).
15. Blinc, R., E. Pirkmajer, J. Slivnik and I. Zupančič, *J. Chem. Phys.*, **45**, 1488 (1966).
15a. Brauer, G., *Handbook of Preparative Chemistry*, Academic Press, New York, 1965, p. 1601.
16. Braune, H., and S. Knoke, *Naturwissenschaften*, **21**, 349 (1933).
17. Braune, H., and K. Stute, *Angew. Chem.*, **51**, 528 (1938).
18. Brizard, L., *Ann. Chim. Phys.*, **21**, 375 (1900).
19. Brizard, L., *Compt. Rend.*, **123**, 182 (1896).
20. Brockway, L. O., *Rev. Mod. Phys.*, **8**, 260 (1936).
21. Brown, D. H., D. R. Russell and D. W. A. Sharp, *J. Chem. Soc., Ser. A*, **1966**, 18.
21a. Brown, D. H., K. R. Dixon, R. D. W. Kemmitt and D. W. A. Sharp, *J. Chem. Soc.*, **1965**, 1559.
22. Brunot, F., *J. Ind. Hyg.*, **15**, 136 (1933).
23. Bublitz, D. E., W. E. McEwan and J. Kleinberg, *J. Am. Chem. Soc.*, **84**, 1845 (1962).
24. Buckingham, D. A., F. P. Dwyer, H. A. Goodman and A. M. Sargeson, *Australian J. Chem.*, **17**, 315, 325 (1964).
24a. Buckingham, D. A., F. P. Dwyer and A. M. Sargeson, *Australian J. Chem.*, **17**, 622 (1964).
24b. Buckingham, D. A., F. P. Dwyer and A. M. Sargeson, *Inorg. Chem.*, **5**, 1243 (1966).
25. Buell, G. R., W. E. McEwen and J. Kleinberg, *J. Am. Chem. Soc.*, **84**, 40 (1962).
26. Burstall, F. H., F. P. Dwyer and E. C. Gyarfas, *J. Chem. Soc.*, **1950**, 953.
27. Busev, A. I., and M. I. Ivanyutin, *Tr. Komiss. PO Analit. Khim., Akad. Nauk. SSSR, Inst. Geokhim. i Analst. Khim.*, **11**, 172 (1960); *Chem. Abstr.*, **55**, 24381b (1961).
28. Cabrera, B., and A. Duperier, *Compt. Rend.*, **185**, 414 (1927).
29. Cady, G. H., and G. B. Hargreaves, *J. Chem. Soc.*, **1961**, 1563.
30. Cady, G. H., and G. B. Hargreaves, *J. Chem. Soc.*, **1961**, 1568.
31. Campion, R., N. Purdie and N. Sutin, *J. Am. Chem. Soc.*, **85**, 3528 (1963).
32. Carrington, A., and C. K. Jorgensen, *Mol. Phys.*, **4**, 395 (1961).
33. Charronat, R. in *Nouveau Traite de Chimie Minerale* (Ed. P. Pascal), Masson et cie, Paris, 1958, p. 265.

34. Chatt, J., and R. G. Hayter, *J. Chem. Soc.*, **1961**, 896.
35. Chatt, J., and B. L. Shaw, *Chem. Ind. (London)*, **1960**, 931.
35a. Chatt, J., B. L. Shaw and A. E. Field, *J. Chem. Soc.*, **1964**, 3466.
36. Chatt, J., and R. G. Hayter, *J. Chem. Soc.*, **1961**, 2605.
37. Chatt, J., and R. G. Hayter, *J. Chem. Soc.*, **1963**, 6017.
38. Child, M. S., *Mol. Phys.*, **3**, 601, 605 (1960).
39. Child, M. S., and H. C. Longuet-Higgins, *Phil. Trans. Roy. Soc. (London), Ser. A*, **254**, 259 (1961); Child, M. S., and A. C. Roach, *Mol. Phys.*, **9**, 281 (1965).
40. Classen, H. H., H. Selig and J. G. Malm, *J. Chem. Phys.*, **36**, 2888 (1962).
41. Classen, H. H., H. Selig and J. G. Malm, *J. Chem. Phys.*, **36**, 2890 (1962).
42. Classen, H. H., *J. Chem. Phys.*, **30**, 968 (1959).
43. Claus, C., *J. Prakt. Chem.*, **90**, 83 (1863); **43**, 631 (1847).
44. Clifford, A. F., and C. S. Kobayashi, *Inorg. Syn.*, **6**, 204, 206, 207 (1960).
44a. Collmann, J. P., and W. R. Roper, *J. Am. Chem. Soc.*, **88**, 3504 (1966).
44b. Collmann, J. P., and W. R. Roper, *Chem. Commun.*, **1966**, 244.
45. Corey, E. R., and L. F. Dahl, *Inorg. Chem.*, **1**, 521 (1962).
46. Corey, E. R., and L. F. Dahl, *J. Am. Chem. Soc.*, **83**, 2203 (1961).
47. Cover, R. E., and L. Meites, *J. Am. Chem. Soc.*, **83**, 4706 (1961).
48. Criegee, R., *Ann.*, **522**, 75 (1936).
49. Criegee, R., B. Manchard and H. Wannowius, *Ann.*, **550**, 99 (1942).
50. Criegee, R., W. Horauf and W. D. Schellenberg, *Ber.*, **86**, 126 (1953).
50a. Crosby, G. A., D. M. Klassen and S. L. Sabath, *Mol. Crystals*, **1**, 166 (1966).
51. Crowell, W. R., R. K. Brinton and R. F. Evenson, *J. Am. Chem. Soc.*, **60**, 1105 (1938).
52. Crowell, W. R., and H. L. Baumbach, *J. Am. Chem. Soc.*, **57**, 2607 (1935).
53. Csanyi, L. J., *Acta Chim. Acad. Sci. Hung.*, **21**, 35 (1959).
54. Curphy, T. J., J. O. Santer, M. Rosenblum and J. H. Richards, *J. Am. Chem. Soc.*, **82**, 5249 (1960).
55. Dietrich, M. and A. C. Wahl, *J. Chem. Phys.*, **38**, 1591 (1963).
56. Dillard, J. G. and R. W. Kiser, *J. Phys. Chem.*, **69**, 3893 (1965).
56a. Dingle, R., *J. Mol. Spectry.*, **18**, 276 (1965).
57. Dodd, R. E., *Trans. Faraday Soc.*, **55**, 1480 (1959).
58. Dodge, R. P., O. S. Mills and V. Schomaker, *Proc. Chem. Soc. (London)*, **1963**, 380.
59. Dreyer, R., and I. Dreyer, *Z. Chem.*, **4**, 106 (1964).
60. Dwyer, F. P., and S. W. Hogarth, *J. Proc. Roy. Soc. N. S. Wales*, **84**, 194 (1950).
61. Dwyer, F. P., and J. W. Hogarth, *J. Proc. Roy. Soc. N. S. Wales*, **84**, 117 (1950).
62. Dwyer, F. P., and J. W. Hogarth, *J. Proc. Roy. Soc. N. S. Wales*, **85**, 113 (1951).
63. Dwyer, F. P., and J. W. Hogarth, *J. Am. Chem. Soc.*, **77**, 6152 (1955).
64. Dwyer, F. P., and A. M. Sargeson, *J. Am. Chem. Soc.*, **77**, 1285 (1955).
65. Dwyer, F. P., N. A. Gibson and E. C. Gyarfas, *J. Proc. Roy. Soc. N. S. Wales*, **84**, 80 (1950).
66. Dwyer, F. P., and E. C. Gyarfas, *J. Am. Chem. Soc.*, **74**, 4699 (1952).
66a. Dwyer, F. P., and E. C. Gyarfas, *J. Am. Chem. Soc.*, **73**, 2322 (1951).
67. Dwyer, F. P., N. A. Gibson and E. C. Gyarfas, *J. Proc. Roy. Soc. N. S. Wales*, **84**, 68 (1950).

68. Dwyer, F. P., and E. C. Gyarfas, *Nature*, **166**, 481 (1950).
69. Dwyer, F. P., and J. W. Hogarth, *Inorg. Syn.*, **5**, 204, 206 (1957).
70. Dwyer, F. P., R. S. Nyholm and B. T. Tyson, *J. Proc. Roy. Soc. N. S. Wales*, **81**, 272 (1947).
71. Earnshaw, A., B. N. Figgis, J. Lewis and R. D. Peacock, *J. Chem. Soc.*, **1961**, 3132.
72. Eichler, E., and A. C. Wahl, *J. Am. Chem. Soc.*, **80**, 4145 (1958).
73. Eisenstein, J. C., *J. Chem. Phys.*, **34**, 310 (1961).
74. Elwell, D., *Proc. Phys. Soc.* (*London*), **84**, 409 (1964).
75. Englman, R., *Mol. Phys.*, **6**, 345 (1964).
76. Evans, D. F., D. Jones and G. Wilkinson, *J. Chem. Soc.*, **1964**, 3164.
77. Fenn, E., R. S. Nyholm, P. G. Owston and A. Turco, *J. Inorg. Nucl. Chem.*, **17**, 387 (1961).
78. Fergusson, J. E., B. H. Robinson and W. R. Roper, *J. Chem. Soc.*, **1962**, 2113.
78a. Fergusson, J. E., and G. M. Harris, *J. Chem. Soc.*, *Ser. A*, **1966**, 1293.
79. Figgis, B. N., J. Lewis and F. E. Mabbs, *J. Chem. Soc.*, **1961**, 3138.
80. Figgis, B. N., and J. Lewis, *Progr. Inorg. Chem.*, **6**, 162 (1964).
81. Figgis, B. N., R. G. Kidd and R. S. Nyholm, *Proc. Roy. Soc.* (*London*), *Ser. A*, **269**, 469 (1962).
82. Fischer, E. O., and A. Vogler, *Z. Naturforsch.*, *Ser. B*, **17**, 421 (1962).
83. Fischer, E. O., K. Bittler and H. P. Fritz, *Z. Naturforsch.*, *Ser. B*, **18**, 83 (1963).
83a. Fischer, E. O., M. von Foerster, C. G. Kreiter and K. E. Schwarzans, *J. Organomet. Chem.*, **7**, 113 (1967).
84. Fischer, E. O., and J. Muller, *Ber.*, **96**, 3217 (1963).
84a. Fischer, E. O., and H. Grubert, *Ber.*, **92**, 2302 (1959).
85. Fischer, R. D., and A. Vogler, *Angew. Chem.*, **4**, 700 (1965).
86. de Ford, P., and A. W. Davidson, *J. Am. Chem. Soc.*, **73**, 1469 (1951).
87. Fraenkel, G., R. E. Carter, A. McClachan and J. H. Richards, *J. Am. Chem. Soc.*, **82**, 5846 (1960).
88. Fremy, E., *J. Prakt. Chem.*, **33**, 412 (1844).
89. Fritz, H. P., and R. Schneider, *Ber.*, **93**, 1171 (1960).
90. Fritz, H. P., *Ber.*, **92**, 780 (1959).
90a. Fritzmann, E., and L. Tchugaev, *Z. Anorg. Allgem. Chem.*, **172**, 213 (1938).
90b. Fritzsche, J., and H. Struve, *J. Prakt. Chem.*, **41**, 111 (1847).
91. Fulop, K., and L. J. Csányi, *Acta Chim. Acad. Sci. Hung.*, **38**, 193 (1963).
91a. Gans, P., A. Sabatini and L. Sacconi, *Inorg. Chem.*, **5**, 1877 (1966).
91b. Gibbs, L., Am. J. Chem., **3**, 233 (1881).
92. Gilchrist, R., *Bur. Standards J. Res. Washington*, **9**, 282 (1932).
93. Ginsberg, A. P., and E. Koubek, *Inorg. Chem.*, **4**, 1186 (1965).
93a. Glemser, O., H. W. Roesky, K-H. Hellberg and H-U. Werther, *Ber.*, **99**, 2652 (1966).
94. Goldschmidt, V. M., *Skrifter Norke Videnskaps-Akad Oslo, Mat. Naturv. Kl.*, **1**, 10 (1926).
95. Goldstein, G., *Inorg. Chem.*, **2**, 425 (1963).
96. Gordon, B. M., L. L. Williams and N. Sutin, *J. Am. Chem. Soc.*, **83**, 2061 (1961).
96a. Goubeau, J., *Angew. Chem.*, **5**, 571 (1966).
97. Gray, H. B., and N. A. Beach, *J. Am. Chem. Soc.*, **85**, 2922 (1963).

98. Griffith, J. S., *Theory of Transition Metal Ions*, Cambridge University Press, Cambridge, 1961.
99. Griffith, J. S., *Discussions Faraday Soc.*, **26**, 173 (1959).
100. Griffith, W. P., *J. Chem. Soc.*, **1966**, 899.
101. Griffith, W. P., *Unpublished work.*
101a. Griffith, W. P., *J. Chem. Soc.*, *Ser. A*, **1966**, 1467.
102. Griffith, W. P., *J. Chem. Soc.*, **1964**, 245.
103. Griffith, W. P., *J. Chem. Soc.*, **1962**, 3248.
104. Griffith, W. P., *J. Chem. Soc.*, **1965**, 3694.
105. Griffith, W. P., *Quart. Rev. London*, **19**, 254 (1965).
106. Griffiths, J. H. E., J. Owen and I. M. Ward, *Proc. Roy. Soc.* (*London*), *Ser. A*, **219**, 526 (1953).
107. Grimley, R. T., R. P. Burns and M. G. Inghram, *J. Chem. Phys.*, **33**, 308 (1960).
108. Gunstone, F. D., *Advances in Organic Chemistry*, Interscience Publishers, New York, **1**, 110 (1960).
108a. Haas, T. E., and E. P. Marram, *J. Chem. Phys.*, **43**, 3985 (1965).
109. Hair, M. L., and P. L. Robinson, *J. Chem. Soc.*, **1960**, 2775; **1958**, 106.
110. Hargreaves, G. B., and R. D. Peacock, *J. Chem. Soc.*, **1960**, 2618.
111. Hargreaves, G. B., and R. D. Peacock, *Proc. Chem. Soc.* (*London*), **1959**, 85.
112. Hatem, S., *Compt. Rend.*, **240**, 977 (1955).
112a. Henbest, H. B., W. R. Jackson and B. C. G. Robb, *J. Chem. Soc.*, *Ser. B*, **1966**, 803.
113. Hepworth, M. A., P. L. Robinson and G. J. Westland, *J. Chem. Soc.*, **1954**, 4269.
114. Hepworth, M. A., and P. L. Robinson, *J. Inorg. Nucl. Chem.*, **4**, 24 (1957).
115. Hepworth, M. A., P. L. Robinson and G. Westland, *Chem. Ind.* (*London*), **1955**, 1516.
116. Hepworth, M. A., K. H. Jack and G. J. Westland, *J. Inorg. Nucl. Chem.*, **2**, 79 (1956).
117. Hepworth, M. A., P. L. Robinson and G. J. Westland, *J. Chem. Soc.*, **1958**, 611.
117a. Hewkin, D., and W. P. Griffith, *J. Chem. Soc.*, *Ser. A*, **1966**, 472.
118. Hieber, W., and T. Kruck, *Angew. Chem.*, **73**, 580 (1961).
119. Hieber, W., and H. Stallmann, *Ber.*, **75**, 1472 (1942).
120. Hieber, W., and H. Stallmann, *Z. Elektrochem.*, **49**, 288 (1943).
120a. Hieber, W., and V. Frey, *Z. Naturforsch.*, *Ser. B*, **21**, 704 (1966).
121. Hill, E. A, and J. H. Richards, *J. Am. Chem. Soc.*, **83**, 3840 (1961).
122. Hofmann, K. A., O. Erhardt and O. Schneider, *Ber.*, **46**, 1657 (1913).
123. Huggins, D. K., N. Flitcroft and H. D. Kaesz, *Inorg. Chem.*, **4**, 166 (1965).
124. Hunter, D., *J. Pharm. Pharmacol.*, **5**, 149 (1953); *Brit. Med. Bull.*, **7**, 11 (1950).
125. Irvine, D. H., *J. Chem. Soc.*, **1958**, 2166.
126. Irvine, D. H., *J. Chem. Soc.*, **1959**, 2977.
127. Irvine, D. H., *J. Chem. Soc.*, **1957**, 1841.
128. Ito, K., D. Nakamura, K. Ito and M. Kubo, *Inorg. Chem.*, **2**, 690 (1963).
129. Jaeger, F. M., and J. E. Zanstra, *Proc. Acad. Sci. Amsterdam*, **35**, 610 (1932).
130. Jahn, H. A., and E. Teller, *Proc. Roy. Soc.* (*London*), *Ser. A*, **161**, 220 (1937).
131. Jellinek, F., *Z. Naturforsch.*, *Ser. B*, **14**, 737 (1959).

131a. Jezowska-Trzebiatowska, B., J. Hanuja and W. Wojciechowski, *J. Inorg. Nucl. Chem.*, **28**, 2701 (1966).
132. Johannesen, R. B., and G. A. Candela, *Inorg. Chem.*, **2**, 67 (1963).
132a. Johnson, B. F. G., J. Lewis, I. G. Williams and J. Wilson, *Chem. Commun.*, **1966**, 391, 851; *J. Chem. Soc., Ser. A*, **1967**, 341.
133. Jones, L. H., *J. Chem. Phys.*, **41**, 856 (1964).
134. Jorgensen, C. K., *Mol. Phys.*, **3**, 201 (1960).
135. Jorgensen, C. K., *Acta Chem. Scand.*, **17**, 1043 (1963).
136. Jorgensen, C. K., *Acta Chem. Scand.*, **17**, 1034 (1963); **16**, 793 (1962).
137. Jorgensen, C. K., and J. S. Brinen, *Mol. Phys.*, **5**, 535 (1962).
138. Jorgensen, C. K., *Mol. Phys.*, **2**, 309 (1959).
139. Jorgensen, C. K., *J. Inorg. Nucl. Chem.*, **24**, 1587 (1962).
140. Juza, R., *Z. Anorg. Chem.*, **219**, 129, 137 (1934).
141. Kamimura, H., S. Koide, H. Sekiyama and S. Sugano, *J. Phys. Soc Japan.*, **15**, 1264 (1960).
142. Keen, I. M., *Platinum Metal Rev.*, **8**, 143 (1964).
143. Keisel, K., *Z. Anorg. Allgem. Chem.*, **219**, 141 (1934).
144. Kemmitt, R. D., D. R. Russell and D. W. A. Sharp, *J. Chem. Soc.*, **1963**, 4408.
145. Kirschmann, H. D., and W. R. Crowell, *J. Am. Chem. Soc.*, **59**, 20 (1937); **55**, 488 (1933).
146. Kolbin, N. I., I. N. Semenov and Yu. M. Shutov, *Russ. J. Inorg. Chem. Eng. Transl.*, **8**, 1270 (1963); **9**, 108 (1964).
146a. Korn, E. D., *Biochim. Biophys. Acta*, **116**, 317, 325 (1966).
147. Kotani, M., *J. Phys. Soc. Japan*, **4**, 293 (1949).
148. Krauss, F., and D. Wilken, *Z. Anorg. Allgem. Chem.*, **145**, 151 (1925).
149. Krauss, F., and D. Wilken, *Z. Anorg. Allgem. Chem.*, **137**, 349 (1924).
150. Krauss, F., and G. Schrader, *J. Prakt. Chem.*, **120**, 36 (1929).
151. Krauss, F., and G. Schrader, *J. Prakt. Chem.*, **119**, 279 (1928).
151a. Krauss, F., and G. Schrader, *Z. Anorg. Allgem. Chem.*, **176**, 385 (1928).
151b. Krauzman, M., *Compt. Rend., Ser. B*, **262**, 765 (1966).
151c. Kruck, Th., *Angew. Chem.*, **6**, 53 (1967).
152. Kruse, F. H., *Acta Cryst.*, **14**, 1035 (1961).
153. Kuwana, T., D. E. Bublitz and G. Hoh, *J. Am. Chem. Soc.*, **82**, 5811 (1960).
154. Langseth, A., and B. Quiller, *Z. Physik. Chem., Ser. B*, **27**, 79 (1934).
154a. Levin, I. W., and S. Abramowitz, *Inorg. Chem.*, **5**, 2024 (1966).
155. Lewis, J., and G. Wilkinson, *J. Inorg. Nucl. Chem.*, **6**, 12 (1958).
156. Lewis, J., R. S. Nyholm and G. A. Rodley, *J. Chem. Soc.*, **1965**, 1483.
157. Liehr, A. D., *J. Phys. Chem.*, **67**, 464 (1963).
158. Lippincott, E. R., and R. D. Nelson, *Spectrochim. Acta*, **10**, 307 (1958).
159. Liu, F., N. C. Liu and J. C. Bailar, *Inorg. Chem.*, **3**, 1085 (1964).
160. Lott, K. A. K., and M. R. C. Symons, *J. Chem. Soc.*, **1960**, 973.
161. McCullough, J. D., *Z. Krist., Ser. A*, **94**, 143 (1936).
162. McDonald, A., and J. Trotter, *Acta Cryst.* (1965).
162a. McDonald, C. G., and J. S. Shannon, *Australian J. Chem.*, **19**, 1545 (1966).
163. McDonald, J. E., and J. W. Cobble, *J. Phys. Chem.*, **66**, 791 (1962).
164. McGlynn, S. P., and M. Kasha, *J. Chem. Phys.*, **24**, 481 (1956).
165. McLaughlin, A. I. G., R. Milton and K. M. A. Perry, *Brit. J. Ind. Med.*, **3**, 183 (1946).
166. Marcus, R. A., *J. Chem. Phys.*, **24**, 966 (1956); **26**, 867 (1957); *J. Phys. Chem.*, **67**, 853 (1963).

167. Mark, V., and M. D. Rausch, *Inorg. Chem.*, **3**, 1067 (1964).
168. Marr, G., and D. E. Webster, *J. Organometal. Chem.*, **2**, 99 (1964).
169. Martius, C. A., *Ann.*, **117**, 357 (1861).
170. Masuno, K., and S. Waku, *Nippon Kagaku Zasshi*, **83**, 116 (1962).
171. Mathieu, J-P., and H. Poulet, *Compt. Rend.*, **248**, 2315 (1959).
171a. Mathieu, J-P., and H. Poulet, *Spectrochim. Acta*, **19**, 1966 (1964).
172. Mathieu, J-P., and S. Cornevin, *J. Chim. Phys.*, **36**, 271 (1939).
173. Mattraw, H. C., N. J. Hawkins, D. R. Carpenter and W. W. Sabol, *J. Chem. Phys.*, **23**, 985 (1955).
174. Meites, L., *J. Am. Chem. Soc.*, **79**, 4631 (1957).
175. Meyer, E. von, *J. Prakt. Chem.*, **16**, 77 (1877).
176. Miano, R. R., and C. S. Garner, *Inorg. Chem.*, **4**, 337 (1965).
176a. Michelotti, F. W., and W. P. Keaveney, *J. Polymer Sci., Ser. A*, **3**, 695 (1965).
177. Moffitt, W., G. L. Goodman, M. Fred and B. Weisntock, *Mol. Phys.*, **2**, 109 (1959).
178. Moraht, H., and C. Wischin, *Z. Anorg. Allgem. Chem.*, **3**, 153 (1893).
179. Morgan, G., and F. H. Burstall, *J. Chem. Soc.*, **1937**, 1649.
180. Mugdan, M., and D. P. Young, *J. Chem. Soc.*, **1949**, 2988.
180a. Mulay, L. N., and V. Withstandley, *J. Chem. Phys.*, **43**, 4522 (1965).
180b. Müller, H., *Z. Anorg. Allgem. Chem.*, **342**, 177 (1966).
180c. Müller, H., *J. Inorg. Nucl. Chem.*, **28**, 2081 (1966).
181. Nakagawa, I. and T. Shimanouchi, *Spectrochim. Acta*, **18**, 101 (1962).
181a. Nikol'skii, A. B., and A. N. Ryabov, *Russ. J. Inorg. Chem. Eng. Transl.*, **10**, 1 (1965).
181b. Nowotny, H., and E. Henglein, *Naturwissenschaften*, **27**, 167 (1939).
182. Nyholm, R. S., and G. J. Sutton, *J. Chem. Soc.*, **1958**, 572.
182a. Nyholm, R. S., and K. Vrieze, *J. Chem. Soc.*, **1965**, 5337.
183. Ogawa, E., *Bull. Chem. Soc. Japan*, **6**, 302 (1931).
184. Orioli, P. L., and L. Vaska, *Proc. Chem. Soc.*, **1962**, 333.
185. Ortner, M. H., *J. Chem. Phys.*, **34**, 556 (1961).
185a. Paal, C., and C. Amberger, *Ber.*, **40**, 1382 (1907).
186. Palmer, J. W., and F. Basolo, *J. Inorg. Nucl. Chem.*, **15**, 279 (1960).
186a. Patterson, F. K., and R. Ward, *Inorg. Chem.*, **5**, 1312 (1966).
187. Peacock, R. D., 'Fluorine Compounds of Transition Elements,' in *Progr. Inorg. Chem.*, **2** (1960), Interscience Publishers, New York.
188. Peacock, R. D., and D. W. A. Sharp, *J. Chem. Soc.*, **1959**, 2762.
189. Perichon, J., S. Palous and R. Buvet, *Bull. Soc. Chim. France*, **1963**, 982.
190. Pilipenko, A. T., and I. P. Sereda, *Russ. J. Inorg. Chem. Eng. Transl.*, **6**, 209 (1961).
190a. Pitwell, L. R., *Nature*, **207**, 1181 (1965).
191. Porai-Koshits, N. A., L. A. Atovyman and V. G. Adrianov, *J. Struct. Chem. USSR Engl. Transl.*, **2**, 686 (1960).
192. Preetz, W., *Angew. Chem.*, **4**, 710 (1965).
193. Rallo, F., *J. Chromatog.*, **8**, 132 (1962).
194. Rausch, M. D., E. O. Fischer and H. Grubert, *J. Am. Chem. Soc.*, **82**, 76 (1960).
195. Rausch, M. D., and V. Mark, *J. Org. Chem.*, **28**, 3225 (1963).
196. Ray, M. M., *Science and Culture*, **30**, 190 (1964).

197. Razunas, V., G. Macur and S. Katz, *J. Chem. Phys.*, **43**, 1010 (1965).
198. Robin, M. B., *Inorg. Chem.*, **1**, 337 (1962).
199. Rosenblum, M., J. O. Santer and W. G. Howells, *J. Am. Chem. Soc.*, **85**, 1450 (1963).
200. Rosenblum, M., *Chemistry of the Iron Group Metallocenes*, John Wiley and Sons, New York, 1965.
201. Rosenheim, A., and E. A. Sasserath, *Z. Anorg. Allgem. Chem.*, **21**, 122 (1889).
202. Rosenheim, A., *Z. Anorg. Allgem. Chem.*, **24**, 420 (1900).
203. Rossini, F. D., D. D. Wayman, W. H. Evans, S. Lewis, and I. Yaffe, *Selected Values of Chemical Thermodynamic Properties*, Nat. Bur. Standards, Washington, 1952.
204. Ruff, O., and F. W. Tchirch, *Ber.*, **46**, 929 (1913).
204a. Ruff, O., and F. Bornemann, *Z. Anorg. Allgem. Chem.*, **65**, 434 (1910).
205. Ruff, O., and H. Rathsburg, *Ber.*, **50**, 487, 497 (1917).
206. Sachs, A., *Z. Krist.*, **34**, 166 (1901).
207. Sailer, G., *Z. Anorg. Allgem. Chem.*, **116**, 212 (1921).
208. Sauerbrann, R. D., and E. B. Sandell, *J. Am. Chem. Soc.*, **75**, 3554 (1953); *Anal. Chim. Acta*, **9**, 86 (1953).
209. Sawyer, D. T., and D. S. Tinti, *Inorg. Chem.*, **2**, 796 (1963).
209a. Scagliarini, G., and A. Masetti Zannini, *Gazz. Chim. Ital.*, **53**, 504 (1923).
210. Schaaf, R. L., *J. Inorg. Nucl. Chem.*, **25**, 903 (1963).
211. Schilt, A. A., *Inorg. Chem.*, **3**, 1323 (1964).
212. Schilt, A. A., *J. Am. Chem. Soc.*, **85**, 904 (1963).
213. Schmidt, G. B., and W. Herr, *Z. Naturforsch.*, *Ser. A*, **16**, 748 (1961).
214. Scholder, R. and G. Schatz, *Angew. Chem.*, **2**, 264 (1963).
215. Scholder, R., *Angew. Chem.*, **70**, 591 (1958).
215a. Schrauzer, G. N., V. Mayweg, U. Muller-Westerhoff and W. Heinrich, *Angew. Chem.*, **3**, 381 (1964); G. N. Schrauzer and V. Mayweg, *Z. Naturforsch. Ser. B*, **19**, 192 (1964).
216. Schukarev, S. A., N. I. Kolbin and I. N. Semenov, *Russ. J. Inorg. Chem. Eng. Transl.*, **6**, 638 (1961).
216a. Seip, H. M., and R. Stølevik, *Acta Chem. Scand.*, **20**, 385 (1966).
217. Semenov, I. N., and N. I. Kolbin, *Russ. J. Inorg. Chem. Eng. Transl.*, **7**, 111 (1962).
218. Sleight, A. W., J. Longo and R. Ward, *Inorg. Chem.*, **1**, 245 (1962); **1**, 723 (1962).
218a. Spacu, P., C. Gheorghiu and L. Zubov, *Rev. Chim. Acad. Rep. Populaire Roumaine*, **6**, 323 (1961); *Chem. Abstr.*, **57**, 4294e.
219. Stevens, K. W. H., *Proc. Roy. Soc.* (*London*), *Ser. A*, **219**, 542 (1953).
220. Stokinger, H. E., *J. Occupational Medicine*, **5**, 491 (1963).
221. Tchugaev, L., *Z. Anorg. Allgem. Chem.*, **148**, 65 (1925).
222. Thomassen, L., *Z. Phys. Chem.*, **2**, (B), 349 (1929).
223. Thorsen, W. R., *J. Chem. Phys.*, **29**, 938 (1958).
224. Tirouflet, J., E. Laviron, R. Dabard and J. Komenda, *Bull. Soc. Chim. France*, **1963**, 857.
225. Trifan, D. W., and R. Bacskai, *J. Am. Chem. Soc.*, **82**, 5010 (1960).
226. Turner, A. G., A. F. Clifford and C. N. R. Rao, *Analyt. Chem.*, **30**, 1708 (1958).
227. Ueki, T., A. Zalkin and D. H. Templeton, *Acta Cryst.*, **19**, 157 (1965).

228. Vauquelin, N., *Ann. Chim. Phys.*, **89** (1), 248 (1841).
229. Vaska, L., and J. W. diLuzio, *J. Am. Chem. Soc.*, **83**, 1262 (1961).
230. Vaska, L., *J. Am. Chem. Soc.*, **86**, 1943 (1964).
231. Vaska, L., and E. M. Sloane, *J. Am. Chem. Soc.*, **82**, 1263 (1960).
232. Vaska, L., *Chem. Ind. (London)*, **1961**, 1402.
233. Vaska, L., *Inorg. Nucl. Chem. Letters*, **1**, 89 (1965).
234. Viste, A., and H. B. Gray, *Inorg. Chem.*, **3**, 1113 (1964).
235. van Vleck, J. H., *J. Chem. Phys.*, **7**, 61, 72 (1939).
236. Volkov, V. M., and M. E. Dyatkina, *Proc. Acad. Sci. USSR, Chem. Ser. Eng. Transl.*, **134**, 1007 (1960).
237. Wahl, A., *Z. Elektrochem.*, **64**, 90 (1960).
238. Waters, W. A., *Ann. Rep. Progr. Chem. (Chem. Soc. London)*, **42**, 152 (1945).
239. Watt, G. W., and L. Vaska, *J. Inorg. Nucl. Chem.*, **6**, 246 (1958).
240. Watt, G. W., and E. M. Potrafke, *J. Inorg. Nucl. Chem.*, **17**, 248 (1961).
240a. Watt, G. W., J. T. Summers, E. M. Potrafke and E. R. Birnbaum, *Inorg. Chem.*, **5**, 857 (1966).
241. Watt, G. W., and L. Vaska, *J. Inorg. Nucl. Chem.*, **5**, 308 (1958).
242. Watt, G. W., E. M. Potrafke and D. S. Klett, *Inorg. Chem.*, **2**, 868 (1963).
243. Watt, G. W., and L. Vaska, *J. Inorg. Nucl. Chem.*, **5**, 304 (1958).
244. Watt, G. W., and W. C. McCordie, *J. Inorg. Nucl. Chem.*, **27**, 2013 (1965).
244a. Watt, G. W., and J. T. Summers, *J. Am. Chem. Soc.*, **88**, 431 (1966).
245. Weinstock, B., and J. G. Malm, *J. Am. Chem. Soc.*, **80**, 4466 (1958).
246. Weinstock, B., and J. G. Malm, *Proc. U.N. Intern. Conf. Peaceful Uses At. Energy, Geneva*, **28**, 125 (1958).
247. Weinstock, B., H. H. Claassen and J. G. Malm, *J. Chem. Phys.*, **32**, 181 (1960).
248. Weinstock, B., and G. L. Goodman, *Adv. Chem. Phys.*, **9**, 169 (1965).
249. Weinstock, B., H. H. Claassen and C. L. Chernick, *J. Chem. Phys.*, **38**, 1470 (1963).
250. Wells, A. F., *Structural Inorganic Chemistry* Oxford University Press, Oxford, 1962, p. 215, 456 and 920.
251. Werner, A., and K. Dinklage, *Ber.*, **34**, 2698 (1901).
252. Westland, A. D., *Can. J. Chem.*, **41**, 2692 (1963).
253. Westland, A. D., and N. C. Bhiwandker, *Can. J. Chem.*, **39**, 1284 (1961).
254. Westland, A. D., and N. C. Bhiwandker, *Can. J. Chem.*, **39**, 2353 (1961); **41**, 2692 (1963).
255. Wilson, R. F., and P. Merchant, *J. Inorg. Nucl. Chem.*, **26**, 1057 (1964); *Talanta*, **12**, 1 (1965).
256. Wilson, R. F., and J. James, *Z. Anorg. Allgem. Chem.*, **321**, 180 (1963).
256a. Winkhaus, G., H. Singer and M. Kricke, *Z. Naturforsch., Ser. B*, **21**, 1109 (1966).
257. Wintrebert, L., *Ann. Chim. Phys.*, **28** (7), 15 (1903).
258. Wintrebert, L., *Compt. Rend.*, **140**, 585 (1905).
258a. Wöhler, L., K. Ewald and H. G. Krall, *Ber.*, **66**, 1638 (1933).
259. Woodward, L. A., and M. J. Ware, *Spectrochim. Acta*, **20**, 711 (1964).
260. Woodward, L. A., and J. A. Creighton, *Spectrochim. Acta*, **17**, 594 (1961).
261. Woodward, L. A., and H. L. Roberts, *Trans. Faraday Soc.*, **52**, 615 (1956).
262. Woodward, L. A., and M. J. Ware, *Spectrochim. Acta*, **19**, 775 (1963).
263. Woodward, L. A., J. A. Creighton and K. A. Taylor, *Trans. Faraday Soc.*, **56**, 1267 (1960).

4 RUTHENIUM

Ruthenium resembles osmium far more than it does iron, and also shows certain similarities to iridium and rhodium in the trivalent state. The greatest similarities between ruthenium and osmium are found in the oxides and fluorides and in the chemistry of the lower oxidation states (II to O), and the greatest differences between the two arise in the trivalent state. Amongst the platinum metals ruthenium has two outstanding features. One is its tendency, particularly when in the tetravalent state, to form polynuclear complexes with oxide, nitride or hydroxy bridges; this is shared by osmium, but to a more limited extent. Secondly, ruthenium forms more nitrosyl complexes than any other metal; possible reasons for this are discussed later (p. 174).

Ruthenium (VIII), (VII) and (VI)

The octavalent state is less stable for ruthenium than for osmium, and the only established compound is the tetroxide, which is an even more powerful oxidizing agent than its osmium analogue. The heptavalent state is represented only by the perruthenates. Although several ruthenium (VI) complexes are known, this is a less important state than for osmium; whereas the latter forms many osmyl complexes, only a few ruthenyl salts have been prepared.

Ruthenium (V), (IV) and (III)

The pentafluoride and the derived complexes $[RuF_6]^-$ are the only known ruthenium (V) compounds. Whereas osmium forms all four tetrahalides, ruthenium tetrabromide and tetraiodide have not been made and the hexahaloruthenates (IV) are much more easily reduced to the trivalent species than their osmium analogues. The trivalent is the commonest oxidation state of the element and its chemistry is much closer to that of rhodium and iridium than to osmium, particularly with Group VII and Group V donors.

Ruthenium (II), (I) and (O)

Apart from the many ruthenium (II) nitrosyl complexes, there are a number of phosphine, arsine and stibine compounds, which show marked similarities to the analogous osmium species. The monovalent state is represented only by the carbonyl halides, and the zerovalent state only by carbonyl and phosphine complexes. The only real similarities between iron and ruthenium are found in the carbonyls and in the sandwich-type organometallic compounds.

GROUP VII DONORS

The fluorine chemistry of ruthenium resembles that of osmium except that osmium trifluoride is not known. There are similarities between the halogen chemistries of ruthenium (IV) and iridium (IV) complexes and between those of ruthenium (III) and rhodium (III): thus both the latter metals form polymeric halo species, and their two chloro-aquo systems have a number of features in common. There is considerable doubt about the existence of ruthenium (II) and (I) halides.

Ruthenium (VI)

Ruthenium hexafluoride, RuF_6, can be made by direct fluorination of the metal (dark brown crystals, m.p. 54°) [57]. The infrared spectrum of the vapour has been recorded[304] (cf. p. 101, Table 3.1) and confirms that the molecule is octahedral. X-ray powder pattern photographs show the solid to be isostructural with other platinum metal hexafluorides[57]. The compound is even more reactive than its osmium analogue and for this reason, together with its colour, the Raman spectrum could not be measured; however, the infrared active $(\nu_2 + \nu_3)$ combination mode was extremely broad suggesting that a dynamic Jahn–Teller effect might be operative in the molecule[304,305] (cf. p. 48).

$RuOF_4$ can be made as very pale green crystals (m.p. 115°, b.p. 184°) by the action of a mixture of bromine trifluoride and bromine on the metal[143]. In contrast to $OsOF_4$ it is paramagnetic ($\mu_{eff} = 2{\cdot}91$ BM at room temperature; see Table 4.11) [143]. The heat of vaporization is 11·97 kcal/mole and the entropy of vaporization is 26·1 cal/mole deg[143].

Attempts to prepare ruthenium (VI) oxychlorides analogous to $OsOCl_4$ have failed[135], although salts of $[RuO_2Cl_4]^{2-}$ are known.

'$K_2[RuF_8]$', made by the action of fluorine on potassium hexachlororuthenate (IV) at 200° [14], has been shown to be $KHF_2 . K[Ru^{V}F_6]$ [134].

$Cs_2[RuO_2Cl_4]$ has been made as deep red crystals by the action of hydrochloric acid on ruthenium tetroxide in the presence of caesium chloride; it is diamagnetic[147]. The lattice is cubic (a = 10·22 Å), and the infrared spectrum suggests that there is a linear O═Ru═O grouping similar to the O═Os═O found in the 'osmyl' complexes[313]. The free acid $H_2[RuO_2Cl_4]$aq can be obtained from ruthenium tetroxide, chlorine and hydrochloric acid[9].

Ruthenium (v)

Ruthenium pentafluoride, $[RuF_5]_4$, has been made by the reaction between the metal and bromine trifluoride, a procedure which initially gives $RuBrF_8$ (which is probably a salt $BrF_2{}^+RuF_6{}^-$), and this may then be decomposed *in vacuo* to the pentafluoride[134]. Alternatively, it can be prepared by direct fluorination of the metal. It forms dark green crystals, which melt at 85·6° to give a green liquid, and this boils at 227° to give a colourless vapour. The heat and entropy of vaporization have been found to be 15·23 kcal/mole and 30·4 cal/mole deg, respectively[143].

The structure of the solid has been determined by x-ray methods. The molecule is tetrameric, the four ruthenium atoms in Ru_4F_{20} lying at the corners of a rhombus; there is a fluorine bridge between each pair of metal atoms, with a metal–fluorine(bridge)–metal angle of 127° and a mean metal–fluorine distance of 1·90 Å[142] (Figure 4.1). The magnetic properties of the compound have been studied from 100 to 292°K (see Table 4.11, p. 214)[143]. The moment of 3·60 BM at room temperature is very close to that of $K[RuF_6]$ (3·48 BM[306]) suggesting

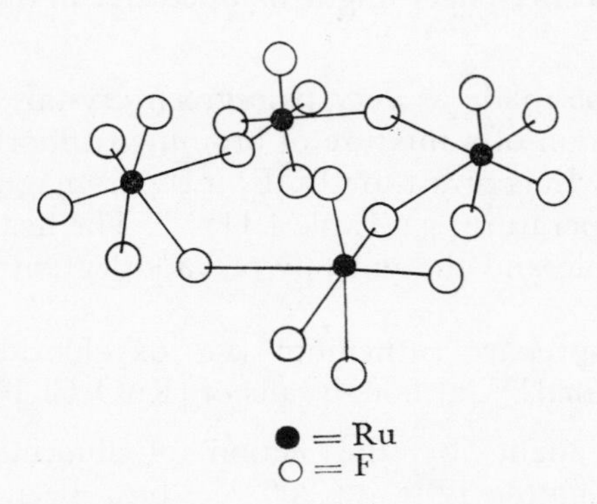

Figure 4.1 Molecular structure of $[RuF_5]_4$

that there is little metal–metal magnetic interaction in the pentafluoride, although osmium pentafluoride, which probably has a similar structure, has a moment considerably lower than that of $K[OsF_6]$ (cf. p. 51).

$K[RuF_6]$ can be made by the action of bromine trifluoride and bromine on ruthenium tetrabromide in the presence of potassium bromide[134]. The colour of the potassium salt varies from blue to pink according to the conditions of its preparation. The crystal structures of the salts of $[RuF_6]^-$ are similar to those of $[OsF_6]^-$; the lithium and sodium salts have the rhombohedral (distorted sodium chloride type) $Li[SbF_6]$ structure, the potassium, caesium, rubidium and thallous salts have the $K[OsF_6]$ (caesium chloride type) structure and the silver salt, the tetragonal $K[NbF_6]$ lattice[173].

The infrared spectrum of $K[RuF_6]$ has been measured above 400 cm^{-1} (cf. p. 102, Table 3.2) and the electronic spectrum of the solid measured from 10,000 to 40,000 cm^{-1}, assignments of the latter being made on the basis of Tanabe–Sugano diagrams[32,167]. The magnetic properties of the potassium and caesium salts are summarized in Table 4.11.

Various 'addition compounds' of bromine trifluoride, bromine pentafluoride and selenium tetrafluoride such as $BrF_3.RuF_5$, $BrF_5.RuF_5$ and $SeF_4.RuF_5$ have been reported[138a] and may be salts of $[RuF_6]^-$, e.g. $[SeF_3]^+[RuF_6]^-$ [138a]. The xenon compound $Xe[RuF_6]_n$ can be made from ruthenium hexafluoride and xenon[17].

Ruthenium (IV)

Ruthenium tetrafluoride, RuF_4, can be made as yellow crystals by heating the pentafluoride with iodine and iodine pentafluoride. The magnetic properties have been measured from 88 to 291°K (the moment is 3·04 BM at room temperatures) (cf. Table 4.11)[144].

Ruthenium tetrachloride, $RuCl_4$. There seems to be some doubt about the existence of this compound in the solid state, though it apparently exists in the vapour phase above 750°. The chlorination of ruthenium trichloride at 750° is said to give the tetrachloride, which can be condensed at −30° (above which temperature it apparently decomposes unless chlorine is also present)[178,275]. It is also said that the prolonged action of hydrochloric acid on the tetroxide gives $RuCl_4.5H_2O$[266]. Either or both of these species may well be oxy or hydroxy chloride species.

Studies on the ruthenium–chlorine system at high temperatures show that the two main species are the tri- and tetrachlorides. For the reaction

$$Ru(s) + 2\ Cl_2 \rightarrow RuCl_4(g)$$

values of $\Delta H^0_{298} = -22{\cdot}3 \pm 4$ kcal/mole and $\Delta S^0_{298} = -24{\cdot}0 \pm 4$ e.u. were found[19].

Ruthenium tetrabromide and tetraiodide are unknown; attempts to prepare them have given the trihalides. The only known ruthenium (IV) bromo or iodo species are $RuOBr_2.2NH_3$ and $RuOI_2.2NH_3$ (cf. Table 4.2).

$Ru(OH)Cl_3$ can be made as a deep brown substance by the action of hydrochloric acid on ruthenium tetroxide[27c,45]. It is very soluble in water, and the solution is reduced by stannous chloride to ruthenium trichloride[255]. Its reaction with ozone has been investigated[115a]. For **$Ru_3O_2Cl_6(H_2O)_6$**, see p. 135.

Ru_2OCl_6 and **Ru_2OCl_5** (the latter formally contains 'ruthenium 3.5'[95]) can be made by the action of chlorine on a solution of commercial ruthenium trichloride[95].

The hexahaloruthenates (IV), $[RuX_6]^{2-}$ (X = F, Cl, Br)

The magnetic properties are dealt with in a separate section (see Table 4.11, and p. 133).

$K_2[RuF_6]$ can be prepared by the action of water on $K[RuF_6]$[134]. It forms golden-yellow crystals and has the trigonal potassium hexafluorogermanate crystal structure. The infrared spectrum has been measured above 400 cm^{-1} (cf. Table 3.2) and the electronic spectrum measured over the range 10,000–40,000 cm^{-1} [32]. The sodium salt has a hexagonal structure ($a = 9{\cdot}32$, $c = 5{\cdot}15$ Å)[32a].

$K_2[RuCl_6]$ can be made by passing chlorine through solutions of $K_2[RuCl_5H_2O]$, or by fusing potassium chlorate with ruthenium; (in the latter method the binuclear salt $K_4[Ru_2OCl_{10}]$ may sometimes appear as an impurity)[10,27c,148,249] Rubidium, caesium and ammonium salts have also been made. On heating to 250° they evolve chlorine and give salts of $[RuCl_5]^{2-}$. The potassium salt forms black crystals which have a cubic lattice ($a = 9{\cdot}738 \pm 0{\cdot}001$ Å) and a ruthenium–chlorine distance $2{\cdot}29 \pm 0{\cdot}04$ Å[3]. The infrared spectrum of the potassium salt has been measured[2] (cf. p. 103, Table 3.3) and the electronic absorption spectrum of the $[RuCl_6]^{2-}$ ion has been measured in aqueous solution and assignments proposed[170].

Polarographic reduction studies on $[RuCl_6]^{2-}$ and on a number of other ruthenium chloro complexes have been reported. $[RuCl_6]^{2-}$ is reversibly reduced to $[RuCl_5H_2O]^{2-}$, probably via $[RuCl_6]^{3-}$ ($E_{1/2} = -0{\cdot}76$ v versus s.c.e.)[249].

$K_2[RuBr_6]$ can be made by the action of bromine on a solution of the aquo complex $K_2[RuBr_5H_2O]$. It forms black crystals which give a deep blue aqueous solution, and it can be reduced by alcohol to $K_2[RuBr_5H_2O]$. Rubidium, caesium and ammonium salts have also been made[148].

$K_2[RuI_6]$ is not known nor are any salts containing $[RuI_6]^{2-}$ (or $[RuI_6]^{3-}$) anions.

Magnetic properties of the hexahaloruthenates (IV)

These are summarized in Table 4.11 (see also p. 59). Figgis and coworkers interpreted the temperature dependence of the susceptibilities of the fluoro, chloro and bromo complexes on the assumption that the spin–orbit and interelectronic repulsion factors are close to those expected for a free Ru^{4+} ion, and conclude that there is little electron delocalization from the metal to the ligands[78]. Later measurements on $K_2[RuCl_6]$ by Johannesen and Candela were interpreted as indicating that the temperature dependence of the susceptibility arises from occupancy of higher electronic states in the complex[158]. The susceptibility of $K_2[RuCl_6]$ in solid solution in the isomorphous (diamagnetic) $K_2[PtCl_6]$ was found to be almost the same as for the pure solid complex alone, whereas in the case of $K_2[OsCl_6]$ the susceptibility of the anion increases considerably on such dilution (see p. 102)[309]. It has been suggested that there is magnetic superexchange in $K_2[OsCl_6]$ but not in $K_2[RuCl_6]$, the reason for the difference being that the 5*d* orbitals of osmium extend further in space than the 4*d* ruthenium orbitals, and are thus more easily involved in exchange via halogen ligands[309] (cf. also p. 58).

Electron spin resonance measurements were made on $K_2[RuCl_6]$ and a very weak signal observed; the *g* value was isotropic as expected from the cubic symmetry of the crystal (no such resonance could be found for $K_2[OsCl_6]$)[119].

$K_4[Ru_2OCl_{10}]$, originally formulated as $K_2[RuCl_5OH]$, can be made by the action of hydrochloric acid on ruthenium tetroxide with

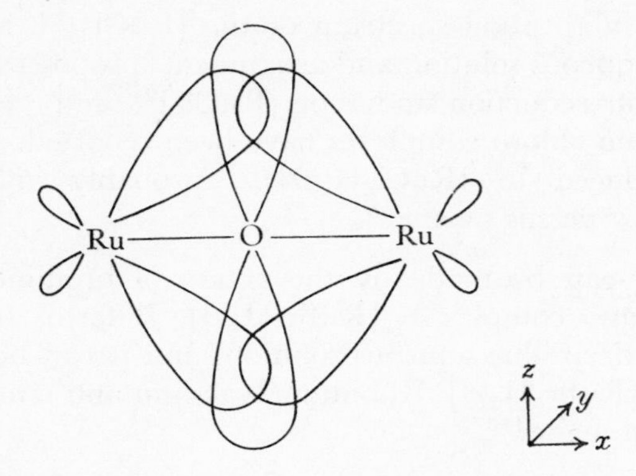

Figure 4.2 Bonding in $[Ru_2OCl_{10}]^{4-}$: $4d_{xz}$–$2p_z$–$4d_{xz}$ overlap (there will be a similar $4d_{xy}$–$2p_y$–$4d_{xy}$ three-centre orbital)

potassium chloride. The potassium salt forms deep red crystals, and rubidium, caesium and ammonium salts have also been prepared[27c,147,249]. The formulation as a binuclear complex* followed the observation that the complex was diamagnetic[219], and a subsequent x-ray crystal study showed that the compound is indeed binuclear, and that the Ru—O—Ru group is linear; (Ru—Cl = 2·34 Å and Ru—O = 1·80 Å)[217]. A molecular-orbital description of the bonding in this complex has been given and satisfactorily explains the diamagnetism[72]. The electron pairs in the $2p_y$ and $2p_z$ orbitals on oxygen (taking Ru—O—Ru as the *x* axis) are assumed to interact with the singly occupied $4d_{xz}$ and $4d_{xy}$ ruthenium orbitals to form two three-centre molecular orbital sets (Figure 4.2). Each of these will contain four electrons which are paired, and since the 'non-bonding' $4d_{yz}$ orbitals on the ruthenium atoms will each contain an electron pair, overall diamagnetism will result (see also osmyl complexes on p. 72: the bonding in these is somewhat analogous). The electronic absorption spectrum has been measured[168,170] and interpreted on the basis of this molecular-orbital treatment[168], and the infrared spectrum of the potassium salt has also been measured and skeletal modes assigned[138c,313]. The polarographic reduction of $[Ru_2OCl_{10}]^{4-}$ has been studied[249].

A salt $(\mathbf{enH_2})_2[\mathbf{Ru(OH)Cl_7}]$ has been described[45,125].

* Although some earlier authors had also suggested that it was a binuclear species[255].

The ruthenium (IV) chloro-aquo system

The addition of increasing amounts of chloride ion to ruthenium (IV) perchlorate in aqueous solution produces the following sequences of colour changes:

Ru(IV) red → yellow → violet → yellow ((Cl$^-$) > 0·1M, (H$^+$) > 0·4M)
Ru(IV) red → violet → yellow ((Cl$^-$) > 0·1M, (H$^+$) < 0·4M)

Equilibrium, kinetic and spectrophotometric studies on this complicated system indicate that the yellow colours arise from hydroxyaquo-chloro species such as **$[Ru(H_2O)(OH)_2Cl_3]^-$** and **$[Ru(OH)_2Cl_4]^{2-}$** (polynuclear complexes are also present)[278,301], while the violet colour arises from the uncharged species **$Ru(H_2O)_2(OH)_2Cl_2$**[301]. Fletcher and coworkers, however, suggest that the latter may be polymeric, $Ru_3O_2Cl_6(H_2O)_6$, with a linear Ru—O—Ru—O—Ru system as in ruthenium red[96] (see p. 168). Ruthenium (IV) chloro complexes in aqueous solution are reduced by molecular hydrogen under ambient conditions to ruthenium (III) probably by a mechanism involving catalytic ruthenium (III) (cf. p. 141 below)[132].

$K_4[Ru_2OBr_{10}]$ (black crystals) has been made from ruthenium tetroxide, potassium bromide and hydrobromic acid; infrared spectra indicate that it has a structure similar to $K_4[Ru_2OCl_{10}]$[138c].

$K_2[RuBr_5(OH)]$ (black crystals) has been reported; it can be made from ruthenium tribromide and potassium bromide in aqueous solution[120], and may well have the binuclear formulation $K_4[Ru_2OBr_{10}]$[138c].

Ruthenium (III)

Ruthenium trifluoride, RuF_3, has been made by the action of excess iodine on the pentafluoride at 150°[14]:

$$5\,RuF_5 + I_2 \rightarrow 5\,RuF_3 + 2\,IF_5$$

The solid has a somewhat distorted hexagonal structure (a = 5·408 ± 0·001 Å, α = 54·67 ± 0·01°; both a and α may vary slightly from sample to sample, due perhaps to some non-stoichiometry in the lattice)[137]. Neutron diffraction powder patterns of the trifluoride taken at 4·2 and 298°K suggest that the compound is not magnetically ordered[310].

Ruthenium trichloride, $RuCl_3$, is the commonest compound of ruthenium. Like many trichlorides it exists in both water-insoluble and water-soluble forms.

Water-insoluble $RuCl_3$. There are two modifications. The dark brown β form is obtained by heating ruthenium sponge at 330° in a 1:3 mixture of carbon monoxide and chlorine[153,274b], and the black α form by heating the β form in a current of chlorine to 700°[153]. The β–α transition occurs at 450° and is irreversible[290].

The α form is isomorphous with violet chromic chloride. It has a trigonal trapezoidal lattice ($a = 5{\cdot}96 \pm 0{\cdot}04$ and $c = 17{\cdot}2 \pm 0{\cdot}01$ Å), the chloride ions having a slightly distorted cubic close-packed arrangement[30,290]. In the β form it appears that the ruthenium is tetrahedrally coordinated, and the lattice is hexagonal ($a = 6{\cdot}12$, $c = 5{\cdot}66$ Å)[95]. However, a recent report claims that the ruthenium has octahedral coordination with a Ru–Cl distance of 2.83 Å and Ru–Ru distance of 2·83 Å[274b].

The α form becomes antiferromagnetic at low temperatures with a Néel point of 30°K (close to the Néel points for the isomorphous chromic and ferric chlorides, 17 and 15°K, respectively)[95]; the β form has very much lower magnetic susceptibilities than the α form at all temperatures[95].

For the reaction

$$Ru(s) + \tfrac{3}{2}\,Cl_2 \rightarrow RuCl_3(g)$$

$\Delta H^0_{298} = 13{\cdot}4 \pm 3$ kcal/mole and $\Delta S^0_{298} = 8{\cdot}3 \pm 3$ e.u.[19], values very similar to those found for chromic chloride (cf. also reference 276).

Water-soluble hydrated $RuCl_3$. This can be got by the prolonged action of hydrochloric acid on ruthenium tetroxide[27c,256]. The aqueous solution is red and at first contains no ionized chloride, but aquation of the complex slowly occurs, and the resulting solutions are fairly easily hydrolysed. The monomeric species present in aqueous solutions of the trichloride are considered below (p. 139) but polymeric complexes are undoubtedly present in the solutions (cf. also p. 139). A brown, anhydrous water-soluble form is also known[141].

Commercial ruthenium trichloride frequently contains polynuclear ruthenium (IV) oxy and hydroxy chloro species and may often contain the nitrosyl chloride $[Ru(NO)Cl_3]_n$[95]. Chemical reactions of ruthenium trichloride are summarized in Figure 4.3; catalytic properties of ruthenium trichloride are considered below (p. 140). It has recently been reported that methanolic solutions of ruthenium trichloride in the presence of zinc will absorb molecular nitrogen to give a ruthenium (II) nitrogeno species[277a].

Ruthenium tribromide, $RuBr_3$. There is some uncertainty as to the existence of this compound. Two methods have been given for

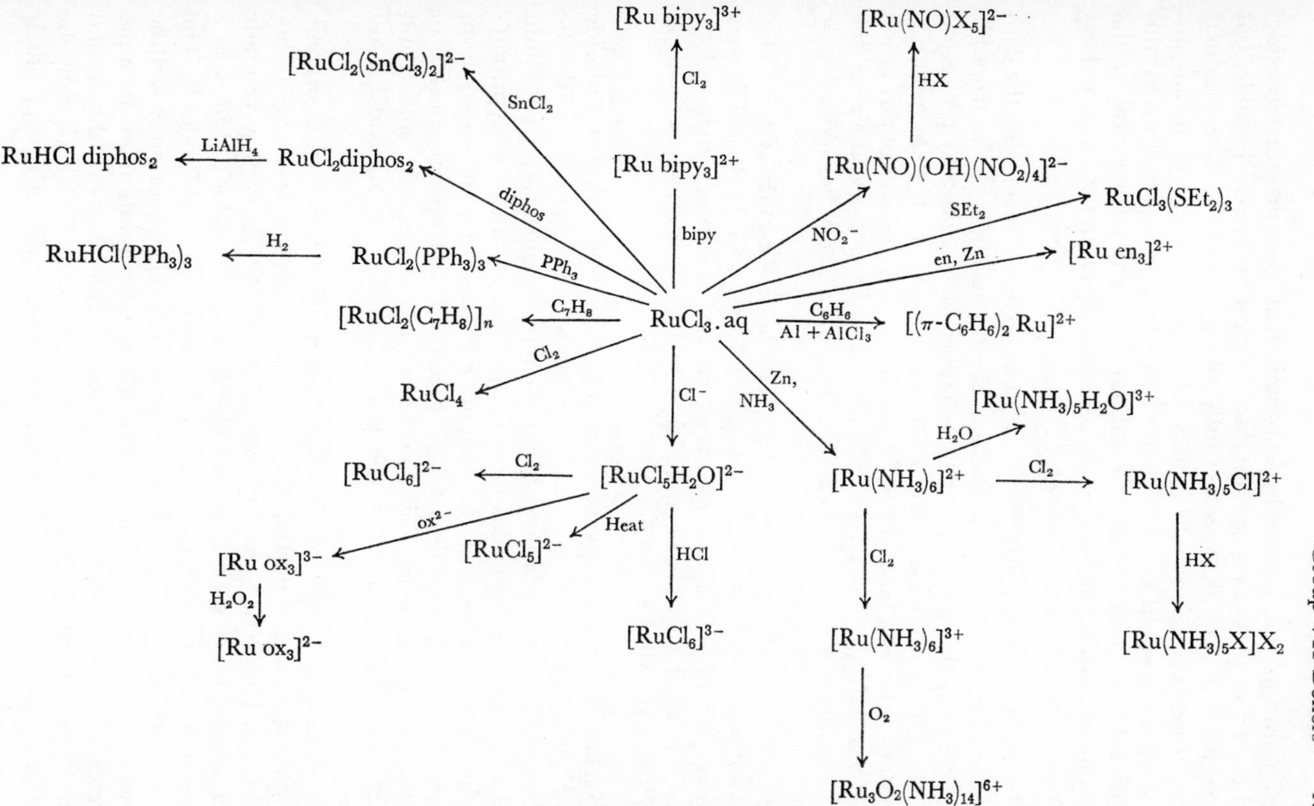

Figure 4.3 Reactions of ruthenium trichloride

its preparation, the action of hydrobromic acid on ruthenium tetroxide, and the treatment of ruthenium dioxide with hydrogen bromide, but in neither case was the product fully characterized[179]. The products form brown crystals which readily dissolve in water, giving an unstable brown solution. Addition of alkali metal bromides to this yields salts of $[RuBr_5(H_2O)]^{2-}$. A more recent preparation of the tribromide shows that the unit cell has D_6^6 symmetry and is hexagonal; $a = 12{\cdot}924$, $c = 5{\cdot}860$ Å)[274a].

Ruthenium triiodide, RuI_3. Iodine does not react directly with the metal, and the best method for the preparation of the triiodide is to dissolve the tetroxide in hydrochloric acid and add potassium iodide. The compound forms a fine black powder. The thermal dissociation between 590 and 660° was studied and the heat of formation obtained ($\Delta H^0_{298} = 38{\cdot}2 \pm 1{\cdot}4$ kcal/mole); the only products of the decomposition are the elements[277]. The unit cell is hexagonal ($a = 6{\cdot}982$, $c = 6{\cdot}231$ Å)[274a].

The violet solid reported as **$Ru(OH)Cl_2$** or **$Ru_2(OH)_2Cl_2$**[160] may be identical with $Ru(H_2O)_2(OH)_2Cl_2$[301] (see p. 135); **Ru_2OCl_4** may be a product of the chlorination of commercial ruthenium trichloride[95]. **$Ru(OH)(H_2O)Cl_2$** has been claimed to be a hydrolysis product of $K_2[RuCl_5H_2O]$[148].

$K_3[RuCl_6]$ is normally made by the action of hydrogen chloride on $K_2[RuCl_5H_2O]$[49]. The red crystals are isomorphous with the corresponding rhodium and iridium complexes, and sodium, rubidium and caesium salts have also been made. The magnetic susceptibility of the dodecahydrate of the sodium salt has been measured from 90 to 291°K[40] (see Table 4.11). Electronic absorption spectra of $[RuCl_6]^{3-}$ in aqueous solution have been measured and band assignments proposed[169,170]. Chemical reactions of $K_3[RuCl_6]$ are summarized in Figure 4.3.

A number of salts of $[RuCl_5]^{2-}$ and $[RuCl_7]^{4-}$ with organic cations have been reported, similar to the chloro complexes of rhodium (III). The **$(NR_4)_2[RuCl_5]$** salts (R = Me, Et, Pr, etc.) were made from a solution of ruthenium trichloride in hydrochloric acid with a four- or five-fold excess of the tetraalkylammonium chloride[124]. The crystals are black or very dark red in colour. The anion may well be dimeric with chloro bridges, although the formulation as an aquo species, $(NR_4)_2[RuCl_5H_2O]$, is equally feasible. Salts of the second type, **$(NR_4)_4[RuCl_7]$**, can be similarly prepared[124]. They may be crystal aggregates of the base chloride with $(NR_4)_3[RuCl_6]$—their red-brown colours are similar to those of $[RuCl_6]^{3-}$ salts—but it is curious that very few salts of the form $(NR_4)_3[RuCl_6]$ have been reported, while $(NR_4)_2[RuCl_6]$ salts are common.

$K_2[RuCl_5]$ is obtained as brown crystals by heating $K_2[RuCl_5H_2O]$ to 200° or by heating $K_2[RuCl_6]$ to 600° in a stream of dry hydrogen chloride[148,149]. It has been claimed that it exists in two forms[9], and that both may be converted into $K_2[RuCl_6]$ by heating in a chlorine stream to 500°. In water it will slowly aquate to $K_2[RuCl_5H_2O]$, the colour of the solution changing from light yellow to red. A monohydrate has been claimed, and also pyridine and ammonia adducts; rubidium, caesium and ammonium salts are also known. Magnetic susceptibility measurements on $K_2[RuCl_5]$ over the range 80–300°K have been made (see Table 4.11[79]); the rather low values as compared with those found for $Na_3[RuCl_6]$[40] suggest that there is spin–spin interaction; the anion is probably dimeric with chloro bridges[79], and this would explain the slowness of aquation.

The catalytic activity of ruthenium (III) chloro and chloro-aquo complexes is dealt with below (p. 141).

$K_3[RuBr_6]$ has apparently not been isolated and nor have any other $[RuBr_6]^{3-}$ salts. The electronic spectrum of a solution claimed to contain $[RuBr_6]^{3-}$ has been reported (the solution was made by boiling $K_2[RuCl_5H_2O]$ with sodium bromide and hydrobromic acid)[169,170].

$K_2[RuBr_5]$ has been reported but its constitution is uncertain[121].

$(NH_4)[RuBr_4]$. It has been claimed that the water may be removed from $NH_4[RuBr_4(H_2O)_2]$ at 170°[37] but this seems a doubtful proposition; the product is probably polymeric.

Salts such as **$(NR_4)_2[RuBr_5]$** and **$(NR_3H)_2[RuBr_5]$** (R = Me, Et, Pr, Bu) can be obtained by reaction of ruthenium tetroxide with hydrobromic acid and the base chloride[124,125], while the salts **$(NR_4)_4[RuBr_7]$** and **$(NR_3H)_4[RuBr_7]$** are made from ruthenium tribromide, hydrobromic acid and the base chloride[124,125]; as with the chloro analogues, the rarity of $(NR_4)_3[RuBr_6]$ should be noted, though $(NR_4)_2[RuBr_6]$ salts are better known.

No ruthenium (III) iodo complexes are known.

The ruthenium (III) chloro-aquo system

Ion-exchange techniques have been used to study the species present in aqueous solutions of ruthenium trichloride. Assuming that the ruthenium is octahedrally coordinated and that any of the six positions not occupied by chloride ions are filled by water molecules, the species present are: $[\mathbf{RuCl(H_2O)_5}]^{2+}$, *cis-* and *trans-* $[\mathbf{RuCl_2(H_2O)_4}]^+$, $[\mathbf{RuCl_4(H_2O)_2}]^-$, 1,2,3- and 1,2,6-$\mathbf{RuCl_3(H_2O)_3}$, $[\mathbf{RuCl_5H_2O}]^{2-}$ and $[\mathbf{RuCl_6}]^{3-}$ [42,60,61]. Rates and rate laws of interconversion of these species have been determined, and it was found that the rate of replacement of chloride ion by water increases with an increase in the number of chloride groups bound to the metal: the half-time for loss of chloride from $[RuCl(H_2O)_5]^{2+}$ is of the order of a year, while the aquation of $[RuCl_6]^{3-}$ to $[RuCl_5H_2O]^{2-}$ takes only a few seconds. This may be a crystal-field effect, chloride having a smaller crystal-field splitting effect than water, or may arise from the greater polarizability of chloride [60]. Some evidence was found for a *trans* labilizing effect; the position *trans* to chloride in a complex appears to have a greater reactivity than the position *trans* to water. For example 1,2,6-$RuCl_3(H_2O)_3$ loses a chloride ion at least ten times faster than does 1,2,3-$RuCl_3(H_2O)_3$ [60]. The dipole moments of 1,2,3- and 1,2,6-$RuCl_3(H_2O)_3$ in ethyl acetate solution were found to be 7·5 and 4·5 D, respectively [221]. The x-ray crystal structure of *cis*-$(AsPh_4)[RuCl_4(H_2O)_2]$ shows that the metal–oxygen bond distance is 2·12 ± 0·01 Å and the metal–chlorine distance 2·34 ± 0·01 Å [145a].

A number of these chloro-aquo and other halo-aquo complexes have been isolated as indicated below.

$\mathbf{K_2[RuCl_5H_2O]}$ can be made as red crystals by ethanolic reduction of a solution of ruthenium tetroxide in hydrochloric acid in the presence of potassium chloride, or by reduction of $K_4[Ru_2OCl_{10}]$ [61,149]. It is isomorphous with the corresponding rhodium complex; rubidium, caesium and ammonium salts were also made. Magnetic susceptibilities of the potassium, ammonium and caesium salts were measured from 80 to 293°K [40] (see Table 4.11). The x-ray crystal structure of the caesium salt shows the metal–oxygen and metal–chlorine bond lengths to be 2·10 ± 0·01 and 2·34 ± 0·01 Å, respectively [145a], while for the potassium salt the values are 2·12 ± 0·05 and 2·33 ± 0·02 Å [175].

A salt $(\mathbf{en_2\ H_2})_5[\mathbf{Ru(OH)Cl_5}]$ has been claimed [45].

$(\mathbf{NH_4})[\mathbf{RuCl_4(H_2O)_2}]$ can be prepared by the action of stannous chloride and hydrochloric acid on ammonium ruthenate (rubidium and caesium salts were also made) [38]. It was originally formulated as $(NH_4)[RuCl_4].2H_2O$, but it is likely that the water groups are coordinated (it is possible that coordinated $SnCl_3^-$ groups may be present as well, since the method of preparation is of the type used to make $SnCl_3^-$ complexes). $Rb[RuCl_4(H_2O)_2].2H_2O$ and a caesium salt are also known[38].

The free acid $H[RuCl_4].2H_2O$ can be made from ruthenium tetroxide, alcohol and hydrochloric acid. It exists in two forms, a red and a green, both very soluble in water; the green form can be made by persistent treatment of the red with alcohol[49]. These may be *cis* and *trans* forms of $H[RuCl_4(H_2O)_2]$, but if so at least one more molecule of water would be present to give $(H_3O)[RuCl_4(H_2O)_2]$.

Catalytic activity of ruthenium (III) chloro complexes

A solution of ruthenium trichloride in hydrochloric acid will catalyse the reduction of iron (III) or ruthenium (IV) by molecular hydrogen. The rate law is

$$-d[H_2]/dt = k_1[H_2][Ru^{III}]$$

(at 80°, $k_1 = 1{\cdot}1$ l/M sec for the reduction of iron (III) in 3 M hydrochloric acid; $\Delta H^\ddagger = 23{\cdot}1$ kcal/mole and $\Delta S^\ddagger = 6$ e.u., values very close to those obtained for the corresponding reaction with rhodium trichloride as catalyst). It was suggested that $[RuCl_6]^{3-}$, $[RuCl_5H_2O]^{2-}$ and $[RuCl_4(H_2O)_2]^-$, which are all fairly labile, were probably the catalytic active species in the reactions. The mechanism proposed involves the heterolytic splitting of hydrogen[132]:

$$Ru^{III} + H_2 \underset{k_{-1}}{\overset{k_1}{\rightleftharpoons}} [Ru^{III}H]^- + H^+ \quad (1)$$

$$[Ru^{III}H]^- + 2\,Ru^{IV} \xrightarrow{k_2} 3\,Ru^{III} + H^+ \quad (2)$$

$$[Ru^{III}H]^- + 2\,Fe^{III} \longrightarrow Ru^{III} + 2\,Fe^{II} + H^+ \quad (3)$$

Ruthenium (III) chloro complexes will also catalyse the isotopic exchange between water and molecular deuterium; the kinetics are similar to those found for the above reactions, suggesting that step (1), the heterolytic splitting step, is common to both reactions (cf. also p. 194)[130a] and determines the rates.

Solutions of ruthenium trichloride in hydrochloric acid are also effective catalysts for the hydration of acetylene and mono- and di-substituted acetylenes (acetylene gives acetaldehyde, methyl acetylene gives acetone). For acetylene the rate law is[129]

$$-d[C_2H_2]/dt = k[C_2H_2][Ru^{III}]$$

and, in contrast to the hydrogen activation experiments described above, k is markedly dependent on the concentration of hydrochloric acid, passing through a maximum at 4 M acid. The variation in k follows closely the change in the *sum* of the concentrations of the species $[RuCl_5H_2O]^{2-}$ and $[RuCl_4(H_2O)_2]^{-}$ [61], so it appears that these are the catalytically active species. Both have a coordinated water molecule, and both are labile in substitution reactions. The proposed mechanism [129] is

$$\underset{CH\equiv CH}{[RuCl_5-OH_2]^{2-} + } \rightleftharpoons \underset{\pi\ \text{Complex}}{\underset{CH\equiv CH}{[Cl_4Ru-OH_2]^{-}\uparrow}} \xrightarrow{\text{Insertion}}$$

$$\left[Cl_4Ru(H)C{=}C(H)\overset{+}{O}H_2 \right]^{-} \xrightarrow[-H^+]{+Cl^-} \left[Cl_4Ru{-}Cl \;\; (H)C{=}C(H)OH \right]^{3-} \xrightarrow[\text{Acid hydrolysis}]{H_3O^+}$$

$$\underset{\text{Regenerated}}{\left[Cl_4Ru(Cl)OH_2 \right]^{2-}} + \left(H_2C{=}C(H)OH \right) \rightarrow CH_3{-}C(=O)H$$

The observed decline in catalytic activity at high chloride ion concentrations would then be due to the need for a coordinated water molecule, and the decrease in activity at low chloride concentration (<2 M) is presumably due to the fact that ruthenium (III) is then present mainly as neutral and cationic ruthenium (III) chloro species which are relatively inert to substitution [60,61,129].

Ruthenium trichloride will catalyse the dimerization of olefins [5a]; the mechanism probably resembles that proposed for the corresponding rhodium trichloride catalysis (see p. 395). It will also catalyse the polymerization of norbornene, but less effectively than iridium or osmium trichlorides [221c] and catalyses the polymerization of cyclobutenes [230a].

$K_2[RuBr_5H_2O]$ can be made by reduction with alcohol and bromine of $K_4[Ru_2OBr_{10}]$; it forms brown crystals [148].

Salts of $[RuBr_4(H_2O)_2]^-$ have been made by reduction of ruthenium tetroxide with stannous bromide [37].

Ruthenium (II)

Ruthenium dichloride, $RuCl_2$, does not seem to have been made as a pure solid. Joly claimed to have isolated a blue dichloride by evaporation of an alcoholic solution of the trichloride, but hydrolysis to $Ru(OH)Cl_2$ or a similar compound may have occurred[159]. Howe and coworkers made a brown powder which may have been the dichloride by heating ruthenium metal in a stream of chlorine; it was insoluble in water but dissolved in alcohol to give a blue solution which had a ruthenium:chlorine ratio of 1:2[150]. Gall and Lehmann reported a dark blue solid with a similar metal:chlorine ratio[103].

Blue aqueous or alcoholic solutions which may contain $RuCl_2$ or a complexed form of this can be made by electrolytic or hypophosphite reduction of ruthenium trichloride solutions[203,209a]; this blue colour was noted as long ago as 1804 by Fourcroy and Vauquelin, who attributed it to a compound of osmium, ruthenium not having been discovered at that time[101].

The powerful reducing properties of the solutions make it likely that the ruthenium really *is* in the divalent form; quite possibly the main species in solution is $RuCl_2(H_2O)_4$ (the idea that monovalent ruthenium was present was suggested in the earlier literature, but no evidence has been brought forward to support this).

Ruthenium dibromide, $RuBr_2$. Reduction of ruthenium tribromide in alcoholic solution by hydrogen (in the presence of a platinum catalyst and bromoform) gives a violet-blue solution which, on evaporation, yields the black crystalline dibromide. The solution slowly absorbs carbon monoxide to give $[Ru(CO)Br_2]_n$[103].

Ruthenium diiodide, RuI_2. The green alcoholic solution of ruthenium triiodide can be reduced by hydrogen in the presence of a platinum catalyst and ammonia. The resulting blue solution is believed to contain the diiodide[103].

The ruthenium (II) chloro-aquo system

Jorgensen has given a partial review of the literature on the blue solutions of ruthenium (II) in hydrochloric acid and has measured the electronic absorption spectra of such solutions in the visible region. The results were said to be consistent with the presence of planar $[RuCl_4]^{2-}$ ions[169]. On standing, the species in these blue solutions slowly disproportionate to the metal and trivalent chloro species. Rechnitz has prepared solutions of '$[RuCl_4]^{2-}$' (no evidence for this formulation being given) by electrolytic reduction of solutions of $K_2[RuCl_6]$ in 4 M hydrochloric acid; coulometric measurements showed that the ruthenium was in the divalent state[253]. These solutions are oxidized by water, the overall reaction being

$$Ru(II) + H_2O \rightarrow Ru(III) + \tfrac{1}{2} H_2 + OH^-$$

Studies of the kinetics of this reaction with water and with heavy water suggested that the rate-determining step does not involve hydrogen–oxygen bond rupture. The observed kinetics were consistent with the scheme

$$\text{Ru(II)} + H_2O \xrightarrow{\text{Slow}} \text{Ru(III)} + H_2O^-$$

and

$$H_2O^- + H^+ \xrightarrow{\text{Fast}} H + H_2O$$

The reaction follows pseudo first-order kinetics with k equal to 4×10^{-5} sec^{-1} (at pH 1·5 at 30° in 2·5 M chloride ion concentration)[254].

The blue solutions in hydrochloric acid (made in this instance by reduction of $K_2[RuCl_6]$ with titanium (III) chloride) will catalyse the hydrogenation of a number of olefins by molecular hydrogen under homogeneous conditions, and they will also absorb ethylene and propylene to give fairly stable 1:1 olefin:ruthenium complexes. Hydrogenation of maleic or fumaric acid to succinic acid took place in 3 M acid at measurable rates from 70 to 90° according to the rate law

$$\text{Rate} = k[H_2][\text{Ru}^{\text{II}}\ \text{olefin}]$$

where [Ru^{II} olefin] is a 1:1 complex formed prior to the homogeneous hydrogenation to succinic acid. The values of k (at 80° in 3M hydrochloric acid) with corresponding activation parameters are: for maleic acid, $k = 2{\cdot}3 \pm 0{\cdot}1$ M^{-1} sec^{-1}, $\Delta H^{\ddagger} = 14$ kcal/mole, $\Delta S^{\ddagger} = -17$ e.u.; for fumaric acid, $k = 3{\cdot}6 \pm 0{\cdot}6$ M^{-1} sec^{-1}, $\Delta H^{\ddagger} = 17$ kcal/mole and $\Delta S^{\ddagger} = -8$ e.u. The mechanism proposed involves a heterolytic splitting of hydrogen to give a hydrido ruthenium (II) species followed by 'insertion' of the olefin into the metal–hydrogen bond[130,130d]:

$$-\text{Ru}- + \text{C}{=}\text{C} \xrightarrow{\text{Fast}} -\text{Ru}-(\text{C}{=}\text{C}) \xrightarrow[H_2]{\text{Slow}} \text{H}^-{-}\text{Ru}-(\text{C}{=}\text{C}) \longrightarrow \text{H}^-\cdots\text{Ru}\cdots(\text{C}{-}\text{C})$$

$$\text{H}^-\cdots\text{Ru}\cdots(\text{C}{-}\text{C}) \xrightarrow{H^+} -\text{Ru}-\text{C}{-}\text{C}{-}\text{H} \longrightarrow -\text{Ru}- \ (\text{regenerated})$$

Although ethylene cannot be hydrogenated with this ruthenium (II) chloro catalyst, aqueous solutions of ruthenium (II) chloride absorb the gas to form a relatively stable 1:1 complex; at constant ethylene and hydrochloric acid concentrations the uptake follows pseudo first-order kinetics with the rate being proportional to the residual concentration of uncomplexed ruthenium (II):

$$-\mathrm{d}[\mathrm{Ru^{II}}]/\mathrm{d}t = k'[\mathrm{Ru^{II}}]$$

There is a marked inverse dependence of the rate on the concentrations both of H^+ and of chloride ion. It was suggested that the formation of the complex proceeds through a two-step S_N1 mechanism[130a]:

$$\mathrm{Ru^{II}Cl}_n \rightleftharpoons \mathrm{Ru^{II}Cl}_{n-1} + \mathrm{Cl^-}$$

$$\mathrm{Ru^{II}Cl}_{n-1} + \mathrm{C_2H_4} \rightleftharpoons \mathrm{Ru^{II}Cl}_{n-1}(\mathrm{C_2H_4})$$

Some rather ill-defined ruthenium (II) salts have been described in the literature. Addition of caesium ion to the above blue solutions in hydrochloric acid gives a green salt said to be **$Cs_3[Ru_2Cl_7(H_2O)_2]$**[147], and rubidium ion gives $RbRuCl_3$[147]; addition of certain organic bases to the blue solutions gives green diamagnetic salts containing **$[RuCl_4]^{2-}$** and **$[RuCl_5H_2O]^{3-}$**[112], but clearly more investigation of this topic is needed.

For *carbonyl halo complexes* of ruthenium (II) see p. 184 and Table 4.10; for *nitrosyl halo complexes* see p. 175 and Table 4.9.

Ruthenium (I)

Ruthenium monochloride, RuCl, can be made in aqueous solution, according to Manchot and Düsing, by the action of hypophosphorous acid on ruthenium trichloride. The solution slowly evolves hydrogen[204]. There are no definite reports of a solid monochloride, but the same authors report that **RuBr** and **RuI** can be made in solution by reduction of the tribromide and triiodide with hypophosphorous acid[204]. It is possible that these solutions contain hydridic halo ruthenium (II) or ruthenium (III) species.

GROUP VI DONORS

In its higher oxidation states the unsubstituted oxide complexes are tetrahedral (as in RuO_4, $[RuO_4]^-$ and $[RuO_4]^{2-}$), and in forming the latter two ions the element displays an unexpected similarity to manganese. The rarity of *trans*-dioxo ruthenium complexes has already been remarked. Both osmium and ruthenium form few complexes in which there is only a single oxide ligand per metal atom. Ruthenium in its lower oxidation states has a more extensive oxygen and sulphur chemistry than osmium; in particular there is ample evidence for hexaaquo species of the tetra-, tri- and divalent states. The formation of sulphur dioxide complexes by ruthenium (II) ammines (cf. p. 162) is an unusual feature, apparently not shared by the other metals.

Ruthenium (VIII)

Ruthenium tetroxide, RuO_4, is most readily prepared by fusing ruthenium with potassium hydroxide in the presence of an oxidizing agent[266] and then oxidizing the product (potassium ruthenate) with chlorine or permanganate in acid[27c]. A convenient method of preparation from the dioxide is to oxidize the latter with sodium metaperiodate in aqueous solution and in the presence of carbon tetrachloride; the tetroxide then passes into the organic layer[230].

Physical properties. Ruthenium tetroxide forms yellow crystals (m.p. 25·4°, b.p. 40°) which, like osmium tetroxide, were once claimed to exist in two allotropic forms, but this has now been disproved[233].

No crystal-structure studies appear to have been carried out on the compound. An early electron-diffraction study on the vapour[28] may be discounted because of omissions from the calculations[70]. The Raman spectrum has not been measured but the infrared spectrum is consistent with the expected tetrahedral symmetry for the molecule[70,239] (see p. 65). From the rotational contour of the ν_3 band an approximate value for the moment of inertia and hence the ruthenium–oxygen bond length (assuming tetrahedral symmetry) was calculated: it was 2·23 Å[70], but this seems too large; similar calculations with the ν_3 band of osmium tetroxide give 1·85 Å for the osmium–oxygen distance[70] (the actual bond length being 1·717 Å). It seems highly unlikely that the metal–oxygen distance in ruthenium tetroxide should be substantially greater than that in osmium tetroxide. The electronic spectrum of aqueous solutions of ruthenium tetroxide has been measured[18,62] and assignments proposed[18,296].

Thermodynamic properties of the gaseous tetroxide have been obtained by study of the ruthenium–oxygen system at high temperatures[20,271] and have also been derived by statistical thermodynamic methods from the infrared spectrum[239]. For

$$Ru(s) + 2\,O_2 \rightarrow RuO_4(g)$$

$\Delta H^0_{298} = -46{\cdot}7 \pm 5$ kcal/mole and $\Delta S^0_{298} = -39{\cdot}3 \pm 5{\cdot}0$ e.u. have been obtained[20]. The ionization potential of the gaseous tetroxide is $12{\cdot}3_3$ ev[68]. A review is available on the thermochemistry of ruthenium oxides[233a].

The compound is sparingly soluble in water to give a golden-yellow solution; its solubility in grammes of tetroxide per 100 g of water is 1·71 at 0°, 2·03 at 20° and 2·1 at 40°, about a quarter of the values for osmium tetroxide. It is very soluble in organic solvents such as carbon tetrachloride.

Chemical properties. In most respects ruthenium tetroxide is less stable than osmium tetroxide, and it is a much more powerful oxidizing agent. It forms loose complexes of unknown structures with ammonia, phosphorus trifluoride[128] and pyridine[176]. Unlike osmium tetroxide, it is reduced by alkalis to give the ruthenate ion, $[RuO_4]^{2-}$, although Krauss has described a very unstable salt $(NH_4)_2[RuO_5]$ which might be $(NH_4)_2[RuO_4(OH)_2]$, analogous to the perosmates[182]. Most acids will reduce the compound (the volatility of ruthenium tetroxide in solutions of oxidizing acids such as perchloric and nitric has been studied[177]). It is soluble without apparent decomposition in bromine and in liquid sulphur dioxide (evaporation of the latter solution gives colourless crystals, which are very unstable and of unknown constitution[181]). Distribution experiments with dilute alkalis indicate that an aqueous solution of the tetroxide behaves like a weak acid ($K_1 = 6{\cdot}8 \times 10^{-12}$), and it was suggested that $H_2[RuO_5]$ was present[211] (see also discussion of $H_2[OsO_5]$, p. 70). Studies on the polarographic reduction of the tetroxide in various media have been reported[282]. Further chemical properties are summarized in Figure 4.4.

Ruthenium tetroxide in organic chemistry. Little use has been made of ruthenium tetroxide as an oxidizing agent in organic chemistry, owing perhaps to its cost and its instability. Berkowitz and Rylander have made a study of the oxidizing properties of a solution of the compound in carbon tetrachloride[23]: they found that aldehydes were oxidized to acids, alcohols to aldehydes or ketones, olefins to aldehydes, amides to imides and ethers to esters. The reaction with olefins differs from that observed with osmium tetroxide; with the latter, *cis* hydroxylation of the double bond occurs (cf. p. 66), however with ruthenium tetroxide there is carbon–carbon bond cleavage.

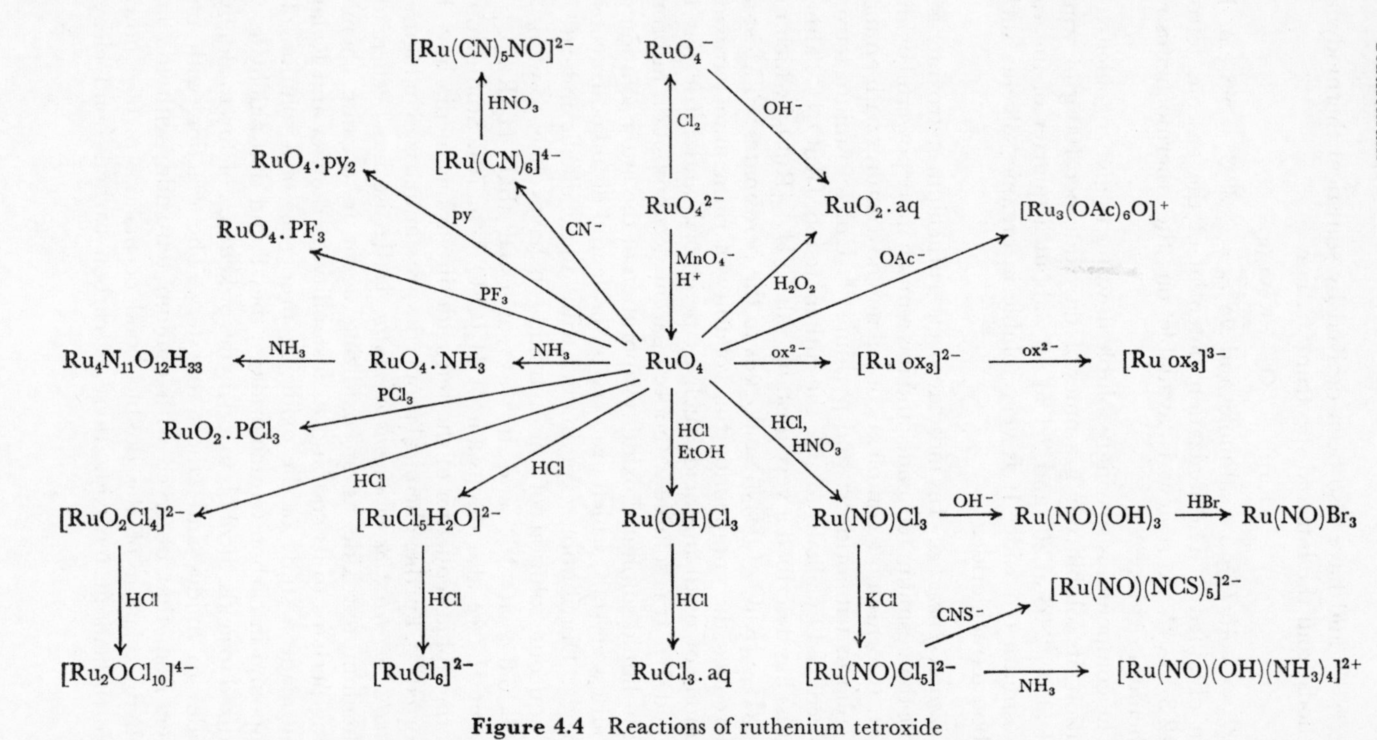

Figure 4.4 Reactions of ruthenium tetroxide

Ruthenium (VI) cyclic esters may be involved as intermediates; for example the conversion of cyclohexene to adipaldehyde may proceed as follows

$$C_6H_{10} + RuO_4 \longrightarrow C_6H_{10}O_2RuO_2 \longrightarrow (CH_2)_4(CHO)_2 + RuO_2$$

The solvents normally used for osmium tetroxide reactions (ether, benzene, pyridine) cannot be used as they react violently with ruthenium tetroxide, and only carbon tetrachloride was found to be satisfactory[69]. A convenient method for the preparation of such solutions has been described by Nakata[230] (cf. p. 146). Specific applications of the use of the reagent are the oxidation of glycosides to glyculopyranosides[24,24a] and of steroid alcohols to ketones[230].

Cleavage of isolated double bonds in steroids and triterpenes by ruthenium tetroxide has been used to identify the compounds and the positions of their double bonds[285a].

Biological and physiological properties. These have not been as extensively studied as those of osmium tetroxide. It appears that the ruthenium compound is somewhat less toxic, but it does exert a powerfully irritant effect on the eyes and on the respiratory system[122] and should be regarded as a dangerous poison.

$(NH_4)_2[RuO_4(OH)_2]$ may, as already mentioned, be the formula of the very unstable species formed by the treatment of the tetroxide with concentrated ammonia; Krauss formulated the compound as $(NH_3)_2[RuO_5].nH_2O$ (n = 1 or 2)[182]. Trenkner, on the other hand, claims that the aqueous ammonia–ruthenium tetroxide reaction gives a dark brown crystalline compound $[Ru^{IV}O(OH)_2(NH_3)_2]aq$[293]. Since treatment of osmium tetroxide with aqueous ammonia yields ammonium osmiamate, it is possible that the above compounds are ruthenium nitrido species. The $[RuO_4(OH)_2]^{2-}$ ion has been suggested as an intermediate in the alkaline decomposition of perruthenate ion (see below)[44].

There is no evidence for ruthenium (VIII) sulphides, selenides or tellurides; species such as RuS_6 and RuS_8 are probably polysulphides of tetravalent ruthenium.

Ruthenium (VII)

Potassium perruthenate, $K[RuO_4]$, is a fairly common compound of ruthenium. It can be made by passing chlorine into an aqueous solution of potassium ruthenate ($K_2[RuO_4]$) until this becomes green, or by fusing ruthenium with potassium nitrate and potassium hydroxide[27c,67,123]. The compound forms small black crystals which decompose at 440° to potassium ruthenate and ruthenium dioxide (a sodium salt has also been made). The x-ray crystal structure of the potassium salt shows that the anion has the tetragonal bisphenoidal structure (a tetrahedron slightly flattened along one axis). The ruthenium–oxygen bond length is 1·79 Å and the $O\hat{Ru}O$ angle is 106°; the overall crystal structure is of the Scheelite (calcium tungstate) type, and potassium perruthenate is isomorphous with potassium osmiamate and potassium periodate, but not with potassium permanganate[281]. Electronic spectra of the perruthenate ion[62,315] have been assigned[296]. The infrared spectrum of the solid was also measured[117b,315].

In aqueous solution the compound is unstable, and decomposes to oxygen and the orange ruthenate. The kinetics of the decomposition in alkali have been studied: the rate law is[44]

$$dx/dt = k_{app}[RuO_4^-]^2[OH^-]^3$$

and it has been suggested that the mechanism involves the intermediate formation of hydroperoxide[44]:

$$RuO_4^- + 2\,OH^- \underset{k_{-1}}{\overset{k_1}{\rightleftharpoons}} [RuO_4(OH)_2]^{3-}$$

$$[RuO_4(OH)_2]^{3-} + RuO_4^- + OH^- \underset{-2}{\overset{k_2}{\rightleftharpoons}} 2[RuO_4]^{2-} + OOH^- + H_2O$$

$$OH^- + OOH^- \xrightarrow{k_3} H_2O + O_2 \text{ (Catalysed)}$$

The rate of the electron exchange reaction between perruthenate and ruthenate ions was found too fast to measure: at 0° the second-order rate constant was probably greater than $3{\cdot}3 \times 10^4\ \text{M}^{-1}\ \text{sec}^{-1}$. However, for the perruthenate–manganate (VI) reaction in aqueous alkali the specific rate constant is $5{\cdot}7 \times 10^2\ \text{M}^{-1}\ \text{sec}^{-1}$ at 20° in 0·2M sodium hydroxide. The thermodynamic and activation parameters are $\Delta H^\circ = 4$ kcal/mole, $\Delta S^\circ = -11$ e.u., $E_a = 7{\cdot}7$ kcal/mole, $\Delta H^\ddagger = 7$ kcal/mole, $\Delta S^\ddagger = -11$ e.u.). The reactions probably proceed via an outer-sphere mechanism[195a].

Studies of the electronic spectra of ruthenium tetroxide in these alkali solutions indicated the presence of a new species, either of ruthenium (VIII) or (VII), which may be $[RuO_4(OH)_2]^{2-}$ or the $[RuO_4(OH)_2]^{3-}$ postulated in the above mechanism; the spectra differed from those of perruthenate and ruthenate, which were also measured[62]. It has been claimed that acidification of solutions of potassium perruthenate gives a hydrated ruthenium (V) oxide together with the tetroxide[235].

The oxidation potential for the perruthenate/ruthenate couple is 0·59 v, and for the ruthenate/dioxide couple 0·35 v[62]. Polarographic studies on solutions of ruthenium tetroxide and of potassium perruthenate and ruthenate gave a similar value for the ruthenate/perruthenate couple, while the E_0 for ruthenium tetroxide/perruthenate was found to be 1·00 v[282]; thus the potential diagram for ruthenium oxy species in alkaline solutions is[62,282]

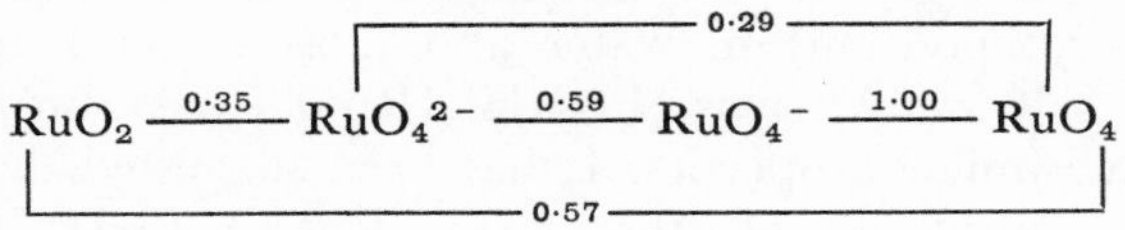

$$RuO_2 \xrightarrow{0{\cdot}35} RuO_4^{2-} \xrightarrow{0{\cdot}59} RuO_4^{-} \xrightarrow{1{\cdot}00} RuO_4$$

(RuO_4^{2-} — RuO_4: 0·29; RuO_2 — RuO_4: 0·57)

Assignments of charge-transfer transitions in perruthenate and ruthenate ions have been made[199].

Ruthenium (VI)

Ruthenium trioxide, RuO_3, has been detected in the vapour phase near 1200° and thermodynamic data determined[20,271]. For the reaction

$$Ru(s) + \tfrac{3}{2}\,O_2 \rightarrow RuO_3(g)$$

$\Delta H^0_{298} = -18{\cdot}0 \pm 4$ kcal/mole and $\Delta S^0_{298} = -16{\cdot}6 \pm 4$ e.u.[20], and the ionization potential of the gaseous species as measured by electron impact is 11·2 ev[68]. There is, however, no evidence for its existence in the solid state, although it has been suggested as an intermediate in the organic oxidation reactions of the tetroxide (cf. above).

$RuO_2.S_2O_7$ is said to be formed by the action of ultraviolet light on solutions of ruthenium tetroxide in sulphuric acid[138].

Potassium ruthenate, $K_2[RuO_4]$, is normally made by fusion of ruthenium metal with potassium nitrate and potassium hydroxide[123]. The crystals are black with a green metallic lustre; sodium, rubidium, caesium and alkaline earth salts are also known[27c,123,180].

Aqueous solutions of potassium ruthenate are orange and very unstable, tending to disproportionate to the perruthenate and ruthenium dioxide; acidification of ruthenates is said to give a ruthenium pentoxide and the perruthenate[235]. Polarographic and oxidation potential studies are considered above (cf. perruthenate). The absorption spectrum of the solution has been measured[62] and charge-transfer bands assigned[199].

Infrared spectra of barium ruthenate have been measured[117b]. The electron spin resonance of sodium ruthenate was measured at 20° K and a g value of 2·0 with an isotropic splitting of 0·02 cm^{-1} established for the $[RuO_4]^{2-}$ ion[44a].

There is a curious reaction between potassium ruthenate and aqueous ammonia: a compound which analyses as $(NH_4)_2[RuO_4]$ is formed, but its properties suggest that it is not ammonium ruthenate. The small black crystals are very stable, and are slightly soluble (without decomposition) in water and most mineral acids. A triethylamine salt analysing as $(Et_3NH)_2[RuO_4]$ has also been made, and this has similar properties. It has been suggested that these are 'ruthenyl' complexes of the form $Ru^{VI}O_2(OH)_2(NH_3)_2$ and $Ru^{VI}O_2(OH)_2(Et_3N)_2$[180].

'Ruthenyl' complexes, like their osmium analogues, have the form $[RuO_2X_4]^{2-}$; presumably the two oxygen atoms are *trans*, although there is no x-ray evidence for this (however, infrared spectra of $Cs_2[RuO_2Cl_4]$ suggest that this is so: the spectra are very similar to those of *trans*-$K_2[OsO_2Cl_4]$[313]). The complexes are diamagnetic, probably due to the low symmetry of the ligand field (see p. 72).

$RuO_2(NH_3)_2(OH)_2$ and **$RuO_2(Et_3N)_2(OH)_2$** have already been mentioned; they are made by the action of ammonia and triethylamine on potassium ruthenate[180]. Their formulation as 'ruthenyl' complexes has not been established but seems reasonable. Treatment of the ammine with hydrochloric acid gives a brown complex which is probably $[RuO_2(NH_3)_2(H_2O)_2]Cl_2$[180]. These may possibly be nitrido complexes.

Another complex which may involve the 'ruthenyl' groups is the green $[RuO_2(SO_4)_2]^{2-}$ ion (no salts isolated), made by dissolving ruthenium tetroxide in sulphuric acid in the presence of reducing agents[211].

$RuO(SO_4)_2$ is claimed to be the product of the reaction between ruthenium tetroxide and α-sulphur trioxide in a sealed tube under ultraviolet light; the compound is dark brown[138].

Ruthenium (V)

Oxides and oxy complexes of this oxidation state are not well established, apart from $Ba_3Ru_2MgO_9$.

Ru_2O_5 and **Ru_4O_9** have been claimed, the pentoxide by the action of heat on ruthenium tetroxide[67] and Ru_4O_9 by the action of heat on the pentoxide[67]. Remy also reports a pentoxide made by aerial oxidation of '$Ru(OH)_2$' (itself made from alkali and blue ruthenium dichloride solutions)[257], and it is said that acidification of solutions of ruthenates or perruthenates gives hydrated ruthenium (V) oxides[235]; it seems probable that all of these compounds are various hydrates of the dioxide[311]. Dehydration studies of the hydrated 'pentoxide' have been made[15]. Species such as **$K_2O.6Ru_2O_5$** (made by prolonged heating of potassium perruthenate at 440°)[161] and **$K_2O.3Ru_2O_5$**[162] have been claimed. Recently, **$Ba_3Ru_2MgO_9$** was obtained by heating together an appropriate mixture of barium carbonate, magnesium oxide and ruthenium metal to 1200°. The compound has the hexagonal barium titanate structure ($a = 5{\cdot}75$, $c = 14{\cdot}12$ Å); a compound with nickel replacing magnesium was also made[71a]. Magnetic measurements were made on $Ba_3Ru_2MgO_9$[42a].

Ruthenium (IV)

Ruthenium dioxide, RuO_2, can be made by heating the metal or the trichloride in a stream of oxygen at 1000°[258] or by the reduction of ruthenium (VI) complexes[10]. It is not affected by acids in the cold. The anhydrous oxide forms blue crystals of the rutile type ($a = 4{\cdot}49 \pm 0{\cdot}005$ Å, $c = 3{\cdot}11 \pm 0{\cdot}005$ Å)[272], and its magnetic susceptibility has been measured from 298 to 673°K; at room temperatures the moment is 0·78 BM[126]. This low moment might suggest some metal–metal interaction in the solid, but a recent x-ray study shows the Ru–Ru distance to be 3·107 Å, which is too long to account for substantial interaction; however, the oxide has a very high electrical conductivity. The ruthenium–oxygen distances were found to be 1·917 and 1·999 ± 0·008 Å[64a]. Thermodynamic data for the dioxide have been obtained by studies of the ruthenium–oxygen system over a wide temperature range[4,5,20,233a,271,272]. For the reaction

$$Ru(s) + O_2 \rightarrow RuO_2(g)$$

$\Delta H^0_{298} = -72{\cdot}2 \pm 2$ kcal/mole and $\Delta S^0_{298} = 12{\cdot}5 \pm 2$ e.u.[20]. The ionization potential of the gas is 10·6 ev[68]. The oxidation potential of the perruthenate/ruthenium dioxide couple is 0·57 v[62].

A monohydrate can be prepared by heating the tetroxide in a current of hydrogen[314]. The kinetics of the reaction

$$RuO_2.H_2O(s) \rightarrow RuO_2(s) + H_2O(g)$$

have been studied and the activation energy (21·5 kcal/mole) determined. The ability of both the hydrated and anhydrous forms to catalyse the decomposition of hydrogen peroxide was investigated[171a].

The dioxide appears to be somewhat more stable than its osmium analogue; it is not attacked by acids in the cold, but when heated is reduced to the metal by hydrogen or by carbon monoxide. It has been used as a catalyst for hydrogenation of ketones and allyl alcohol[291].

$RuO(OH)_2$ ('ruthenium hydroxide') is said to be formed by reduction of the tetroxide or a ruthenate in alkaline solution[45].

The ruthenites

Ruthenites of the alkaline earth metals can be made by heating together ruthenium metal and the appropriate carbonate or peroxide. **$SrRuO_3$** has the perovskite structure (a = 3·93 Å)[174]; **$BaRuO_3$** has a rhombohedral lattice in which BaO_3 layers are stacked and the ruthenium has slightly distorted octahedral coordination such that there are strings of three face-sharing RuO_6 octahedra, the strings being linked by the sharing of corners. The ruthenium–ruthenium distance is only 2·55 ± 0·01 Å, suggesting metal–metal interaction; about each metal atom three oxygen atoms are 2·02 ± 0·01 Å distant and the other three are 1·96 ± 0·01 Å distant[71]. X-ray studies are also reported on the systems $Ba_{1-n}Sr_nRuO_3$ and on $BaRu_{1-n}M_nO_3$ (M = Ir, Mn, Ni and n ranging from 1 to 0)[71a].

Magnetic susceptibilities were measured from 77 to 1000°K of $M^{II}RuO_3$ (M = Sr, Ca, Ba), Sr_2RuO_4, $Ba_{5/6}Sr_{1/6}RuO_3$ and $Ba(Ru_{2/3}Mg_{1/3})O_3$: the latter species also contains pentavalent ruthenium[42a].

Aquo complexes

Ruthenium (IV) perchlorate can be made in solution by the reduction of a solution of ruthenium tetroxide in perchloric acid with hydrogen peroxide[114,232,302]. A number of hydrolysed species are present in solution, one of which with two positive charges per ruthenium atom, is present in large concentration; ion-exchange experiments suggest that this is the **$RuOaq^{2+}$** ion[114,175d,295a]. The various other polymers can be broken down to this monomeric oxy species during the course of elution from an ion-exchange resin[11]. Polarographic studies have been reported on ruthenium (IV) aquo complexes[12,232] and it was observed that there was no dependence of the polarographic behaviour on the degree of polymerization of the cation[11]. For perchloric acid solutions the following potential diagram was derived (pH 1)[12]:

$$Ru(\text{II}) \xrightarrow{-0.11} Ru(\text{III}) \xrightarrow{+0.42} Ru(3.5) \xrightarrow{+0.56} Ru(\text{IV})$$
$$Ru(\text{III}) \xrightarrow{+0.49} Ru(\text{IV})$$

Shukla has reported the preparation in solution of the $[\mathbf{Ru(H_2O)_6}]^{4+}$ ion by allowing solutions of $[RuCl_5H_2O]^{2-}$ to age[280]. The effect of adding chloride ion to ruthenium (IV) aquo species has been discussed above (p. 135).

$\mathbf{K_2[Ru\ ox_3]}$ can be made by the oxidation of trisoxalato ruthenate (III) with hydrogen peroxide. The salt is black and the aqueous solution is also said to be black[46]. Polarographic studies have been made on oxalato complexes of ruthenium (IV), (III) and (II)[298].

Nitrates

A solution of ruthenium tetroxide in nitric acid is reduced by hydrogen peroxide to give a deep red solution. Although it has been suggested that this contains complexes of the form $[Ru(OH)_n(H_2O)_{6-n}]^{(4-n)+}$ [7], it seems more likely that these are nitrosyl complexes. The reaction of ozone with 'ruthenium (IV) nitrate' has been studied[115a].

Sulphates

It is said that $Ru(SO_4)_2$ can be made in solution by dissolving barium ruthenite in sulphuric acid[8] or by oxidation of $Ru(S_2O_5)_2$[120]. The product is red and is not hydrolysed in aqueous solution; studies have recently been reported on the species in such solutions[295a]. The complex $RuO_2S_2O_7$ (cf. p. 151) reacts with dilute sulphuric acid to give a brown solution which, it is believed, contains $\mathbf{RuO(SO_4)}$[138].

Sulphur, selenium and tellurium compounds

$\mathbf{RuS_2}$, $\mathbf{RuSe_2}$ and $\mathbf{RuTe_2}$ can all be made from the elements at high temperatures[165,292,312]. They have the pyrites structure (for the disulphide, the cell element is 5·601 ± 0·003 Å and the ruthenium–sulphur distance is 2·31 Å[165]; the cell elements are 5·921 ± 0·002 Å for the diselenide and 6·36 ± 0·002 Å for the ditelluride[292]). There are thermodynamic data for the sulphide[198].

The polysulphides $\mathbf{RuS_3}$[8] and $\mathbf{RuS_6}$[156] can be made from potassium hexachlororuthenate (IV) and hydrogen sulphide; RuS_6 can be oxidized in air to a pyrosulphite, $\mathbf{Ru(S_2O_5)_2}$[156]. A 'thiometallate', possibly $[\mathbf{Ru(SH)_6}]^{3-}$, can be got from polysulphides and $[RuCl_6]^{2-}$ [245a].

Selenourea complexes

These complexes are formed in solution from the ligand and ruthenium (IV) species [245].

Ruthenium (III)

$\mathbf{Ru_2O_3}$ has been claimed as a product of the oxidation of ruthenium in oxygen and also as a reduction product of $K_2[RuCl_5OH]$, but the x-ray studies of Lunde suggest that neither Ru_2O_3 nor RuO exists in the solid state [195]. There is also some doubt concerning the constitution of $Ru(OH)_3$, made by the addition of hydroxide ion to solutions of ruthenium trichloride [183]; Charronat has suggested that some of the reported preparations of this may in fact have given $Ru^{IV}O(OH)_2$ [45].

Aquo complexes*

The ruthenium (III) chloro-aquo system has already been considered (see p. 139). Evidence for the existence of $[\mathbf{Ru(H_2O)_6}]^{3+}$ has been obtained from polarographic reduction studies on ruthenium (IV) perchlorate solutions (p. 154) [11,232] and from the oxidation of $[Ru(H_2O)_6]^{2+}$ [221a]. An intermediate species said to contain 'ruthenium 3·5' was detected by these measurements; its constitution is unknown but it might be regarded as a reduction product of $[RuO(H_2O)_5]^{2+}$ with one or more oxygen or hydroxy bridges, such as $[(H_2O)_5Ru—O—Ru(H_2O)_5]^{5+}$, the metal atoms being in equivalent environments with a formal oxidation state between (III) and (IV).

No *hydroxy* ruthenium (III) complexes are reported.

Acetylacetone complexes

The tris species, **Ru acac**$_3$, can be prepared as a red powder by the action of acetylacetone on ruthenium trichloride. It is insoluble in water but readily dissolves in most organic solvents to give red solutions. The solid sublimes to a red, inflammable vapour [16]. The magnetic susceptibility of the compound has been measured from 80 to 295°K (see Table 4.11) [40,90a], the rather low moment of 1·98 BM as compared with other ruthenium (III) complexes may arise from the lower symmetry (D_3) of the complex. The near infrared spectrum has been measured and assigned [68a].

The proton magnetic resonance spectrum of the complex in solution

* See also pp. 154 and 160.

has been measured and values for the contact shifts recorded. These were compared with those of the dia- and paramagnetic trisacac complexes of other metals, and it was concluded that they were predominantly contact shifts and that ligand–to–metal charge transfer was more important than metal–to–ligand transfer[80].

The reaction of dibenzoylmethane and *p,p'*-dinitrodibenzoylmethane with Ru acac$_3$ yields, respectively, **Ru**$(\mathbf{C_{15}H_{11}O_2})_3$ and **Ru**$(\mathbf{C_{15}H_9O_6N_2})_3$[312a]; a similar complex with benzoylacetone was also prepared, and the magnetic properties and electronic spectra of this, Ru acac$_3$ and Ru$(C_{15}H_{11}O_2)_3$ were studied[119a]—the magnetic data covered the range 80–293°K.

Carboxylic acid complexes

Acetates. The ruthenium acetate system is complicated. The action of glacial acetic acid on 'Ru_2O_3' was reported to give a series of binuclear ruthenium (III) species of the form $Ru_2(OAc)_4(OH)_2(H_2O)_2$, $Ru_2(OAc)_3(OH)_3(H_2O)_2$, $Ru_2(OAc)(OH)_5(H_2O)_2$ and $Ru_2(OAc)_5$-(OH)[224]. However, Martin[213] pointed out that the ruthenium (III) oxide used probably contained some dioxide. He obtained a ruthenium (III) acetate by treating a solution of ruthenium tetroxide in carbon tetrachloride with glacial acetic acid and acetaldehyde: the compound is blue and is formulated as $\mathbf{[Ru_3(OAc)_6O]OAc.7H_2O}$.

Ferric and chromic analogues of these, $[Fe_3(OAc)_6O]OAc$ and $[Cr_3(OAc)_6O](OAc)$, have been described[303], and the x-ray crystal structure of the latter determined; the three chromium atoms are trigonally disposed about and coplanar with the oxygen atom[89].

A pyridine complex, $\mathbf{[Ru_3(OAc)_6py_5]Cl.PtCl_6.7H_2O}$, was also made[213].

$\mathbf{Ru_2(OCOR)_4Cl}$ (R = Me, Et, n-Pr) can be made from the appropriate acid with its anhydride on hydrated ruthenium trichloride. The complexes are 1:1 electrolytes in aqueous solution, and have been formulated as containing ruthenium (III) and (II). They will react with donors such as pyridine to give green compounds of composition $\mathbf{Ru(OCOR)_2py_2}$ and yellow compounds $\mathbf{Ru(OCOR)_2py_4}$ (R = Me, Et); in these complexes the carboxylate groups are monodentate. The magnetic moments of $Ru_2(OCOR)_4Cl$ (Table 4.11) are abnormally high and may mean that in these complexes the ruthenium atoms are spin-free, a very unusual occurrence for a second-row element[287]. There was no evidence of anti- or ferromagnetism. Complexes of the form $\mathbf{[Ru_2(OCOR)_3(OH)(H_2O)]^+}$

(R = Me, Et) were also made and also have high magnetic moments; infrared spectra of these complexes were measured[287].

EDTA complexes (ethylenediaminetetraacetic acid is H_4EDTA). Reaction of ruthenium trichloride with the disodium dihydrogen salt of EDTA yields **Ru(H.EDTA)H_2O** and **RuCl(H_2EDTA)H_2O**; the infrared and electronic spectra of these products were recorded[228a]. Some ruthenium EDTA complexes are reported to react reversibly with molecular oxygen[86a], and peroxy EDTA species were isolated[86a].

Formates. The action of formic acid on 'Ru_2O_3' gives a complex said to be **[$Ru_3(HCOO)_7(OH)_2$].$5H_2O$**[224]; but in view of the above discussion on the acetates it is likely to be **[$Ru_3(HCOO)_6O$](HCOO).$6H_2O$**.

Oxalates. The known oxalato complexes of ruthenium are summarized in Table 4.1, p. 196.

K_3(Ru ox_3).$4\frac{1}{2}H_2O$ can be made by the action of potassium oxalate on $K_2[RuCl_5(H_2O)]$; an addition compound, **KCl.2 K_3-[Ru ox_3].$8H_2O$**, is often formed in the above preparation. Dehydration of K_3[Ru ox_3].$4\frac{1}{2}H_2O$ gives a monohydrate and finally the hemihydrate; the anhydrous salt does not appear to have been made. The potassium salt is green; sodium, ammonium, barium and silver salts are also known[46,73]. The curious hydration properties of this complex suggest that it may have a structure similar to that of the so-called K_3[Rh ox_3] (p. 337) which is (in the solid state and probably in solution) K_6[Rh ox_2(Hox)(OH)][Rh ox_3][246].

Magnetic susceptibility measurements were made on the potassium salt from 90 to 298°K (see Table 4.11); the moment for the solid sample at room temperature was very close to that for the salt in the aqueous solution[237]. The electronic spectrum was measured and assignments proposed[237]. Exchange between the complex and oxalate ion in aqueous solution was measured; the order of reactivity for such exchange in trisoxalato complexes of trivalent metals is: (fast) Mn ~ V ~ Fe > Ru ~ Cr > Co > Rh > Ir (slow), in agreement with predictions from ligand-field stabilization energies[238]. Attempts to resolve [Ru ox_3]$^{3-}$ with strychnine or quinoline salts were unsuccessful[47], as were attempts using the 'active racemates' method[73]; it was suggested that rapid racemization through seven- or eight-coordinate intermediates involving aquo groups might occur[73], (or that the presence of aquo oxalates in solution might be involved[298]).

Ruthenium tetroxide is rapidly reduced to the (IV) state by oxalate ion (presumably to $[Ru\ ox_3]^{2-}$: it is interesting to note that there is no evidence of a 'ruthenyl' oxalate, $[RuO_2\ ox_2]^{2-}$, although the corresponding osmium (VI) species is very stable). The tetravalent complex is reduced polarographically to the trivalent and then to the divalent state[298]. The stability constants of some ruthenium (III) aquooxalato species have been determined[298].

Nitrato complexes

These complexes, which are numerous for ruthenium (II), have not been established for the trivalent state. Fletcher and Woodhead have studied the behavior of ruthenium (III) in nitric acid; oxidation to ruthenium (IV) polymers occurs, and some $Ru(NO)aq^{3+}$ is formed, but there is no evidence for coordinated nitrato groups in these trivalent species[97].

Sulphur, selenium and tellurium donors

No sulphides, selenides or tellurides of ruthenium (III) are known.

Sulphito complexes

$Ru_2(SO_3)_3$, presumably aquated, can be made as blue crystals by the action of sulphur dioxide on ruthenium (IV) aquo complexes[8].

A number of ill-defined ruthenium sulphito complexes have been reported, namely **$6K_2SO_3 . Ru_2O(SO_3)_2 . 4H_2O$**, **$K_2[Ru_2(OH)_2(SO_3)_3] . 3H_2O$** and some even more unlikely sodium salts[259,260]. No **thiourea** complexes seem to have been isolated, but $[Ru(thiourea)(H_2O)_5]^{3+}$ has been claimed to exist in solution[318]; **selenourea** complexes are formed in solution and have been used in analysis for the metal[244].

Dithiocarbamato complexes

$Ru(R_2NCS_2)_3$ (R = Me, Et, Bu) can be made from the ligand and potassium hexachlororuthenate (IV); they are paramagnetic[200] (see Table 4.11) and their infrared spectra have been measured[50]. An x-ray study on the diethyl complex shows a ruthenium–sulphur bond length of $2{\cdot}385 \pm 0{\cdot}005$ Å[70a]. The reaction of tetrabenzylthiouram disulphide with carbon monoxide and ruthenium trichloride in alcoholic solution yields the light brown species **$[Ru((Ph_2CH_2)_2NCS_2]_2(CO)_2]Cl$**; ruthenium (II) carbonyl dithiocarbamato species are also formed in this reaction[175c] (see also p. 163 and Table 4.10).

6*

Thiocyanato complexes

These complexes of ruthenium are not well established apart from the nitrosyl complex (see p. 176). The formation of a blue colour when ruthenium (IV) complexes are mixed with thiocyanate has been noted, and it has been suggested that this may arise from trivalent complexes[100,279], possibly $[Ru(SCN)(H_2O)_5]^{2+}$[317].

Alkyl sulphides

$\mathbf{RuCl_3(SEt_2)_3}$ and $\mathbf{[RuCl_3(SEt_2)_2]_2}$ are both formed from diethyl sulphide and ruthenium trichloride, and can be separated by fractional crystallization; the electronic spectra were recorded and assignments proposed. The monomer has a magnetic moment of 2·1 BM at room temperature whereas that of the dimer is only 0·95 BM, suggesting metal–metal interaction in the latter, probably through chloro bridges[88].

Miscellaneous complexes

Aqueous solutions of dithiophosphate[41] and dithiooxamide[319] complexes of ruthenium (III) have been used for analysis for the metal. Absorption spectra of Ru dpt_3 (dpt = diethyl dithiophosphate) have been measured[169a].

Ruthenium (II)

There is no real evidence for the existence of **ruthenium monoxide, RuO**, although it was said that it could be made by heating the alleged dichloride in carbon dioxide[58] or as a 'hydroxide' by adding alkali to the blue solutions of 'ruthenium dichloride'[257]. Studies on the ruthenium–oxygen system at high temperatures give no evidence for its existence in the gas phase[20,271]; however, band spectra attributed to the gaseous monoxide have been observed[252] and an ionization potential estimated[68].

Aquo and hydroxy complexes

$\mathbf{[Ru(H_2O)_6]^{2+}}$ has been obtained in aqueous solution by electrolytic reduction of mono- and dichloroaquo ruthenium (III) species in the presence of tetrafluoroborate ion; the cation was separated from ruthenium (II) chloro-aquo complexes by cation exchange. The electronic absorption spectra were measured and assigned: the D_q value of 2100 cm^{-1} is close to that of $[RhCl_6]^{3-}$, suggesting that the decrease in ligand-field splitting caused by the lower charge of the ruthenium complex is counter-balanced by the presence of water rather than chloride as a ligand. The cation was polarographically oxidized to the trivalent species ($E_{1/2} = -0{\cdot}02$ v versus S.C.E. in the presence of *p*-toluenesulphonic acid)[221a]. There is also independent polarographic evidence for the existence of ruthenium (II) aquo complexes[114,232].

The potential of the Ru(III)–Ru(II) couple in 0.1M *p*-toluenesulphonic acid was found to be −0.2487v; for the cell reaction

$$Ru^{2+} + H^{+} \rightarrow Ru^{3+} + \tfrac{1}{2} H_2$$

$\Delta H^{\circ} = 10{\cdot}1$ kcal/mole and $\Delta S^{\circ} = 53$ e.u. at 25°[35a].

Nitrosyl aquo and hydroxy complexes. These complexes are summarized in Table 4.9, p. 210.

The *acetylacetone complex* **[Ru(acac)(phen)$_2$](ClO$_4$)** has been made[74] (Table 4.4).

Carboxylic acid complexes

Nitrosyl acetates. Some rather obscure ruthenium nitrosyl acetates have been claimed; these were made from ruthenium tetroxide, nitric acid and acetic acid, and the parent compound was formulated as **[Ru(NO)(OAc)$_2$]**. In the presence of sodium acetate a sodium salt is produced, said to be **Na[Ru(NO)(OAc)$_3$]**[321], and its electrolytic reduction properties were studied[322]. If nitric oxide is a three-electron donor here, these complexes should contain ruthenium (I) and hence be paramagnetic, a situation otherwise unknown for ruthenium nitrosyl complexes. It seems more likely that these are conventional Ru^{II}(NO) complexes and that a hydroxide group should be added to the above formulae.

Nitrosyl oxalates. A few nitrosyl oxalates of ruthenium (II) have been made (see Table 4.1)[46]; the complex $H_2[Ru(NO)ox_2]$.aq[322] should probably be reformulated as **H$_2$[Ru(NO)ox$_2$(OH)]** (see discussion on nitrosyl acetates above). There is polarographic evidence for the existence of **[Ru ox$_3$]$^{4-}$** in solution[298].

Mixed ruthenium (II)–(III) carboxylates have already been discussed (cf. p. 157).

Nitrato complexes

All those reported for ruthenium (II) also contain the nitrosyl group, and such species are summarized in Table 4.9. The only complex which requires separate mention here is $\mathbf{Ru_2N_6O_{15}}$, got by the reaction of nitric oxide with a solution of ruthenium tetroxide in carbon tetrachloride. Two formulations have been proposed: firstly, $Ru_2O(NO)_2(NO_3)_4$ involving bidentate nitrato groups[269], and secondly $Ru_2O_5(NO)_4(NO_3)_2$ involving monodentate nitrato groups[215]. The former is the preferred structure[269].

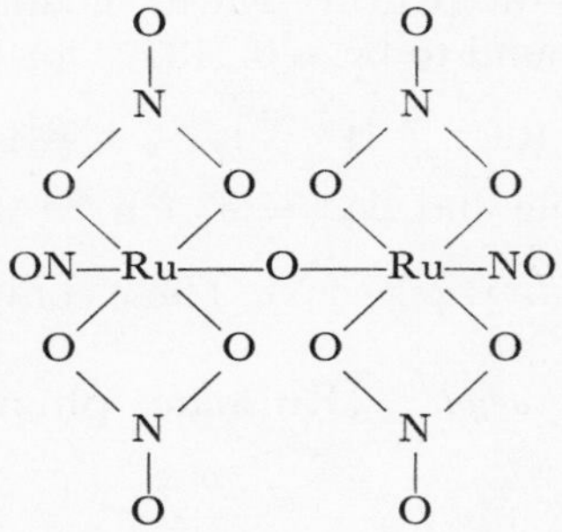

```
          O                 O
          |                 |
          N                 N
        /   \             /   \
      O       O         O       O
        \   /             \   /
   ON—Ru———————O———————Ru—NO
        /   \             /   \
      O       O         O       O
        \   /             \   /
          N                 N
          |                 |
          O                 O
```

There are some ruthenium (I) nitrosyl nitrato species claimed[321], but these are almost certainly complexes of ruthenium (II) (cf. also p. 161).

Sulphur, selenium and tellurium complexes

There is no evidence for monosulphides, -selenides or -tellurides.

Sulphito complexes

Some ill-defined species such as $\mathbf{K_2SO_3.}\boldsymbol{n}\mathbf{RuSO_3.aq}$ have been made from potassium sulphite and $K_4[Ru_2OCl_{10}]$[259], and sodium salts were also prepared. Both the nature of the bonding of the sulphite group and the oxidation state of the ruthenium are in question in these compounds.

Some sulphite complexes containing ammine groups are better defined (cf. Table 4.2), and there are a few hydro–sulphite ammines. **Nitrosyl sulphito** complexes of uncertain composition can be made from $Na_2[Ru(NO)Cl_5]$ and sodium bisulphite.

$\mathbf{RuS_2O_6}$ (deep yellow crystals) can be made from sulphur dioxide and ruthenium (IV) sulphate[8]. It is very soluble in water, and the solution evolves sulphur dioxide when heated to 80°.

Sulphur dioxide complexes

More of these complexes are formed by ruthenium than by any other element; they all contain ammine groups (see Table 4.2)[107].

The preparation and constitution of most of these complexes have recently been confirmed. An x-ray crystal structure analysis of $[Ru(NH_3)_4(SO_2)Cl]Cl$ shows this to have an orthorhombic unit cell (a = 13·962, b = 9·308, c = 7·312 Å). The sulphur dioxide molecule functions as a monodentate ligand coordinated through the sulphur atom, and the bond parameters of the ligand are virtually the same as for solid sulphur dioxide. The ruthenium–nitrogen distance is 2·127 ± 0·006 Å, ruthenium–chlorine 2·415 ± 0·003 Å, ruthenium–sulphur 2·072 ± 0·003 Å, and the chlorine is *trans* to the sulphur giving the molecule an overall C_{4v} skeletal configuration. There are two sulphur–oxygen bond lengths of 1·462 and 1·394 ± 0·01 Å, but no significance is to be attached to the difference, which is probably dictated by crystal-packing effects; the $O_{S}O$ angle is 113·8 ± 0·6°. The infrared spectra of this complex and of $[Ru(NH_3)_5(SO_2)]X_2$ and $[Ru(NH_3)_4(SO_2)X]X$ (X = Cl, Br) were measured, and it was found that there was very little difference between the spectra of free and coordinated sulphur dioxide[297].

Dithiocarbamato complexes

Reaction of ruthenium trichloride in ethanolic solution with dithiocarbamates in the presence of carbon monoxide yields **$Ru(CO)_2(R_2NCS_2)_2$** (R = Me, Et, $C_6H_5CH_2$). These are yellow solids[175c]. The nitrosyl species $Ru(NO)(Et_2NCS_2)_3$ is considered on p. 176. The **bisdithione** complex

Ph S S Ph
Ru
Ph S S Ph

has been made from ruthenium trichloride and phosphorothioic esters of dithioacyloins; this is the only established example of a planar ruthenium (II) complex. The osmium analogue was also made. The ruthenium complex is blue in the solid state and green in organic solution, and the solid melts at 225°[274b]. Reaction of thiophenol with an ethanolic solution of ruthenium trichloride in the presence of carbon monoxide gave the light brown compound **$(Ru(C_6H_5S)_2(CO)_2)_3$**. A similar preparation using ethanedithiol yielded a yellow complex which was thought to be **$(Ru(S(CH_2)_2S)(CO)_2)_n$**[175c].

An *alkyl sulphide* complex **$[Ru(SEt_2)_3(CO)_2(SnCl_3)]^+$** is known (Table 4.10)[175c].

No ruthenium (I) or (0) complexes of Group VI donor ligands have been reported.

GROUP V DONORS

Ruthenium forms many more ammine complexes than either osmium or iron (iridium and rhodium, however, form a comparable range of ammines). In particular the interesting complexes of the type $[Ru^{II}(NH_3)_5X]^{n+}$ (X = NO, SO_2, HSO_3, N_2) should be noted; the ligands X are all good π acceptors. The nitrogeno complex $[Ru(NH_3)_5N_2]I_2$ recently claimed may involve end-bonded co-ordinated nitrogen. The tendency of ruthenium (II) to form nitrosyl complexes has already been noted. As with osmium (but unlike iron) a wide range of phosphine, arsine and stibine complexes has been prepared.

Ruthenium (VIII)

Only a few complexes with Group V ligands have been reported. $\mathbf{RuO_4.NH_3}$, a very unstable and explosive species, is made by the action of ammonia on ruthenium tetroxide at $-30°$[128], while $\mathbf{RuO_4py_2}$ is much more stable and can be made at room temperature by the action of pyridine on a solution of the tetroxide in carbon tetrachloride[176]. With phosphorus trifluoride, the tetroxide will give (at low temperatures) $\mathbf{RuO_4.PF_3}$ and $\mathbf{(RuO_4)_2.PF_3}$, but phosphorus trichloride and tribromide reduce the tetroxide to give $RuO_2.PCl_3$ and $RuO_2.PBr_3$, respectively[128].

The absence of a compound analogous to the very stable potassium osmiamate, $K[OsO_3N]$, is striking, since osmium and ruthenium are otherwise fairly similar in their high oxidation state chemistry.

Ruthenium (VII)

No complexes are known with Group V donors.

Ruthenium (VI)

Nitrido complexes

The reaction of ammonia with ruthenium tetroxide is much more violent than with osmium tetroxide. At $-70°$ the product is said to be $\mathbf{Ru_4N_{11}O_{12}H_{33}}$, a complex which is believed to have nitride ligands. The infrared spectrum was reported. On heating the compound decomposes to a compound thought to be $RuO.NH_2$[300].

Ammines

The ammine complexes $\mathbf{RuO_2(NH_3)_2(OH)_2}$, $\mathbf{[RuO_2(NH_3)_2(H_2O)_2]Cl_2}$ and $\mathbf{RuO_2(Et_3N)_2(OH)_2}$ have already been mentioned[180] (p. 152), although their formulation as 'ruthenyl' complexes has not been fully established. No complexes analogous to the very stable $(OsO_2(NH_3)_4)Cl_2$ have been reported. Fletcher and coworkers mention that oxidation of 'ruthenium red' (p. 168) at 100° with ceric sulphate in acid solution gives colourless solutions which may contain the $[RuO_2(OH)_2(NH_2)_2]^{2-}$ ion[96]; however, terminal amido groups are as yet unknown in coordination chemistry and such a species seems unlikely. A more likely formulation would be $[RuO_4(NH_3)_2]^{2-}$.

Ruthenium (V)

No complexes are known with Group V donors.

Ruthenium (IV)

Ammines

The only examples are the rather ill-defined oxy species $\mathbf{RuOX_2.2NH_3}$ (X = Cl, Br, I) and $\mathbf{RuO(OH)_2.2NH_3.2H_2O}$ (see Table 4.2)[293]; they are presumably polymeric.

Complexes with heterocyclic bases

Ru py$_2$Cl$_4$ can be made from ruthenium trichloride and pyridinium chloride in the presence of hydrogen peroxide; it forms yellow crystals, sparingly soluble in water, but soluble in hydrochloric acid to give a pink solution which becomes emerald green on heating[49]. **RuCl$_4$ bipy** and **RuCl$_4$ phen** are also known (Table 4.4)[74].

The reaction of phosphorus trichloride or tribromide with ruthenium tetroxide yields $\mathbf{RuO_2.PCl_3}$ and $\mathbf{RuO_2.\ PBr_3}$[128].

Ruthenium (III)

$\mathbf{RuO(NH_2)}$ is said to be formed by decomposition of the reaction product of ruthenium tetroxide and ammonia[300].

Ammines

These are summarized in Table 4.2.

$\mathbf{[Ru(NH_3)_6]^{3+}}$ salts are most easily prepared by the treatment of the hexammine ruthenium (II) species with chlorine[187]. Most of the salts are colourless: a chloride, nitrate, sulphate and bromide have been reported[108]. The salts are very stable toward acids, even to concentrated mineral acids, but with alkalis they give curious colour reactions: they become yellow and evolve ammonia, and on subsequent addition of hydrochloric or nitric acids bright blue solutions are obtained. These reactions are not observed with the pentammines, although both the hexammines and the pentammines give the intensely coloured 'ruthenium red' on boiling with alkali in the presence of oxygen.

Magnetic susceptibility measurements have been made on the nitrate and the chloride from 80 to 300°K[40,90,90a] (see Table 4.11). No electron spin resonance signals could be observed from powdered samples of the pure trichloride, but resonance was observed for $[Ru(NH_3)_6]Cl_3$ in solid solutions (dilution 1:200) in $[Co(NH_3)_6]Cl_3$; three sets of principal g values were obtained, apparently due to the presence of three environments of $[Ru(NH_3)_6]^{3+}$ ion in the crystal, each of the three having different rhombic distortions and hence different g values. The hyperfine structure arising from the ^{99}Ru and ^{101}Ru isotopes was resolved and the nuclear spin of these isotopes shown to be $\frac{5}{2}$. Electron spin resonance was also observed in the mercuric chloride adduct, $[Ru(NH_3)_6]Cl_3 . 3HgCl_2$[119].

For the electron-transfer reaction

$$[Ru(NH_3)_6]^{3+} + Cr^{2+} \rightarrow [Ru(NH_3)_6]^{2+} + Cr^{3+}$$
$$(k = 1 \times 10^2 \text{ M}^{-1} \text{ sec}^{-1} \text{ at } 25°)$$

a 1:1 stoichiometry was established and a specific rate constant measured; although the reaction is fairly fast it is some eighty times slower than that of chromous ion with $[Ru(NH_3)_5Cl]^{2+}$[82]. For reasons which are not clear, chloride ion accelerates the reaction, and in the presence of chloride the rate law becomes[83]

$$d[Ru^{II}]/dt = (k_1 + k_2[Cl^-])[Ru(NH_3)_6{}^{3+}][Cr^{2+}]$$

The potential of the couple $[Ru(NH_3)_6]^{3+}/[Ru(NH_3)_6]^{2+}$ was measured (0·214 v)[82]. The rate of exchange of deuterium (in acetic acid-d_1) with the hydrogen in the hexammino ruthenium (III) ion has been measured and compared with rates found for other hexammines (see also p. 290)[241]. Infrared and Raman spectra of $[Ru(NH_3)_6]Cl_3$ above 200 cm^{-1} have been reported (cf. Table 3.7, p. 106)[117a] and the electronic spectrum has been measured[40].

Substituted ruthenium (III) **ammines**. Many are known (see Table 4.2); the most important are the halo- and aquopentammines.

$[Ru(NH_3)_5Cl]Cl_2$ (yellow needles, readily soluble in hot water) can be made by the prolonged action of chlorine on $[Ru(NH_3)_6]Cl_2$ or from the hexammine and hydrochloric acid[108,187]. The x-ray crystal structure determination shows that the metal–nitrogen distance is $2{\cdot}09 \pm 0{\cdot}09$ Å and the metal–chlorine distance is $2{\cdot}34 \pm 0{\cdot}05$ Å[248]. The magnetic susceptibility has been studied over a temperature range (see Table 4.11)[90a], and the electron spin resonance absorption of the powdered solid gives a broad line, the broadening probably being due to the very large anisotropy of the crystal[119]. The electronic absorption spectrum has been measured[40].

The rates of acid and base hydrolysis of $[Ru(NH_3)_5Cl]^{2+}$ have been measured; under comparable conditions, the base hydrolysis is some 10^6 times faster than the acid, a situation found also for cobalt (III) chloropentammine ion but not for rhodium (III) and chromium (III) chloropentammines, where the difference in rates of acid and base hydrolysis is much less. The acid hydrolysis of the ruthenium complex cannot be explained by a single mechanism—the rate law corresponds to an opposed first- and second-order reaction

$$[Ru(NH_3)_5Cl]^{2+} + H_2O \underset{k_2}{\overset{k_1}{\rightleftharpoons}} [Ru(NH_3)_5H_2O]^{3+} + Cl^-$$

The equilibrium constant for the acid hydrolysis process was obtained as a function of the temperature[31]. In aqueous sulphuric acid a sulphato pentammine is formed, the mechanism being[31]

$$[Ru(NH_3)_5Cl]^{2+} + H_2O \rightarrow [Ru(NH_3)_5(H_2O)]^{3+} + Cl^- \quad \text{(Slow)}$$

$$[Ru(NH_3)_5(H_2O)]^{3+} + SO_4^{2-} \rightarrow [Ru(NH_3)_5SO_4]^+ + H_2O \quad \text{(Fast)}$$

The fast base hydrolysis is likely to proceed via a conjugate base mechanism in which an amido complex is formed as an intermediate:

$$[Ru(NH_3)_5Cl]^{2+} + OH^- \rightarrow [Ru(NH_3)_4(NH_2)Cl]^+ + H_2O$$

and in the case of this reaction (but not in the case of the analogous reactions with cobalt and chromium pentammines, in which π bonding from the amide group is likely to be important) a seven-coordinate intermediate may well be involved; the low base hydrolysis rate for $[Rh(NH_3)_5Cl]^{2+}$ is explicable on the basis of a low ammine acidity[241] and the presence of large ligand-field effects[31]. For the reaction

$$[Ru(NH_3)_5Cl]^{2+} + Cr^{2+}(aq) + H_2O \rightarrow [Ru(NH_3)_5H_2O]^{2+} + CrCl^{2+}(aq)$$

the specific rate constant at 25° is about 8×10^3 M^{-1} sec^{-1} [82], compared with 1×10^2 M^{-1} sec^{-1} for the chromous ion reduction of $(Ru(NH_3)_6)^{3+}$. This comparative similarity in rate constant is in striking contrast to the behaviour for the reduction by chromous ion of $[Co(NH_3)_5Cl]^{2+}$, which is some 10^{10} times faster than the reduction of $[Co(NH_3)_6]^{3+}$. This difference is thought to arise from the fact that it is a t_{2g} electron which is added to ruthenium (III) and an e_g electron to cobalt (III); since the t_{2g} electron density lies between the ligand orbitals there is less interelectronic repulsion than with the e_g electron which lies on the metal–ligand axes[83]. There is substantial evidence for the transfer of chlorine directly from ruthenium to chromium in the reaction of $[Ru(NH_3)_5Cl]^{2+}$ with chromous ion[83].

$[Ru(NH_3)_5Br]Br_2$ and **$[Ru(NH_3)_5I]I_2$** can be made from the hexammine or chloropentammine and the halogen acid[40,108]; they are orange and much less soluble in water than the corresponding chloropentammines. Their absorption spectra have been measured[40]. The rates of formation of these complexes from the aquopentammine and bromide and iodide ions have been measured[82].

$[Ru(NH_3)_5(H_2O)]Cl_3$ (yellow crystals) can be made by the action of hydrochloric acid on $[Ru(NH_3)_6]Cl_2$[187]. The magnetic moment of the dithionate salt is 1·95 BM at room temperatures[109]; electronic spectra of the cation have been measured[40] and the oxidation potential of the couple $[Ru(NH_3)_5(H_2O)]^{3+}/[Ru(NH_3)_5(H_2O)]^{2+}$ was found to be $0{\cdot}11 \pm 0{\cdot}01$ v[82].

Ruthenium red. This intensely red species can be made in a number of ways, of which the commonest is the aerial oxidation of $[Ru(NH_3)_6]Cl_3$. The complex has been isolated and it has been suggested that it is a trimer, with a linear Ru—O—Ru—O—Ru system[96]:

$$[(NH_3)_5Ru^{III}—O—Ru^{IV}(NH_3)_4—O—Ru^{III}(NH_3)_5]^{6+}$$

The complex is diamagnetic, and the diamagnetism can be explained by the use of polycentric molecular orbitals similar to those used for $[Ru_2OCl_{10}]^{4-}$. The infrared spectrum of the complex and its deuterate have been interpreted on the basis of this structure[64c]. Oxidation of ruthenium red with ceric ion gives the paramagnetic brown cation:

$$[(NH_3)_5Ru^{IV}—O—Ru^{III}(NH_3)_4—O—Ru^{IV}(NH_3)_5]^{7+}$$

in which the magnetic moment per ruthenium atom is 1·13 BM at room temperatures[96]. Ruthenium red can be seen in solutions as dilute as 1 p.p.m., and the substance will dye animal fibres red. It has been used as a sensitive test for the element.

Amine complexes*

These are somewhat rare for ruthenium (III) though common for the divalent state.

[Ru en_2(OH)Cl]Cl (deep brown) is formed by reaction of ruthenium trichloride with ethylenediamine; hydrochloric acid reacts with this complex to give **[Ru en_2Cl_2]Cl** and potassium iodide gives **[Ru en_2(OH)I]I**[225]. **[Ru$(EtNH_2)_4Cl_2$]Cl** and **[Ru$(EtNH_2)_4$Cl-(OH)]Cl** can be made from ruthenium trichloride and ethylamine[225].

Complexes with heterocyclic bases

A number of ruthenium (III) **pyridine** complexes are known (see Table 4.3), but in none of these does the pyridine: metal ratio exceed 4:1; this is also the case with all the other platinum metals (it may be sterically difficult for six pyridine groups to be bonded to each metal atom). The infrared spectra of Ru py_3Cl_3 and pyH[Ru py_2Cl_4][286] and of their methyl substituted analogues have been measured.

A wide range of *o*-phenanthroline and 2,2′-bipyridyl complexes of ruthenium (III) with other ligands in mixed complexes have been made, and these are summarized in Table 4.4. The tris complexes are of particular interest.

[Ru $bipy_3$]Cl_3 has been made by oxidation of [Ru $bipy_3$]Cl_2 with ceric ion[75] but has not been isolated from solution. Oxidation potentials for the $[Ru\ bipy_3]^{3+}/[Ru\ bipy_3]^{2+}$ couple have been measured at different temperatures and ionic strengths, and from these results thermodynamic data for the reaction

$$[Ru\ bipy_3]^{3+} + \tfrac{1}{2} H_2 \rightarrow [Ru\ bipy_3]^{2+} + H^+$$

deduced[104].

Electron-transfer reactions of $[Ru\ bipy_3]^{3+}$. As with the corresponding bipyridyl complexes of osmium, these are often very fast and only lower limits for the second-order rate constants have been determined. In all these cases cited in Table 4.5 it is likely that the reactions are of the outer-sphere activated complex type[113]. Curiously, although $[Ru\ bipy_3]^{3+}$ will oxidize $[Fe(CN)_6]^{4-}$ and $[Fe\ bipy_3]^{2+}$, it will not (unlike $[IrCl_6]^{2-}$) oxidize ferrous haemoglobin and myoglobin, but

* See Table 4.6.

instead reacts preferentially with other groups on the globin molecule[105].

[Ru phen$_3$]Cl$_3$ (red crystals) can be made by oxidation of [Ru phen$_3$]Cl$_2$ with chlorine[75].

Spectrophotometric evidence for the intermediate existence of **[Ru bipy]$^{3+}$aq** and **[Ru phen]$^{3+}$aq** in the formation of [Ru bipy$_3$]$^{2+}$ and [Ru phen$_3$]$^{2+}$ from the bases and ruthenium trichloride has been presented; [Ru bipy$_2$](ClO$_4$)$_3$.3H$_2$O was isolated and evidence for the existence of [Ru^{IV} bipy$_2$Cl$_2$]$^{2+}$ found[223].

The complexes [RuL$_3$]$^{3+}$ (L = 2,2′-bipyridyl, 5-methyl-*o*-phenanthroline, 5,6-dimethyl- and 3,5,6,8-tetramethyl-*o*-phenanthroline) will chemiluminesce when added to an aqueous solution of a base; in the case of the trisbipyridyl complex the orange chemiluminescence was clearly visible in a dimly-lit room, although it lasted no longer than one second[138b].

No ruthenium (III) **nitro** or **nitrosyl** complexes are known.

Hydrazine complexes

Addition of hydrazine to K$_2$[RuCl$_5$(H$_2$O)] or K$_2$[RuCl$_5$] is said to yield a wide range of paramagnetic binuclear hydrazine complexes such as [Ru$_2$(N$_2$H$_4$)$_5$Cl$_2$]Cl$_4$[13]; however, x-ray examination of the latter showed it to be [Ru(NH$_3$)$_5$Cl]Cl$_2$[248], so there is some doubt as to whether much reliance is to be placed on the original reports. Some hydrazine species may, however, be present since some of the products are explosive. It is also possible that they may be nitrogeno ammine complexes, the method of preparation being similar to that recently reported for salts of [Ru(NH$_3$)$_5$N$_2$]$^+$[6a]. There is some evidence for the existence of a 1:2 ruthenium:azide complex[297a].

Phthalocyanine complexes

The reaction of phthalonitrile with ruthenium trichloride gives **PcCl.RuCl** (PcH$_2$ = C$_{32}$H$_{18}$N$_8$) which in hydrochloric acid yields PcClRu(HSO$_4$)[22]; a similar reaction gives PcRuCl.C$_6$H$_4$(CN)$_2$[172]. The electronic absorption and infrared (700–5000 cm^{-1}) spectra of the complex were measured, and the adducts PcRuCl.C$_6$H$_4$(CN)-(CONH$_2$) and PcRuCl.py$_n$ (n = 4 or 5) were made[172].

Biguanide complexes [Ru(Bgh)$_3$] X$_3$

These can be made from the ligand and ruthenium trichloride; the unit cell dimensions of the sulphate have been determined[112a].

Miscellaneous nitrogen donor complexes

Pyrazole (Pz) and 3,5-dimethylpyrazole (DPz) react with blue 'ruthenium dichloride' solutions to give $(RuCl_3Pz_3)^-$, $RuCl_2Pz_3$-(H_2O) and $[RuCl_3(DPz)_3]^-$[178a].

Phosphine, arsine and stibine complexes

These are listed in Table 4.7. The main types are $RuX_3(LR_3)_3$ (X = Cl, Br; L = P, As)[54,76], $[RuCl_4(PR_3)_2]^-$[288] and $RuX_3(LR_3)_2(MeOH)$[288]. The diarsine complexes $[Ru\,diars_2X_2]^+$ have magnetic moments between 1·83 and 1·97 BM at room temperatures—unlike their osmium analogues they cannot be oxidized to the tetravalent state[236]. The infrared spectrum of $[Ru\,diars_2Cl_2](ClO_4)$ suggests that this has a *trans* structure[189].

No *hydrides* of ruthenium (III) phosphines or arsines are known.

Ruthenium (II)

Nitrogeno complexes

$[\mathbf{Ru(NH_3)_5N_2]I_2}$ is claimed as the product of reaction between ruthenium trichloride and an aqueous solution of hydrazine hydrate. The complex is diamagnetic and the infrared spectrum suggests that a nitrogen molecule is coordinated to the ruthenium[6a] †. Molecular nitrogen reacts with methanolic solutions of ruthenium trichloride or $Ru(OH)Cl_3$ in the presence of zinc powder to give a ruthenium (II) nitrogen° complex[277a].

Ammines*

$[\mathbf{Ru(NH_3)_6]Cl_2}$ can be made by the action of zinc dust with ammonia and ammonium chloride on ruthenium trichloride solution. The complex forms orange crystals which are very sensitive to aerial oxidation[187]. The infrared spectrum has been measured[87a].

Studies of the reduction of ruthenium (III) pentammino species with chromous ion show that $[\mathbf{Ru(NH_3)_5}]^{2+}$ or $[\mathbf{Ru(NH_3)_5(H_2O)}]^{2+}$ is formed[82], and that this species is comparatively stable in aqueous solution in the absence of oxygen[83].

Decomposition of $[Ru(NH_3)_6]^{2+}$ and $[Ru(NH_3)_5H_2O]^{2+}$ species on standing in aqueous solution yields at least three unidentified products. One of these, which is formed in strong acid, is bright blue and comparatively stable in air although, very remarkably, it is oxidized by cobalt (III) hexammines[83]. This may be the blue product

* See Table 4.2.

† X-ray studies show that the Ru—N—N group is linear, with Ru—N = 2·11Å and N—N = 1·12Å[27b].

obtained by boiling $[Ru(NH_3)_6]^{3+}$ with alkali followed by hydrochloric acid (p. 166).

The reduction of perchlorate ion by $[Ru(NH_3)_6]^{2+}$ and by $[Ru(NH_3)_5H_2O]^{2+}$ follows in each case the rate law

$$-d[Ru^{II}]/dt = k[Ru^{II}][ClO_4^-]$$

This is unlikely to be an electron-transfer process since even sodium dissolved in liquid ammonia will not reduce perchlorate ions. A mechanism involving a seven-coordinate ruthenium (IV) oxy intermediate was proposed, this intermediate being reduced by ruthenium (II) to ruthenium (III)[83].

The reduction of the halopentammines (chloride, bromide, iodide) of cobalt (III) by $[Ru(NH_3)_6]^{2+}$ was also studied and found to follow the rate law

$$\text{Rate} = k[Ru^{II}][Co^{III}]$$

For the chloro complex, the specific rate (at 25° and infinite dilution) was 17 M^{-1} sec^{-1}. Some evidence for a direct group-transfer mechanism was found for the reaction with cobalt (III) iodopentammine[83].

Most of the known substituted ruthenium (II) ammines, apart from the aquopentammine[82], all contain coordinated sulphite, sulphur dioxide, nitrogen or nitrosyl groups (see Table 4.2). A large number of nitrosyl ammines are known (Table 4.2); the crystal structure of *trans*-$[Ru(NH_3)_4(NO)(OH)]Cl_2$ is discussed on p. 174.

Amine complexes

Apart from one mixed ethylenediamine complex with *o*-phenanthroline and the trisethylenediamine complexes mentioned below, all of these contain the nitrosyl group and are listed in Table 4.6.

[Ru en$_3$]Br$_2$ can be made from ruthenium trichloride and ethylenediamine in the presence of zinc powder (the iodide and perchlorate were also made)[6,188]. Infrared spectra of these and the deuterated derivatives were recorded and band assignments proposed[6,188].

Complexes with heterocyclic bases*

A number of mixed **pyridine** *o*-phenanthroline and 2,2′-bipyridyl complexes are listed in Table 4.3—in no case does the pyridine:ruthenium (II) ratio exceed 2:1.

[Ru bipy$_3$]Cl$_2$ can be made by the action of the ligand on ruthenium trichloride at 250°[39]. The reaction is apparently

$$2RuCl_3 + 8C_{10}H_8N_2 \rightarrow 2[Ru(C_{10}H_8N_2)_3]Cl_2 + C_{20}H_{14}N_4 + 2HCl$$

* See Tables 4.3 and 4.4.

The complex forms red crystals which are very soluble in water; the solid hexahydrate does not lose its water until 200°. A bromide, iodide, perchlorate and nitrate are known (all hexahydrated), while the hydroxide is an octahydrate and the carbonate a decahydrate. Partial asymmetric synthesis of the complex was achieved by using $K_2[RuCl_5(H_2O)]$ as starting material together with the ligand and optically active tartrates, a method also used to make optically active salts of $[Ru\ phen_3]^{2+}$ and $[Os\ bipy_3]^{2+}$ [193].

Electron-transfer reactions of $[Ru\ bipy_3]^{2+}$ (see also Table 4.5). Kinetics of reduction of persulphate ion by $[Ru\ bipy_3]^{2+}$ in aqueous solution were studied under various conditions of temperature and ionic strength. Under equivalent conditions this reaction proceeds some 5,000 times faster than the persulphate oxidation of $[Os\ bipy_3]^{2+}$, and it was suggested that this arose from the difference in redox potentials of the $[Ru\ bipy_3]^{3+}/[Ru\ bipy_3]^{2+}$ and $[Os\ bipy_3]^{3+}/[Os\ bipy_3]^{2+}$ systems [154]. Studies on oxidation of ruthenium (II) bipyridyl and *o*-phenanthroline complexes by thallic ion suggest that a thallium (II) intermediate is involved [222a].

$[Ru\ phen_3]Cl_2$ can be made in the same way as the bipy complex [75,193]. Oxidation of *d*- or *l*-$[Ru\ phen_3]^{2+}$ ion with ceric ion gives the corresponding optically active blue $[Ru\ phen_3]^{3+}$ which can be reduced back to $[Ru\ phen_3]^{2+}$ without change of optical configuration [77]. The circular dichroism of $[Ru\ phen_3]^{2+}$ in solution has been measured [197].

Absorption and luminescence spectra and mean lifetimes of the luminescence of $[Ru\ bipy_3]Cl_2$ and $[Ru\ phen_3]I_2$ were measured. The energy levels were analysed and possible applications of the compounds for lasers discussed [65,247].

$[Ru\ terpy_2]Cl_2$ has been prepared by fusing the ligand with ruthenium trichloride and metallic ruthenium. It forms red crystals which are unaffected by acids or alkalis [227].

Nitro complexes

All the known ruthenium nitro complexes also contain the nitrosyl group*—it is remarkable that unsubstituted complexes of the form $[M(NO_2)_6]^{2-}$ or $[M(NO_2)_6]^{3-}$ are not known for either ruthenium or osmium, since the hexanitro iridium (III) and rhodium (III)

* Two nitro species of uncertain composition have been claimed [29,164] but these are very likely to contain nitrosyl groups also. The carbonyl nitro species $Ru(CO)_2(NO_2)_2$ has, however, recently been made [43a] (cf. Table 4.10).

complexes are very stable. The known nitrosyl nitro and nitrosyl nitrato nitro complexes are summarized in Table 4.9, and the crystal structure of $Na_2[Ru(NO)(OH)(NO_2)_4]$ is considered on p. 175. The salts made from ruthenium trichloride and nitrites and formulated as $M^I_2[Ru(NO_2)_5]$[164] are in fact the nitrosyl nitro complexes M^I_2-$[Ru(NO)(OH)(NO_2)_4]$[283].

Nitrosyl complexes

Ruthenium is unique in that it forms more nitrosyl complexes than any other element; in most of these the metal is formally in the divalent state, assuming the nitric oxide to function as a three-electron donor. The Ru(NO) group in such species is extraordinarily stable, whether the complex be anionic, neutral or cationic, and it is exceedingly difficult to break the ruthenium–nitrosyl bond by normal chemical substitution or oxidation–reduction methods. The reason for this stability is not clear; it is noteworthy that in the majority of such complexes, the other ligands present are not particularly good π acceptors, so it appears that ruthenium (II) is best stabilized when one good π-acceptor group is present. This is particularly the case for other ruthenium (II) ammines. The analogous osmium (II) nitrosyl species are easily oxidized, in line with the general tendency of third-row elements to prefer higher oxidation states than second-row elements.

Because of the large number of nitrosyl complexes of ruthenium (there are over a hundred) it is impracticable to deal with them all in this section. Table 4.9 provides a summary of information and gives cross-references where relevant. A few of the more important nitrosyl complexes are dealt with separately below; firstly, however, it is necessary to comment on the conflicting data which have been presented on the structures of ruthenium nitrosyls.

Structures of nitrosyl complexes. The available data are summarized in Table 4.8. Since the infrared spectra of the coordinated nitrosyl group in these complexes are all very similar[58a,190] it seems unlikely that the spread in ruthenium–nitrogen and nitrogen–oxygen distances should be so great; the x-ray determination for $K_2[Ru(NO)Cl_5]$ seems particularly suspect. The definitive structural data are clearly those for $Na_2[Ru(NO)(OH)(NO_2)_4]$ (see below), and it seems to the author that some other results given in Table 4.8 are to be regarded with some caution; no error limits are given, and the claims that the metal–nitrogen–oxygen angle in some of these complexes is less than 180° certainly needs further substantiation.

The structure of $\mathbf{Na_2[Ru(NO)(OH)(NO_2)_4]}$ has been obtained from neutron diffraction studies, and the results so obtained are among the most accurate bond parameters yet available for any of the compounds of these four platinum metals. The nitrosyl group is *trans* to the hydroxyl, and the various parameters are as follows: metal–nitro grouping, Ru—N = 2·079 ± 0·003 Å, N—O = 1·21 ± 0·005 Å, $\widehat{ONO}$ = 118°; metal–nitrosyl grouping, Ru—N = 1·748 ± 0·003 Å and N—O = 1·127 ± 0·007 Å (the Ru—N—O group is linear); metal–hydroxyl grouping, Ru—O = 1·950 ± 0·005 Å, O—H = 0·921 ± 0·06 Å and Ru—O—H = 108° ± 0·1° [283]. The difference in metal–nitrogen distances in the nitro and nitrosyl groupings is very striking and can be used as an argument for π bonding in the latter case. An earlier (two-dimensional) x-ray structural study of $K_2[Ru(NO)(OH)(NO_2)_4]$ indicated that the $\widehat{RuNO}$ angle was 170° [27], and it is likely that the report of an $\widehat{RuNO}$ angle of 150° in $[Ru(NH_3)_4(NO)(OH)]Cl_2$ is also in error (p. 209).

Nitrosyl halides

$\mathbf{[Ru(NO)X_3]_n aq}$ (X = Cl, Br, I) are probably all hydrated to various degrees. The chloride, which is dark red, can be made by evaporating a solution of ruthenium tetroxide in hydrochloric and nitric acids[163]; the bromide can be made in a similar fashion[159] and the iodide (which is supposedly anhydrous) from the chloride and hydriodic acid[159]. A compound claimed to be $H[Ru(NO)Cl_3(H_2O)_2]$, made from ruthenium tetroxide, nitric acid and hydrochloric acid[322], is almost certainly $[Ru(NO)Cl_3]_n aq$, since it is diamagnetic (the formulation as an acid requires it to be a paramagnetic species of ruthenium (I)).

$\mathbf{K_2[Ru(NO)X_5]}$ X = Cl, Br, I) can be made from $[Ru(NO)X_3]_n aq$ and the appropriate potassium halides[163]; ammonium, rubidium and caesium salts are also known. The solubilities of the salts at 25° (g/100 ml of water) of $M^I_2[Ru(NO)Cl_5]$ are K, 12; NH_4, 5; Rb, 0·6; Cs, 0·2. The x-ray crystal structure of the potassium salt indicates that the metal–nitrosyl group is linear; the Ru—Cl distance is 2·35 Å (see Table 4.9)[175]. Infrared spectra of $K_2[Ru(NO)X_5]$ (X = Cl, Br, I) have been measured (both ^{14}N- and ^{15}N-substituted) from 4000 to 200 cm^{-1} [58a,72a,103a,221b,221d].

The hydrolysis of $[Ru(NO)Cl_5]^{2-}$ yields, as the first products, $[Ru(NO)Cl_4(H_2O)]^-$ and $[Ru(NO)(OH)Cl_4]^{2-}$. Measurements of the electronic absorption spectra of these and other products were made[284a].

The kinetics of oxidation of $(NH_4)_2[Ru(NO)Cl_5]$ with periodate have been studied. The overall reaction is given as[115]

$$(NH_4)_2[Ru(NO)Cl_5] + 14\,KIO_4 \rightarrow RuO_4 + 2\tfrac{1}{2}\,Cl_2 + 14\,KIO_3 + 2\,HNO_3 + NO_2 + 3\,H_2O$$

It was found that sodium bismuthate was a faster oxidant in this reaction[115]. The heat of solution of $(NH_4)_2[Ru(NO)Cl_5]$ in water has been measured[171] and the hydrolysis of the complex anion studied[284a].

Aquo–chloro species of the form $[Ru(NO)Cl_n(H_2O)_{5-n}]^{(4-n)+}$ are also known (cf. Table 4.9).

Miscellaneous nitrosyl complexes

$\mathbf{K_2[Ru(NO)(NCS)_5]}$ can be made by the action of potassium thiocyanate on $K_2[Ru(NO)Cl_5]$. The chemical-shift position in the ^{14}N nuclear magnetic resonance absorption of an aqueous solution of the complex compared with those found in other thiocyanates suggests that the thiocyanate group was bonded to the ruthenium through its nitrogen atom, an interesting result because most other platinum metal thiocyanates are sulphur bonded[146].

Reaction of nitric oxide with $Ru(Et_2NCS_2)_3$ yields $\mathbf{Ru(NO)(Et_2NCS_2)_3}$[200]. A recent x-ray study of this shows that there are two bidentate dithiocarbamate ligands (Ru—S = 2·415 ± 0·005 Å) and one monodentate dithiocarbamate group (Ru—S = 2·398 ± 0·005 Å) *cis* to the nitrosyl group, giving an octahedral structure[70a]. The Ru—N distance is 1·72 Å[70a] (see also Table 4.8).

The only example reported of an unsubstituted nitrosyl is of $\mathbf{[Ru(NO)_5]_n}$, made by the action of nitric oxide under pressure on ruthenium pentacarbonyl[205]. However, the analyses of the compound were unsatisfactory, and the complex could have been a carbonyl nitrosyl such as $Ru(CO)_2(NO)_2$ or perhaps an analogue of $Fe(NO)_4$[118,206]. The reaction of $Ru_3(CO)_{12}$ with moist nitric oxide gives a brown material which may be $Ru(CO)_2(NO_2)_2$[43a] or could contain nitrosyl groups.

Infrared spectra have been measured for a number of ruthenium (II) nitrosyl species and discussed in terms of the *trans* effect of the (NO^+) group[72a,221a,284], and solvent effects on N—O stretching frequencies in some ruthenium (II) nitrosyl phosphine complexes were measured[87]. The thermal stability of certain ruthenium nitrosyls has been studied[284a], and extraction of $[Ru(NO)(OH)(NO_2)_4]^{2-}$ by amines effected[321a].

Reduction of nitrosyl ruthenium (II) **complexes.** Polarographic experiments on ruthenium nitrosyl chloro and nitrosyl nitrato complexes show a five-electron reduction at the dropping electrode, and slow chemical reductions to as yet unspecified products may be achieved with hydrazine[156b]. Treatment of $K_2[Ru(NO)Cl_5]$ or $K_2[Ru(NO)(OH)(NO_2)_4]$ with stannous chloride is said to give binuclear amido complexes such as $K_3[Ru_2(NH_2)X_8H_2O)]$[48]; reduction of $[Ru(NO)Cl_3]_n$ with zinc is said to give $[Ru(NH_2)$-$Cl(H_2O)]_n$, which is paramagnetic[322]; and reduction of $[Ru(NO)$-$(OH)_3]_n$ with formaldehyde yields $[Ru_2H_2(NO)(OH)_3]aq$[48]. None of these formulations is convincing and clearly this is a field which should be more fully investigated.

Phthalocyanine complexes. The ruthenium (II) species **PcRu.2C$_6$H$_5$-NH$_2$** ($PcH_2 = C_{32}H_{18}N_8$) has been prepared by the reaction of aniline with $PcRuCl.C_6H_4(CN)_2$. It is purple, and its infrared and electronic absorption spectra were recorded[172]. Other adducts of ruthenium(II) phthalocyanine were also made[184b].

Phosphine, arsine and stibine complexes

These complexes are listed in Table 4.7. The main types are $RuX_2(LR_3)_4$ (X = Cl, Br; L = P, As)[54,76], $RuX_2(LR_3)_3$ (X = Cl, Br; L = P, Sb)[288], and the binuclear species $[Ru_2Cl_3(PR_3)_6]Cl$[51]. Chelating diphosphine ligands react with ruthenium trichloride to give *cis*- and *trans*-$RuCl_2$(diphosphine)$_2$[51], and the bidentate ligand diarsine gives *trans*-$RuCl_2$diars$_2$[189,236].

RuCl$_2$(PPh$_3$)$_3$ can be prepared by the action of an excess of triphenylphosphine on ruthenium trichloride[288]. The x-ray crystal structure analysis of this complex[186] shows that it is pentacoordinated, the metal atom lying close to the centre of a distorted square-based pyramid. The two *trans* chlorine atoms in the basal plane are each 2·387 ± 0·007 Å from the metal and the two metal–phosphorus distances in this plane are 2·38 Å, while the apical metal–phosphorus bond length is only 2·23 Å. The base is not quite flat, the phosphorus atoms being a little above and the chlorine atoms a little below the hypothetical plane. The next closest approach to the ruthenium, in the position *trans* to the apical phosphorus atom, is made by a hydrogen atom on a β carbon of a phenyl ring; the metal–hydrogen distance is approximately 2·59 Å, but there is no evidence for a metal–hydrogen interaction[186]. The conclusion drawn from this x-ray study was that the complex is a true pentacoordinated species, and that its stability arises from intramolecular blocking of the unused octahedral site by the phenyl ring[186].

[$Ru_2Cl_3(PEt_2Ph)_6$]Cl reacts with butyraldehyde to give propene[247a]

$$[Ru_2Cl_3(PEt_2Ph)_6]Cl + 4\ C_3H_7CHO \rightarrow 2RuCl_2(CO)(PEt_2Ph)_3 + 2C_3H_6 + 2C_3H_7CH_2OH$$

Catalytic activity of ruthenium (II) phosphines. Both $RuCl_2(PPh_3)_4$ and $RuCl_2(PPh_3)_3$ dissociate in benzene–ethanol solutions and lose a molecule of phosphine. The vacant coordination site is probably occupied by a weakly bound solvent molecule[85]:

$$RuCl_2(PPh_3)_4 \underset{-S}{\overset{S}{\rightleftharpoons}} RuCl_2(PPh_3)_3(S) + PPh_3$$

$$RuCl_2(PPh_3)_3(S) \underset{-S}{\overset{+S}{\rightleftharpoons}} RuCl_2(PPh_3)_2(S)_2$$

$$RuCl_2(PPh_3)_3 \underset{-S}{\overset{S}{\rightleftharpoons}} RuCl_2(PPh_3)_2(S)_2 + PPh_3$$

S = Solvent molecule

As with the similar rhodium (III) complexes the dissociation probably occurs because of the strong *trans* effect of triphenylphosphine; the vacant site is then readily occupied in substitution reactions. Both of the solution species above will catalyse the homogeneous reduction by molecular hydrogen of alkenes and alkynes under ambient conditions (if ethanol is not present the reductions are very slow, unlike the corresponding rhodium (III) reactions). In the absence of olefins the solutions will catalyse the molecular hydrogen–deuterium exchange. It is very likely that the hydride $RuHCl(PPh_3)_3$ is involved in these reactions, since it is formed by passing molecular hydrogen into the solutions[85].

Hydrido phosphine, arsine and stibine complexes

These are listed in Table 4.7.

$RuHCl(PPh_3)_3$ can be made by the action of molecular hydrogen under normal conditions on solutions of $RuCl_2(PPh_3)_3$ or $RuCl_2(PPh_3)_4$; its infrared and proton magnetic resonance spectra were measured. As mentioned above, it is likely to be the catalytic intermediate in the hydrogenation reactions of its parent phosphine complexes[85]. All the other ruthenium (II) hydrides so far reported involve chelating diphosphine or diarsine ligands.

Reaction of *cis*-RuX_2(diphosphine)$_2$ (X = Cl, Br, I) with lithium aluminium hydride gives *trans*-**RuHX(diphosphine)$_2$** (a similar change of configuration was observed with the osmium analogues); the products are colourless or pale yellow. In the case of RuHCl-(diphosphine)$_2$ the chloride is labile to substitution by other anionic X groups to give RuHX(diphosphine)$_2$ (X = I, NCS, CN, NO_2, H) (the chloride ligands in *cis*-$RuCl_2$(diphosphine)$_2$ are inert to substitution, perhaps due to steric blocking by phenyl groups). The *trans* configuration of the hydrido complexes was shown by dipole moment and proton magnetic resonance measurements. The infrared spectra were also measured and the ruthenium–hydrogen stretching frequencies assigned; they decreased in the sequence[52]: $I^- > Br^- > Cl^- > SCN^- > NO_2^- > CN^- > H^-$, and this series can be correlated with the *trans* effect of the ligand X. Variations of the metal–hydrogen stretching frequency with the nature of the chelating diarsine were also noted.

cis-**RuH_2(diphosphine)$_2$** (diphosphine = $Me_2P(CH_2)_2PMe_2$) can be prepared by the reaction between sodium naphthalene and *trans*-RuHBr(diphosphine)$_2$, or by reduction of *trans*-$RuCl_2$(diphosphine)$_2$ with molten potassium. The complex forms colourless crystals; the infrared spectrum, nuclear magnetic resonance and dipole moment support the *cis* assignment of configuration[53].

trans-**RuH_2(diphosphine)$_2$** was made by reaction of *trans*-RuHCl(diphosphine)$_2$ with lithium aluminium hydride; infrared, dipole moment and nuclear magnetic resonance measurements were made[52].

$Ru^{II}H(CH_2PMe.(CH_2)_2PMe_2)(PMe_2(CH_2)_2PMe_2)$ was prepared by reducing *trans*-$RuCl_2$(diphosphine)$_2$ with sodium naphthalene and then heating the product (see also p. 187). The complex is said to have dual properties, since it may be regarded as a tautomer of the above hydridic formulation and of Ru^0(diphosphine)$_2$. Its chemical properties are consistent with the formulation as a zerovalent complex since with hydrogen chloride a mole of hydrogen is evolved:

$$Ru^0\,(\text{diphosphine})_2 + 2HCl \rightarrow H_2 + cis\text{-}Ru^{II}Cl_2(\text{diphosphine})_2$$

but the physical properties (infrared and nuclear magnetic resonance spectra and the dipole moment) all suggest the hydridic formulation, one proton having been removed from the methyl group of one of the diphosphine ligands[53]. The tautomerism envisaged is given in Figure 4.5.

The complex [**Ru(QAS)Br$_2$**] (QAS = tris-[*o*-diphenylarsinophenyl-arsine], made from $[Ru(NO)Br_3]_n$ and the ligand, has been shown by

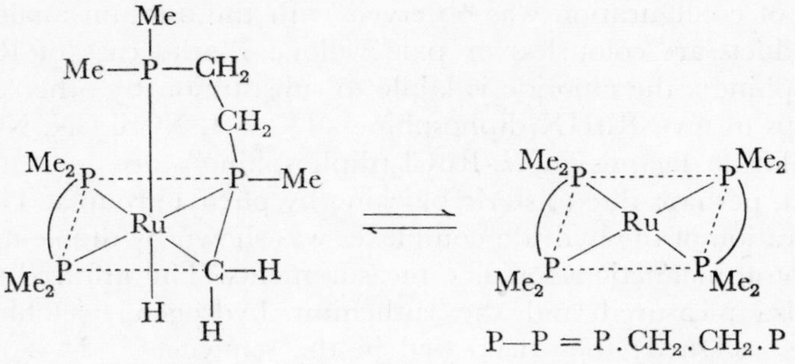

Figure 4.5 Tautomerism in Ru (diphosphine)$_2$

P—P = P.CH$_2$.CH$_2$.P

x-ray crystal structure analysis to be octahedral; the ruthenium–bromine distances are 2·615 ± 0·005 Å and ruthenium–arsenic bond lengths are 2·4 ± 0·1 Å[199a]. **$RuH_2(PF_3)_4$** is also reported[184a].

Nitrosyl phosphines, arsines and stibines*

A wide range of complexes of the form $Ru(NO)Cl_3L_2$ (L = phosphines, arsines and stibines) have been recently made, and their infrared spectra recorded[54a,87a].

Ruthenium (I)

$[Ru(NO)X_2]_n$ (X = Br, I) can be made by the action of nitric oxide at 230° on $[RuX_2(CO)_2]_n$; the chloro complex could not be obtained free of impurity[209]. The iodo complex reacts with ligands L (L = py, ½ bipy, Ph_2MeAs) to give **$[Ru(NO)I_2L_2]_2$**[155a].

Ruthenium (O)

The known examples are Ru(diphosphine)$_2$ (p. 179), $Ru(PF_3)_5$[184a], and **Na[RuH (diphosphine)$_2$]** was detected as an intermediate in the reaction between sodium naphthalene and *trans*-RuHBr(diphosphine)$_2$: it was not isolated[53].

Carbonyl, alkyl and aryl phosphines, arsines and stibines are considered below (p. 185. Tables 4.7 and 4.10).

GROUP IV DONORS

Almost all the ligands involved have carbon donor atoms and are π acceptors; there are also a few complexes containing the $(SnCl_3)^-$

* See Table 4.9 and reference 87.

group with tin as the donor atom. The organometallic chemistry of ruthenium in general closely resembles that of osmium but has been more extensively investigated than the latter. Most of the complexes contain divalent ruthenium.

Ruthenium (IV)

$\mathbf{K_2[Ru(CN)_6]}$ and $\mathbf{(amineH)_2[Ru(CN)_6]}$ have been reported but should certainly be reformulated as $K_4[Ru(CN)_6]$ and $(amineH)_2H_2$-$[Ru(CN)_6]$[118a].

$[(\pi\text{-}\mathbf{Cp})_2\mathbf{Ru(OH)}]^+$ is probably the product of oxidation of ruthenocene[186].

Allyl complexes

The two complexes in this section are bis-π-allyls and so are regarded as ruthenium (IV) complexes; as with the nitrosyl group, however, this is the formal oxidation state only.

$\mathbf{RuCl_2(C_{10}H_{16})}$ can be made from an ethanolic solution of ruthenium trichloride and isoprene; the material is reddish-brown and polymeric in nature. Preliminary x-ray results indicate that the coordination about the metal is approximately trigonal bipyramidal, the axial positions being occupied by two bridging chlorine atoms and the equatorial positions by a terminal chlorine atom and two π-allylic groups from the $(C_{10}H_{16})$ ligand[245b]. A solution of the compound in dichloromethane will react with carbon monoxide to give $\mathbf{Ru(CO)Cl_2(C_{10}H_{16})}$, and this species will then react in methanolic solution with pyridine to give $\mathbf{RuCl_2.py.(C_{10}H_{16})}$, and with further carbon monoxide to give $RuCl_2(CO)_4$[245b].

A related complex is $\mathbf{RuCl_2(C_{12}H)_{18}}$, dodeca-2,6,10-triene-1,12-diyl chlororuthenate (IV), which can be made from butadiene and ruthenium trichloride in 2-methoxyethanol; it forms yellow-brown prisms[231a]. A preliminary x-ray structure analysis shows that the ruthenium has approximately trigonal bipyramidal coordination with the two chlorine atoms in the axial positions (Figure 4.6). The chain ligand has been formed by the catalytic trimerization of butadiene, and it functions in the complex as a 'tridentate' molecule with two allyl and one olefinic donor centres[196]. This structure receives support from studies of the proton magnetic resonance of the compound[231a]. The ruthenium (II) species obtained by reduction of ruthenium

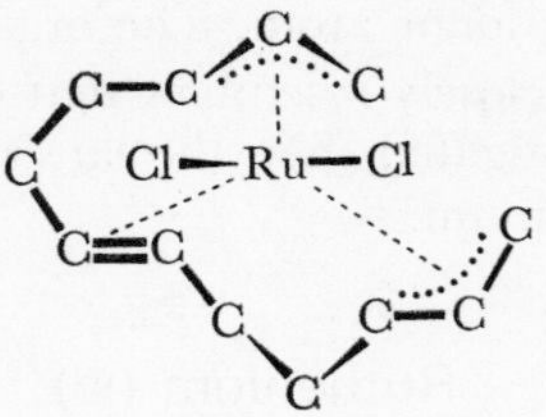

Figure 4.6 Molecular structure of $RuCl_2(C_{12}H_{18})$

trichloride with allyl alcohol is a powerful catalyst for inter- and intramolecular hydrogen-transfer reactions[231] of the type

$$2CH_2{=}CH.CH_2OH \rightarrow CH_2{=}CH.CH_3 + CH_2{=}CH.CHO + H_2O$$

$$CH_2{=}CH.CH_2OH \rightarrow CH_3.CH_2.CHO$$

Presumably an allyl complex of ruthenium (IV) or (III) is involved.

Ruthenium (III)

$Ru(CN)_3$ (green powder) is said to be formed when chlorine is passed into a solution of $K_4[Ru(CN)_6]$[184]; addition of ammonia to this yields **$Ru(CN)_3(NH_3)_2(H_2O)$**[184]. With sulphuric acid a solution of $K_4[Ru(CN)_6]$ gives **$Ru_2(CN)_5.H_2O$** as a blue powder[184].

$[Ru(CN)_6]^{3-}$ salts have not been isolated, but there is titrimetric, spectrophotometric and polarographic evidence for the existence of the ion; the oxidation potential of the $[Ru(CN)_6]^{3-}/[Ru(CN)_6]^{4-}$ couple is $-0{\cdot}86$ v[99].

Carbonyl complexes

$Ru(CO)Br_3(PPh_3)_2$ and $[Ru(CO)Cl_4py]^-$ have been reported (Table 4.10)[288].

Solutions of $[RuCl_5(H_2O)]^{2-}$ will absorb carbon monoxide to give **$[Ru(CO)Cl_5]^{2-}$**, and salts containing this anion have been isolated. At constant hydrochloric acid concentrations the formation of this carbonyl complex was found to obey a second-order rate law[130c]:

$$-d[Ru^{III}(CO)]/dt = k_1[Ru^{III}][CO]$$

The complex will readily absorb molecular hydrogen to give the ruthenium(II) species $[Ru(CO)Cl_4(H_2O)]^{2-}$ [130c] (see below).

Salts containing the **$[Ru(CO)Cl_4(H_2O)]^{2-}$** ion can be prepared by the reaction of 'ruthenium dichloride' solutions in hydrochloric acid with carbon monoxide, or by reaction of $[Ru(CO)Cl_5]^{2-}$ with molecular hydrogen[130c], or by the decarbonylation of formic acid with 'ruthenium dichloride' in hydrochloric acid[130b] (the kinetics of this latter reaction were studied[130b]). The complex functions as a catalyst for the exchange of deuterium with water and also for the hydration of acetylene[130c]. Solutions of $[Ru(CO)Cl_4(H_2O)]^{2-}$ as prepared by reaction of $(Ru(CO)Cl_5)^{2-}$ with molecular hydrogen reacts with carbon monoxide to yield $\mathbf{[Ru(CO)_2Cl_4]^{2-}}$, isolated as a yellow crystalline salt; this reacts with triphenylphosphine to give the neutral species $\mathbf{Ru(CO)_2Cl_2(PPh_3)_2}$[130c].

'Sandwich' compounds

Ruthenicinium salts containing the Cp_2Ru^+ cation can be made by the anodic oxidation of ruthenocene. The perchlorate and tri-iodide were isolated as pale yellow salts, and the electronic spectra and polarographic reduction properties were measured[240].

For *allyl complexes* see above, p. 181.

Stannous chloride complexes

Salts of $\mathbf{[RuCl_2(SnCl_3)_2]^-}$ can be precipitated from mixed solutions of ruthenium trichloride and stannous chloride. The electronic absorption spectra were recorded[320].

Ruthenium (II)

Cyanide complexes

$\mathbf{K_4[Ru(CN)_6]}$ can be made by the action of potassium cyanide on potassium ruthenate[151], or by boiling a solution of ruthenium trichloride with an excess of potassium cyanide until the solution loses its colour[151]; sodium, copper and silver salts have also been made, and the anhydrous free acid can be prepared by addition of hydrochloric acid and ether to the potassium salt. The electronic spectrum has been measured[216,262] and assignments proposed[116], and the infrared[218,229] and Raman spectra[218] have been recorded (see Table 3.12, p. 113). The infrared spectra of solid $H_4[Ru(CN)_6]$ and $D_4[Ru(CN)_6]$ have been measured and suggest that, as for ferrocyanic and osmocyanic acids, there are unsymmetrical (N—H···N) hydrogen bonds[86]; these measurements have been made over a temperature range[106]. Studies have been reported on the shifts in the electronic spectra of Prussian Blue caused by the substitution of Ru^{II} and Os^{II} for Fe^{II} in the lattice[262]. It is said that bromine reacts with aqueous solutions of $[Ru(CN)_4]^{4-}$ to give $[Ru(CN)_5H_2O]^{3-}$[186a].

$Ru(CN)_2$ can be made as a grey-green powder by addition of potassium cyanide to the blue 'ruthenium dichloride' solutions[261]; the product obtained by addition of ammonia to $Ru_2(CN)_5.H_2O$ is claimed to be **$NH_4[Ru_2(NH_3)_4(CN)_5]$**[184].

$K_2[Ru(NO)(CN)_5]$ is the only fully established nitrosyl cyanide complex of the platinum metals. It is a product of the complicated reaction between nitric acid and $K_4[Ru(CN)_6]$, and forms red-brown crystals; sodium, copper, silver, cobalt and nickel salts are also known[204a]. The infrared spectrum has been measured.

$K_2[Ru(CN)_2(CO)_2I_2]$ can be got from potassium cyanide and ruthenium carbonyl iodide[139].

$Ru(CN)_2bipy_2$ was prepared from sodium cyanide, bipyridyl and $K_2[RuCl_5(H_2O)]$ followed by reduction with bisulphite ion[274]. The proton affinity[274] and infrared spectrum have been measured[273]. The analogous species with *o*-phenanthroline could not be made.

Isocyanide complexes

Both *cis*- and *trans*-**$Ru(CNR)_4X_2$** (X = Cl, Br, I, CN; R = Me, Et, C_7H_7 and $C_{13}H_{11}$) can be made, and also polybromides and polyiodides such as **$RuBr_2I_9(CNC_7H_7)_4$**[201,202].

Carbonyl complexes

See Table 4.10.

Carbonyl halides. These are of the form **$Ru(CO)_4X_2$** (X = Cl, I) and **$[Ru(CO)_2X_2]_n$** (X = Cl, Br, I).

cis-**$Ru(CO)_4I_2$** can be made by the reaction between ruthenium triiodide and carbon monoxide (at 200 atmospheres pressure) at 170° in the presence of copper powder. The complex forms yellow crystals which sublime at 126°[63]. The x-ray crystal structure determination shows that the configuration is *cis*, the coordination being octahedral. The metal–iodine distance is 2·72 ± 0·1 Å, the metal–carbon distance 2·01 ± 0·06 Å and the carbon–oxygen distance 1·04 ± 0·05 Å[66]. The infrared spectrum also supports the *cis* assignment[63].

$Ru(CO)_4Cl_2$ can be made from carbon monoxide and $RuCl_2$-$C_{10}H_{16}$[245b]; for $[Ru(CO)_2Cl_4]^{2-}$, see p. 183.

$[Ru(CO)_2X_2]_n$ (X = Cl, Br, I) are made from the trihalides and carbon monoxide at 200° (see Table 4.10); with a wide variety of donor ligands L the iodo complex gives a series of species of the form

$Ru(CO)_2L_2I_2$, and the infrared spectrum of $[Ru(CO)_2I_2]_n$ indicates that this has a polymeric structure with bridging iodo groups[155].

Carbonyl phosphine complexes and hydrido carbonyl phosphines. These are summarized in Table 4.10 and some of their preparations and reactions in Figure 4.7. Both *cis*- and *trans*-**$RuX_2(CO)_2(PR_3)_2$** were made, the configurations being established by infrared measurements and dipole moment determinations[54]; the *cis* isomers were got by the action of the phosphine on ruthenium trichloride in the presence of 2-methoxyethanol (or in some cases potassium hydroxide). Infrared measurements have been made on some of the *cis* species with a view to locating the metal–carbonyl deformation modes, and these were found near 500 cm^{-1} [2a]. The *trans* isomers (which are less stable than the *cis*) were made by heating

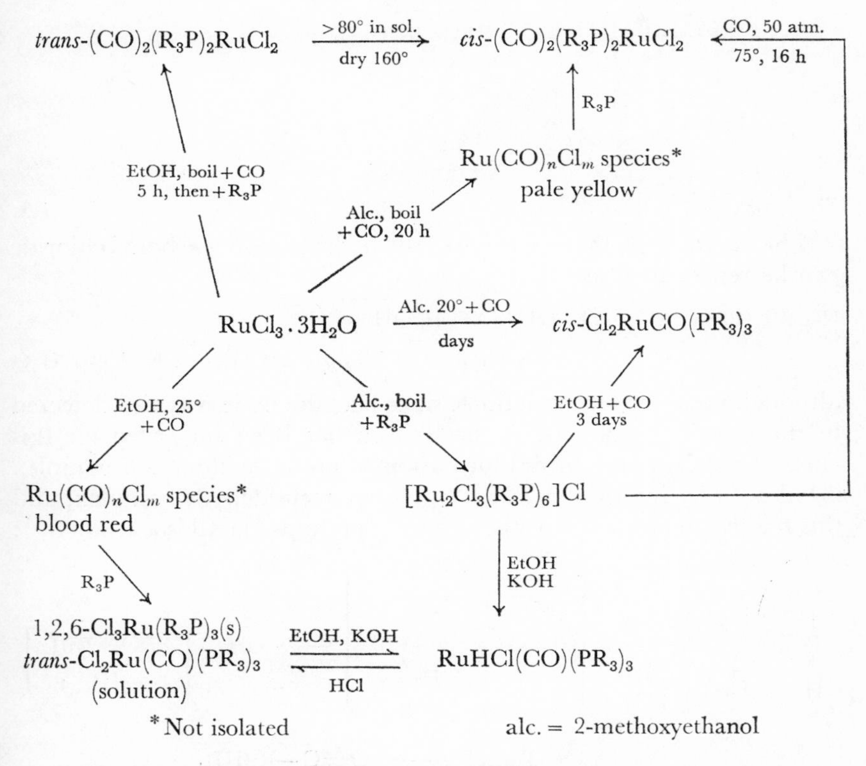

Figure 4.7 Reactions of ruthenium carbonyl phosphine complexes

an ethanolic solution of ruthenium trichloride with the tertiary phosphine and carbon monoxide. In addition monocarbonyl species of the form **RuHX(CO)(PR$_3$)$_3$** (X = Cl, Br, I) can be got from $[Ru_2Cl_3(PR_3)_6]Cl$ with ethanol in the presence of potassium hydroxide, the bromo and iodo complexes being made from $[Ru_2Cl_3(PR_3)_6]Cl$, potassium hydroxide and bromides or iodides in the presence of a high-boiling alcohol[54]. From these, dihalo species $RuX_2(CO)(PR_3)_3$ (X = Cl, I) can be made. Dipole moment and nuclear magnetic resonance studies suggested the configurations of the hydrido halo and dihalo complexes to be **1** and **2**.

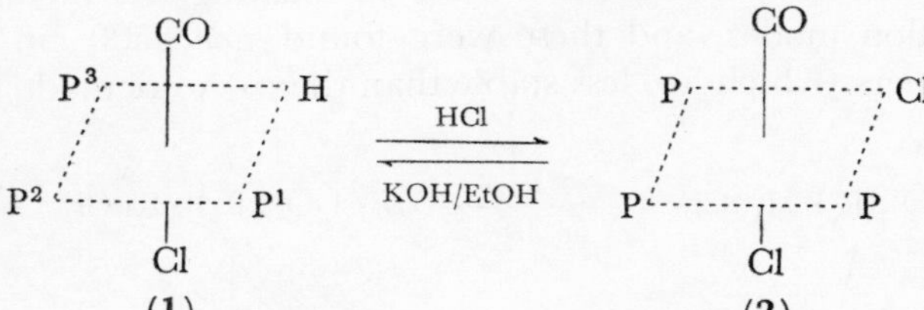
CO
P3
H
P2
P1
Cl
HCl
KOH/EtOH
CO
P
Cl
P
P
Cl

(1) (2)

Figure 4.8

The net reaction for formation of the hydrido monocarbonyl chloride can be represented as

$$[Ru_2Cl_3(PR_3)_6]Cl + 2\,KOH + 2\,C_2H_5OH \rightarrow 2\,RuHCl(CO)(PR_3)_3 + 2\,CH_4 + 2\,KCl + 2\,H_2O$$

although there are side reactions, since acetaldehyde was also detected in the reaction products. A mechanism has been suggested for this curious reaction: the initial formation of an ethoxide-metal complex is followed by hydride transfer to give an acetaldehyde complex, and this finally breaks down to the product, perhaps via an isocarbonyl[54]:

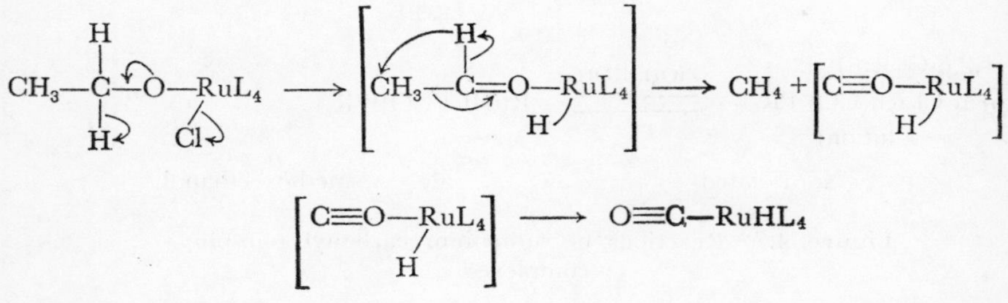
CH3—C—O—RuL4
H
H
Cl
CH3—C=O—RuL4
H
H
CH4 +
C≡O—RuL4
H
C≡O—RuL4
H
O≡C—RuHL4

Carbonyl phosphine complexes containing metal–metal bonds

Species of the form **[XHg—RuX(CO)$_3$(PPh$_3$)$_2$]HgX$_3$** (X = Cl, Br, I) have been prepared by the reaction of mercury dihalides with the zero-valent carbonyl phosphine Ru(CO)$_3$(PPh$_3$)$_2$[59a].

Alkyl and aryl phosphines

The known **alkyl and aryl complexes** (cf. Table 4.7) are formed with chelating diphosphines and diarsines. They are of the form *trans*-RuXR(diphosphine)$_2$ (X = H, Cl, Br, I, SCN; R = Me, Et, Ph) and *cis*-RuR$_2$(diphosphine)$_2$ (R = Me, Et, Ph), the configurations having been established from the dipole moments together with infrared and proton magnetic resonance measurements; the arsine complex RuClMe(*o*-C$_6$H$_4$(AsMe$_2$)$_2$)$_2$ was also made[55]. The *trans* complexes (monoalkyl or aryl) can be made from both *cis*- or *trans*-RuCl$_2$(diphosphine)$_2$ using lithium methyl, aluminium triethyl or lithium phenyl; substitution of the chloride in RuClR(diphosphine)$_2$ by bromide, iodide or thiocyanate can be effected by metathesis. The *cis*- dialkyl and diaryl complexes are made from the monoalkyl or -aryls with the appropriate lithium compound.

Hydrido alkyl and aryl complexes of the *trans*-**RuHR(diphosphine)$_2$** (R = Me, Et, Ph) can be made from the corresponding halo complex and lithium aluminium hydride (Table 4.7)[55].

cis-**RuH(aryl)(diphosphine)$_2$** (aryl = phenyl, 2-naphthyl, anthryl, phenanthryl) can be got by reducing *cis*- or *trans*-RuCl$_2$-(diphosphine)$_2$ with the arene anions in tetrahydrofuran solution[53]. As with Ru^0(diphosphine)$_2$ (p. 179), the chemical properties are consistent with a formulation Ru^0(arene)(diphosphine)$_2$—thus, the pyrolysis and iodination reactions give C$_{10}$H$_8$:

$$\mathrm{Ru^0(C_{10}H_8)(diphosphine)_2} \xrightarrow[10^{-3}\mathrm{mm}]{150°} \mathrm{Ru^0(diphosphine)_2 + C_{10}H_8}$$

$$\mathrm{Ru(C_{10}H_8)(diphosphine)_2 + I_2} \longrightarrow cis\text{-}\mathrm{RuI_2(diphosphine)_2 + C_{10}H_8}$$

The physical properties (infrared and nuclear magnetic resonance spectra with dipole moment data) suggest a hydridic formulation, *cis*-RuH(aryl)(diphosphine)$_2$, and so does the reaction with ethyl bromide:

$$cis\text{-}\mathrm{RuH(2\text{-}C_{10}H_7)(diphosphine)_2 + C_2H_5Br} \rightarrow trans\text{-}\mathrm{RuBr(2\text{-}C_{10}H_7)(diphosphine)_2 + C_2H_6}$$

while the reaction with deuterium chloride suggests that the complex

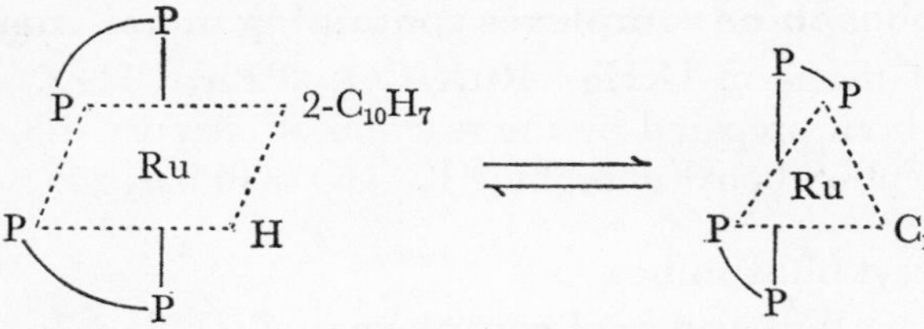

P—P = $Me_2P.CH_2.CH_2.PMe_2$

Figure 4.9 Tautomerism in Ru (diphosphine)$_2$ ($C_{10}H_8$)

is a mixture of the two tautomers. The tautomerism is represented as shown in Figure 4.9, and the arene form represented as a pentacoordinate complex with ruthenium (0) while the aryl form has octahedral ruthenium (II)[53].

The electronic absorption spectra of complexes of the form *trans*-RuXY(diphosphine)$_2$ (X = Y = Cl, Br, I; X = H, Me, Ph, *p*-tolyl with Y = Cl) have been measured and assignments proposed; from these it was deduced that the hydride, alkyl and aryl groups have almost as high a ligand-field splitting effect as the cyanide group[56].

Olefin complexes*

With monoolefins. As is the general case with these four metals, dienes are much more effective ligands than monoolefins. The blue solutions of 'ruthenium dichloride' will absorb ethylene and propylene in a 1 : 1 metal : olefin ratio, but no complexes were isolated[130,130a] (cf. p. 144).

With chelating diolefins. A number of these are known, all with ruthenium (II).

Cycloocta-1,5-diene, C_8H_{12}, reacts with $[Ru_2Cl_3(PEt_2Ph)_6]Cl$ to give **$RuCl_2(C_8H_{12})(PEt_2Ph)_2$**[127], with a solution of ruthenium trichloride in ethanol and carbon monoxide to give **$[Ru(C_8H_{12})(CO)Cl_2]_2$**[263], and with ruthenium trihalides to give **$[RuX_2(C_8H_{12})]_n$** (X = Cl, Br, I)[21]. The latter will undergo bridge-splitting reactions with other donor groups—thus, *p*-toluidine gives monomeric **$RuCl_2(C_8H_{12})(p\text{-tol})_2$**[21].

* For ruthenium (0) olefins see p. 193; for olefin intermediates in catalytic hydrogenation, see pp. 142 and 144.

Norbornadiene (bicyclo[2.2.1]hepta-2,5-diene, C_7H_8) reacts with ruthenium trichloride to give $[\mathbf{RuCl_2(C_7H_8)}]_n$ (the bromo analogue can be made by methathesis with lithium bromide), which with *p*-toluidine yields $\mathbf{RuCl_2(C_7H_8)}$***p*****-tol**$_2$[1,21]. With ruthenium trichloride, ethanol and carbon monoxide, C_7H_8 gives $[RuCl_2(CO)(C_7H_8)]_2$ and the bromo complex was also isolated[263]. The ligand will also react with an ethanolic solution of ruthenium trichloride and carbon monoxide to give $[Ru(C_7H_8)(CO)Cl_2]_2$, and with $Ru(PPh_3)_4X_2$ to form $\mathbf{Ru(PPh_3)_2(C_7H_8)X_2}$ (X = Cl, Br)[263].

Cycloocta-1,3,5-triene (C_8H_{12}) and cycloocta-diene react with ruthenium trichloride to give $\mathbf{(C_8H_{10})Ru^{II}(C_8H_{12})}$, and the infrared and proton magnetic resonance spectra of the products were measured[93].

Catalysis of olefin polymerization by ruthenium (III) chloro complexes is considered above (p. 142) and the catalysis of the hydrogenation of olefins by ruthenium (II) chloro complexes is discussed on p. 144 and 194.

'Sandwich' complexes

Ruthenocene*, $\mathbf{Cp_2Ru}$ (π-C_5H_5 = Cp), can be made from ruthenium trichloride in tetrahydrofuran with sodium cyclopentadienide. It forms light-yellow crystals[34] (m.p. 200°). X-ray crystal structure analyses show that, unlike ferrocene but like osmocene, the rings are eclipsed (cf. Figure 3.7, p. 96) the average carbon–carbon distance being 1·43 Å, the metal–carbon distance 2·21 Å and the perpendicular ring–ring distance 3·69 Å[131]. In ferrocenyl ruthenocenyl ketone, where both Cp_2Fe and Cp_2Ru units are in the same molecule, each pair of rings is eclipsed[285], and this is also the case in diacetyl ruthenocene[294] and in dibenzoyl ruthenocene[295].

Infrared and Raman studies have been made on ruthenocene and the skeletal modes assigned[191,192] (cf. Table 3.15, p. 116). Thermodynamic data for the compound are given in Table 3.14, p. 116. The proton magnetic resonance spectrum of the compound in carbon tetrachloride solution shows a single sharp line indicating that all the protons are in an equivalent environment[102]; broad line proton magnetic resonance spectra on the solid suggest that the rotational energy barrier in ruthenocene and in substituted ruthenocenes is about 1 kcal/mole higher than for the corresponding ferrocenes[263a].

* See also osmocene, p. 96.

Electronic absorption spectra of solutions of ruthenocene have been measured[263a] but no attempt at assignment of the bands was made. Polarographic and chronopotentiometric[185] studies on the compound are discussed on p. 97.

Acylruthenocenes[35,251] and acetylruthenocenes[35,36,140] have been prepared by Friedel–Crafts syntheses, and trimethylsilylruthenocene has recently been made[210]. Kinetic studies on the solvolysis of α-ruthenocenyl ethyl acetate[251] and the acid-catalysed decomposition of trimethylsilylruthenocene[210] are considered on p. 97, as also are the kinetics of the acid-catalysed decomposition of ruthenocenyl phenylcarbinyl azide[35], protonation of ruthenocene, and proton magnetic resonance studies on acyl and acetyl ruthenocenes. The kinetics of the oxidation of ruthenocene and ferrocene by iodine in benzene have been investigated; the reaction is first order in the metallocene and second order in iodine[267].

A review on the chemistry of ferrocene, ruthenocene and osmocene has recently been published[263a].

Cp $Ru^{II}(CO)_2Br$ is formed as a yellow, diamagnetic solid by the action of bromine on $[Cp\,Ru^{O}(CO)_2]_2$[92,94], and salts of **$[Cp\,Ru(CO)_2(C_2H_4)]^+$** can be made from ethylene, aluminium tribromide and $(Cp\,Ru(CO)_2)_2$[92,94].

The orange crystalline complex **$CpRu(CO)_2I$** was prepared by the action of a solution of iodine in carbon tetrachloride on $[CpRu(CO)_2]_2$; on reaction with sodium borohydride it gives the hydride **$CpRuH(CO)_2$** as a colourless liquid. The sodium salt of this, **$Na[CpRu(CO)_2]$** was got from sodium amalgam in tetrahydrofuran with $[CpRu(CO)_2]_2$, and this sodium salt will react with methyl or ethyl iodide to give the alkyl derivatives **$CpRuMe(CO)_2$** and **$CpRuEt(CO)_2$**. The proton magnetic resonance spectra of these complexes, $CpRuX(CO)_2$ (X = H,D,I,Me,Et), were measured and the results compared with those obtained for non-transition metal complexes[66a].

Diindenyl ruthenium (II), **$(\pi\text{-}C_9H_7)_2Ru$,** can be prepared as an air-stable orange crystalline solid (m.p. 200°) from indenylsodium, anhydrous ruthenium trichloride and ruthenium metal. Treatment of a solution of this compound in ethanol with hydrogen in the presence of Adams catalyst yields the bistetrahydroindenyl product, **$(\pi\text{-}C_9H_{11})_2Ru$,** as a white solid (m.p. 66°). The infrared, electronic absorption and proton magnetic resonance spectra of both these materials and of their iron analogues were measured, and indicated that in all of them the five-membered C_5H_3 parts of the molecule were bonded to the metal atoms[102a, 239a]. The crystal structure of $(\pi-C_9H_7)_2$ Ru has recently been determined[300a].

Arene complexes*

Dibenzene ruthenium (II) perchlorate, $[(\pi\text{-}C_6H_6)_2Ru](ClO_4)_2$, can be made by a reaction under Friedel–Crafts conditions with benzene, ruthenium trichloride, aluminium and aluminium trichloride. It forms pale yellow crystals which, though they are air-stable at room temperatures, explode when heated. The infrared and proton magnetic resonance spectra were consistent with the above formulation[166]. With lithium phenyl, yellow air-stable crystals of **[π-1-endo-**$C_6H_5.C_6H_6]_2Ru^{II}$ are produced, the formulation being supported by infrared and proton magnetic resonance spectra[166].

Dimesitylene ruthenium (II) perchlorate, $[(\pi\text{-}C_6H_3Me_3)_2Ru]$-$(ClO_4)_2$ is made in a similar way to its benzene analogue, and forms yellow needles[91]. The absence of a ruthenium (III) mesitylene complex is singular—in this connection one may recall that the unusual oxidation state of two for rhodium is found in $(\pi\text{-}C_6Me_6)_2{}^{2+}Rh$, the trivalent species again being unknown.

Di-π-cyclohexadienyl ruthenium (II), $(\pi\text{-}C_6H_7)_2Ru$, can be got from dibenzene ruthenium perchlorate and lithium aluminium hydride, but the main product of the reaction is the isomeric $(\pi\text{-}C_6H_6)Ru^0(C_6H_8)$ (see p. 194). Infrared and proton magnetic resonance spectra were measured[166].

For **allyl complexes** see p. 181.

Stannous halide complexes

$(Me_4N)_2[Ru^{II}Cl_2(SnCl_3)_2]$ and $(Ph_3PH)_2[Ru^{II}Cl_2(SnCl_3)_2]$ can be made from ruthenium trichloride, stannous chloride, hydrochloric acid and the chloride of the base. The salts are yellow and are diamagnetic[320]. $[RuX_2(CO)_2(SnX_3)_2]^{2-}$ (X = Cl, Br) can be got from ruthenium trichloride in ethanol with carbon monoxide and SnX_2[175c]. Other stannous chloride complexes are listed in Table 4.10.

Ruthenium (I)

$[Ru(CO)Br]_n$ is made from the trihalides and carbon monoxide at 180° and 350 atmospheres pressure[208]; $[Ru(CO)_xI]_n$ can be got by the action of iodine on a ruthenium carbonyl or by the action of

* Complexes with six-membered rings.

carbon monoxide under pressure on ruthenium triiodide[205]. The fact that it is soluble in benzene suggests that it is not highly polymeric, and may be dimeric, like $[Os(CO)_4I]_2$.

Ruthenium carbonyl hydride is discussed on p. 193.

Reaction of $Ru_3(CO)_{12}$ with tetramethyldiphosphine gives a dimeric species of ruthenium (I), $[Ru(CO)_3(PMe_2)]_2$, thought to have the structure[43a]

```
              Me2
               P
              / \
(OC)3Ru............Ru(CO)3
              \ /
               P
              Me2
```

Sandwich complexes

$[\mathbf{CpRu(CO)_2}]_2$ can be made from ruthenium dicarbonyl diiodide and sodium cyclopentadienide; its infrared[64b] and proton magnetic resonance spectra were measured[92,94]. In solution it exists as an equilibrium mixture of carbonyl-bridged and non-bridged forms[94].

Ruthenium (0)

Ruthenium pentacarbonyl, $\mathbf{Ru(CO)_5}$, can be made by heating finely divided ruthenium metal with carbon monoxide to 180° under a pressure of 200 atmospheres, or by the action of carbon monoxide on ruthenium triiodide at 170° (in this case atmospheric pressure suffices)[205]. It is a colourless liquid (m.p. 22°, vapour pressure at 18° is equal to 50 mm). Like iron and osmium pentacarbonyls it is monomeric and probably has a trigonal bipyramidal structure.

$\mathbf{Ru_3(CO)_{12}}$, formerly believed to be the ennea complex $Ru_2(CO)_9$, can be made by heating a solution of the pentacarbonyl in benzene or by irradiating it in sunlight[205] or from a methanolic solution of ruthenium trichloride, zinc and carbon monoxide (10 atmospheres, 65°)[33a]. It forms yellow-green crystals (m.p. 150°) which are soluble in organic solvents, and it is isomorphous with $Os_3(CO)_{12}$[64]. Infrared studies on the complex also suggest that the two compounds have similar structures[64] (see p. 99). Mass spectroscopic measurements on the compound shows that, as with osmium dodecacarbonyl, the metal cluster is not disrupted until all the carbonyl groups have been stripped[158a,b].

$[\mathbf{Ru(CO)}]_n$ is formed in small amounts in the preparation of $Ru_3(CO)_{12}$ from the pentacarbonyl, and can also be made by the action of alkali on $Ru_3(CO)_{12}$. It is soluble in aqueous alcohol but not in benzene or ether, and forms green crystals[205,208].

A ruthenium carbonyl hydride, $\mathbf{H_nRu_4(CO)_{12}}$ ($n \approx 3$ or 4) has been prepared by the action of hydrogen and carbon monoxide (at 120 atmospheres and 75°) on a solution of ruthenium trichloride with silver powder. The complex is orange (m.p. 147°), and its infrared and proton magnetic resonance spectra were measured[156a]. Treatment of $Ru_3(CO)_{12}$ with sodium borohydride followed by acidification yields $\mathbf{H_2Ru_4(CO)_{13}}$ and $\mathbf{H_4Ru_4(CO)_{12}}$; infrared and mass spectra of these were measured[158a].

Carbonyl phosphine complexes

$\mathbf{Ru(CO)_3(PPh_3)_2}$ can be made by the reduction of $RuCl_2(CO)_2(PPh_3)_2$ with zinc in dimethylformamide under 4 atmospheres pressure of carbon monoxide. The complex is pale yellow and will undergo a number of reactions of the type

$$Ru(CO)_3(PPh_3)_2 + X_2 \rightarrow Ru(CO)_2X_2(PPh_3)_2 \ (X = Cl, Br)$$

$$Ru(CO)_3(PPh_3)_2 + HX \rightarrow Ru(CO)_2HX(PPh_3)_2 \ (X = Cl, Br)$$

With mercuric halides and with methyl iodide, products containing ruthenium–mercury and ruthenium–carbon bonds are formed[59].

Reaction of $Ru_3(CO)_{12}$ with triphenylphosphine gives a deep red trimeric material $\mathbf{Ru_3(CO)_9(PPh_3)_3}$[43a].

The complex functions as a hydroformylation catalyst; for example pent-1-ene will give hexaldehyde when treated with carbon monoxide in the presence of the complex[85].

Olefin complexes

$\mathbf{(C_8H_{10})Ru^0(C_8H_{10})}$, cycloocta-1,3,5-triene ruthenium bicyclo-[4.2.0]octa-2,4-diene, was prepared from anhydrous ruthenium trichloride, isopropyl magnesium bromide and cycloocta-1,3,5-diene, and the same product could also be made from $[(C_7H_8)RuCl_2]_n$, the Grignard solution and the 1,3,5-diene. In both preparations ultraviolet irradiation was used. The infrared and proton magnetic resonance spectra were consistent with the proposed formulation[228b].

$\mathbf{(C_8H_{12})Ru(C_7H_8)}$, cycloocta-1,5-diene ruthenium cycloheptatriene, was got from $(C_8H_{12})RuCl_2$, cycloheptatriene and an ethereal solution of isopropyl magnesium bromide; in similar fashion the interaction of $[(C_7H_8)RuCl_2]_n$ (C_7H_8 = norbornadiene), the Grignard and cycloheptatriene yields $\mathbf{(C_7H_8)Ru(C_7H_8)}$, norbornadiene ruthenium cycloheptatriene. The infrared and proton magnetic resonance spectra of both these products were consistent with their formulation as diene complexes of ruthenium (o) [228b]. Reaction of cycloocta-1,3-diene with $Ru_3(CO)_{12}$ yields $Ru_3(CO)_{10}(C_8H_{12})$ [43a].

Reaction of $[\pi\text{-}(C_6H_6)_2Ru]^{2+}$ salts with lithium aluminium hydride will give yellow crystals of $(\pi\text{-}C_6H_6)Ru^0(C_6H_8)$, where (C_6H_8) is cyclohexa-1,3-diene[166].

HOMOGENEOUS CATALYSIS BY RUTHENIUM COMPLEXES

Rather less work has been reported on this topic than on the corresponding rhodium systems, and up to now more attention has been paid to catalytic hydrogenations than to other types of catalysis.

Catalytic hydrogenation

The reduction of iron (III) or ruthenium (IV) by molecular hydrogen in the presence of anionic ruthenium (III) chloro complexes probably involves a heterolytic splitting of the hydrogen molecule and formation of an intermediate hydride (p. 141)[130a,132]. This conclusion is supported by isotope experiments which show that $[RuCl_6]^{3-}$ catalyses the molecular deuterium–water exchange, and the rate law is similar to that established for the reduction of ferric ion by hydrogen catalysed by ruthenium (III)[130a]:

$$[RuCl_6]^{3-} + D_2 \rightarrow D^+ + Cl^- + [DRuCl_5]^{3-} \begin{cases} \xrightarrow{HCl} HD + [RuCl_6]^{3-} \\ \xrightarrow{H_2O} [HRuCl_5]^{3-} \rightarrow \tfrac{1}{2}H_2 \end{cases}$$

$$[HRuCl_5]^{3-} + 2\,Fe^{III} \rightarrow [RuCl_6]^{3-} + 2\,Fe^{II} + \tfrac{1}{2}H_2$$

A basically similar type of mechanism involving heterolytic fission and hydride formation has been proposed for the ruthenium (II) catalysed reductions of maleic and fumaric acids in the presence of molecular hydrogen (p. 144). The chloro species in acidic solutions of ruthenium (II) chloride form (1: 1) complexes with the acids and these are reduced by hydrogen[130a,130d].

The ruthenium (II) chloro system will only catalyse the reduction of activated double bonds. The ruthenium (II) chlorophosphine species

$RuCl_2(PPh_3)_4$ and $RuCl_2(PPh_3)_3$ in benzene–ethanol solutions will, however, catalyse the reduction by molecular hydrogen of ethylene and other nonactivated olefins; the reductions are very slow if ethanol is not present. In such solutions it appears that there is dissociation of the phosphine groups to give $RuCl_2(PPh_3)_2$; this has 'vacant' coordination sites which can be occupied by the hydride ion and by the coordinating olefin. The phosphines stabilize the intermediate hydride, which in this case can be detected directly and has been shown to be $RuHCl(PPh_3)_3$; it is, however, sufficiently labile to be catalytically active[85] (p. 178). The course of the reaction is then likely to be similar to that given for the ruthenium (II) chloro system on p. 178.

These reactions, all of which appear to involve a *heterolytic* splitting of the hydrogen molecule, differ in mechanism from those involved in homogeneous catalysis by rhodium (I) species (cf. p. 367); in the latter case the oxidation state of the metal atom changes from (I) to (III) by the *homolytic* addition of hydrogen.

Hydroformylation reactions

The ruthenium (0) complex $Ru(CO)_3(PPh_3)_2$ which, as has already been mentioned, shows addition reactions involving a change in oxidation state[59]:

$$Ru^{0}(CO)_3(PPh_3)_2 + X_2 \rightarrow Ru^{II}X_2(CO)_2(PPh_3)_2$$

will function as a hydroformylation catalyst. Another but less efficient ruthenium catalyst for this type of reaction is $RuCl_3(PPh_3)_2(MeOH)$ (p. 178)[85]. A general discussion of such catalysed hydroformylation reactions is given on p. 403.

Miscellaneous catalysed reactions

The hydration of acetylenes by ruthenium (III) chloro species is discussed on p. 141[129], and hydrogen-transfer reactions with allylic alcohols catalysed by ruthenium (II) chloro species are discussed on p. 181[231]. The non-catalytic hydrogen transfer during formation of ruthenium (II) hydrido carbonyl phosphine species is also relevant (p. 186)[54]. Ruthenium trichloride will also function as a catalyst for the polymerization of olefins (see p. 142).

Table 4.1 Oxalate complexes of ruthenium

Oxidation state	Complex	Colour	Physical properties	Preparation	Ref.
IV	$K_2[Ru\ ox_3]$	Black	pol[298]	$K_3[Ru\ ox_3] + H_2O_2$	46
III	$K_3[Ru\ ox_3]$	Green	el[237]pol[298]	$K_2[RuCl_5H_2O] + ox^{2-}$	46, 73
	$K_3[Ru\ ox_2Cl_2]$			$K_2[RuCl_5H_2O] + ox^{2-}$	46
	cis- and *trans*-$[Ru\ ox_2py_2]^-$	Orange		$K_3[Ru\ ox_3] + py$	46
II	$K_4[Ru\ ox_3]$ (soln. only)		pol[298]	Reduction of $[Ru\ ox_3]^{3-}$	298
	$K_2[Ru\ ox_2(NO)Cl]$	Red		$K_2[Ru(NO)Cl_5] + ox^{2-}$	46
	cis-$K[Ru\ ox_2(NO)py]$			$K_2[Ru\ ox_2(NO)Cl)] + py$	46, 47
	? $H_2[Ru\ ox_2(NO)]$			$RuO_4 + H_2ox + NO$	322
	$K_2[Ru\ ox(NO)I_3]$	Black		$K_2[Ru(NO)I_5] + ox^{2-}$	46
	$Ru\ ox\ phen_2$	Red		$Ru\ phen_2Cl_2 + ox^{2-}$	74

Table 4.2 Ammine complexes of ruthenium[a]

Oxidation state	Complex	Colour	Physical properties	Preparation	Ref.
VIII	$RuO_4 . NH_3$			$RuO_4 + NH_3$	128
VI	$RuO_2(NH_3)_2X_2$	Brown		$K_2[RuO_4] + NH_3 + HCl$	180
IV	$RuO(OH)_2(NH_3)_2 . 2\ H_2O$	Brown		$RuO_4 + NH_3 + H_2O$	293
	$RuOX_2(NH_3)_2$ (X = Cl, Br, I)	Brown		$RuO(OH)_2(NH_3)_2 + HX$	293
IV–III	$[Ru_3O_2(NH_3)_{14}]^{6+}$	Red	mag, el[96]	$[Ru(NH_3)_6]Cl_3 + NH_3 + O_2$	96
	$[Ru_3O_2(NH_3)_{14}]^{7+}$	Brown	mag, el[96]	$[Ru_3O_2(NH_3)_{14}]^{6+}$ + Ce(IV)	96
III	$[Ru(NH_3)_6]Cl_3$	Colourless	mag, kin, el, R, i.r., pot, e.s.r. (p. 165)	$[Ru(NH_3)_6]Cl_2 + Cl_2$	187
	$[Ru(NH_3)_5Cl]Cl_2$	Yellow	kin, el, i.r., e.s.r., X (p. 167)	$[Ru(NH_3)_6]Cl_3 + HCl$	108
	$[Ru(NH_3)_5Br]Br_2$	Yellow	kin[82], el[40]	$[Ru(NH_3)_6]Cl_3 + HBr$	108
	$[Ru(NH_3)_5I]I_2$	Blue-purple	kin[82], el[40]	$[Ru(NH_3)_5Cl]Cl_2 + HI$	40
	$[Ru(NH_3)_5OH]S_2O_6$			$[Ru(NH_3)_5Cl]Cl_2 + NH_3 + S_2O_6^{2-}$	109
	$[Ru(NH_3)_5H_2O](NO_3)_3$			$[Ru(NH_3)_5Cl]Cl_2 + NH_3 + NO_3^-$	109
	$[Ru(NH_3)_5NO_3](NO_3)_2$			$[Ru(NH_3)_5H_2O](NO_3)_3$ + Heat	109
	$[Ru(NH_3)_5S_2O_3]Cl$	Yellow		$[Ru(NH_3)_6]Cl_2 + SO_2$	187
	cis-$[Ru(NH_3)_4X_2]X$	Orange		$[Ru(NH_3)_4(SO_2)X]X + HX$	111
	trans-$[Ru(NH_3)_4X_2]X$ (X = Cl, Br)	Orange		$[Ru(NH_3)_4ox]^+ + HX$	111, 225
	cis-$[Ru(NH_3)_4I_2]I$			$[Ru(NH_3)_4ox]^+ + HI$	40
	$[Ru(NH_3)_4I_2]^+$ (*trans*?)	Black		$[Ru(NH_3)_4(OH)I]I + HI$	225

Table 4.2 (*continued*)

Oxidation state	Complex	Colour	Physical properties	Preparation	Ref.
III (*continued*)	$[Ru(NH_3)_4(OH)X]X$ (X = Cl, I)	Brown		$RuX_3 + NH_3 + H_2O$	111, 226
	$[Ru(NH_3)_4(OH)Br]Br$	Purple		$[Ru(NH_3)_4Br_2]Br + NH_3 + H_2O$	226
	$[Ru(NH_3)_4ClBr]^+$ (solution only)			$[Ru(NH_3)_4Cl_2]^+ + HBr$	111
	$[Ru(NH_3)_4Cl(NO_3)](NO_3)$	Brown		$[Ru(NH_3)_4(OH)Cl]Cl + HNO_3$	226
	2 $RuX.7NH_3$ (X = Cl, Br, I)			$RuX_3 + NH_3$	120, 160, 293
	?*cis*-$Ru(NH_3)_3Cl_3$	Red		*cis*-$[Ru(NH_3)_4Cl_2]Cl + NH_3$	111
	$Ru(NH_3)_3Cl_3$	Black		$RuCl_3 + NH_3$	160
	$Ru(NH_3)_3Br_3$			$RuBr_3 + NH_3$	160
	?$Ru_2(NH_3)_6(NH_2)(H_2O)Br_5$			$[Ru_2(NO)Br_8]^{5-}$(?) $+ NH_3$	29
II	$[Ru(NH_3)_6]Cl_2$	Orange	kin, el, pot (p. 171)	$RuCl_3 + Zn + NH_3$	187
	$[Ru(NH_3)_5SO_2]Cl_2$	Red		$Ru(NH_3)_5SO_3 + HCl$	107
	$Ru(NH_3)_5SO_3$	Colourless			107
	$[Ru(NH_3)_5(HSO_3)]^+$ (solution only)			$[Ru(NH_3)_4(SO_2)Cl]Cl + NH_3$	107
	$[Ru(NH_3)_5NO]Cl_3$	Orange	i.r.[87a]	$[Ru(NH_3)_6]Cl_2 + NO_2^- + HCl$	110, 187
	trans-$[Ru(NH_3)_4(SO_2)Cl]Cl$	Red	X, i.r.[297]	$Ru(NH_3)_4(HSO_3)_2 + HCl$	107, 297
	trans-$[Ru(NH_3)_4(SO_2)Br]Br$		i.r.[297]	$Ru(NH_3)_4(HSO_3)_2 + HBr$	297
	trans-$Ru(NH_3)_4(HSO_3)_2$	Colourless	i.r.[297]	$Ru(NH_3)_5Cl]Cl_2 + HSO_3^-$	107, 297
	$[Ru(NH_3)_4(SO_2)(H_2O)]S_2O_6$	Yellow		$Ru(NH_3)_4(HSO_3)_2 + S_2O_6^{2-}$	107

Table 4.2 (*continued*)

Oxidation state	Complex	Colour	Physical properties	Preparation	Ref.
II (*continued*)	*trans*-$[Ru(NH_3)_4(NO)Cl]Cl_2$	Red	i.r.[87a,270,284]	$[Ru(NH_3)_4(NO(OH)]Cl_2$ + HCl	307
	$[Ru(NH_3)_4(NO)Br]Br_2$	Orange		$[Ru(NH_3)_4(NO)H_2O]Br_3$ + HBr	307
	$[Ru(NH_3)_4(NO)I]I_2$	Violet		$[Ru(NH_3)_4(NO)(OH)]I_2$ + HI	163
	trans-$[Ru(NH_3)_4(NO)(OH)]Cl_2$	Yellow	X,[26] i.r.[87a,270,284]	$[Ru(NO)Cl_5]^{2-} + NH_3$	307
	$[Ru(NH_3)_4(NO)(NO_3)](NO_3)_2$			$[Ru(NH_3)_4(NO)Cl]Cl_2$ + $AgNO_3$	163
	$[Ru(NH_3)_4(NO)(H_2O)]Cl_3$	Orange		$[Ru(NH_3)_4(NO)(OH)]Br_2$ + HCl	307
	$[Ru(NH_3)_4(NO)(SO_4)]_2(SO_4)$	Rose		$[Ru(NH_3)_4(NO)(OH)]Cl_2$ + H_2SO_4	163
	$[Ru(NH_3)_2phen_2]I_2$			$RuCl_2phen_2 + NH_3 + I^-$	74
	$[Ru(NH_3)_2py_2bipy]^{2+}$	Red		$[Rupy_4bipy]Cl_2 + NH_3$	74
	$[Ru(NH_3)_2en(NO)(OH)]I_2$	Yellow		$[Ru\ en_2(NO)I]I_2 + NH_3$ + H_2O	49
	$Ru(NH_3)_2(NO_2)_2(NO)(OH)$			$[Ru(NO)(OH)(NO_2)_4]^{2-}$ + NH_4OH	243
	$Na_4[Ru(NH_3)_2(SO_3)_2(HSO_3)_2]$	Colourless		$[Ru(NH_3)_5Cl]Cl_2 + HSO_3^-$	107
	$Ru(NH_3)_2(CO)_2I_2$		i.r.[155]	$[Ru(CO)_2I_2]_n + NH_3$	155
	$Ru(NH_3)_3Cl_2(H_2O)$	Violet		$H_2[RuO_2Cl_4]aq + NH_3$	9

[a] See also pp. 164–169 and 171–172

Table 4.3 Pyridine complexes of ruthenium (cf. also Table 4.10)

Oxidation state	Complex	Colour	Physical properties	Preparation	Ref.
VIII	RuO_4py_2			RuO_4 + py	176
IV	Ru py_2Cl_4	Yellow		pyHCl + $RuCl_3$ + H_2O_2	49
III	[Ru py_4Cl_2]Cl	Yellow		[Ru py_4Cl(OH)]Cl + HCl	226
	[Ru py_4Cl(OH)]Cl	Yellow		$RuCl_3$ + py	226
	Ru py_3Cl_3 (also methyl pyridine analogues)		i.r.[286]	pyH[Ru py_2Cl_4] + py (pressure)	286
	pyH[Ru py_2Cl_4] (also methyl pyridine analogues)		i.r.[286]	$H_2[RuCl_6]$aq + py	286
	[Ru py_2acac bipy]$(ClO_4)_2$	Blue		[Rupy_4bipy]Cl_2 + acac + Ce(IV)	74
	[Ru py_2X_2L]X (X = Cl, Br, I, SCN; L = bipy, phen)			Ru py_2X_2L + Ce(IV)	74
	[Ru py_2bipy ox]Cl			Ru py_2bipy ox + Ce(IV)	74
	pyH[Ru py(CO)Cl_4]		i.r.[288]	$RuCl_3$ + py + CO + EtOH	288
	[$Ru_3py_2(OAc)_6$]Cl$PtCl_6$			RuO_4 + HOAc + py + $PtCl_6^{2-}$	213
	$(pyH)_2$[Ru$pyCl_5$]	Red		$RuCl_3$ + pyHCL	45
II	[Ru py_4bipy]$(ClO_4)_2$	Brown		$RuCl_4$bipy + py + ClO_4^- + EtOH	74
	[Ru py_3Xbipy]$^+$ (X = Cl, Br)	Brown		$RuCl_4$bipy + py + X^- + EtOH	74

Table 4.3 (*continued*)

Oxidation state	Complex	Colour	Physical properties	Preparation	Ref.
II (*continued*)	Ru py_2X_2L (X = Cl, Br, I, SCN; L = bipy, phen)	Brown		$RuCl_4.L$ + py + X^- + EtOH	74
	[Ru py_2phen_2]$(ClO_4)_2$	Orange		$RuCl_2phen_2$ + py	74
	[Ru py_2acac bipy](ClO_4)	Violet		[Ru py_4bipy]Cl_2 + acac	74
	Ru py_2ox bipy	Red		[Ru py_4bipy]Cl_2 + ox^{2-}	74
	[Ru $py_2(NH_3)_2$bipy]$(ClO_4)_2$	Red		[Ru py_4bipy]Cl_2 + NH_3	74
	cis-Ru $py_2(CO)_2X_2$ (X = Cl, I)		i.r.[155]	$[Ru(CO)_2I_2]_n$ + py; $RuCl_3$ + CO + EtOH + py	155, 288
	[Ru pyCl $phen_2$](ClO_4)			Ru $phen_2Cl_2$ + py + NaCl + $NaClO_4$	74
	[Ru py$(H_2O)phen_2$]$(ClO_4)_2$	Brown		[Ru $phen_2py_2$]$(ClO_4)_2$ + H_2O	74
	[Ru py bipy terpy]$(ClO_4)_2$			[RuCl terpy bipy](ClO_4) + py	74
	cis-K[Ru py(NO)Cl_4]	Orange		$K_2[Ru(NO)Cl_5]$ + py	46
	cis-K[Ru py(NO)ox_2]	Red		$K_2[Ru(NO)ox_2Cl]$ + py	46
	Ru py_2(NO)Cl ox			$K_2[Ru(NO)Cl_5]$ + py + ox^{2-}	49
	[Ru py_2en(NO)(OH)]I_2			Ru en(NO)I_3 + py	49
	[Ru $py_3(H_2O)$bipy]$(ClO_4)_2$	Brown		[Ru py_4 bipy]Cl_2 + py	74
	Ru $py_2(NO)Cl_3$	Red		Ru(NO)Cl py_2ox + HCl	49
	Ru $py_n(OCOR)_2$ (n = 2, 4; R = Me, Et, Ph)	Green		$Ru_2(OCOR)_4Cl$ + py	287

Table 4.4 Complexes of ruthenium with heterocyclic bases[c]

Oxidation state	Complex[a]	Colour	Physical properties	Preparation[a]	Ref.
IV	$RuL.Cl_4$	Purple		$L.H[RuL.Cl_4] + HNO_3$	74
	$[Ru\ bipy_2Cl_2]^+$ (solution only)			$RuCl_3$ + bipy	223
III	$[Ru\ bipy_3]Cl_3$	Red	kin[b] (p. 169)	$RuCl_3$ + bipy + Ce(IV)	75
	$[Ru\ phen_3]Cl_3$	Red		$RuCl_3$ + phen + Ce(IV)	75
	$K[RuL.X_4]$	Brown		$K_2[RuCl_5OH] + L + X^-$	74
	$[RuL_2Cl_2](ClO_4)$	Brown	el[88a]	$RuL_2Cl_2 + Cl_2 + ClO_4^-$	74
	$[Ru\ phen_2(OH)_2](ClO_4)$	Blue-green		$Ru\ phen_2Cl_2 + AgNO_3 + ClO_4^-$	74
	$[Ru\ bipy_2]^{3+}$; $[Ru\ bipy]^{3+}$ (solution only)			$RuCl_3$ + bipy	223
	$[Ru\ bipy_2](ClO_4)_3$	Green		$RuCl_3 + bipy + ClO_4^-$	223
	$[RuL.Cl_2(H_2O)_2]^+$	Brown		$RuL.Cl_4 + H_2SO_4$	74
	$RuL.Cl_2acac$	Green		$RuL.Cl_4$ + acac	74
	$[Ru\ bipy\ acac_2]Cl$	Red		$Ru\ bipyCl_2acac$ + acac	74
	$Ru\ bipyCl_3(H_2O)$	Yellow		$Ru\ bipyCl_4 + H_2O + EtOH$	74
	$[Ru\ bipyXterpy](ClO_4)_2$	Brown		$Ru\ bipyCl_4 + terpy + X^-$	74

Table 4.4 (*continued*)

Oxidation state	Complex[a]	Colour	Physical properties	Preparation[a]	Ref.
II	$[Ru\ bipy_3]Cl_2$	Red	Kin[b], el[88a]	$RuCl_3$ + bipy	39, 193
	$[Ru\ phen_3]Cl_2$	Red		$RuCl_3$ + phen	39, 193
	$Ru\ bipy_2X_2$ (X = Cl, Br, I, $\frac{1}{2}$ ox)			$K_2[RuCl_5OH] + X^- +$ bipy	88a, 193
	$Ru\ phen_2X_2$	Violet		$phenH[RuCl_4phen) + X^-$ + Heat	74
	$RuL(acac)_2$	Blue		$[RuL.acac_2]^+ + S_2O_4^{2-}$	74
	$[Ru\ phen_2acac](ClO_4)$	Red		$Ru\ phen_2Cl_2$ + acac	74
	$Ru\ bipy(CO)_2I_2$		i.r.[155]	$[Ru(CO)_2I_2]_n$ + bipy	155
	$Ru\ bipy(NO)X_3$			$K_2[Ru(NO)X_5]$ + bipy	228
	$[Ru\ terpy(NO)Cl_2]Cl$	Brown		$K_2[Ru(NO)Cl_5]$ + terpy	228
	$[Ru\ tetrapy(NO)Cl]Cl_2$	Brown		$K_2[Ru(NO)Cl_5]$ + tetrapy	228
	$[Ru\ terpy\ bipyX]^+$			$Ru\ bipyCl_4$ + terpy + X^-	74

[a] L = phen or bipy; X = Cl or Br.
[b] See pp. 169 and 172.
[c] See also Tables 4.1, 4.2, 4.3, 4.6 and 4.9.

Table 4.5 Second-order rate constants for electron-exchange reactions of ruthenium complexes (cf. pp. 169 and 173)

Oxidant	Reductant[a]	T(°C)	Medium	k(M^{-1} sec^{-1})	Method[b]	Ref.
$[Ru\ bipy_3]^{3+}$	$[Os\ bipy_3]^{2+}$	0°	0·1M H_2SO_4	$>5 \times 10^4$	(b)	81
$[Ru\ bipy_3]^{3+}$	$[Os\ bipy_3]^{2+}$	25°	0·5M $HClO_4$	$>10^8$	(a)	113
$[Ru\ bipy_3]^{3+}$	$[Fe(CN)_6]^{4-}$	18°	10^{-3}M HNO_3	$>10^5$	(c)	105
$[Ru\ bipy_3]^{3+}$	$[Fe\ bipy_3]^{2+}$	18°	10^{-3}M HNO_3	$>10^5$	(c)	105
$[Ru\ bipy_3]^{3+}$	$[Fe(t\text{-phen})_3]^{2+}$	25°	0·5M H_2SO_4	$>10^8$	(a)	113
$[Ru\ bipy_3]^{3+}$	$[Fe(p\text{-phen})_3]^{2+}$	25°	0·5M H_2SO_4	$>10^8$	(a)	113
$[Ru\ bipy_3]^{3+}$	$[Fe\ phen_3]^{2+}$	0°	0·1M H_2SO_4	$>3 \times 10^6$	(b)	81
Tl^{3+}	$[Ru\ bipy_3]^{2+}$	25°	4·8M $HClO_4$	0·19	(e)	222a
Tl^{3+}	$[Ru\ terpy_2]^{2+}$	25°	4·8M $HClO_4$	0·83	(e)	222a
Ce^{4+}	$[Ru\ bipy_3]^{2+}$	18°	M $HClO_4$	$>10^5$	(c)	105
$[RhCl_6]^{2-}$	$[Ru\ phen_3]^{2+}$	10°	0·5M Cl^-	$>2{\cdot}5 \times 10^9$	(d)	152
Ce^{4+}	$[Ru\ bipy_3]^{2+}$	25°	0·5M H_2SO_4	$8{\cdot}8 \times 10^3$	(c)	222, 222a
Ce^{4+}	$[Ru\ phen_3]^{2+}$	25°	0·5M H_2SO_4	$5{\cdot}8 \times 10^3$	(c)	222, 222a
Ce^{4+}	$[Ru\ terpy_2]^{2+}$	23°	0·5M H_2SO_4	7×10^3	(c)	222, 222a

[a] t-phen = 3,4,7,8-tetramethyl-1,10-phenanthroline, p-phen = 5-phenyl-1,10-phenanthroline.
[b] The methods of determining the rate constants are as follows:
(a) continuous flow.
(b) isotopic tracer.
(c) spectrophotometric.
(d) temperature-jump.
(e) optical activity.

Table 4.6 Diamine complexes of ruthenium

Oxidation state	Complex	Colour	Physical properties	Preparation	Ref.
III	?$Ru_4en_7ox_{12}.12\ H_2O$	Green		$K_3[Ru\ ox_3]$ + en	49
	$[Ru\ en_2Cl_2]Cl$	Brown		$[Ru\ en_2(OH)Cl]Cl + HCl$	226
	$[Ru\ en_2(OH)Cl]Cl$	Brown		$RuCl_3$ + en	226
	$[Ru\ en_2(OH)I]I$	Brown		$[Ru\ en_2(OH)Cl]Cl + HI$	226
	$[Ru(EtNH_2)_4Cl_2]Cl$	Red		$RuCl_3 + EtNH_2$	226
	$[Ru(EtNH_2)_4(OH)Cl]Cl$	Brown		$Ru(EtNH_2)_4Cl_2 + NH_3 + H_2O$	226
II	$[Ru\ en_3]Br_2$		i.r.[6,188]	$Ru\ Cl_3$ + en + Zn	6,188
	$[Ru\ en_2(NO)Cl]Cl_2$			$[Ru\ en_2(NO)Br]Br_2 + AgCl$	49
	$[Ru\ en_2(NO)Br]Br_2$	Orange		$[Ru\ en_2(NO)(OH)]I_2 + AgBr + Br^-$	49
	cis-$[Ru\ en_2(NO)I]I_2$	Red		$[Ru\ en_2(NO)(HClOH]I_2$ + heat	49
	trans-$[Ru\ en_2(NO)I]I_2$	Orange		$[Ru\ en_2(NO)(OH)]I_2 + HI$	49
	$[Ru\ en_2(NO)(OH)]Br_2$	Yellow		$[Ru(NH_3)_4(NO)(OH)]Br_2$ + en	308
	$[Ru\ en_2(NO)(OH)]Cl_2.HCl$	Orange		$[Ru\ en_2(NO)(OH)]I_2 + HCl + AgCl$	49
	$Ru\ en(NO)Cl_3$	Brown		$Ru\ en(NO)I_3 + Cl_2$	49
	$Ru\ en(NO)I_3$	Red		$K_2[Ru(NO)Cl_5]$ + en + I^-	49
	$[Ru\ en(NH_3)_2(NO)(OH)]I_2$			$Ru\ en(NO)I_3 + NH_3$	49
	$[Ru\ en\ phen_2]I_2$	Orange		$RuCl_2\ phen_2$ + en + I^-	74

Table 4.7 Phosphine, arsine and stibine complexes of ruthenium[f]

Oxidation state	Complex	Colour	Physical properties	Preparation	Ref.
III	$RuX_3(LR_3)_3$ (X = Cl, Br; $LR_3 = AsMePh_2, AsMe_2Ph, AsEt_2Ph, PMe_2Ph, PEt_2Ph$)	Brown		$RuX_3 + LR_3 + EtOH$	54, 76
	$RuX_3(LR_3)_2L'$ (X = Cl, Br; $LR_3 = PPh_3, AsPh_3$, L′ = MeOH, EtOH, Me_2CO)	Red-green		$RuX_3 + LR_3 + L'$	288
	$[RuCl_4(PR_3)_2]^+$ ($PR_3 = PEt_2Ph, PEt_3$)	Green		$RuCl_3 + CO + EtOH + PR_3$	288
	trans-[Ru $diars_2X_2$]X (X = Cl, Br, I)		i.r.[189]	Ru $diars_2X_2 + Cl_2 + X^-$	236
	[Ru $diarsX_4$][Ru $diars_2X_2$]			Ru $diars_2X_2 + Cl_2$	236
	$[Ru\ diars_3]^+[Ru\ diars\ I_4^-]^-$			$RuCl_3$ + diars + NaI	236
II	$[Ru_2Cl_3(PR_3)_6]Cl$ ($PR_3 = PMe_2Ph, PEt_2Ph, PMePh_2, PEtPh_2$)			$RuCl_3 + PR_3$ + 2-methylethanol,	51, 54
	$RuX_2(LR_3)_4$ (X = Cl, Br; $LR_3 = PPh_3, PHR_2$) (R = Et,Ph) $AsMe_2Ph$	Yellow		$RuCl_3 + PR_3 + X^-$	133, 288
	$RuX_2(AsMePh_2)_4$ (X = Cl, Br, I)			$RuX_3(AsMePh_2)_3 + H_3PO_2$	76
	$RuX_2(PPh_3)_3$ (X = Cl, Br)	Red-brown	X[186]	$RuCl_3 + PPh_3 + X^-$	288
	$RuCl_2(SbPh_3)_3$	Red		$RuCl_3 + SbPh_3$	288
	$RuHCl(PPh_3)_3$	Yellow	i.r.,n.m.r.[85]	$H_2 + RuCl_2(PPh_3)_3$	85

Table 4.7 *(continued)*

Oxidation state	Complex	Colour	Physical properties	Preparation	Ref.
II *(continued)*	*trans*-Ru $diars_2X_2$		i.r.[189]	$RuCl_3$ + diars + X^- (X = Cl, Br, I, SCN)	236
	cis- and *trans*-$RuX_2(diphosphine)_2$[a] (X = Cl, Br, I, CN, OAC, SCN)		D[51]	RuX_3 + diphosphine	51
	cis- and *trans*-$RuH_2(diphosphine)_2$[b]		i.r., n.m.r.[52]	*trans*-$RuX_2(diphosphine)_2$ + $LiAlH_4$	52, 53
	trans-$RuXR(diphosphine)_2$[c] (X = Cl, Br, I, SCN, H; R = Me, Et, Ph)		i.r., n.m.r., D[55], El[56]	$RuX_2(diphosphine)_2$ + LiR	55
	cis -and *trans*-$RuHR(diphosphine)_2$[d] (R = Me, Et, Ph)		i.r., n.m.r., D[55], El[56]	*trans*-$RuXR(diphosphine)_2$ + $LiAlH_4$	55
	$RuClMe(o\text{-}C_6H_4(AsMe_2)_2)_2$		i.r., n.m.r., D[55]	$RuCl_2(o\text{-}C_6H_4(AsMe_2)_2)_2$ + LiMe	55
	cis-$RuR_2(diphosphine)_2$[d] (R = Me, Et, Ph)		i.r., n.m.r., D[55], El[56]	$RuClR(diphosphine)_2$ + LiR	55
	trans-$RuHX(diphosphine)_2$[a] (X = Cl, Br, I, SCN, CN, NO_2, H)		i.r., n.m.r.[52]	*cis*- or *trans*-RuX_2(diphos-phine)$_2$ + $LiAlH_4$	52
	Na[RuH(diphosphine)$_2$] (solution only)			*trans*-$RuHBr(diphosphine)_2$ + Na napth.	53
	cis = $RuHR(diphosphine)_2$[e]		i.r., n.m.r.[53]	R^- + *cis*- or *trans*-$RuCl_2$-(diphosphine)$_2$	53

Table 4.7 *(continued)*

Oxidation state	Complex	Colour	Physical properties[a]	Preparation	Ref.
II *continued)*	$RuX_2(PPh_3)_2L$ ($X = Cl, Br$); $L = C_7H_8, C_8H_{12}$	Yellow		$RuX_2(PPh_3)_4 + L$	127, 263
	trans-$RuHCl(o\text{-}C_6H_4(AsMe_2)_2)_2$		i.r., n.m.r.[52]		52
	$Ru(NO)X_3(LR_3)_2$ ($X = Cl, I$; $LR_3 = PR_3, PEt_3, PBu_3$, As Ph_3, Ph_2MeAs, diars, $SbPh_3$, PhSMe)		i.r.[87,87a]	$[Ru(NO)Cl_3]_n + LR_3$	87a
I	$[Ru(NO)I_2(Ph_2MeAs)_2]_2$		i.r.[155a]	$[Ru(NO)I_2]_n + Ph_2MeAs$	155a
O	$Ru(diphosphine)_2$		i.r., n.m.r., D[53]	*trans*-$RuCl_2(diphosphine)_2$ + Na napth	53
	$Na[RuH(diphosphine)_2]^e$ (soln. only)			$[RuHBr(diphosphine)_2]$ + Na napth	53

[a] Diphosphine = $C_2H_4(PR_2)_2$(R = Me, Et, Ph); $CH_2(PPh_2)_2$ and $O^-C_5H_4(PEt_2)_2$
[b] Diphosphine = $C_2H_4(PR_2)_2$(R = Me, Et) and $O^-C_6H_4(PEt_2)_2$
[c] Diphosphine = $C_2H_4(PR_2)_2$(R = Me, Ph); $CH_2(PPh_2)_2$
[d] Diphosphine = $C_2H_4(PR_2)_2$(R = Me, Ph)
[e] Diphosphine = $C_2H_4(PMe_2)_2$
[f] See also pp. 171 and 177 and also Tables 4.9 and 4.10

Table 4.8 Structural data on ruthenium (II) nitrosyl complexes

Complex	Ru—N distance (Å)	N—O distance (Å)	Ru$\hat{N}$O angle	Ref.
$Na_2[Ru(NO)(OH)(NO_2)_4]$[a]	1·748	1·127	180°	283
$K_2[Ru(NO)(OH)(NO_2)_4]$	1·85	1·10	170°	27
$K_2[Ru(NO)Cl_5]$	1·70	1·25	180°	175
$[Ru(NO)(OH)(NH_3)_4]Cl_2$	2·07	1·14	150°	26
$(NH_4)_2[Ru(NO)(OH)Cl_4]$	2·04	1·13	153°	242
$Ru(NO)(Et_2NCS_2)_3$	1·72	1·17	170°	70a
$[Ru(NO)(NH_3)_5]Cl_3$	1·80	1·10	167°	175

[a] Neutron diffraction measurements; others by x-rays.

Table 4.9 Nitrosyl complexes of ruthenium[a]

Oxidation state	Complex	Colour	Physical properties	Preparation	Ref.	Pages in text
II	$[Ru(NO)(OH)_3]_n$	Brown		$[Ru(NO)Cl_3]_n + OH^-$	163	
	$[Ru(NO)X_3]_n$ (X = Cl, Br, I)			$RuO_4 + HX + HNO_3$	159, 163	175
	$[Ru(NO)X_5]^{2-}$	Red	i.r.[58a,103a]	$[Ru(NO)X_3]_n + X^-$	163	175
	$[Ru(NO)(NO_3)_3]_n$			$RuO_4 + NO + HNO_3$	214	
	$[Ru(NO)Cl_n(H_2O)_{5-n}]^{(3-n)+}$		i.r.[220]	$[Ru(NO)Cl_3]_n + HCl$	43, 220	
	$Ru(NO)(NO_3)_y(OH)_{3-y}(H_2O)_2$			$[Ru(NO)(OH)3]_n + HNO_3$	98	
	$[Ru(NO)(H_2O)_5]^{3+}$			$[Ru(NO)(OH)_3]_n + HNO_3$	268, 299	
	$[Ru(NO)(NO_3)_n(H_2O)_{5-n}]^{(3-n)+}$			$[Ru(NO)(OH)_3]_n + HNO_3$	98a, 268	
	$[Ru(NO)(NO_3)_x(NO_2)_{3-x}(H_2O)_2]$		i.r.[33]	$[Ru(NO)(NO_3)_3]_n + NO$	33	
	$[Ru(NO)(NO_3)_3(OP(OBu)_3)]$	Red		$Bu_3PO_4 + [Ru(NO)(NO_3)_3]_n$	269	
	$Ru_2N_6O_{15}$		i.r.[215,269]	$RuO_4 + NO$	215, 269	162
	$K_2[Ru(NO)(NCS)_5]$		n.m.r.[146]	$K_2[Ru(NO)Cl_5] + KNCS$	146	176
	$Na_2[Ru(NO)(OH)(NO_2)_4]$	Orange	i.r.[190,270]	$RuCl_3 + NaNO_2$	164	175
	$K_2[Ru(NO)(CN)_5]$	Brown	i.r.[190]	$K_4[Ru(CN)_6] + HNO_3$	204a	184
	$Ru(NO)Cl_3L_2$ (L = PR_3, AsR_3, SbR_3, $\frac{1}{2}$ diars; $\frac{1}{2}$ bipy, $\frac{1}{2}$ phen)		i.r.[54a,87a]	$[Ru(NO)Cl_3]_n + L$	54a, 87a	180
	$Ru(NO)(S_2CNEt_2)_3$	Red	X[70a]	$NO + Ru(S_2CNEt_2)_3$	200	176
I	$[Ru(NO)X_2]_n$ (X = Br, I)			$[RuX_2(CO)_2]_n + NO(230°)$	209	180
	$[Ru(NO)I_2L_2]_2$ (L = py, $\frac{1}{2}$ bipy, Ph_2MeAs)		i.r.[155a]	$[Ru(NO)I_2]_n + L$	155a	180
	$[Ru(NO)Cl_2(acac)_2]_2$		i.r.[87a]	$[Ru(NO)Cl_3]_n + acac$	87a	
?	$[Ru(NO)_5]_n$	Black		$Ru(CO)_5 + NO$	205	176

[a] Other references in text: nitrosyl oxalates (Table 4.1); nitrosyl acetates (p. 161); nitrosyl ammines (Tables 4.2 and 4.8); nitrosyl complexes with heterocyclic bases (Tables 4.3 and 4.4); nitrosyl amines (Table 4.6); nitrosyl phosphines and arsines (Table 4.7). See also p. 174 and Table 4.8.

Table 4.10 Carbonyl complexes of ruthenium

Oxidation state	Complex	Colour	Physical properties	Preparation	Ref.
III	$Ru(CO)(PPh_3)_2Br_3$	Red		$(NH_4)_2[RuBr_5] + PPh_3 + MeOH$	288
	$[Ru(CO)Cl_5]^{2-}$	Red		$[RuCl_5(H_2O)]^{2-} + CO$	130c
	$[Ru(CO)_2((PhCH_2)_2NCS_2)_2]Cl$	Brown		$RuCl_3 + CO + EtOH + (Ph^- - CH_2)_2NCS_2^-$	175c
	$[Ru(CO)Cl_4py]^-$			$RuCl_3.aq + CO + py$	288
II	*cis*-$Ru(CO)_4I_2$	Yellow	i.r.[63]X[66]	$RuI_3 + Cu + CO$ (200 atm, 170°)	63
	$[Ru(CO)_2Cl_2]_n$	Yellow		$RuCl_2 + CO$ (210°)	59, 103, 207a
	$[Ru(CO)_2Br_2]_n$	Orange		$RuBr_3 + CO$ (270°)	207a
	$Ru(CO)(R_2NCS_2)_2$	Yellow	i.r.[175c]	$RuCl_3 + CO + EtOH + R_2NCS_2^-$	175c
	$[Ru(CO)_3(PMe_2)]_2$		i.r.[43a]	$Ru_3(CO)_{12} + P_2Me_4$	43a
	$[Ru(CO)_2I_2]_n$	Orange	i.r.[155]	$RuI_3 + CO$ (270°)	207a
	$Ru(CO)_2(R_2NCS_2)_2$ ($R = Me, C_6H_5CH_2$)	Yellow	i.r.[175c]	$RuCl_3 + CO + EtOH + R_2NCS_2^-$	175c
	$[Ru(CO)_2(C_6H_5S)_2]_3$	Brown	i.r.[175c]	$RuCl_3 + CO + EtOH + C_6H_5SH$	175c
	$[Ru(CO)_2(NO_2)_2]_n$	Brown	i.r.[43a]	$NO + H_2O + Ru_3(CO)_{12}$	43a
	$Ru(CO)_3I_2(PPh_3)$	Brown	i.r.[43a]	$Ru_3(CO)_9(PPh_3)_3 + I_2$	43a
	$[Ru(CO)_3I(PMe_2)]_2$	Yellow	i.r.[43a]	$[Ru(CO)_3(PMe_2)]_2 + I_2$	43a
	$[Ru(CO)Cl_4(H_2O)]^{2-}$	Yellow	i.r.[130c]	$H_2 + [Ru(CO)Cl_5]^{2-}$	130c
	$Ru(CO)_2I_2L_2$ ($L = PPh_3$, py, NH_3, $AsMePh_2$)		i.r.[155]	$[Ru(CO)_2I_2]_n + L$	155
	cis-$Ru(CO)_2X_2(LPh_3)_2$ (X = Cl, Br, I; L = P, As, Sb)	Colourless	i.r.[288]	$RuCl_3 + EtOH + CO + LR_3 + X^-$	288

Table 4.10 (*continued*)

Oxidation state	Complex	Colour	Physical properties	Preparation	Ref.
II (*continued*)	*trans*-$Ru(CO)_2X_2(PPh_3)_2$ (X = Cl, Br, I)	Yellow		$RuX_2(PPh_3)_4 + CO + Me_2CO$	155, 288
	cis-$Ru(CO)_2Cl_2(PEt_3)_2$	Colourless	i.r.[54], D[54]	$RuCl_3 + PEt_3 + KOH$ + allyl alcohol	54
	cis-$Ru(CO)_2(AsMePh_2)_2I_2$	Yellow	i.r.[155]	$[Ru(CO)_2I_2] + AsMePh_2$	155
	trans-$Ru(CO)_2(PEt_3)_2Cl_2$		i.r.[54], D[54]	$RuCl_3 + CO + PEt_3$ (80°)	54
	trans-$Ru(CO)_2(PEt_2Ph)_2Cl_2$		i.r., D[54]	$RuCl_3 + CO + PEt_2Ph$	54
	$Ru(CO)_2Cl_2L_2$ (L = py, β-pic, quinoline)		i.r.[288]	$RuCl_3 + CO + L$	288
	$[Hg—RuX(CO)_3(PPh_3)_2]HgX_3$ (X = Cl, Br, I)		i.r.[59a]	$Ru(CO)_3(PPh_3)_2 + HgX_2$	59a
	$RuXY(CO)(PMe_2Ph)_3$ (X = Y = Cl, Br, I, SCN; X = Br, I, Y = Cl; X = H, Y = Cl, Br, I)		n.m.r.[156c]		156c
	$RuX_2(CO)_2(PMe_2Ph)_3$ (X = Cl, Br, I)		n.m.r.[156c]		156c
	$Ru(CO)(PEt_2Ph)_3Cl_2$	Colourless	i.r., D[54]	$RuCl_3 + PEt_2Ph$ + 2-methoxyethanol	54
	$RuBr_2(CO)(PEt_2Ph)_3$	Yellow	i.r., D[54]	$[Ru_2Cl_3(PEt_2Ph)_6]Cl + LiBr$	54
	$Ru(CO)I_2(PEt_2Ph)_3$	Yellow	i.r., D[54]	$Ru(CO)HI(PEt_2Ph) + EtOH + KI$	54
	$RuHX(CO)(PR_3)_3$ (X = Cl, Br, I; PR_3 = PPh_3, PEt_2Ph)		i.r., D[54]	$[Ru_2Cl_3(PR_3)_6]Cl + EtOH + KOH + X^-$	54
	$[Ru(CO)(S_2CNR_2)_2]_n$			$RuCl_3 + R_2NCS_2 + CO$	175c
	$Ru(CO)_2X_2L_2$ (X = Cl, Br; L = $PhNH_2$, $PhCH_2NH_2$, $\frac{1}{2}$ phen)		i.r.[175b]	$RuCl_3 + CO + L + Br^-$	175b

Table 4.10 (*continued*)

Oxidation state	Complex	Colour	Physical properties	Preparation	Ref.
II (*continued*)	$Ru(CO)_2(C_6H_4(S)NH_2)_2$		i.r.[175b]	$RuCl_3 + CO + C_6H_4(S)NH_2$	175b
	$Ru(CO)_2Cl_2$ bipy		i.r.[175b]	$RuCl_3 + CO +$ bipy	175b
	$[Ru(CO)_2(SEt_2)_3(SnCl_3)]^+$		i.r.[175b]	$RuCl_3 + CO + SnCl_2 + Et_2S$	175b
	$CpRu(CO)_2Br$			$[CpRu(CO)_2]_2 + Br_2$	92, 94
	$[Ru(CO)_2(SnX_3)_2X_2]^{2-}$ (X = Cl, Br)			$SnX_3^- + RuCl_3 + EtOH + CO$	175b, 288
	$Ru_2Cl_3(SnCl_3)(CO)_2(PPh_3)_3L$ ($L = PPh_3$, 2 Me_2CO)	Yellow		$RuCl_3 + CO + PPh_3 + L + SnCl_3^-$	288
	$[RuCl_2(CO)diene]_2$ (diene = C_7H_8, C_8H_{12})			$RuCl_3.aq + CO +$ diene + EtOH	263
	$RuCl_2(CO)py_3$			$RuCl_2(CO)$ diene + py	263
I	$[Ru(CO)Br]_n$	Colourless		$RuBr_3 + CO$ (350 atm, 180°)	208
	$[Ru(CO)_xI]_n$	Orange		$RuI_3 + CO$ (500 atm, 170°) + Ag	205
	$H_3Ru_4(CO)_{12}$	Orange		$RuCl_3 + CO + H_2$ (200 atm)	156a
	$[CpRu(CO)_2]_2$			$[Ru(CO)_2I_2]_2 + NaCp$	92, 94
0	$(Ru(CO)_5$	Colourless		$RuI_3 + CO(170°)$	205
	$Ru_3(CO)_{12}$	Yellow	i.r.[64]	Heat $Ru(CO)_5$	205
	?$[Ru(CO)]_n$	Green		$KOH + Ru_3(CO)_{12}$	205, 208
	$Ru(CO)_3(PPh_3)_2$	Yellow		$[RuCl_2(CO)_2(PPh_3)_2] + Zn + CO$	59
	$Ru_3(CO)_9(PPh_3)_3$		i.r.[43a]	$Ru_3(CO)_{12} + PPh_3$	43a

[a] See also pp. 182 and 185.

Table 4.11 Magnetic measurements on ruthenium complexes[a]

Complex	X_A (× 10^6 c.g.s. units)[a]		μ_{eff} (BM)		Ref.
$RuOF_4$	9508 (102°)	3655 (287°)	2·80 (102°)	2·91 (287°)	143
$[RuF_5]_4$	13653 (100°)	5516 (292°)	3·32 (100°)	3·60 (292°)	143
$K[RuF_6]$	15800 (90°)	4996 (295°)	3·40 (90°)	3·48 (295°)	306
$Cs[RuF_6]$	17190 (90°)	5335 (295°)	3·54 (90°)	3·60 (295°)	306
$[RuF_4]_n$	8941 (88°)	3959 (291°)		3·04 (291°)	144
$K_2[RuF_6]$	3853 (89°)	3397 (297°)		2·86 (297°)	78
$K_2[RuCl_6]$	3870 (78°)	3450 (298°)		2·88 (298°)	158
$Rb_2[RuCl_6]$	4266 (93°)	3765 (296°)		3·01 (296°)	78
$K_2[RuBr_6]$	3573 (96°)	3338 (297°)		2·84 (297°)	78
$Rb_2[RuBr_6]$	3433 (89°)	3194 (293°)		2·81 (293°)	78
$RuCl_3$	8150 (77°)	2310 (294°)			84, 153
$Na_3[RuCl_6].12H_2O$	4725 (90°)	2140 (291°)	1·85 (90°)	2·24 (291°)	40
$K_2[RuCl_5(H_2O)]$	4983 (90°)	1872 (291°)	1·90 (90°)	2·19 (291°)	40
$Cs_2[RuCl_5(H_2O)]$	4670 (90°)	1755 (291°)	1·84 (90°)	2·14 (291°)	40
$K_2[RuCl_5]$			1·14 (80°)	1·64 (300°)	79
$[Ru(NH_3)_6]Cl_3$	4331 (90°)	1984 (291°)	1·77 (90°)	2·15 (291°)	40, 90a
Ru $acac_3$	4004 (90°)	1438 (291°)	1·70 (90°)	1·93 (291°)	40, 90a
$Ru(Me_2NCS_2)_3$	1930 (191°)	1115 (373°)	1·74 (191°)	1·83 (373°)	200
$[Ru_2(OCOMe)_4Cl]$	8578 (106°)	3446 (291°)		2·88 (291°)	287
$[Ru(NH_3)_5Cl]Cl_2.H_2O$	5213 (78°)	2093 (293·2°)	1.81 (78°)	2·23 (293°)	90a
bipy H[Ru bipy Cl_4]	5340 (78°)	2244 (295°)	1·82 (78°)	2·31 (295°)	90a
$[Ru(NH_3)_6](NO_3)_3.3H_2O$	5096 (87°)	1994 (292°)	1·90 (87°)	2·17 (292°)	90a

[a] Temperatures (in parentheses) in °K.

Table 4.12 Selected data on polarography of ruthenium complexes

Complex	Process	$E_{1/2}$ (versus s.c.e.)	Medium	Ref.
RuO_4	VIII→VII	$+1{\cdot}00^{a,b}$	ClO_4^-	282
$[RuO_4]^-$	VII →VI	$+0{\cdot}61^{a,b}$	ClO_4^-	282
$[Ru(H_2O)_6]^{4+}$	IV →III	$-0{\cdot}22$	$HClO_4$	232
	III →II	$-0{\cdot}81$	$HClO_4$	232
$[Ru(CN)_6]^{3-}$	III →II	$-0{\cdot}72^{b}$	0·2M KCl	99

[a] Hydrogen electrode.
[b] Reversible.

REFERENCES

1. Abel, E. W., M. A. Bennett and G. Wilkinson, *J. Chem. Soc.*, **1959**, 3178.
2. Adams, D. M., and H. A. Gebbie, *Spectrochim. Acta*, **19**, 925 (1963).
2a. Adams, D. M., *J. Chem. Soc.*, **1964**, 1771.
3. Adams, D., and D. P. Mellor, *Austr. J. Sci. Res.*, **5** (A), 577 (1952).
4. Alcock, C. B., and G. W. Hooper, *Proc. Roy. Soc.* (*London*), *Ser A*, **254**, 551 (1960).
5. Alcock, C. B., *Trans. Brit. Ceram. Soc.*, **60**, 147 (1961).
5a. Alderson, T., E. L. Jenner and R. V. Lindsey, *J. Am. Chem. Soc.*, **87**, 5638 (1965).
6. Allen, A. D., and C. V. Senoff, *Can. J. Chem.*, **43**, 888 (1965).
6a. Allen, A. D., and C. V. Senoff, *Chem. Commun.*, **1965**, 621.
7. Anderson, J. S., and J. D. M. McConnell, *J. Inorg. Nucl. Chem.*, **1**, 371 (1955).
8. Anthony, U., and A. Lucchesi, *Gazz. Chim. Ital.*, **30**, II, 71, 539 (1900).
9. Aoyama, S., *Z. Anorg. Allgem. Chem.*, **138**, 249 (1924).
10. Aoyama, S., *Z. Anorg. Allgem. Chem.*, **138**, 263 (1924); *Sci. Rept. Tohôku Univ., First Ser.*, **14**, 16 (1925).
11. Atwood, D. K., and T. de Vries, *J. Am. Chem. Soc.*, **83**, 1509 (1961).
12. Atwood, D. K., and T. de Vries, *J. Am. Chem. Soc.*, **84**, 2659 (1962).
13. Avtokratova, T. D., and V. I. Goremykin, *Izv. Akad. Nauk. SSSR*, **1947**, 427; *Chem. Abstr.*, **42**, 1839.
14. Aynsley, E. E., R. D. Peacock and P. L. Robinson, *Chem. Ind.* (*London*), **1952**, 1002.
15. Baranaev, M. K., V. G. Vereskunov and K. P. Zakharova, *At. Energ.* (*USSR*), **17**, 502 (1964).
16. Barbieri, G. A., *Atti Acad. Linc.*, **23** (5), I, 336 (1914).
17. Bartlett, N., and N. K. Jha, in *Noble Gas Compounds* (Ed. H. H. Hyman), Chicago, 1963.
18. Barton, G. B., *Spectrochim. Acta*, **19**, 1619 (1963).
19. Bell, W. E., M. C. Garrison and U. Merten, *J. Phys. Chem.*, **65**, 517 (1961).
20. Bell, W. E., and M. Tagami, *J. Phys. Chem.*, **67**, 2432 (1963).
21. Bennett, M. A., and G. Wilkinson, *Chem. Ind.* (*London*), **1959**, 1516.
22. Berezin, B. D., and G. V. Sennikova, *Proc. Acad. Sci. USSR* (*Eng. Transl.*) **159**, 1127 (1964).

23. Berkowitz, L. M., and P. N. Rylander, *J. Am. Chem. Soc.*, **80**, 6682 (1958).
24. Beynon, P. J., P. M. Collins and W. G. Overend, *Proc. Chem. Soc.* (*London*), **1964**, 342.
24a. Beynon, P. J., P. M. Collins, P. T. Doganges and W. G. Overend, *J. Chem. Soc.*, *Ser. C*, **1966**, 1131.
25. Biltz, W., and H. Ehrhon, *Z. Anorg. Allgem. Chem.*, **240**, 117 (1939).
26. Bokii, G. B., and N. A. Parpiev, *Soviet Phys. Cryst.* (*Eng. Transl.*), **2**, 681 (1957).
27. Bokii, G. B., Wang Ang-nu and T. S. Khodashova, *J. Struct. Chem. USSR, Eng. Transl.*, **3**, 149 (1962).
27a. Bottomley, F., and S. C. Nyburg, *Chem. Commun.*, **1966**, 897.
27b. Brandstetr, J., and J. Vrestal, *Coll. Chem. Czech. Commun.*, **31**, 58 (1966).
27c. Brauer, G., *Handbook of Preparative Inorganic Chemistry*, Academic Press, New York, 1965, p. 1597.
28. Braune, H., and K. Stute, *Angew. Chem.*, **51**, 528 (1938).
29. Brizard, L., *Ann. Chim. Phys.*, **21** (7), 311 (1900); Compt. Rend., **123**, 182 (1896).
30. Brodersen, K., F. Moers and H. G. Schnering, *Naturwiss.*, **52**, 205 (1965).
31. Broomhead, J. A., F. Basolo and R. G. Pearson, *Inorg. Chem.*, **3**, 826 (1964).
32. Brown, D. R., D. R. Russell and D. W. A. Sharp, *J. Chem. Soc.*, **1966**, Ser. A, 18.
32a. Brown, D. H., K. R. Dixon, R. D. W. Kemmitt and D. W. A. Sharp, *J. Chem. Soc.*, **1965**, 1559.
33. Brown, P. G. M., *J. Inorg. Nucl. Chem.*, **13**, 73 (1960).
33a. Bruce, M. I., and F. G. A. Stone, *Chem. Commun.*, **1966**, 684.
34. Bublitz, D. E., W. E. McEwen and J. Kleinberg, *Org. Syn.*, **41**, 96 (1961).
35. Bublitz, D. E., W. E. McEwen and J. Kleinberg, *J. Am. Chem. Soc.*, **84**, 1845 (1962).
35a. Buckley, R. R., and E. E. Mercer, *J. Phys. Chem.*, **70**, 3103 (1966).
36. Buell, G. R., W. E. McEwen and J. Kleinberg, *J. Am. Chem. Soc.*, **84**, 40 (1962).
37. Buividaite, M., *Z. Anorg. Allgem. Chem.*, **230**, 286 (1937).
38. Buividaite, M., *Z. Anorg. Allgem. Chem.*, **222**, 279 (1935).
39. Burstall, F. H., *J. Chem. Soc.*, **1936**, 173.
40. Buschbeck, C., and H. Hartmann, *Z. Physik. Chem.* (*Frankfurt*), **11**, 120 (1957).
41. Busev, A. I., and M. I. Ivanyutin, *Tr. Komis. Analit. Khim. Akad. Nauk SSSR, Inst. Geokhim. i Analit. Khim.*, **11**, 172 (1960).
42. Cady, H. H., and R. E. Connick, *J. Am. Chem. Soc.*, **80**, 2646 (1958).
42a. Callaghan, A., C. W. Moeller and R. Ward, *Inorg. Chem.*, **5**, 1572 (1966).
42b. Cambi, L., and L. Malatesta, *Rend. Ist. Lombardo. Sci. Lettere A*, **71**, 118 (1938).
43. Campbell, W. M., and R. M. Wallace, *U.S. At. Energy Comm., TID-15360* (1962).
43a. Candlin, J. P., K. K. Joshi and D. T. Thompson, *Chem. Ind.* (*London*), **1966**, 1960.
44. Carrington, A., and M. C. R. Symons, *J. Chem. Soc.*, **1960**, 284.
44a. Carrington, A., D. J. E. Ingram, D. Schonland and M. C. R. Symons, *J. Chem. Soc.*, **1956**, 4710.

44b. Chalandon, P., and B. P. Susz, *Helv. Chim. Acta*, **41**, 697 (1958).
45. Charronat, R., *Ann. Chim.* (*Paris*), **16** (10), 40, 68 (1931).
46. Charronat, R., *Ann. Chim.* (*Paris*), **16** (10), 123, 168, 188 (1931).
47. Charronat, R., *Compt. Rend.*, **178**, 1279, 1423 (1924).
48. Charronat, R., in P. Pascal, *Traité de Chimie Minerale, Paris*, **11**, 433 (1932).
49. Charronat, R., *Ann. Chim.* (*Paris*), **16** (10), 179, 188, 235 (1931).
50. Chatt, J., L. A. Duncanson and L. M. Venanzi, *Suomen Kemistilehti*, **29B**, 75 (1956).
51. Chatt, J., and R. G. Hayter, *J. Chem. Soc.*, **1961**, 896.
52. Chatt, J., and R. G. Hayter, *J. Chem. Soc.*, **1961**, 2605.
53. Chatt, J., and J. M. Davidson, *J. Chem. Soc.*, **1965**, 843.
54. Chatt, J., B. L. Shaw and A. E. Field, *J. Chem. Soc.*, **1964**, 3466.
54a. Chatt, J., and B. L. Shaw, *J. Chem. Soc., Ser. A*, **1966**, 1811.
55. Chatt, J., and R. G. Hayter, *J. Chem. Soc.*, **1963**, 6017.
56. Chatt, J., and R. G. Hayter, *J. Chem. Soc.*, **1961**, 772.
57. Claassen, H. H., H. Selig, J. G. Malm, C. L. Chernick and B. Weinstock, *J. Am. Chem. Soc.*, **83**, 2390 (1961).
58. Claus, C., *Ann.*, **54**, 236 (1846).
58a. Cleare, M., and W. P. Griffith, *J. Chem. Soc.*, **1967**, *Ser. A, in press.*
59. Collmann, J. P., and W. R. Roper, *J. Am. Chem. Soc.*, **87**, 4008 (1965).
59a. Collmann, J. P., and W. R. Roper, *Chem. Commun.*, **1966**, 244.
60. Connick, R. E., in *Advances in the Chemistry of the Co-ordination Compounds* (Ed. S. Kirschner), Macmillan, New York, 1961, p. 15.
61. Connick, R., and D. A. Fine, *J. Am. Chem. Soc.*, **83**, 3414 (1961); **82**, 4187 (1960).
62. Connick, R. E., and C. R. Hurley, *J. Am. Chem. Soc.*, **74**, 5012 (1952).
63. Corey, E. R., M. V. Evans and L. F. Dahl, *J. Inorg. Nucl. Chem.*, **24**, 926 (1962).
64. Corey, E. R., and L. F. Dahl, *J. Am. Chem. Soc.*, **83**, 2203 (1961).
64a. Cotton, F. A., and J. T. Mague, *Inorg. Chem.*, **5**, 317 (1966).
64b. Cotton, F. A., and G. Yagupsky, *Inorg. Chem.*, **6**, 15(1967).
64c. Cram, R., and W. P. Griffith, *Unpublished observations.*
65. Crosby, G. A., W. G. Perkins and D. M. Klassen, *J. Chem. Phys.*, **43**, 1498 (1965).
66. Dahl, L. F., and D. L. Wampler, *Acta Cryst.*, **15**, 946 (1962).
66a. Davison, A., J. A. McCleverty and G. Wilkinson, *J. Chem. Soc.*, **1963**, 1133.
67. Debray, H., and H. Joly, *Compt. Rend.*, **106**, 331, 1499 (1888).
68. Dillard, J. G., and R. W. Kiser, *J. Phys. Chem.*, **69**, 3893 (1965).
68a. Dingle, R., *J. Mol. Spectry.*, **18**, 276 (1965).
69. Djerassi, C., and R. R. Engle, *J. Am. Chem. Soc.*, **75**, 3838 (1953).
70. Dodd, R. E., *Trans. Faraday Soc.*, **55**, 1480 (1959).
70a. Domenicano, A., A. Vaciago, L. Zambonelli, P. L. Loader and L. M. Venanzi, *Chem. Commun.*, **1966**, 476.
71. Donohue, P. C., L. Katz and R. Ward, *Inorg. Chem.*, **4**, 306 (1965).
71a. Donohue, P. C., L. Katz and R. Ward, *Inorg. Chem.*, **5**, 335, 339 (1966).
72. Dunitz, J., and L. E. Orgel, *J. Chem. Soc.*, **1953**, 2594.
72a. Durig, J. R., W. A. McAllister, J. N. Willis and E. E. Mercer, *Spectrochim. Acta*, **22**, 1091 (1966).

73. Dwyer, F. P., and A. M. Sargeson, *J. Phys. Chem.*, **60**, 1331 (1956).
74. Dwyer, F. P., H. A. Goodwin and E. C. Gyarfas, *Australian J. Chem.*, **16**, 42, 544 (1963).
75. Dwyer, F. P., and E. C. Gyarfas, *J. Proc. Roy. Soc. N. S. Wales*, **83**, 170, 174 (1949).
76. Dwyer, F. P., J. E. Humpoletz and R. S. Nyholm, *J. Proc. Roy. Soc. N. S. Wales*, **80**, 217 (1946).
77. Dwyer, F. P., and E. C. Gyarfas, *Nature*, **163**, 918 (1949).
78. Earnshaw, A., B. N. Figgis, J. Lewis and R. D. Peacock, *J. Chem. Soc.*, **1961**, 3132.
79. Earnshaw, A., B. N. Figgis, J. Lewis and R. S. Nyholm, *Nature*, **179**, 1121 (1957).
80. Eaton, D. R., *J. Am. Chem. Soc.*, **87**, 3097 (1965).
81. Eichler, E. and A. C. Wahl, *J. Am. Chem. Soc.*, **80**, 4145 (1958).
82. Endicott, J. F., and H. Taube, *J. Am. Chem. Soc.*, **84**, 4984 (1962).
83. Endicott, J. F., and H. Taube, *Inorg. Chem.*, **4**, 437 (1965).
84. Epstein, C., and N. Elliott, *J. Chem. Phys.*, **22**, 634 (1954).
85. Evans, D., F. H. Jardine, J. A. Osborn and G. Wilkinson, *Nature*, **205**, 1203 (1965).
86. Evans, D. F., D. Jones and G. Wilkinson, *J. Chem. Soc.*, **1964**, 3164.
86a. Ezerskaya, N. A., and T. P. Solobykh, *Zh. Neorgan. Khim.*, **11**, 1462, 1855, 2179 (1966).
87. Fairy, M. B., and R. J. Irving, *Spectrochim. Acta*, **20**, 1757 (1964).
87a. Fairy, M. B., and R. J. Irving, *Spectrochim. Acta*, **22**, 359 (1966); *J. Chem. Soc., Ser. A*, **1966**, 475.
88. Fergusson, J. E., J. D. Karran and S. Seevaratnan, *J. Chem. Soc.*, **1965**, 2627.
88a. Fergusson, J. E., and G. M. Harris, *J. Chem. Soc., Ser. A.*, **1966**, 1293.
89. Figgis, B. N., and G. B. Robertson, *Nature*, **205**, 694 (1965).
90. Figgis, B. N., and J. Lewis, *Progr. Inorg. Chem.*, **6**, 37 (1965).
90a. Figgis, B. N., J. Lewis, F. E. Mabbs and G. A. Webb, *J. Chem. Soc., Ser. A*, **1966**, 422.
91. Fischer, E. O., and R. Böttcher, *Z. Anorg. Allgem. Chem.*, **291**, 305 (1957).
92. Fischer, E. O., and A. Vogler, *Z. Naturforsch.*, **17B**, 421 (1962).
93. Fischer, E. O., and J. Müller, *Ber.*, **96**, 3217 (1963).
94. Fischer, R. D., and A. Vogler, *Angew. Chem.*, **4**, 700 (1965); Fischer, R. D., A. Vogler and K. Noack, *J. Organomet. Chem.*, **7**, 135 (1967); Noack, K., *J. Organomet. Chem.*, **7**, 151(1967).
95. Fletcher, J. M., W. E. Gardner, E. W. Hooper, K. R. Hyde, F. H. Moore and J. L. Woodhead, *Nature*, **199**, 1089 (1963).
96. Fletcher, J. M., B. F. Greenfield, C. J. Hardy, D. Scargill and J. L. Woodhead, *J. Chem. Soc.*, **1961**, 2000.
97. Fletcher, J. M., and J. L. Woodhead, *J. Inorg. Nucl. Chem.*, **27**, 1517 (1965).
98. Fletcher, J. M., I. L. Jenkins, F. M. Lever, F. S. Martin, A. R. Powell and R. Todd, *J. Inorg. Nucl. Chem.*, **1**, 378 (1955).
98a. Fletcher, J. M., C. E. Lyon and A. G. Wain, *J. Inorg. Nucl. Chem.*, **27**, 1841 (1965).

99. de Ford, D., and A. W. Davidson, *J. Am. Chem. Soc.*, **73**, 1469 (1951).
100. Forsythe, J. H. W., R. J. Magee and C. L. Wilson, *Talanta*, **3**, 324 (1960).
101. Fourcroy, and Vauquelin, *Ann. Chim.* (*Paris*), **50**, 5 (1804); **49**, 188 (1804).
102. Fraenkel, G., R. E. Carter, A. McLachlan and J. H. Richards, *J. Am. Chem. Soc.*, **82**, 5846 (1960).
102a. Fritz, H. P., and C. G. Kreiter, *J. Organomet. Chem.*, **4**, 198 (1965).
103. Gall, H., and G. Lehmann, *Ber.*, **59**, 2856 (1926).
103a. Gans, P., A. Sabatini and L. Sacconi, *Inorg. Chem.*, **5**, 1877 (1966).
104. George, P., G. I. H. Hanania and D. H. Irvine, *J. Chem. Soc.*, **1959**, 2548.
105. George, P., and D. H. Irvine, *J. Chem. Soc.*, **1954**, 587.
106. Ginsberg, A. P. and E. Koubek, *Inorg. Chem.*, **4**, 1186 (1965).
107. Gleu, K., W. Breuel and W. Rehm, *Z. Anorg. Allgem. Chem.*, **235**, 201, 211 (1938).
108. Gleu, K., and K. Rehm, *Z. Anorg. Allgem. Chem.*, **227**, 237 (1936); **235**, 356 (1938).
109. Gleu, K., and W. Cuntze, *Z. Anorg. Allgem. Chem.*, **237**, 187 (1938).
110. Gleu, K., and I. Buddecker, *Z. Anorg. Allgem. Chem.*, **268**, 202 (1952).
111. Gleu, K., and W. Breuel, *Z. Anorg. Allgem. Chem.*, **237**, 197, 335 (1938).
112. Godward, L. W. N., and W. Wardlaw, *J. Chem. Soc.*, **1938**, 1422.
112a. Goswani, K. N., and S. K. Datta, *Ind. J. Phys.*, **37**, 604 (1963).
113. Gordon, B. M., L. L. Williams and N. Sutin, *J. Am. Chem. Soc.*, **83**, 2061 (1961).
114. Gortsema, F. P., and J. W. Cobble, *J. Am. Chem. Soc.*, **83**, 4317 (1961).
115. Goryunov, A. A., and L. L. Sveshnikova, *Russ. J. Inorg. Chem.*, *Eng. Transl.*, **6**, 793 (1961).
115a. Goryunov, A. A., Vestnik Leningrad Univ. No. 16, *Ser. Fiz. i Khim.* No. 1, 105 (1961).
116. Gray, H. B., and N. A. Beach, *J. Am. Chem. Soc.*, **85**, 2922 (1963).
117. Griffith, W. P., unpublished results.
117a. Griffith, W. P., *J. Chem. Soc.*, *Ser. A*, **1966**, 899.
117b. Griffith, W. P., *J. Chem. Soc.*, *Ser. A*, **1966**, 1467.
118. Griffith, W. P., J. Lewis and G. Wilkinson, *J. Chem. Soc.*, **1958**, 3993.
118a. Griffith, W. P., *Quart. Rev.* (*London*), **16**, 188 (1962).
119. Griffiths, J. H. E., Owen, J. and I. M. Ward, *Proc. Roy. Soc.* (*London*), *Ser. A*, **219**, 526 (1953).
119a. Grobelny, R., B. Jezowska-Trzebiatowski and W. Wojciechowski, *J. Inorg. Nucl. Chem.* **28**, 2715 (1966).
120. Gutbier, A., and C. Trennkner, *Z. Anorg. Allgem. Chem.*, **45**, 166 (1905).
121. Gutbier, A., F. Falco and Th. Vogt, *Z. Anorg. Allgem. Chem.*, **115**, 225 (1921).
122. Gutbier, A., *Angew. Chem.*, **22**, 487 (1909).
123. Gutbier, A., F. Falco and H. Zwicker, *Angew. Chem.*, **22**, 490 (1909).
124. Gutbier, A., and F. Krauss, *J. Prakt. Chem.*, **91** (2), 103 (1915).
125. Gutbier, A., *Ber.*, **56**, 1008 (1923); *Z. Anorg. Allgem. Chem.*, **129**, 83 (1923).
126. Guthrie, A. N., and L. T. Bourland, *Phys. Rev.*, **37** (2), 303 (1931).
127. Guy, R. G., and B. L. Shaw, *Adv. Inorg. Chem. Radiochem.*, **4**, 77 (1962).

128. Hair, M. L., and P. L. Robinson, *J. Chem. Soc.*, **1960**, 2775; **1958**, 106.
129. Halpern, J., B. R. James and A. L. W. Kemp, *J. Am. Chem. Soc.*, **83**, 4097 (1961).
130. Halpern, J., J. F. Harrod and B. R. James, *J. Am. Chem. Soc.*, **83**, 753 (1961).
130a. Halpern, J., and B. R. James, *Can. J. Chem.*, **44**, 495, 671 (1966).
130b. Halpern, J., and A. L. W. Kemp, *J. Am. Chem. Soc.*, **88**, 5147 (1966).
130c. Halpern, J., B. R. James and A. L. W. Kemp, *J. Am. Chem. Soc.*, **88**, 5142 (1966).
130d. Halpern, J., J. F. Harrod and B. R. James, *J. Am. Chem. Soc.*, **88**, 5150 (1966).
131. Hardgrove, G. L., and D. H. Templeton, *Acta Cryst.*, **12**, 28 (1959).
132. Harrod, J. F., S. Ciccone and J. Halpern, *Can. J. Chem.*, **39**, 1372 (1961).
133. Hayter, R. G., *Inorg. Chem.*, **3**, 301 (1964).
134. Hepworth, M. A., R. D. Peacock and P. L. Robinson, *J. Chem. Soc.*, **1954**, 1197.
135. Hepworth, M. A., and P. L. Robinson, *J. Inorg. Nucl. Chem.*, **4**, 24 (1957).
136. Hepworth, M. A., P. L. Robinson and G. J. Westland, *J. Chem. Soc.*, **1954**, 4269.
137. Hepworth, M. A., K. H. Jack, R. D. Peacock and G. J. Westland, *Acta Cryst.*, **10**, 63 (1957).
138. Hepworth, M. A., and P. L. Robinson, *J. Chem. Soc.*, **1953**, 3330.
138a. Hepworth, M. A., P. L. Robinson and G. Westland, *Chem. Ind.* (*London*), **1955**, 1516.
138b. Hercules, D. M., and F. E. Lytle, *J. Am. Chem. Soc.*, **88**, 4745 (1966).
138c. Hewkin, D., and W. P. Griffith, *J. Chem. Soc.*, A, **1966**, 472.
139. Hieber, W., and H. Heusinger, *Angew. Chem.*, **68**, 678 (1956).
140. Hill, E. A., and J. H. Richards, *J. Am. Chem. Soc.*, **83**, 3840 (1961).
141. Hill, M. A., and F. E. Beamish, *J. Am. Chem. Soc.*, **72**, 4855 (1950).
142. Holloway, J. H., R. D. Peacock and R. W. H. Small, *J. Chem. Soc.*, **1964**, 644.
143. Holloway, J. H., and R. D. Peacock, *J. Chem. Soc.*, **1963**, 527.
144. Holloway, J. H., and R. D. Peacock, *J. Chem. Soc.*, **1963**, 3892.
145. Holm, C. H., and J. A. Ibers, *J. Chem. Phys.*, **30**, 885 (1959).
145a. Hopkins, T. E., A. Zalkin, D. H. Templeton and M. G. Adamson, *Inorg. Chem.*, **5**, 1427, 1431 (1966).
146. Howarth, O. W., R. E. Richards and L. M. Venanzi, *J. Chem. Soc.*, **1964**, 3335.
147. Howe, J. L., *J. Am. Chem. Soc.*, **23**, 779 (1901).
148. Howe, J. L., *J. Am. Chem. Soc.*, **26**, 543 (1904); **49**, 2381 (1927).
149. Howe, J. L., and L. P. Haynes, *J. Am. Chem. Soc.*, **47**, 2922 (1925).
150. Howe, J. L., J. L. Howe, Jr. and S. C. Ogburn, *J. Am. Chem. Soc.*, **46**, 337 (1924).
151. Howe, J. L., *J. Am. Chem. Soc.*, **18**, 981 (1896).
152. Hurwitz, P., and K. Kustin, *Inorg. Chem.*, **3**, 823 (1964).
153. Hyde, K. R., E. W. Hooper, J. Waters and J. M. Fletcher, *J. Less-Common Metals*, **8**, 428 (1965).
154. Irvine, D. H., *J. Chem. Soc.*, **1959**, 2977.

155. Irving, R. J., *J. Chem. Soc.*, **1956**, 2879.
155a. Irving, R. J., and P. G. Laye, *J. Chem. Soc.*, **1966** (**A**), 161.
156. Jaeger, F. M., and J. H. de Boer, *Proc. Acad. Amst.*, **23**, 98 (1921).
156a. Jamieson, J. W. S., J. V. Kingston and G. Wilkinson, *Chem. Commun.*, **1966**, 569.
156b. Jenkins, E. N., *A.E.R.E. R-3491*, *Chem. Abstr.*, **55**, 8120d (1961).
156c. Jenkins, J. M., M. S. Lupin and B. L. Shaw, *J. Chem. Soc.*, *Ser. A*, **1966**, 1787.
157. Jezowska-Trzebiatowska, B., *J. Chim. Phys.*, **61**, 765 (1964).
158. Johannesen, R. B., and G. A. Candela, *Inorg. Chem.*, **2**, 67 (1963).
158a. Johnson, B. F. G., J. Lewis, I. G. Williams and J. Wilson, *Chem. Commun.*, **1966**, 391, 851.
158b. J. Lewis, A. R. Manning, J. R. Miller and J. M. Wilson, *J. Chem. Soc.*, *Ser. A*, **1966**, 1663.
159. Joly, A., in H. Remy, *Encyclopedie Chimique*, *Paris* **17**, 156 (1900).
160. Joly, A., *Compt. Rend.*, **114**, 291 (1891); **115**, 1299 (1892).
161. Joly, A., *Compt. Rend.*, **113**, 695 (1891).
162. Joly, A., and E. Leidie, *Compt. Rend.*, **118**, 168 (1894).
163. Joly, A., *Compt. Rend.*, **108**, 854 (1889); **111**, 964 (1890).
164. Joly, A., and M. Vezes, *Compt. Rend.*, **109**, 668 (1889).
165. de Jong, W. F., and A. Hoog, *Rec. Trav. Chim.*, **46**, 173 (1927).
166. Jones, D., L. Pratt and G. Wilkinson, *J. Chem. Soc.*, **1962**, 4458.
167. Jorgensen, C. K., *Acta Chem. Scand.*, **12**, 1539 (1958).
168. Jorgensen, C. K., and L. E. Orgel, *Mol. Phys.*, **4**, 215 (1961).
169. Jorgensen, C. K., *Acta Chem. Scand.*, **10**, 518 (1956).
169a. Jorgensen, C. K., *Acta Chem. Scand.*, **16**, 1048 (1962).
170. Jorgensen, C. K., *Mol. Phys.*, **2**, 309 (1959).
171. Kapustinskii, A. F., and S. I. Drakino, *Izvest. Sektera Platiny i Drug. Balgorodn. Metal. Inst. Obshch. i Neorgan. Khim. Akad. Nauk SSSR*, **27**, 160 (1952).
171a. Keattch, C. J., and J. P. Redfern, *J. Less-Common Metals*, **4**, 460 (1962).
172. Keen, I. M., and B. W. Malerbi, *J. Inorg. Nucl. Chem.*, **27**, 131 (1965).
173. Kemmitt, R. D. W., D. R. Russell and D. W. A. Sharp, *J. Chem. Soc.*, **1963**, 4408.
174. Khanolkar, D. D., *Current Sci.* (*India*), **30**, 52 (1961).
175. Khodashova, T. S., and G. B. Bokii, *J. Struct. Chem. USSR.*, *Eng. Transl.*, **1**, 138 (1960); Khodashova, T. S., *J. Struct. Chem. USSR.*, *Eng. Transl.*, **6**, 678 (1965).
175a. Khodashova, T. S., *J. Struct. Chem. USSR.*, *Eng. Transl.*, **1**, 308 (1960).
175b. Kingston, J. V., J. W. S. Jamieson and G. Wilkinson, *J. Inorg. Nucl. Chem.*, **29**, 133 (1967).
175c. Kingston, J. V., and G. Wilkinson, *J. Inorg. Nucl. Chem.*, **28**, 2709 (1967).
175d. Koch, H., and H. Bruchertseifer, *Radiochim. Acta*, **4**, 82 (1965).
176. Koda, Y., *Inorg. Chem.*, **2**, 1306 (1963).
177. Koda, Y., *J. Inorg. Nucl. Chem.*, **25**, 314 (1963).
178. Kolbin, N. I., A. N. Ryabov and V. M. Samoilov, *Russ. J. Inorg. Chem.*, *Eng. Transl.*, **8**, 805 (1963).
178a. Kralik, F., and J. Vrestal, *Coll. Czech. Chem. Commun.*, **27**, 1651 (1962).
179. Krauss, F., and H. Kukenthal, *Z. Anorg. Allgem. Chem.*, **137**, 32 (1924).

180. Krauss, F., *Z. Anorg. Allgem. Chem.*, **132**, 301 (1924).
181. Krauss, F., and G. Schrader, *Z. Anorg. Allgem. Chem.*, **176**, 385 (1928).
182. Krauss, F., *Z. Anorg. Allgem. Chem.*, **119**, 217 (1921).
183. Krauss, F., and H. Kukenthal, *Z. Anorg. Allgem. Chem.*, **132**, 315 (1924); **136**, 62 (1924).
184. Krauss, F., and G. Schrader, *Z. Anorg. Allgem. Chem.*, **173**, 63 (1928).
184a. Kruck, T., *Angew. Chem.* **6**, 53 (1967).
184b. Krueger, P. C., and M. E. Kenney, *J. Inorg. Nucl. Chem.*, **25**, 303 (1965).
185. Kuwana, T., D. E. Bublitz and G. Hoh, *J. Am. Chem. Soc.*, **82**, 5811 (1960).
186. La Placa, S. J., and J. A. Ibers, *Inorg. Chem.*, **4**, 778 (1965).
186a. Legros, J., *Compt. Rend.*, **248**, 1339 (1959).
187. Lever, F. M., and A. R. Powell, *Chem. Soc. Spec. Publ. No. 13*, 135 (1959).
188. Lever, F. M., and C. W. Bradford, *Platinum Metals Rev.*, **8**, 106 (1964).
189. Lewis, J., R. S. Nyholm and G. A. Rodley, *J. Chem. Soc.*, **1965**, 1483.
190. Lewis, J., R. J. Irving and G. Wilkinson, *J. Inorg. Nucl. Chem.*, **7**, 32 (1958).
Lewis, J. *et al.*, see 158b.
191. Lippincott, E. R. and R. D. Nelson, *J. Am. Chem. Soc.*, **77**, 4990 (1955).
192. Lippincott, E. R., and R. D. Nelson, *Spectrochim. Acta*, **10**, 307 (1958).
193. Liu, C. F., N. C. Liu and J. C. Bailar, *Inorg. Chem.*, **3**, 1085 (1964).
194. Liu, C. F., N. C. Liu and J. C. Bailar, *Inorg. Chem.*, **3**, 1197 (1964).
195. Lunde, G., *Z. Anorg. Allgem. Chem.*, **163**, 345 (1927).
195a. Luoma, E. V., and C. H. Brubaker, *Inorg. Chem.*, **5**, 1618, 1637 (1966).
196. Lydon, J. E., J. K. Nicholson, B. L. Shaw and M. R. Truter, *Proc. Chem. Soc. (London)*, **1964**, 421.
197. McCaffery, A. J., and S. F. Mason, *Proc. Chem. Soc. (London)*, **1963**, 211.
198. McDonald, J. E., and J. W. Cobble, *J. Phys. Chem.*, **66**, 791 (1962).
199. McGlynn, S. P., and M. Kasha, *J. Chem. Phys.*, **24**, 481 (1956).
199a. Mais, R. H. B., and H. M. Powell, *J. Chem. Soc.*, **1965**, 7471.
200. Malatesta, L., *Gazz. Chim. Ital.*, **68**, 195 (1938).
201. Malatesta, L., and G. Padoa, *Rend. Ist. Lombardo Sci. Lettere A*, **91**, 227 (1957).
202. Malatesta, L., G. A. Padova and A. Sonz, *Gazz. Chim. Ital.*, **85**, 1111 (1955).
203. Manchot, W., and H. Schmid, *Z. Anorg. Allgem. Chem.*, **216**, 104 (1934).
204. Manchot, W., and J. Düsing, *Z. Anorg. Allgem. Chem.*, **212**, 29 (1933).
204a. Manchot, W., and J. Düsing, *Ber.*, **63**, 1226 (1930)
205. Manchot, W., and W. J. Manchot, *Z. Anorg. Allgem. Chem.*, **226**, 388, 410 (1936).
206. Manchot, W., and E. Enk, *Ann.*, **470**, 275 (1929).
207. Manchot, W., and J. Düsing, *Z. Anorg. Allgem. Chem.*, **212**, 111 (1933).
207a. Manchot, W., and E. König, *Ber.*, **57**, 2130 (1924).
208. Manchot, W., and E. Enk, *Ber.*, **63**, 1635 (1930).
209. Manchot, W., and H. Schmid, *Z. Anorg. Allgem. Chem.*, **216**, 99 (1933).
209a. Manchot, W., and H. Schmid, *Ber.*, **64**, 2673 (1931).
210. Marr, G., and D. E. Webster, *J. Organometal. Chem.*, **2**, 99 (1964).

211. Martin, F. S., *J. Chem. Soc.*, **1954**, 2564.
212. Martin, F. S., *J. Chem. Soc.*, **1952**, 3055.
213. Martin, F. S., *J. Chem. Soc.*, **1952**, 2682.
214. Martin, F. S., *Chem. Ind.* (*London*), **1953**, 824.
215. Martin, F. S., J. M. Fletcher, P. G. M. Brown and B. M. Gatehouse, *J. Chem. Soc.*, **1959**, 76.
216. Masuno, K., and S. Waku, *Nippon Kagaku Zasshi*, **83**, 116 (1962).
217. Mathieson, A. M., D. P. Mellor and N. C. Stephenson, *Acta Cryst.*, **5**, 185 (1952).
218. Mathieu, J. P., and H. Poulet, *Compt. Rend.*, **248**, 2315 (1959).
219. Mellor, D. P., *J. Proc. Roy. Soc. N. S. Wales*, **77**, 145 (1943).
220. Mercer, E. E., W. M. Campbell and R. M. Wallace, *Inorg. Chem.*, **3**, 1018 (1964).
221. Mercer, E. E., and W. A. McAllister, *Inorg. Chem.*, **4**, 1414 (1965).
221a. Mercer, E. E., and R. R. Buckley, *Inorg. Chem.*, **4**, 1692 (1965).
221b. Mercer, E. E., W. A. McAllister and J. R. Durig, *Inorg. Chem.*, **5**, 1881 (1966).
221c. Michelotti, F. W., and W. P. Keaveney, *J. Polymer Sci.*, *Ser. A*, **3**, 895 (1965).
221d. Miki, E., T. Ishimori, H. Yamatera and H. Okuno, *J. Chem. Soc. Japan*, **87**, 707 (1966).
222. Miller, J. D., and R. H. Prince, *J. Chem. Soc.*, **1965**, 5749.
222a. Miller, J. D., and R. H. Prince, *J. Chem. Soc.*, *Ser. A*, **1966**, 1048, 1370.
223. Miller, R. R., W. W. Brandt and M. Puke, *J. Am. Chem. Soc.*, **77**, 3178 (1955).
224. Mond, A. W., *J. Chem. Soc.*, **1930**, 1247.
225. Morgan, G. T., and F. H. Burstall, *J. Chem. Soc.*, **1936**, 43.
226. Morgan, G. T., and F. H. Burstall, *J. Chem. Soc.*, **1936**, 4.
227. Morgan, G. T., and F. H. Burstall, *J. Chem. Soc.*, **1937**, 1649.
228. Morgan, G. T., and F. H. Burstall, *J. Chem. Soc.*, **1938**, 1675.
228a. Mukaida, M., M. Okuno and T. Ishimori, *Nippon Kagaku Zasshi*, **86**, 598 (1965).
228b. Muller, J., and E. O. Fischer, *J. Organomet. Chem.*, **5**, 277 (1966).
229. Nakagawa, I., and T. Shimanouchi, *Spectrochim. Acta*, **18**, 101 (1962).
230. Nakata, H., *Tetrahedron*, **19**, 1959 (1963).
230a. Natta, G., G. dall'Asta and L. Porri, *Mikroanal. Chem.*, **81**, 253 (1965).
231. Nicholson, J. K., and B. L. Shaw, *Proc. Chem. Soc.* (*London*), **1963**, 282.
231a. Nicholson, J. K., and B. L. Shaw, *J. Chem. Soc.*, *Ser. A*, **1966**, 807.
232. Niedrach, L. W., and A. D. Tevebaugh, *J. Am. Chem. Soc.*, **73**, 2835 (1951).
233. Nikol'skii, A. B., *Russ. J. Inorg. Chem.*, *Eng. Transl.*, **8**, 668 (1963).
233a. Nikol'skii, A. B., and A. N. Ryabov, *Russ. J. Inorg. Chem.*, **12**, 1 (1965).
234. Norman, J. H., and H. G. Staley, quotation ref. (68).
235. Nowogrocki, G., and G. Tridot, *Bull. Chim. Soc. France*, **1965**, 688.
236. Nyholm, R. S., and G. J. Sutton, *J. Chem. Soc.*, **1958**, 567.
237. Oliff, R. W., and A. L. Odell, *J. Chem. Soc.*, **1964**, 2467.
238. Oliff, R. W., and A. L. Odell, *J. Chem. Soc.*, **1964**, 2417.
239. Ortner, M. H., *J. Chem. Phys.*, **34**, 556 (1961).

239a. Osiecki, J. H., C. J. Hofmann and D. P. Hollis, *J. Organomet. Chem.*, **3**, 107 (1965).
240. Page, J. A., and G. Wilkinson, *J. Am. Chem. Soc.*, **74**, 6149 (1952).
241. Palmer, J. W., and F. Basolo, *J. Inorg. Nucl. Chem.*, **15**, 279 (1960).
242. Parpiev, N. A., and G. B. Bokii, *J. Inorg. Chem.* (*USSR*), **2**, 414 (1957).
243. Pichkov, N., N. M. Sinitsyn and O. E. Zvyagintsev, *Proc. Acad. Sci., USSR* (*Engl. Transl.*), **156**, 585 (1964).
244. Pilipenko, A. T., and I. P. Sereda, *Zh. Analit. Khim.*, **16**, 73 (1961).
245. Pilipenko, A. T., and I. P. Sereda, *Vopr. Anal. Blagorodn. Metal.*, **1963**, 64 (*Chem. Abstr.*, **61**, 10039a) (1964).
245a. Pitwell, L. R., *Nature*, **207**, 1181 (1965).
245b. Porri, L., M. C. Gallazzi, A. Colombo and G. Allegra, *Tetrahedron Letters*, **1965**, 4187.
246. Porte, A. L., H. S. Gutowsky and G. M. Harris, *J. Chem. Phys.*, **34**, 66 (1961).
247. Porter, G. B., and H. L. Schaefer, *Ber. Bunsen. Physik. Chem.*, **68**, 316 (1964).
247a. Prince, R. H., and K. A. Raspin, *Chem. Commun.*, **1966**, 156.
248. Prout, C. K., and H. M. Powell, *J. Chem. Soc.*, **1962**, 137.
249. Pshenitsyn, N. K., and N. A. Ezerskaya, *Russ. J. Inorg. Chem., Eng. Transl.*, **6**, 312 (1961); **5**, 513 (1960); **2**, (1), 172 (1957).
250. Rausch, M. D., E. O. Fischer, and H. Grubert, *J. Am. Chem. Soc.*, **82**, 5811 (1960).
251. Rausch, M. D., E. O. Fischer and H. Grubert, *J. Am. Chem. Soc.*, **82**, 76 (1960).
252. Razunas, V., G. Macur and S. Katz, *J. Chem. Phys.*, **43**, 1010 (1965).
253. Rechnitz, G. A., *Inorg. Chem.*, **1**, 953 (1962).
254. Rechnitz, G. A., and H. A. Catherino, *Inorg. Chem.*, **4**, 112 (1965).
255. Remy, H., and A. Luhrs, *Ber.*, **61**, 917 (1928); **62**, 200 (1929).
256. Remy, H., and T. Wagner, *Z. Anorg. Allgem. Chem.*, **168**, 1 (1928).
257. Remy, H., *Z. Anorg. Allgem. Chem.*, **126**, 185 (1923).
258. Remy, H., and M. Kohn, *Z. Anorg. Allchem. Chem.*, **137**, 365 (1924).
259. Remy, H., *Z. Anorg. Allgem. Chem.*, **124**, 268 (1922).
260. Remy, H., and C. Breimeyer, *Z. Anorg. Allgem. Chem.*, **129**, 215 (1923).
261. Remy, H., *Z. Anorg. Allgem. Chem.*, **113**, 229 (1920).
262. Robin, M. B., *Inorg. Chem.*, **1**, 337 (1962).
263. Robinson, S. D., and G. Wilkinson, *J. Chem. Soc., Ser. A.*, **1966**, 300.
263a. Rosenblum, M., *Chemistry of the Iron Group Metallocenes*, John Wiley and Sons, New York, 1965.
264. Ruff, O., *Ber.*, **46**, 920 (1913).
265. Ruff, O., and E. Vidic, *Z. Anorg. Allgem. Chem.*, **143**, 171 (1925).
266. Ruff, O., and E. Vidic, *Z. Anorg. Allgem. Chem.*, **136**, 49 (1924).
267. Savitskii, A. V., and Y. K. Syrkin, *Tr. po Khim. i Khim. Technol.*, **4**, 165 (1961).
268. Scargill, D., C. E. Lyon, N. R. Large and J. M. Fletcher, *J. Inorg. Nucl. Chem.*, **27**, 161 (1965).
269. Scargill, D., and J. M. Fletcher, *Proc. Chem. Soc.* (*London*), **1961**, 251.
270. Scargill, D., *J. Chem. Soc.*, **1961**, 4444.

271. Schäfer, H., A. Tebben and W. Gerhardt, *Z. Anorg. Allgem. Chem.*, **321**, 41 (1963).
272. Schäfer, H., G. Schneidereit and W. Gerhardt, *Z. Anorg. Allgem. Chem.*, **319**, 327 (1963).
273. Schilt, A. A., *Inorg. Chem.*, **3**, 1323 (1964).
274. Schilt, A. A., *J. Am. Chem. Soc.*, **85**, 904 (1963).
274a. von Schnering, H. G., K. Brodersen, F. Moers, H. K. Breitbach and G. Thiele, *J. Less-Common Metals*, **11**, 288 (1966).
274b. Schrauzer, G. N., V. Mayweg, H. W. Finck, U. Müller-Westerhoff and W. Heinrick, *Angew. Chem.*, **3**, 381 (1964); Schrauzer, G. N., and V. Mayweg, *Z. Naturforsch*, **19B**, 192 (1964).
275. Schukarev, S. A., N. I. Kolbin and A. N. Ryabov, *Russ. J. Inorg. Chem., Eng. Transl.*, **4**, 763 (1959).
276. Schukarev, S. A., N. I. Kolbin and A. N. Ryabov, *J. Inorg. Chem., Eng. Transl.*, **3**, 1721 (1958).
277. Schukarev, S. A., N. I. Kolbin and A. N. Ryabov, *Russ. J. Inorg. Chem., Eng. Transl.*, **6**, 517 (1961).
277a. Shilov, A. E., A. K. Shilova and Yu. G. Borod'ko, *Kinetika i Kataliz*, **7**, 786 (1966).
278. Shlenskaya, V. I., and A. A. Biryukov, *Vestn. Mosk. Univ. Ser. II Khim.*, **18**, 75 (1963) (*Chem. Abstr.*, **59**, 13489h (1963)).
279. Shlenskaya, V. I., and E. M. Piskunov, *Vestn. Mosk. Univ. Ser. II, Khim.*, **18**, 35 (1963) (*Chem. Abstr.*, **59**, 2385h).
280. Shukla, S. K., *J. Chromatog.*, **8**, 96 (1962).
281. Silverman, M. D., and H. A. Levy, *J. Am. Chem. Soc.*, **76**, 3317 (1954).
282. Silverman, M. D., and H. A. Levy, *J. Am. Chem. Soc.*, **76**, 3319 (1954).
283. Simonsen, S. H. and M. H. Mueller, *J. Inorg. Nucl. Chem.*, **27**, 309 (1965).
284. Sinitsyn, N. M., and O. E. Zvyagintsev, *Proc. Acad. Sci. USSR*, **145**, 572 (1962).
284a. Sinitsyn, N. M., and O. E. Zvyagintsev, *Russ. J. Inorg. Chem., Eng. Transl.*, **10**, 1397 (1965); **11**, 168 (1966).
285. Small, G. J., and J. Trotter, *Can. J. Chem.*, **42**, 1746 (1964).
285a. Snatzke, G., and H. W. Fehlhaber, *Ann.*, **663**, 123 (1963).
286. Soucek, J., *Collection Czech Chem. Commun.*, **27**, 960 (1962).
287. Stephenson, T. N., and G. Wilkinson, *J. Inorg. Nucl. Chem.*, **28**, 2285 (1966).
288. Stephenson, T. A., and G. Wilkinson, *J. Inorg. Nucl. Chem.*, **28**, 945 (1966).
289. Stevens, K. W. H., *Proc. Roy. Soc.* (*London*), *Ser. A*, **219**, 542 (1953).
290. Stroganov, E. V., and K. V. Ovchinnikov, *Vestn. Leningr. Univ. Ser. Fiz. i Khim. No. 4*, **12**, 152 (1957) (*Chem. Abstr.*, **52**, 13356 (1958)).
291. Tagaki, Y., *Sci. Papers Inst. Phys. Chem. Res.* (*Tokyo*), **57**, 210 (1963).
292. Thomassen, L., *Z. Physik. Chem.* (*Frankfurt*), *Ser. B*, **2**, 349 (1929).
293. Trenkner, K., *Dissert. Erlangen*, **41** (1904) (cf. Gmelin 'Ruthenium,' **63**, 33 (1938)).
294. Trotter, J., *Acta. Cryst.*, **16**, 571 (1963).
295. Trotter, J., and S. H. Whitlow, *Acta Cryst.*, **19**, 868 (1965).
295a. Vdovenko, V. M., L. N. Lazarev and Y. S. Kharitonou, *Radiokhimiya*, **7**, 232 (1965).

296. Viste, A., and H. B. Gray, *Inorg. Chem.*, **3**, 1113 (1964).
297. Vogt, L. H., J. L. Katz and S. E. Wiberley, *Inorg. Chem.*, **4**, 1157 (1965).
297a. Vrestal, J., F. Kralik and J. Soucek, *Coll. Czech. Chem. Commun.*, **25**, 2155 (1960).
298. Wagnerova, D. M., *Collection Czech. Chem. Commun.*, **27**, 1130 (1962).
299. Wallace, R. M., *J. Inorg. Nucl. Chem.*, **20**, 283 (1961).
300. Watt, G. and W. C. McCordie, *J. Inorg. Nucl. Chem.*, **27**, 262 (1965).
300a. Webb, N. C., and R. E. Marsh, *Acta Cryst*, **22**, 382 (1967).
301. Wehner, P., and J. C. Hindman, *J. Phys. Chem.*, **56**, 10 (1952).
302. Wehner, P., and J. C. Hindman, *J. Am. Chem. Soc.*, **72**, 3911 (1950).
303. Weinland, R. F., and E. Gussmann, *Ber.*, **42**, 3888 (1909).
304. Weinstock, B., H. H. Claassen and C. L. Chernick, *J. Chem. Phys.*, **38**, 1470 (1963).
305. Weinstock, B., *Rec. Chem. Progr.* (*Kresge-Hooker Sci. Lib.*), **23**, 23 (1962).
306. Weise, E., and W. Klemm, *Z. Anorg. Allgem. Chem.*, **279**, 74 (1955).
307. Werner, A., *Ber.*, **40**, 2614 (1907).
308. Werner, A., and A. P. Smirnoff, *Helv. Chim. Acta*, **3**, 737 (1920).
309. Westland, A. D., *Can. J. Chem.*, **41**, 2692 (1963).
310. Wilkinson, M. K., E. O. Wollen, H. P. Child and J. W. Cable, *Phys. Rev.*, **121**, 74 (1961).
311. Wohler, L., P. Balz and L. Metz, *Z. Anorg. Allgem. Chem.*, **139**, 205 (1924).
312. Wohler, L., K. Ewald and H. G. Krall, *Ber.*, **66**, 1645 (1933).
312a. Wolf, L., E. Butter and H. Weinelt, *Z. Anorg. Allgem. Chem.*, **306**, 87 (1960).
313. Woodhead, J. L., and J. M. Fletcher, *U.K.A.E.A., A.E.R.E. R-4123.*
314. Woodhead, J. L., and J. M. Fletcher, *J. Less-Common Metals*, **4**, 460 (1962).
315. Woodhead, J. L., and J. M. Fletcher, *J. Chem. Soc.*, **1961**, 5039.
316. Woodward, L. A., and J. A. Creighton, *Spectrochim. Acta*, **17**, 594 (1961).
317. Yaffe, R. P., and A. F. Voigt, *J. Am. Chem. Soc.*, **74**, 2500 (1952).
318. Yaffe, R. P., and A. F. Voigt, *J. Am. Chem. Soc.*, **74**, 2503 (1952).
319. Yaffe, R. P., and A. F. Voigt, *J. Am. Chem. Soc.*, **74**, 3163 (1952).
320. Young, J. F., R. D. Gillard and G. Wilkinson, *J. Chem. Soc.*, **1964**, 5176.
321. Zvyagintsev, O. E., and S. M. Starostin, *J. Inorg. Chem.* (*USSR*), *Eng. Transl.*, **2** (6), 107 (1957).
321a. Zvyagintsev, O. E., N. M. Sinitsyn and V. N. Pichkov, *Russ. J. Inorg. Chem. Eng. Transl.*, **11**, 107 (1966).
322. Zvyagintsev, O. E., and A. Kurbanov, *J. Inorg. Chem.* (*USSR*), *Eng. Transl.*, **3** (10), 108 (1958).

5 IRIDIUM

There is a distinct tendency for iridium to assume higher oxidation states in its complexes than rhodium; for example iridium (IV) is more common than tetravalent rhodium. Its complexes are more inert to substitution than are the corresponding rhodium species; this has been demonstrated quantitatively for the chloro-aquo systems, but appears to be a general phenomenon. A peculiarity of the element is that it will form polynuclear complexes with oxygen or nitrogen bridging groups, while rhodium apparently does not share this property. For iridium, few olefin complexes, but many nitrosyl complexes, are known, while for rhodium the reverse is the case.

Nevertheless, in broad outline iridium and rhodium have similar chemistries, and a number of parallels may be drawn between the properties of ruthenium, iridium and rhodium complexes.

Iridium (VI) and (V)

These oxidation states are established only for the fluorides and fluoro complexes, as is the case with rhodium; oxide species probably do exist but need better characterization.

Iridium (IV) and (III)

These are together the commonest oxidation states of the element. Although the tetrahalides are not characterized the derived hexahalo anions are well known. Most of the chemistry of iridium (IV) involves Group VII and VI donor ligands, while that of iridium (III) involves all four groups. The existence of a large number of iridium (III) hydrido phosphine and arsine species is not paralleled by any of the other platinum metals, and there are also many iridium (III) halo carbonyls. A difficulty often encountered in the practical chemistry of complexes of these oxidation states is that oxidation of tri- to tetravalent or reduction of tetra- to trivalent iridium may very easily occur.

Iridium (II), (I) and (O)

The bivalent state is even rarer for iridium than it is for rhodium: the best established examples are the carbonyl halides $[Ir(CO)_2X_2]_n$ and the nitrosyl $Ir(NO)Br_3(PPh_3)_2$.

A substantial number of monovalent complexes is known and, as with their rhodium analogues, the majority have square planar coordination. A feature of some of these d^8 species, particularly $Ir(CO)Cl(PPh_3)_2$, is the ease of their conversion to octahedral d^6 complexes.

The chemistry of the zerovalent oxidation state is confined to that of the carbonyls. The nitrosyls $Ir(NO)_2X(PPh_3)_2$ and $Ir(NO)(CO)(PPh_3)_2$ formally contain iridium (−I), and $Ir(NO)_2PPh_3$ iridium (−II), but the concept of oxidation state can have little meaning in such cases.

GROUP VII DONORS

The fluorine chemistry of iridium is similar to that of the other three metals except that no tetrafluoride has yet been identified; unlike rhodium it forms a trifluoride. The species $[IrX_6]^{2-}$ (X = F, Cl, Br, I) are known but the tetrahalides IrX_4 are not, although claims have been made for the existence of all of them; however, all four trihalides are known and their derived hexahalo anions with the exception of $[IrF_6]^{3-}$ and $[IrI_6]^{3-}$. As with the other three metals, the existence of di- and monohalides of the element is very unlikely.

There is little oxyhalide chemistry of iridium, but the halo-aquo systems of iridium (IV) and iridium (III) have been much studied.

Iridium (VI)

Iridium hexafluoride, IrF_6, can be made by direct fluorination of the metal at 270°. It is a yellow crystalline solid (m.p. 44·4°, b.p. 53°) and is isomorphous with osmium hexafluoride[271]. Electron-diffraction measurements on the vapour give 1·833 ± 0·005 Å for the metal–fluorine bond length and show the molecule to be octahedral[268]. Infrared and Raman spectra of the compound have been measured[49,194] (see Table 3.1, p. 101) and the possibility of observing Jahn–Teller effects on the vibrational spectra has already been discussed[46] (p. 48). Electronic absorption spectra of iridium hexafluoride have been measured from 3,000 to 40,000 cm^{-1} and band assignments proposed[102,197]. Vapour-pressure measurements have been made for the compound, and thermodynamic data derived: the heats of fusion, transition and vaporization are respectively 1·19, 1·70 and 7·38 kcal/mole and the corresponding entropies are 3·74, 6·21 and 22·6 cal/mole deg[36]. The magnetic properties of the solid compound have been measured over the range 90–293°K (see Table 5.12) (p. 303) and show that the compound is not magnetically dilute[89].

The hexafluoride decomposes in aqueous solution to give the hydrated dioxide and ozone.

An oxy fluoride, **$IrOF_4$**, has been claimed[241] but the product almost certainly is a mixture containing $[IrF_6]^{2-}$ salts[271].

Iridium (v)

Iridium pentafluoride, $[IrF_5]_n$, has only recently been identified. It can be made by fluorination of the metal at 380° and forms yellow crystals (m.p. 104·5°)[16]. The compound is identical with the previously reported 'tetrafluoride', which was made by heating the hexafluoride to 350° with powdered glass. The major reaction is apparently[16]

$$4\,IrF_6 + [SiO_2] \rightarrow 4\,IrF_5 + O_2 + SiF_4$$

The compound is isomorphous with ruthenium pentafluoride and so presumably has the tetrameric structure of the latter (cf. p. 130). Magnetic susceptibility measurements were made over the range 77–296°K (see Table 5.12)[16].

K[IrF$_6$] is prepared by the action of bromine trifluoride on a mixture of potassium bromide and iridium tribromide; other salts can be made similarly. It forms white crystals and has the rhombohedral $K[OsF_6]$ structure (a = 4·98 Å, α = 97·4°)[116]. The lithium and sodium salts have the rhombohedral $Li[SbF_6]$ structure, the potassium, rubidium and caesium salts have the rhombohedral $K[OsF_6]$ lattice and the silver salt is tetragonal with the $K[NbF_6]$ structure[150]. Magnetic susceptibility measurements on the potassium and caesium salts were made from 90 to 294°K (see Table 5.12); the susceptibility is almost independent of temperature[82]. The electronic absorption spectrum of the solid caesium salts has been measured from 10,000 to 40,000 cm^{-1} and assignments proposed on the basis of Tanabe–Sugano diagrams[35]. **NO$^+$[IrF$_6$]$^-$** is formed together with $(NO)_2^{2+}[IrF_6]^{2-}$ when hexafluoride reacts with nitric oxide; it is cubic (a_0 = 10·114 Å)[17]. The species **SeF$_3$.IrF$_6$**, **IrF$_5$.SF$_4$**, **IrF$_5$.SO$_2$** and **[IrF$_5$]$_2$.SeF$_4$** have been made[117, 237a].

Iridium (iv)

Although **IrF$_4$** has been reported[240,271] the product obtained was almost certainly the pentafluoride[116]; there is no evidence for the existence of a tetrafluoride, which is singular, since the derived anion $[IrF_6]^{2-}$ is well known.

It is said that **iridium tetrachloride, IrCl$_4$**, can be got by the action of aqua regia or chlorine on either ammonium hexachloroiridate (iv) or the material obtained by fusing iridium with potassium nitrate[273], but there is some doubt as to whether the product is the pure tetrachloride or the 'free' acid $H_2[IrCl_6]$aq. A method claimed to give the pure substance from iridium (IV) sulphide has been described[156], but again it is likely that the product may have contained some aquated free acid. $\mathbf{IrBr_4}$ and $\mathbf{IrI_4}$ have both been claimed, the bromide as the product of the reaction between the dioxide and hydrobromic acid[23] and the iodide by the addition of potassium iodide to ammonium hexachloroiridate (IV)[160,211], but in the first case at least it is likely that the aquated free acid was formed, and analyses of the product of the second reaction indicated that the compound was mainly the triiodide[152]. A compound analysing as $\mathbf{Ir_2Br_7}$ can be got by prolonged action of hydrobromic acid on $H_2[IrCl_6]$[116].

$\mathbf{Ir(OH)_3Cl}$ (deep blue) is said to be formed by hydrolysis of $Na_2[IrCl_6]$ solutions[208]; the compound $\mathbf{2\,IrBr_3.IrO_2}$ (black needles) has been made by heating iridium dioxide with bromine[94]. The species $\mathbf{IrO_2Cl}$ has been detected in the gas phase[19a].

The hexahaloiridates (IV)

The magnetic and spectral properties of these compounds are considered in a separate section (cf. p. 235) (Table 5.12) and so are the electron-exchange reactions of $[IrCl_6]^{2-}$ and $[IrBr_6]^{2-}$ (p. 237) (Table 5.2).

$\mathbf{K_2[IrF_6]}$ is prepared by the reaction of potassium hydroxide and $K[IrF_6]$[116], or by heating iridium metal with potassium hexafluoroplumbate[246]. It forms red crystals. The barium salt is rhombohedral (a = 4·90 Å, α = 97·8°)[116], but all the other known salts, including the potassium one, have hexagonal lattices (a and c values are: sodium, 9·34 and 5·14 Å; potassium 5·80, 4·63 Å; ammonium 5·98, 4·79 Å; rubidium 5·97, 4·79 Å; caesium, 6·24, 5·00 Å[118]). The magnetic moment of the caesium salt at room temperature is 1·42 BM[118], and the electronic spectrum of the solid salt has been measured from 10,000 to 40,000 cm^{-1}[35]. The metal–fluorine stretching frequency (infrared) in the potassium salt is 568 cm^{-1}[219].

An aqueous solution of the free acid, $H_2[IrF_6]$, has been made by ion-exchange methods, but a solid compound could not be isolated. The solution was yellow, and potentiometric titrations indicated that, on dilution, hydrolysis of the hexafluoro ion occurred[118]:

$$[IrF_6]^{2-} + H_2O \rightleftharpoons [Ir(OH)F_5]^{2-} + HF$$

A nitrosonium compound, $\mathbf{(NO^+)_2[IrF_6]^{2-}}$, can be made, as pale yellow crystals, from nitric oxide and iridium hexafluoride[17], while nitrogen dioxide yields the white nitronium salt $\mathbf{(NO_2)_2[IrF_6]}$[237a].

The nitrosonium salt has a hexagonal structure (a = 10·01, c = 3·53 Å)[17].

$K_2[IrCl_6]$ is best made by double decomposition from the far more soluble sodium salt (the potassium salt is 1·3 g/100 ml soluble in water at 20°, the sodium salt 40, ammonium[145a] 1, rubidium 0·06, caesium 0·01). The sodium salt can be got by the action of chlorine on a heated mixture of iridium and sodium chloride[29a, 111], or by oxidation of $Na_3[IrCl_6]$ with nitric acid or chlorine. The black crystals are isomorphous with $K_2[PtCl_6]$. The x-ray crystal structure of the anhydrous ammonium salt shows this to be cubic (a = 9·87 Å), and the complex anion is octahedral with an iridium–chlorine distance of 2·47 Å[27]. In addition to these salts, caesium, rubidium, magnesium and thallous salts have been reported, and a hydrated ether-soluble free acid $H_2[IrCl_6].6H_2O$ has been made by the action of aqua regia on the ammonium salt[201,276]. The equilibria

$$K_2[IrCl_6] \rightleftharpoons Ir + 2\,KCl + 2\,Cl_2$$

and

$$2\,K_2[IrCl_6] + 2\,KCl \rightleftharpoons 2\,K_3[IrCl_6] + Cl_2$$

were studied by measurements of dissociation pressures over the range 480–840°[229].

Observations have been made of the pure nuclear quadrupole resonances of chlorine in $K_2[IrCl_6]$ and $K_2[OsCl_6]$ at 90, 200 and 300°K. A single resonance line was seen in both cases, suggesting that all chlorine atoms were in equivalent environments, and conclusions were drawn as to the extent of σ and π bonding in the complexes (cf. p. 54)[112a,129]. Infrared spectra of $k_2[IrCl_6]$ were measured[1] (p. 103).

Some briefly reported data are available for the aquation of $[IrCl_6]^{2-}$ ion[187, 195] and suggest that the process is faster than the corresponding reaction for $[OsCl_6]^{2-}$. Studies of the exchange of chloride ion with $[IrCl_6]^{2-}$ and $[IrCl_6]^{3-}$ in weakly acid solutions have been made; evidence was obtained for the presence of the hydroxy chloro species $[IrCl_4(OH)_2]^{2-}$ and $[IrCl_2(OH)_4]^{2-}$ in solutions of $[IrCl_6]^{2-}$[24]. Hydrolysis of $[^{142}Ir^{36}Cl_6]^{2-}$ has been studied[19c].

Polarographic reduction of $[IrCl_6]^{2-}$ is a one-electron reversible process[214a,259a] (cf. also p. 303). The diffusion coefficient of $[IrCl_6]^{2-}$ is $8{\cdot}2 \times 10^{-6}$ cm^2 sec^{-1}[154].

The chemical reactions of $K_2[IrCl_6]$ are summarized in Figure 5.1.

$K_2[IrBr_6]$ can be made by the prolonged action of potassium bromide solution on sodium hexachloroiridate (IV)[23]; it forms brilliant

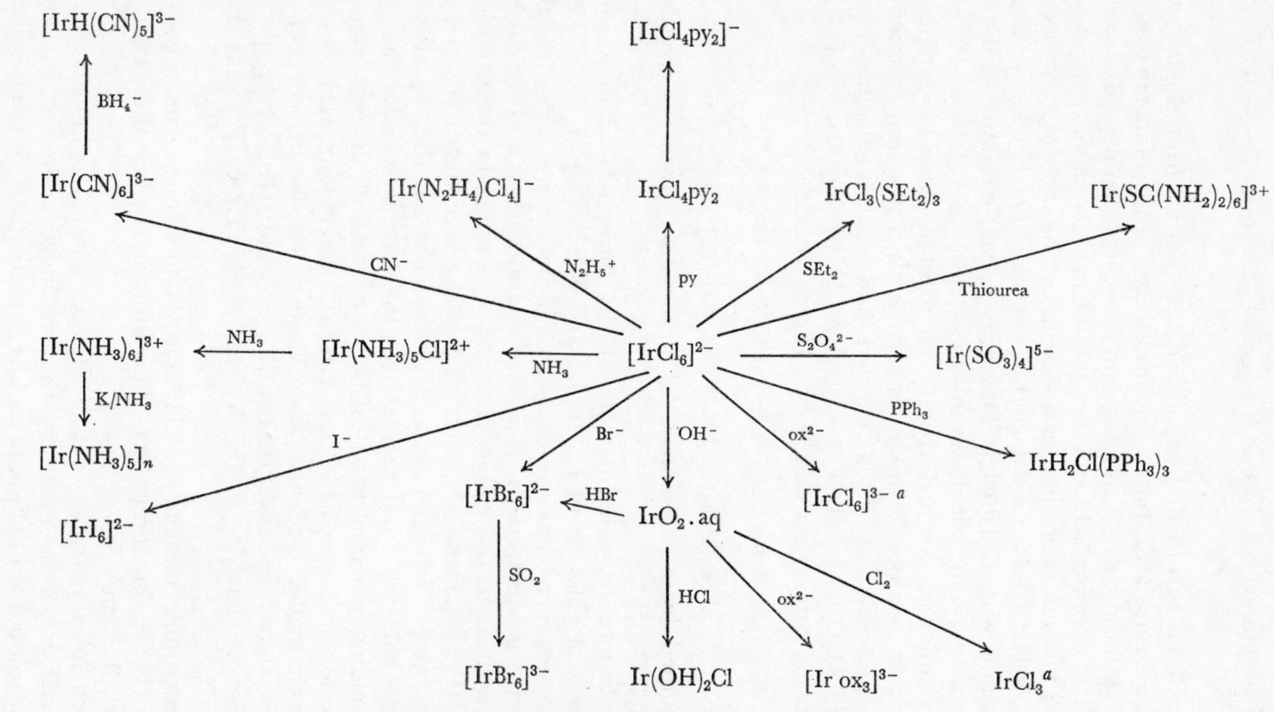

Figure 5.1 Reactions of $[IrCl_6]^{2-}$. [a] Cf. p. 240.

blue-black octahedra, and sodium, rubidium, caesium and ammonium salts are known as well as a hydrated free acid. The hexabromo salts are more soluble than those containing the hexachloro anion, in particular the ammonium salt. The exchange between bromide ion and $[IrBr_6]^{2-}$ has been studied at 40° in 0·1–6 N hydrobromic acid, and the rate law

$$\text{Rate} = k[IrBr_6{}^{2-}][HBr]$$

was established[247].

Mixed chlorobromo complexes

Complexes of the form $[\mathbf{IrCl}_n\mathbf{Br}_{6-n}]^{2-}$ (all five species) have been isolated by high voltage ionophoresis of mixed solutions of bromide ion and $[IrCl_6]^{2-}$. As with the $[OsCl_nBr_{6-n}]^{2-}$ system, the migration velocities of the anions decrease, and wavelengths of the absorption maxima in the electronic spectra increase, as the number of bromine atoms in the complex increases. The (relative) stability constants for the individual species were determined, and it was shown that $[IrBr_6]^{2-}$ was 170 times more stable than $[IrCl_6]^{2-}$[25]. Some evidence for formation of geometrical isomers of $[IrCl_xBr_{6-x}]^{2-}$ ($x = 2, 3, 4$) was found[224].

$\mathbf{K_2[IrI_6]}$ has been made by the action of potassium iodide solution on $H_2[IrCl_6]$aq, or (in small quantities) by the action of iodine and potassium iodide on the powdered metal at 70°. It forms dark brown crystals with a metallic lustre, and gives a ruby-red aqueous solution. Sodium and ammonium salts were also made (this report, the only one to be made of salts of $[IrI_6]^{2-}$, dates from 1857)[211].

$\mathbf{K[IrI_5]}$ has been briefly reported[202].

Magnetic and spectroscopic properties of the hexahalo-iridates (IV)

Electron spin resonance (e.s.r.) data. A classic e.s.r. experiment was performed in 1953 on a dilute solid solution of $K_2[IrCl_6]$ in the diamagnetic salt $K_2[PtCl_6]$ (the sodium and ammonium salts of $[IrCl_6]^{2-}$ were also studied). The resonance signal showed hyperfine structure from the chlorine nuclei, suggesting that the single unpaired electron from the $5d^5$ (low spin) iridium (IV) ion is delocalized over the ligands; from the magnitude of the splitting it appears that it spends about 5% of its time on each chlorine atom (this figure is frequently misquoted as 3%), and 70% on the metal. This delocalization of the unpaired electron on to the ligands was attributed to a weak metal–chlorine π interaction, and is one of the first definite pieces of evidence for the existence of π bonding in transition-metal complexes[108,213,253]. Similar measurements on a solid solution of $Na_2[IrBr_6]$ in a lattice of $Na_2[PtBr_6]$ indicated that here too the unpaired electron spends about a third of its time on the ligands[213].

Magnetic properties. Later e.s.r. measurements on $K_2[IrCl_6]$ and $(NH_4)_2[IrCl_6]$ demonstrated the presence of iridium–iridium electron spin–spin interactions in these salts. It is believed that this interaction operates by a superexchange mechanism (cf. also p. 58) through the intervening chlorine atoms of adjacent ions:

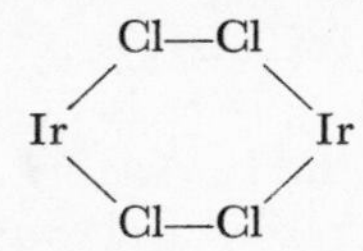

These exchange effects were found in semi-dilute crystals of $(NH_4)_2[Ir, PtCl_6]$ and $K_2[Ir, PtCl_6]$ (Ir:Pt = 1:20): an intense isotropic absorption due to magnetically isolated $[IrCl_6]^{2-}$ centres was observed together with a number of fainter anisotropic lines ascribed to Ir—Ir pairs[109,114a]. The consequence of such exchange is that the pure salts of the iridium complex should be antiferromagnetic at very low temperatures, and this is indeed the case. Near 20°K, the molar susceptibilities are independent of temperature but, below this temperature, they fall sharply at the antiferromagnetic transition points (3·08 and 2·16°K for the potassium and ammonium salts, respectively)[51]. This is in close agreement with the behaviour of the specific heats of the complexes: λ-type anomalies were observed at 3·05 and 2·15°K, respectively[14]. The magnetic measurements have been interpreted in terms of nearest and next-nearest neighbour interactions of iridium atoms[51], and a theory propounded to account for the exchange interactions[143a,214].

Magnetic susceptibility measurements have been made on $K_2[IrCl_6]$ and $(NH_4)_2[IrCl_6]$ from 1 to 297°K[51] and on $K_2[IrCl_6]$, $(NH_4)_2[IrCl_6]$ and $(NH_4)_2[IrBr_6]$ from 78 to 310°K[206] (Table 5.12, p. 303). These latter more restricted data showed that the molar susceptibilities of all three salts drop with increasing temperature, but the Curie–Weiss law is obeyed by the chloro complex only above 190°K, and not at all by the bromo salt. Measurements over the same temperature range on the trimethylammonium, pyridinium and tetraphenylarsonium salts of $[IrCl_6]^{2-}$ showed that at all temperatures these had considerably lower susceptibilities than either the potassium or ammonium salts[206]. This latter observation is contrary to expectation since, if exchange effects are operative, the presence of large cations should lessen the Ir–Cl–Cl–Ir interactions and so increase the observed susceptibility.

Unfortunately there are at present no data on the variation with temperature of the susceptibilities of $[IrF_6]^{2-}$ salts, and no data at all on salts of $[IrI_6]^{2-}$.

Electronic absorption spectra. Electronic spectra of solid $K_2[IrF_6]$[35] and of aqueous solutions of $[IrCl_6]^{2-}$, $[IrBr_6]^{2-}$[135] and $[IrCl_nBr_{6-n}]^{2-}$ (n = 1 to 5)[25] have been measured and assignments of the ligand-field and charge-transfer bands given. As with salts containing $[OsCl_6]^{2-}$ and $[OsBr_6]^{2-}$, the colours of salts of $[IrCl_6]^{2-}$ vary with the nature of the cation in the solid state. Thus, while aqueous solutions of $[IrCl_6]^{2-}$ are orange-red, the rubidium and caesium salts are deep red, the silver salt (which is unstable and easily reduced to $Ag_3[IrCl_6]$) is blue and the thallous salt is blue-green. The reflectance spectra of these four salts were measured and it was shown that the latter two have a new, broad band in the red[15]. Jorgensen has discussed these results in terms of a strong covalent interaction between the cation and complex anion[134]. Vibronic coupling in $[IrCl_6]^{2-}$ has been discussed[46].

As with the corresponding osmium (IV) hexahalides, solvent shifts of electronic bands in organic solvents of $[IrCl_6]^{2-}$ and $[IrBr_2]^{2-}$ can be correlated with the dielectric constants of the solvents[136]. The application of high pressures on the salts $Na_2[IrCl_6]$ and $K_2[IrBr_6]$ in solid solutions causes shifts of some of their electronic absorption bands to the red[15] (cf. p. 61).

Electron-transfer reactions of hexachloroiridates (IV)*

Rate constants for the electron-transfer reactions

$$[IrX_6]^{2-} + (\text{reductant})^{2+} \rightleftharpoons [IrX_6]^{3-} + (\text{oxidant})^{3+}$$

(where X = Cl, Br, and the reductants were other complex ions) have been measured by the temperature-jump relaxation method; they are amongst the highest ever recorded, and certainly the most accurately measured, for this type of reaction (Table 5.1)[113,126]. The values agree with the predictions of the Marcus theory of electron exchange[113,126]. It will be observed from Table 5.1 that the electron-transfer reactions between $[IrCl_6]^{2-}$ and anions such as $[IrBr_6]^{3-}$,

* See Table 5.1.

$[Fe(CN)_6]^{4-}$ and $[W(CN)_8]^{4-}$ are some thousand times slower than those found between $[IrCl_6]^{2-}$ and cationic complexes containing heterocyclic aromatic ligands[103,126,126a]. This is probably due to electrostatic repulsions between reactants of the same charge, which increase the energy necessary to bring them together to form the activated complex[103].

The oxidation of ferrous hexaaquo ion by $[IrCl_6]^{2-}$ ($k = 3{\cdot}2 \times 10^8$ M^{-1} sec^{-1}) is faster than that by $[Fe\ phen_3]^{3+}$ ($k = 3{\cdot}7 \times 10^4$ M^{-1} sec^{-1}, both being measured at 25°) although the standard free energy changes for both reactions are the same. It has been suggested that the rate difference arises from a more positive entropy of activation for the former reaction[103]. In the reaction between $[IrCl_6]^{2-}$ and chromous hexaaquo ion there is no transfer of chlorine to the chromium, but an intermediate green species believed to be $[(H_2O)_5$-$CrClIrCl_5]$ was observed[257,258].

Iridium (IV) chloro-aquo and chlorohydroxy species

Oxidation of $Ir(H_2O)_3Cl_3$ and $[Ir(H_2O)_2Cl_4]^-$ by chlorine gives $\mathbf{[Ir(H_2O)_3Cl_3]^+}$ and $\mathbf{Ir(H_2O)_2Cl_4}$ (characterized by absorption spectra; geometrical structures unknown)[41]. Aquation of $[IrCl_6]^{2-}$ gives $\mathbf{[Ir(H_2O)Cl_5]^-}$ and probably some other aquo species[187]; the existence of $\mathbf{[IrCl_4(OH)_2]^{2-}}$ and $\mathbf{[IrCl_2(OH)_4]^{2-}}$ in weak hydrochloric acid solution of $[IrCl_6]^{2-}$ has already been mentioned (p. 233)[24].

Iridium (III)

Iridium trifluoride, IrF_3, can be made by thermal decomposition of the pentafluoride at 400°, or by reduction of the hexafluoride with metallic iridium: the first method gives a pure sample of poorly formed crystals while the latter gives good crystals which may, however, be contaminated with some unreacted metal[119]. Small variations are found in the unit cell dimensions of samples made by the two methods, although such variation is much smaller than is observed with ruthenium trifluoride (the values are $a = 5{\cdot}418 \pm 0{\cdot}002$ Å and $\alpha = 54{\cdot}13 \pm 0{\cdot}03°$)[119]. In iridium trifluoride (as in rhodium and palladium trifluorides) the fluorine atoms have a hexagonal close-packed arrangement, whereas ruthenium trifluoride has a distorted hexagonal lattice (as in ferric and cobaltic trifluorides). The bridge $Ir\hat{F}Ir$ angle is estimated as 132°[119].

The only iridium (III) fluoro complexes so far made are

$(NO)_2[IrF_5]$ and **$(NO_2)_2[IrF_5]$**, got by heating $(NO)_2[IrF_6]$ and $(NO_2)_2[IrF_6]$, respectively[237a]. Attempts to make $K_3[IrF_6]$ by, for example, the treatment of $K_3[Ir(NO_2)_6]$ with hydrofluoric acid yield only $K_2[IrF_6]$[220].

Iridium trichloride, $IrCl_3$, can be made from the elements at 450–600°, the reaction apparently being accelerated by sunlight[152]. The colour of the product varies from green to dark blue according to the circumstances of its preparation and the compound so prepared is insoluble in water. By heating it to 500–900° in evacuated ampoules, two crystalline, water-insoluble modifications can be obtained: a deep red monoclinic (α) form ($a = 6{\cdot}00 \pm 0{\cdot}02$, $c = 16{\cdot}98 \pm 0{\cdot}21$ Å)[34], and a red orthorhombic (β) form ($a = 6{\cdot}95 \pm 0{\cdot}02$, $b = 9{\cdot}81 \pm 0{\cdot}02$, $c = 20{\cdot}8_2 \pm 0{\cdot}05$ Å)[13]. In both cases the metal atom is at the centre of a distorted octahedron of chlorine atoms, with three pairs of chlorine atoms at 2·30, 2·31 and 2·39 Å distant in the α form[32] and at $2{\cdot}31_0$, $2{\cdot}33_6$ and $2{\cdot}41_0$ in the β form[13]. It is asserted that the difference between the two forms lies in the distribution of iridium atoms in the octahedral holes of the lattice. The α form is said to be weakly diamagnetic and the β form 'non-magnetic' over the range 78–473°K[33]. It is the author's experience that the water-insoluble forms of the trichloride are extremely difficult to attack with any acid, the best method apparently being prolonged digestion with aqua regia, which of course converts the trichloride into hexachloroiridates (IV). For the reaction

$$Ir(s) + \tfrac{3}{2}\,Cl_2 \rightarrow IrCl_3(g)$$

$\Delta H^0_{298} = 24.3 \pm 3$ kcal/mole and $\Delta S^0_{298} = 1.6 \pm 3$ e.u.[19a].

Water-soluble forms of the trichloride can be prepared by treatment of hexachloroiridates (III) with sulphuric acid, or by the action of hydrogen chloride on $Ir(OH)Cl_2$—the products are hydrated[53,152].

The trichloride has been used as a catalyst for the chlorination of organic compounds (rhodium trichloride shows similar properties); for example, a mixture of benzene vapour and chlorine when passed over an iridium trichloride–alumina catalyst at 150° yields *p*-dichlorobenzene[31]. It will also catalyse the polymerization of norbornene[195a]. Chemical properties of the trichloride are summarized in Figure 5.2.

Iridium tribromide, $IrBr_3$, can be made in an anhydrous red-brown form by the action of bromine on the 'dibromide'[152] or as a hydrate by the action of hydrobromic acid on iridium dioxide or on $Ir(OH)Br_2$; the hydrate is dark brown, and on heating decomposes

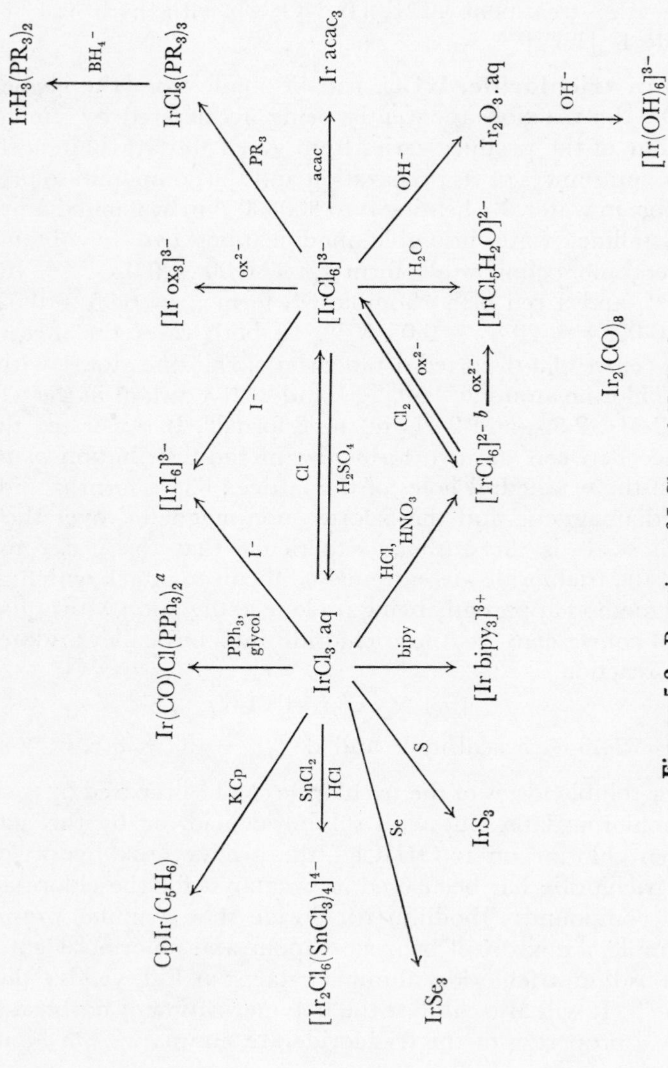

Figure 5.2 Reactions of $IrCl_3$ and $[IrCl_6]^{3-}$.
[a] See p. 278. [b] See p. 234.

to the dibromide[152]. A compound formulated as **$IrBr_3.3HBr.3H_2O$** (blue crystals) can also be made from iridium dioxide and hydrobromic acid[23], and is presumably the free acid $(H_3O)_3[IrBr_6]$. Another iridium (III) bromide is **$IrBr_3.HBr.2H_2O$**, made also from the dioxide and hydrobromic acid[71], and this might be reformulated as $(H_3O)[IrBr_4(H_2O)]$. The compound Ir_2Br_7[116] has already been mentioned (p. 232).

Iridium triiodide, IrI_3, can be made by the action of hydriodic acid on iridium dioxide; this gives the deep yellow trihydrate which, on heating, loses water to give first the dihydrate and finally the dark-brown anhydrous compound, which is slightly soluble in water and reacts with hot alkalis[152].

Various hydroxy halo species have been made: **$Ir(OH)Cl_2aq$** (deep green hygroscopic crystals) results from the action of gaseous hydrogen chloride at room temperature on iridium dioxide; it was suggested that this product might be an acid $H[Ir(OH)_2Cl_2]aq$ since it gives precipitates with cations, but a more reasonable formulation would be **$(H_3O)[IrCl_2(OH)_2(H_2O)_2]$**. The green species **$Ir(OH)Br_2.aq$** is made from hydrogen bromide and hydrated iridium dioxide[152].

$K_3[IrCl_6]$, sometimes called potassium chloroiridite, can be made by reducing $K_2[IrCl_6]$ with oxalate, alcohol or a number of other reducing agents[223,229]. The salt is olive-green, though the colour varies slightly with the degree of hydration. The solubilities of the ammonium, potassium, rubidium and caesium salts in water are, respectively, 9·5, 8·0, 1·0 and 0·5 g/100 ml at 20°. The potassium salt is isomorphous with $K_3[RhCl_6]$, and the monohydrate has a rhombic structure ($a:b:c$ = 1·031:1:1·303)[75]. Although the free acid has not been isolated it can be made in solution by reduction of $H_2[IrCl_6]$ with oxalic acid or alcohol; the solution is red.

The infrared spectrum of $K_3[IrCl_6]$ has been measured (cf. Table 3.3, p. 102)[1,120a,153a], and the electronic absorption spectrum of $[IrCl_6]^{3-}$ measured in aqueous solution and band assignments proposed[135,139]; Englman has studied the intensities of the Laporte-forbidden transitions in the spectrum[84].

Exchange of ^{192}Ir (which has a half-life of seventy-four days) between $[IrCl_6]^{3-}$ and $[IrCl_6]^{2-}$ has been measured, using solutions in molar hydrochloric acid with concentrations of the complexes between 0·1 and 0·0001 M; under such conditions, exchange was always complete within a time interval of about a minute (at 50° and in darkness). The specific rate, assuming no separation-induced exchange, is greater than 290 l/mole sec[252] (later experiments using the temperature-jump method give $k = 2{\cdot}3 \times 10^5$ M^{-1} sec^{-1} at 25°)[126a]. The kinetics of aquation of $[IrCl_6]^{3-}$ and of the replacement of water by Cl^- in $[IrCl_5(H_2O)]^{2-}$ have been studied[155,223].

$$[IrCl_6]^{3-} + H_2O \underset{k_{-1}}{\overset{k_1}{\rightleftharpoons}} [IrCl_5(H_2O)]^{2-} + Cl^-$$

The rate constants were found; at 25°, $k_1 = 9{\cdot}4 \times 10^{-6}$ sec^{-1} and $E_a = 30{\cdot}4 \pm 2$ kcal/mole in M perchloric acid; at 50° in M hydrochloric acid the water-replacement rate law was

$$-d[IrCl_5H_2O^{2-}]/dt = k_{-1}[IrCl_5H_2O^{2-}][Cl^-]$$

with $k_{-1} = 5 \times 10^{-5}$ M^{-1} sec^{-1}[223]. Studies were similarly made on the equilbrium

$$[IrCl_5H_2O]^{2-} + H_2O \underset{k_{-2}}{\overset{k_2}{\rightleftharpoons}} [IrCl_4(H_2O)_2]^- + Cl^-$$

and for this K (= k_2/k_{-2}) is constant at 0·21 M (at 50°, $[H^+]$ from 1·02 to 2·55 M). The rate law is[41]

$$-d[IrCl_4(H_2O)_2{}^-]/dt = k_{-2}[IrCl_4(H_2O)_2{}^-][Cl^-]$$

with $k_{-2} = 6{\cdot}7 \times 10^{-5}$ M^{-1} sec^{-1} at 50°. Preliminary measurements were also made of the aquation[41]

$$[IrCl_4(H_2O)_2]^- + H_2O \xrightarrow{k_3} Ir(H_2O)_3Cl_3 + Cl^-$$

The species $[IrCl_4(H_2O)_2]^-$ and $Ir(H_2O)_3Cl_3$ (geometrical configurations unknown) were characterized by chromatographic methods and their absorption spectra recorded. The two acid dissociation constants of $[IrCl_4(H_2O)_2]^-$ are $pK_a^{(1)} = 8{\cdot}5 \pm 0{\cdot}4$ and $pK_a^{(2)} = 10{\cdot}1 \pm 0{\cdot}5$[41]. Hydrolysis of $[^{192}Ir^{36}Cl_6]^{3-}$ has been studied[19c].

The kinetics of the $[IrCl_6]^{3-}$–chlorate redox reaction have been investigated by means of steady-state controlled potential electrolysis. The overall reaction is

$$6\,[IrCl_6]^{3-} + ClO_3^- + 6\,H^+ \rightarrow 6\,[IrCl_6]^{2-} + Cl^- + 3\,H_2O$$

and the rate law is

$$-d[IrCl_6{}^{3-}]/dt = k[IrCl_6{}^{3-}][ClO_3{}^-]$$

(at 45° and $[H^+] = 0{\cdot}2$ M, $k = (3{\cdot}2 \pm 0{\cdot}1) \times 10^{-4}$ M^{-1} sec^{-1}). The Arrhenius activation energy E_a determined over the range 35–50° is 30 kcal/mole. The rate-determining step is probably

$$[IrCl_6]^{3-} + ClO_3^- \rightarrow [IrCl_6]^{2-} + ClO_3^{2-} \text{ (radical)}$$

It was also found that the rates of reaction of chlorate ion with $[IrCl_6]^{3-}$ and $[IrCl_5H_2O]^{2-}$ are the same under equivalent conditions[236].

The reversibility of the couple

$$[IrCl_6]^{2-} + e^- \rightarrow [IrCl_6]^{3-}$$

has been demonstrated by galvanostatic methods and the diffusion coefficients of the ions calculated: these are $8{\cdot}2 \times 10^{-6}$ cm²/sec for $[IrCl_6]^{2-}$ and $7{\cdot}8 \times 10^{-6}$ cm²/sec for $[IrCl_6]^{3-}$[154]. The oxidation potential of the $[IrCl_6]^{2-}/[IrCl_6]^{3-}$ system is $0{\cdot}032 \pm 0{\cdot}003$ v in 1 M hydrochloric acid and in molar sodium chloride solutions[155].

Chemical reactions of $K_3[IrCl_6]$ are summarized in Figure 5.1.

$K_3[IrBr_6]$ can be made by the action of sulphur dioxide on an aqueous solution of $K_2[IrBr_6]$ or from 'iridium tetrabromide', potassium bromide and hydrogen sulphide[71]. The potassium salt forms olive-green prismatic needles, and ammonium, sodium, rubidium and caesium salts are also known. Absorption spectra of aqueous solutions of $[IrBr_6]^{3-}$ have been reported[135,139] and assignments proposed[84,135].

Although **$K_2[IrBr_5]$** was once claimed[180] it has now been shown that the product was the carbonyl species $K_2[IrBr_5(CO)]$[179].

$(AsPh_4)[IrBr_4(EtOH)]$ can be made by refluxing ethanol with $(AsPh_4)[IrBr_4(CO)_2]$[180]; the product is likely to be dimeric, with bromo bridges.

$Cs_5[Ir_3Br_{14}].2H_2O$ is formed in addition to $Cs_3[IrBr_6].H_2O$ when a caesium salt is added to a solution of $Na_3[IrBr_6]$. It was suggested that the complex has a trinuclear structure[71]:

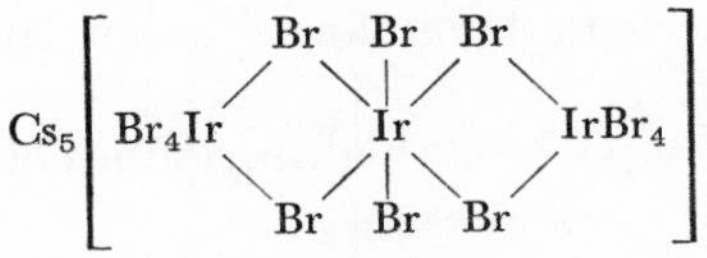

```
      [         Br   Br   Br            ]
      [        /   \  |  /   \          ]
  Cs5 [ Br4Ir        Ir        IrBr4    ]
      [        \   /  |  \   /          ]
      [         Br   Br   Br            ]
```

The tendency to form polynuclear halogen bridged complexes is most marked with rhodium (cf. p. 322) although a few such complexes are known for ruthenium.

$K_3[IrI_6]$ can be made by treating hydrated iridium trichloride with a solution of potassium iodide. It forms green crystals, and is soluble in water and in alcohol; ammonium and silver salts were also made[211].

The supposed $\mathbf{K_2[IrI_5]}$[182] is now known to be $K_2[IrI_5(CO)]$[179].

The iridium (III) chloro-aquo system

This has not been as extensively investigated as those of ruthenium (III) and rhodium (III); the only three aquo species which have been characterized in aqueous solutions of $[IrCl_6]^{3-}$ are $[IrCl_5(H_2O)]^{2-}$, $[IrCl_4(H_2O)_2]^-$ and $IrCl_3(H_2O)_3$[41] (the kinetics of formation of these by aquation reactions have been mentioned previously on p. 242). Of these, salts of the pentachloroaquo anion alone have been isolated. Studies by high-voltage ionophoresis have also demonstrated the existence of the above species and of $[IrCl_2(H_2O)_4]^+$ in acid solutions of $[IrCl_6]^{3-}$, but none of the geometrical isomers was distinguished[26].

$\mathbf{K_2[IrCl_5(H_2O)]}$ (green crystals) can be made by reducing an aqueous solution of $K_2[IrCl_6]$ with potassium oxalate[41,54]. The solubilities of the known salts are: potassium 9·2, ammonium 15·4, rubidium 1·05 and caesium 0·83 g/100 ml of water at 19°. The aquated acid $H_2[IrCl_5H_2O].6H_2O$ can be made by the action of oxalic acid on $H_2[IrCl_6]$ solution[209]. The water-replacement reaction of $[IrCl_5(H_2O)]^{2-}$ has been studied (cf. p. 242)[223] and so has the aquation[41].

Delepine has prepared a salt which appears to be $\mathbf{K_4[NIr_3Cl_{12}(H_2O)_3]}$ and also $\mathbf{Cs_3[NIr_3Cl_{11}]}$[70a]; cf. p. 248.

Iridium (III) chlorohydroxy complexes

These have been postulated as existing in weakly acid or neutral solutions of $[IrCl_6]^{3-}$; they are said to include $[IrCl_4(OH)_2]^{3-}$ and $[IrCl_2(OH)_4]^{3-}$[24].

$\mathbf{K_2[IrBr_5(H_2O)]}$ can be made from iridium dioxide, hydrobromic acid and potassium bromide; it forms yellow needles. A rubidium salt was also isolated[71].

No iridium (III) aquo- or hydroxyiodo complexes have been reported (yet).

Iridium (II)

No halides of this oxidation state have been established. The following species were claimed by early workers but their existence should be regarded with considerable suspicion.

It was said that **iridium dichloride, $IrCl_2$,** could be made by heating the trichloride in a current of chlorine to 770°[273]. The product is brown, and its lattice is believed to be of the cadmium dichloride type[218]. A green form has been claimed (made by heating the disulphide in chlorine)[86] but this is likely to have been a mixture of the metal and the trichloride. Studies on dissociation of the trichloride suggest that $IrCl_2$ does not exist in the vapour or solid phases[19a].

Iridium dibromide, $IrBr_2$, is supposedly obtained by heating the hydrated dioxide or the hydrated tribromide in a stream of hydrogen bromide at 440°. The compound was a very stable, deep reddish-brown graphite-like powder, insoluble in acids and water but soluble in alkalis. Heating it to 485° gave the monobromide[152].

Iridium diiodide, IrI_2, was claimed to be found when the triiodide was heated to 330° in hydrogen iodide; the product has not, however, been made in the pure state[152]. There is also an old report that it can be made by treating an aqueous suspension of the 'tetraiodide' with sulphur dioxide[211].

It is said that **$(NH_4)_2[IrI_4]$** can be got as black crystals from the reaction of ammonium iodide with a hot solution of $(NH_4)_2[IrCl_6]$[211], but the compound is probably $(NH_4)_3[IrI_6]$.

Iridium (I)

These monovalent compounds seem to be somewhat better characterized than the dihalides, but confirmatory work with them would be desirable.

It is said that **iridium monochloride, IrCl**, can be sublimed from the trichloride above 773°. It is a coppery-red substance with a metallic lustre, and is very stable, being insoluble in water, acids and alkalis[273].

Iridium monobromide, IrBr, can be made by heating the dibromide in an atmosphere of hydrogen bromide to 485°. It is dark brown (brown-red by transmitted light), and can be sublimed at 500°. It is slightly soluble in water, acids and bases[152].

Iridium monoiodide, IrI, is made by heating the diiodide in an atmosphere of hydrogen iodide to 355°[152].

GROUP VI DONORS

As is the case with osmium, the cationic hexaaquo species $[M(H_2O)_6]^{4+}$ and $[M(H_2O)_6]^{3+}$ have not been detected, whereas the trivalent species at least are known for rhodium and ruthenium.

The absence of characterized oxy complexes of both iridium and rhodium is in sharp contrast to the chemistry of ruthenium and osmium.

Iridium has a considerable affinity for sulphur.

Iridium (VIII)

IrO_4 was once claimed as an oxidation product of the metal[83]: it was not isolated, and its existence must be regarded as very questionable.

Iridium (VI)

Iridium trioxide, IrO_3, does not appear to exist in the solid state[274], but it has been shown by transpiration and mass spectrometric techniques to exist in the vapour phase near 1200°[19b,205]. From electron impact studies the ionization potential has been estimated as 11·9 ev[205].

Oxy species

Potassium iridates, **$nK_2O.IrO_3$**, can be made by fusion of the metal with potassium nitrate or with a mixture of potassium nitrate and hydroxide. The products are ill-defined, insoluble in water, and will oxidize hydrochloric acid to chlorine. A sodium iridate of equally uncertain composition has been made[95,274]. It has been suggested that the oxidation products of acid iridium (III) solutions contain iridium (VI) as well as (V) and (IV)[255], and it is said that anodic oxidation of iridium (III) species gives **IrO_2^{2+}** species[80a].

Iridium trisulphide, IrS_3, can be got as a dark grey powder by heating the trichloride with an excess of sulphur to 600°. The compound is extraordinarily stable towards acids, and is said to be unaffected by aqua regia[275]; it is a semi-conductor[125a].

$IrSe_3$ and **$IrTe_3$**, have been made by heating the trichloride with selenium or tellurium, respectively, and are similarly inert[21,22]; they are semi-conductors[125a]. **Ir_3S_8** can also be made from the elements[22]. It may contain both iridium (VI) and (IV), or alternatively sulphur chains.

Iridium (V)

The only examples claimed of pentavalent iridium are the species formed by oxidation of iridium (III) mentioned above[255], the species IrO_2Cl which exists only in the gas phase,[19a] and $IrF_5.SO_2$ (p. 231).

Iridium (IV)

Iridium dioxide, IrO_2, can be made by heating the metal in oxygen[19b] or by hydrolysis of solutions of $[IrCl_6]^{2-}$ with alkali and then dehydrating the product under carbon dioxide[274]; the best way of making a very pure product is said to be the careful hydrolysis of salts containing $[IrCl_6]^{2-}$ [29a, 153]. The oxide forms black crystals of the rutile type (a = 4·49, c = 3·14 Å)[172]. The magnetic susceptibility has been measured from 298 to 698°K and suggests that the compound is magnetically non-dilute, as is to be expected for oxides[112]. The gaseous iridium–oxygen system has been studied at high temperatures and an estimate made of the dissociation energy of the dioxide[2,241]. The ionization potential of the gaseous species has been estimated as 10·9 ev from electron impact studies[205].

For the reaction

$$Ir(s) + O_2 \rightarrow IrO_2(s)$$

$\Delta H^0_{298} = -57{\cdot}4$ kcal/mole and $\Delta S^0_{298} = -438$ e.u.[19b]

A hydrated form of the dioxide can be got by the treatment of iridium (IV) complexes with alkali; it is said that this is soluble in water at room temperatures to the extent of 0·002%. It will slowly dissolve in mineral acid to give blue solutions, of uncertain composition—they perhaps contain trimers similar to those described below on p. 249.

Chemical properties of the dioxide are summarized in Figure 5.1.

The iridites

Fusion of iridium with sodium carbonate in air above 600° gives **Na_2IrO_3**, which has a structure similar to that of Na_2SnO_3[245].

$CaIrO_3$ can be made in a hexagonal form (a = 5·44, c = 6·39 Å) by heating together mixtures of iridium dioxide and calcium carbonate, while an orthorhombic form (a = 3·14, b = 9·85, c = 7·29 Å) is formed when the above preparation is carried out in a calcium chloride melt. A fuller x-ray study of the orthorhombic form showed that there is a distorted octahedral arrangement of oxygen atoms about the iridium, with two sets of iridium–oxygen bonds, four of which are long (equatorial, Ir—O = 2·06 Å) and two of which are short (axial, Ir—O = 1·94 Å); each calcium atom is surrounded by nine oxygen atoms[239]. X-ray powder studies have been carried out on **$Sr_4[IrO_6]$** and showed that this had a triply primitive hexagonal unit cell, but no details were given of the preparation of the compound[231]. Alkali metal iridites of ill-defined nature can be made by the reaction between iridium and alkali metal nitrites at high temperatures, followed by extraction of the product with water. With potassium nitrite, $\mathbf{K_2Ir_2O_7}$, $\mathbf{K_2Ir_6O_{13}}$ and $\mathbf{K_2Ir_{12}O_{25}}$ were claimed[132], but it was later suggested that the aqueous solutions from which these were obtained contained colloidal iridium dioxide, stabilized in this condition by the alkali[274].

Oxy, hydroxy and aquo complexes

Iridium (IV) chloroaquo and chlorohydroxy systems have already been mentioned (p. 238).

$\mathbf{[IrO(OH)]^+}$ species, violet in colour, are said to be formed by oxidation of iridium (III) sulphate with permanganate or ceric ion, while reduction of IrO_2^{2+}, formed by anodic oxidation of iridium (III), gives the red-violet $\mathbf{IrO^{2+}}$ species[80a].

$\mathbf{[Ir(OH)_6]^{2-}}$ is said to be formed in solution when solutions of iridium (III) or iridium (IV) chloro complexes are heated to 90° for some time. The electronic absorption spectrum was recorded[73]. At high concentrations of iridium the solutions turn blue, probably due to the formation of polynuclear species[73]. Polarographic reduction of the complex is a reversible one-electron process ($E_{1/2} = -0{\cdot}60$); it was supposed that the reduction product was $[Ir(OH)_5H_2O]^{2-}$[259a].

Polynuclear oxy–aquo complexes

These complexes of iridium (IV) with coordinated sulphate and phosphate groups have received some attention. It has been suggested[137] that the blue-green sulphates of Lecoq de Boisbaudran contain the $[O.Ir_3(SO_4)_9]^{10-}$ ion (these species are made by boiling hexachloroiridates (III) with concentrated sulphuric acid[70a,161]). The bonding in this complex is probably similar to that in the nitrido sulphates, $[N.Ir_3(SO_4)_6(H_2O)_3]^{4-}$ (made by boiling $(NH_4)_3[IrCl_6]$ with sulphuric acid[55,70a]), and in $[NIr_3Cl_{12}(H_2O)]^{4-}$[70a]; it is convenient to discuss them together here.

$\mathbf{[N.Ir_3(SO_4)_6(H_2O)_3]^{4-}}$. It has been shown that the oxidizing power of this species is consistent with it containing one iridium (III) and two iridium (IV) atoms per molecule[70a,137]. The structure suggested for this compound (Figure 5.3(a)) supposes that the three iridium atoms form an equilateral triangle with the nitrogen atom at the centre, the four atoms being coplanar[137,138,212]. This type of structure is also found in $HgO.2HgCl_2$ (where an oxygen atom is surrounded in a plane by three rectilinear HgCl groups)[244], and in $[Cr_3(OAc)_3$-$(H_2O)_3O]Cl$[90]; (cf. also p. 147). The bonding and the observed diamagnetism of the complex are explained as follows: the two iridium (IV) and one iridium (III) atoms, assuming spin-pairing, will have a total of sixteen electrons in their nine t_{2g} orbitals; in addition the lone nitrogen atom will have a pair of electrons in its $2p_z$ orbital (the z axis being perpendicular to the iridium–nitrogen plane). This orbital has the correct symmetry to interact with the appropriate metal t_{2g} orbitals, giving a (stable) bonding and an (unstable) antibonding level; assuming that the antibonding level remains unoccupied, the stability of the sixteen electron system can be understood. Reduction of the green nitrido salt with vanadous ion gives a straw yellow species containing three iridium (III) atoms per molecule[137]; if one assumes the same planar structure, this species will have its extra two electrons paired up in the antibonding orbital[138]. In all these compounds the metal atoms are equivalent.

Other salts of the same type which have been isolated are $[Ir_3N(NH_3)_3(SO_4)_6]^{4-}$ and $[Ir_3N(\beta\text{-pic})_3(SO_4)_6]^{4-}$, obtained as potassium or ammonium salts by interaction of $(NH_4)[Ir(SO_4)_2$-$(H_2O)_2]$ and the appropriate base[66a].

The $[O.Ir_3(SO_4)_9]^{10-}$ ion. This contains two iridium (III) and one iridium (IV) atoms per molecule[137] and so a possible structure would again be that shown by Figure 5.3(b), with a coplanar arrangement of metal and oxygen atoms; to maintain octahedral coordination

(a)
$[N.Ir_3(SO_4)_6(H_2O)_3]^{4-}$
(green)

(b)
$[O.Ir_3(SO_4)_9]^{10-}$
(blue-green)

Figure 5.3 Metal molecular orbitals for trinuclear iridium complexes[138] ((a) and (b)) are as follows:

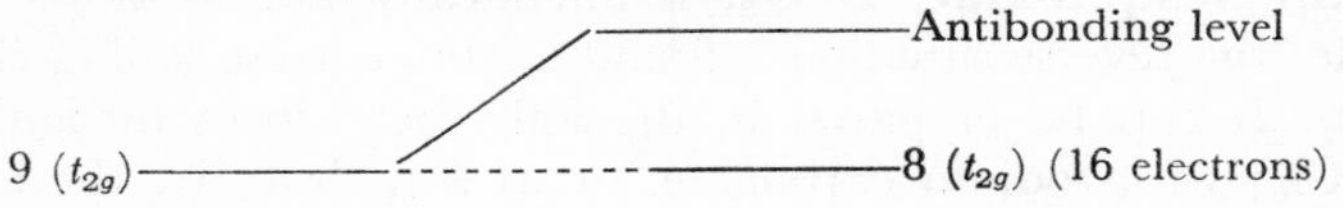

for the iridium atoms, it is now necessary to assume that six of the sulphate groups are bridging and three monodentate. The presence of two iridium (III) and one iridium (IV) atoms implies that there should be one (unpaired) electron in the antibonding orbital indicated in Figure 5.3[138], and this is apparently the case.

A number of other polynuclear iridium (IV)–iridium (III) species of a somewhat ill-defined nature have been reported: these contain coordinated sulphate, hydroxide and phosphate groups, and were made by treatment of iridium (IV) hexachloro complexes with sulphuric perchloric and phosphoric acids[99,225]. They will all catalyse the reaction between cerium (IV) and water[100].

Oxalates

Although $K_2[Ir\ ox_3]$ has been mentioned in the literature and reference[56] given, this latter source refers only to the preparation and resolution of $K_3[Ir\ ox_3]$. Only two iridium (IV) oxalate complexes have been obtained, namely **$Cs_2[IrCl_4\ ox]$**, precipitated on addition of caesium chloride to a solution of $K_3[IrCl_4\ ox]$ through which chlorine has been passed[128a], and **$K[Irpy\ Cl_3\ ox].aq$** from chlorine and $K_2[Irpy\ Cl_3\ ox]$[128a].

Iridium (IV) sulphate, $Ir(SO_4)_2.aq$, can be made by oxidation of the disulphide with nitric acid[237] and appears to form no complexes or 'double salts' with alkali metal sulphates; **$IrO.SO_4.4H_2O$** can be made from sulphur dioxide and iridium dioxide[23].

Compounds containing sulphur, selenium and tellurium

IrS_2, $IrSe_2$ and $IrTe_2$ can be made from the elements in the case of the sulphide[22] or by reduction of $IrSe_3$ and $IrTe_3$ with hydrogen in the case of the selenide and telluride[275]. The heat of formation of the sulphide has been measured, (−30 kcal/mole) and it has been shown that the lattice is of the pyrites type[22]. The semi-conductors IrSSe and $IrSe_{1.5}Te_{0.5}$ have been made by sintering methods[125a]. A mixed species, **$2\ IrS_2.Ir_2S_3$**, is formed as a brown precipitate when hydrogen sulphide is passed into an aqueous solution of $K_2[IrCl_6]$[10].

Iridium (III)

Iridium sesquioxide, Ir_2O_3, is chemically not as stable as the dioxide (the reverse situation is found for the corresponding rhodium oxides). It can be prepared in the anhydrous form by ignition of $K_2[IrCl_6]$ with sodium carbonate, or as a hydrate by the addition of alkali to $K_3[IrCl_6]$ under an inert atmosphere[274]. The anhydrous form is black and the hydrate (which is of uncertain composition) may be green or deep blue, according to the circumstances of preparation. On heating either form to a temperature above 400° a mixture of the metal and iridium dioxide is formed, and on heating above 1000° the metal and oxygen are formed. The sesquioxide is soluble in sulphuric, hydrochloric and hydrofluoric acids, but it is oxidized to the dioxide by nitric acid; the hydrated sesquioxide is slightly soluble in alkalis. There is no evidence for the existence of lower oxides of iridium in the solid state; in the gas phase, however, the trioxide, dioxide and monoxide have been detected, but not the sesquioxide.

Aquo and hydroxy complexes

Apart from the aquochloro, aquobromo and hydroxychloro systems already mentioned (p. 244), the only other species containing these ligands are the $[NIr_3(SO_4)_6(H_2O)_3]^{4-}$ ion (cf. p. 248)[137] and some rather ill-defined aquosulphato and aquophosphato complexes[99,225] made by reduction of the corresponding iridium (IV)–(III) species (see p. 250); it is possible that these too have trinuclear structures with a coplanar arrangement of one oxygen and three iridium atoms. The $\mathbf{[Ir(OH)_6]^{3-}}$ ion may be present in alkaline solutions of the sesquioxide, and there is polarographic evidence for the existence of $[Ir(OH)_5H_2O]^{2-}$[259a].

For *peroxy complexes* see p. 272.

Acetylacetone complexes

Ir acac$_3$, like its rhodium analogue, is difficult to prepare. It is formed in small quantitites as a yellow solid (which may be sublimed at 260° at 1 mm pressure) when the hydrated sesquioxide is treated with acetylacetone at pH 6; as a by-product of this reaction, an unstable reddish-brown substance, probably containing the $\mathbf{[Ir(OH)_2acac_2]^-}$ anion, is formed[80]. The tris complex is yellow (m.p. 269°), and insoluble in water and sparingly soluble in alcohol and ether, but it dissolves easily in benzene or chloroform. Its mass spectrum was measured[174a].

The complex, $\mathbf{IrH_2(acac)(PPh_3)_2}$, has been made by the action of acetylacetone on $IrH_3(PPh_3)_3$[11].

Carboxylic acid complexes

Acetates. The only acetato complex reported seems to be the $[Ir(NH_3)_5(OAc)]^{2+}$ cation, and $[Ir(OAc)_2Cl]_2$[45a] (cf. p. 261).

Formates. Efforts to prepare the complex $[IrCl_5(HCOOH)]^{2-}$ from hexachloroiridates and formic acid[45a] apparently yield the carbonyl species $[Ir(CO)Cl_5]^{2-}$[147a], although it has been claimed that formic acid in ethanolic solution reacts with $[IrCl_6]^{2-}$ to give $(\mathbf{Ir(HCOO)_2Cl_2})^-$: this latter complex reacts with acetic acid to give a dimeric acetate, $(\mathbf{Ir(OAc)_2Cl})_2$[45a]. Clearly a careful investigation of this system is needed. (The decarbonylation of formic acid by ruthenium (II) chloride has already been noted (p. 183).) The only formato complex of iridium which is definitely established is $[\mathbf{Ir(NH_3)_5(HCOO)}](\mathbf{ClO_4})_2$, made as yellow crystals by the action of formic acid on $(Ir(NH_3)_5OH)(ClO_4)_2$[249].

Oxalato complexes. As with rhodium, a fairly large number of these are known for iridium (III) (cf. Table 5.2); the only one which will be dealt with in detail is the tris complex.

$\mathbf{K_3[Ir\,ox_3].4\tfrac{1}{2}H_2O}$ can be made from $K_3[IrCl_6]$ and potassium oxalate, or from oxalic acid, potassium carbonate and freshly-prepared hydrated iridium dioxide[56]. The crystals, triclinic pinaconoidal in shape, are orange-red; the potassium salt is sparingly soluble in the cold but easily dissolves in hot water. The curious hydration number for the potassium salt is reminiscent of the behaviour of the corresponding ruthenium (III) and rhodium (III) salts (cf. p. 158 and 337) and suggests that, like the rhodium complex at least, the structure of the solid salt may be $K_6[Ir\,ox_2(Hox)(OH)][Ir\,ox_3].8H_2O$. Again, like the ruthenium and rhodium salts, adducts with mercuric cyanide, $2\,K_3[Ir\,ox_3].Hg(CN)_2.8H_2O$, and potassium chloride, $2\,K_3[Ir\text{-}ox_3].KCl.8H_2O$, can readily be prepared[56] (however, unlike the ruthenium salt but like the rhodium salt, all the hydrated water can be removed from $K_3[Ir\,ox_3].4\tfrac{1}{2}H_2O$; a tetra- and a dihydrate are also known)[111]. The mixed iridium–rhodium complex $\mathbf{K_3[Ir_{1/2}Rh_{1/2}ox_3]\text{-}4\tfrac{1}{2}H_2O}$ has been made (from optically active forms of the rhodium and iridium tris oxalato salts)[57]. The compound $KH_2[Ir\,ox_3].4H_2O$ is made by the action of sulphuric acid on the tris oxalate[78]: it may contain protonated monodentate oxalate groups and coordinated water. The acid $H_3[Ir\,ox_3].xH_2O$ can be made as a solid from hydrated iridium dioxide and oxalic acid[97].

Resolution of $K_3[Ir\,ox_3]$ has been achieved by using the strychnine salts[56]; the complex is not racemized after boiling in aqueous solution for an hour[59]. The exchange of oxalate ligand with $[Ir\,ox_3]^{3-}$ (the ligand labelled with ^{14}C) is slow, as predicted by crystal-field stabilization arguments[210] (cf. also the $[Ru\ ox_3]^{3-}$–oxalate exchange, p. 158). The electronic absorption spectrum of $[Ir\ ox_3]^{3-}$ in solution has been measured[139,210]. Measurements on the circular dichroism of $[Ir\ ox_3]^{3-}$ are reported[174,189,190] and the magnetic dipole-allowed transitions identified[98].

Nitrato and nitrito complexes

'Iridium nitrate', of unknown constitution, has been made from iridium trichloride and nitric acid at 100°; with nitrate ion in aqueous solution it is said to give salts containing the $\mathbf{[Ir(NO_3)_6]^{3-}}$ anion[88]. A nitrato pentammine, $\mathbf{[Ir(NH_3)_5(NO_3)]^{2+}}$, is known (cf. Table 5.4), and is made by heating $[Ir(NH_3)_5(H_2O)](NO_3)_3$.

The only nitrito complexes reported are salts of $\mathbf{[Ir(NH_3)_5ONO]^{2+}}$ (cf. p. 260).

Phosphato and phosphito complexes

Iridium is unusual amongst the four elements in that it forms a number of such complexes, albeit ill-defined. These include species, probably trinuclear, formed by reduction of the iridium (IV) complex phosphates[99,225] (cf. p. 248); $\mathbf{IrCl_3(H_3PO_3)_3}$ and $\mathbf{2IrCl_3.3H_3PO_3.3HPO_4}$, both made by the action of water on $IrCl_3(PCl_3)_2$ and $IrCl_3(PCl_3)_3$[94]; $\mathbf{K_3[IrCl_3(H_2PO_3)_3]}$ from a potassium salt and $IrCl_3(H_3PO_3)_3$ (more complicated ammonium and silver salts were also described)[94] and the mixed phosphate–arsenate $\mathbf{2IrCl_3.3H_3PO_3.3H_3PO_4.5H_3AsO_3}$[94].

The **peroxy complex** $Ir(CO)O_2Cl(PPh_3)_2$ is considered on p. 272.

Sulphato complexes

$\mathbf{Ir_2(SO_4)_3.aq}$, can be made as a yellow sparingly soluble material by boiling iridium (IV) sulphate with concentrated sulphuric acid[237] or by dissolving the sesquioxide in sulphuric acid in the absence of air; this latter product is said to give salts of the form $\mathbf{M[Ir(SO_4)_2(H_2O)_2]}$ (M = potassium, ammonium, rubidium, caesium, thallous)[184]. Iridium (III) sulphate will catalyse the oxidation of water to oxygen by cerium (IV), and the reaction, which is first order in cerium and in iridium, proceeds according to the rate law[100]:

$$-d[Ce^{IV}]/dt = k[Ce^{IV}][\text{iridium (III)}]$$

A number of sulphato complexes of rather dubious formulations have been claimed. Iridium trichloride and sulphuric acid in the presence of ammonium or sodium salts give salts of $\mathbf{[Ir(SO_4)_2(H_2O)(OH)]^{2-}}$[60], and with pyridine these give $\mathbf{[Ir(SO_4)_2(OH)py]^{2-}}$[61].

$\mathbf{K_3[Ir(SO_4)_3]}$ can be made by fusing iridium (III) salts with potassium bisulphate[62], and a hydrated acid can be made by the action of sulphuric acid on $K_2[IrCl_6]$: it is colourless, becoming blue-green on oxidation[201]. Potassium iridium alum, $\mathbf{K_2SO_4.Ir_2(SO_4)_3.24H_2O}$ can be made from iridium (III) sulphate and potassium sulphate[237]; this may be identical to $K[Ir(SO_4)_2(H_2O)_2]$. A number of trinuclear iridium (III) sulphato complexes were made by Delepine[55] and can be reformulated in the manner described for the iridium (III)–(IV) species (p. 248); the same applies to the complicated iridium (III) polynuclear aquohydroxysulphato complexes more recently reported[99,225].

Dimethylsulphoxide complexes

The reaction between aquated chloroiridous acid, $H_3[IrCl_6]aq$, and dimethylsulphoxide yields the 1,2,3- and 1,2,6-isomers of $\mathbf{IrCl_3(OSMe_2)_3}$; the dipole moments are respectively 3·9 and 2·9 D. The same reaction also gives two forms of $\mathbf{H[IrCl_4(OSMe_2)_2].2Me_2SO}$, and salts of this acid were isolated; analogous complexes with tetramethylene sulphoxide ligands were made in a similar fashion[112b].

These complexes, particularly the acids, will catalyse the hydrogen transfer from propan-2-ol to cyclohexanones and the reduction of the latter to axial alcohols[112b].

Trimethylphosphito complexes

These complexes of iridium (III) are apparently present in mixed solutions of chloroiridous acid and trimethyl phosphite; such solutions will, like the dimethylsulphoxide species, catalyse the reduction of cyclohexanones to axial alcohols[112b].

Sulphur, selenium and tellurium donors

$\mathbf{Ir_2S_3}$ can be made by heating the disulphide, or by passing hydrogen sulphide into an acid solution of the sesquioxide[22]. It is brown and chemically inert, being only slowly attacked by aqua regia. Its heat of formation has been determined and so have the dissociation pressures at various temperatures[22]. A 'hydrosulphide', $\mathbf{Ir_2S_3.3H_2O}$, can be made by the prolonged action of hydrogen sulphide on $(NH_4)_2[IrCl_5H_2O]$. It is brown, slowly blackening in air[227].

The polysulphide $\mathbf{(NH_4)_3IrS_{15}}$ results from the treatment of iridium trichloride with a solution of sulphur in ammonium sulphide; the compound forms brown crystals. A similar platinum compound,

$(NH_4)_2PtS_{15}$, is also known[124]. It is also possible to prepare a salt believed to be **$Na_3[Ir(SH)_6]$** by the action of sodium polysulphide on $Na_3[IrCl_6]$[222a].

Ir_2Se_3 can be made from hydrogen selenide and a solution of iridium trichloride. It is black, and is only partially decomposed at red heat in the presence of potassium nitrate, chlorate or carbonate[39]. Curiously, no iridium (III) telluride has been reported.

Sulphito complexes

The known examples are summarized in Table 5.3. Infrared studies on a number of these complexes suggest that the sulphite group functions as a monodentate ligand with a metal–sulphur rather than a metal–oxygen bond[12], that is

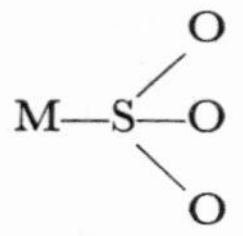

M—S(—O)(—O)—O

(C_{3v} local symmetry)

rather than

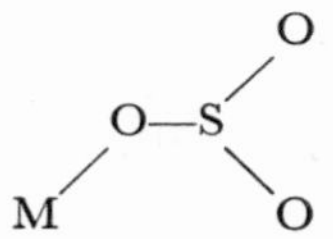

M—O—S(—O)—O

(C_s local symmetry)

In the case of the complexes containing the $[Ir(SO_3)_2Cl_3]^{4-}$ and $[Ir(SO_3)_2(NH_3)_3]^{-}$ ions it was deduced from the spectra that one of the two sulphite groups was bidentate, and the structure **1** below was preferred over **2**:

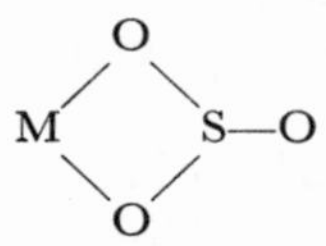

M(—O—)(—O—)S—O

(**1**)

M(—O—)(—S—)[O—S], S—O, S—O

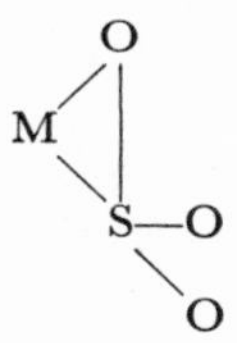

(**2**)

From these infrared studies and by the use of Badger's and Lechner's empirical relationships between force constants and bond lengths, values were deduced for the bond lengths and angles in the coordinated sulphite groups[12], but it is uncertain what validity these calculations have.

The reaction of nitrite ion with $[Ir(SO_3)_2Cl_3]^{4-}$ gives $[Ir(NO_2)_5(SO_3)]^{4-}$, but the remaining sulphite group cannot be removed by excess nitrite to give the hexanitro complex, suggesting that sulphite has a stronger *trans* effect than the nitro group in these species. This is also illustrated by the reaction sequence[45]:

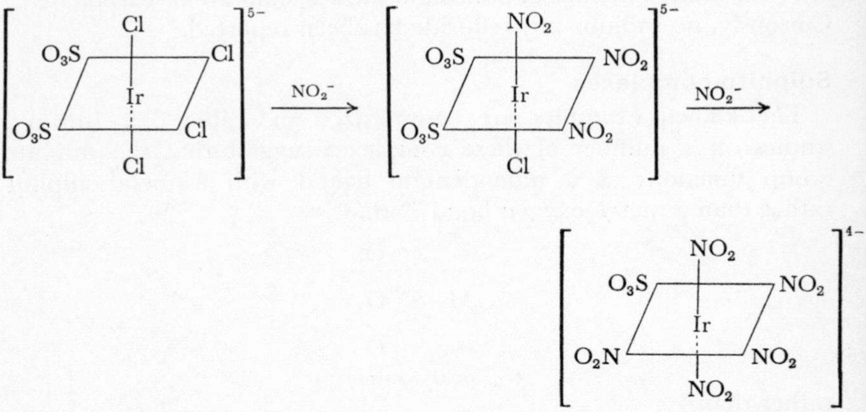

Cl; O_3S, Cl; Ir; O_3S, Cl; Cl]$^{5-}$ $\xrightarrow{NO_2^-}$ NO_2; O_3S, NO_2; Ir; O_3S, NO_2; Cl]$^{5-}$ $\xrightarrow{NO_2^-}$

NO_2; O_3S, NO_2; Ir; O_2N, NO_2; NO_2]$^{4-}$

Preliminary x-ray crystal structure results have been published of $(NH_4)_5[Ir(SO_3)_2Cl_4]$ and $(NH_4)_4[Ir(SO_3)_2Cl_3]$[222b].

Thiourea complexes

[Ir(thiourea)$_6$]Cl$_3$ forms yellow plates, and is made from iridium (IV) chloride solutions, hydrogen sulphide and the ligand. This procedure also gives **[Ir(thiourea)$_5$Cl]Cl$_2$** (olive-green) and **[Ir(thiourea)$_4$Cl$_2$]Cl** (red)[165]. $Na_3[IrCl_6]$ will react with thiourea in acid solutions to give **Ir(thiourea)$_3$Cl$_3$** (golden-yellow), and an adaptation of the method used for preparing the hexa complex yields **(NH$_4$)[Ir(thiourea)$_2$Cl$_4$]** and **(NH$_4$)$_2$[Ir(thiourea)Cl$_5$]** (both orange)[165].

No *dithiocarbamate* complexes seem to have been made. The electronic absorption spectra of the trisdiethyldithiophosphate complex (the ligand is $(EtO)_2PS_2^-$) has been measured and assignments proposed[140].

Thiocyanato complexes

Studies have been made of the position of the chemical shift in the ^{14}N nuclear magnetic resonance spectrum of an aqueous solution of **[Ir(SCN)$_6$]$^{3-}$**, from which it was deduced that there were metal–sulphur rather than metal–nitrogen bonds in the complex[125]. The solution was made from thiocyanate ion and $[IrCl_6]^{3-}$.

Alkyl sulphide complexes

Yellow and red isomers of **$Ir(Et_2S)_3Cl_3$** (yellow, m.p. 131°, red, m.p. 165°) can be made from an ethanolic solution of diethyl sulphide and ammonium hexachloroiridate (IV)[145]. It was originally suggested that these were the 1,2,3- and 1,2,6-isomers, but studies on the dipole moments, electronic spectra, conductivities and proton magnetic resonance spectra show that the yellow form is 1,2,3-$Ir(Et_2S)_3Cl_3$ and that the red form is *trans*-$[Ir(Et_2S)_4Cl_2]^+$-*trans*-$[Ir(Et_2S)_2Cl_4]^-$; other salts of $[Ir(Et_2S)_4Cl_2]^+$ and $[Ir(Et_2S)_2Cl_4]^-$ were also isolated[147]. Assignments have been proposed for the electronic spectral bands in the monomeric 1,2,3-$Ir(Et_2S)_3Cl_3$ complex[87,147] and dissociation pressure data were obtained for the compound[87]. Other complexes of this type are **$Ir_2Cl_5(R_2S)_4$** (R = Me,Et), **$IrCl_3py(Et_2S)_2$**, **$IrCl_3py_2(Et_2S)$** and **$[Ir(Et_2S)(NH_3)_5]Cl_3$**, made from $(NH_4)_2[IrCl_6]$ and the appropriate ligands[232]. The alkyl selenide complexes **$IrCl_3(Me_2Se)_3$** and **$IrCl_3(Et_2Se)_3$** have been made similarly[93].

Miscellaneous complexes

Electronic absorption spectra of iridium (III) (and rhodium (III)) complexes with diethyldithiophosphate, thiosemicarbazide, 2,2′-di(aminoethyl)sulphide and diethyldiselenophosphates have been recorded[140,141]

Iridium (II)

There are no reports of the existence of the monoxide as a solid, but band spectra of the species IrO in the gas phase have been measured[235], and from electron impact studies the ionization potential of the gaseous monoxide has been estimated as 10·1 ev[205]. All the other iridium (II) compounds which have been claimed involve sulphur ligands.

IrS can be made as a deep blue, very inert solid by heating the disulphide in a stream of carbon dioxide[10]. Thermodynamic data have been reported for the iridium–sulphur system of compounds[175].

Sulphito complexes

Such species as **$[Ir(SO_3)_4]^{6-}$** and **$[Ir(SO_3)Cl_6]^{6-}$** are said to be formed by the reaction between iridium (IV) chloride and bisulphites[251], but it is very unlikely that the complexes contain divalent iridium.

The mercaptide **$Ir(SEt)_2$** is said to result from the reaction between ethyl mercaptan and iridium trichloride, and orange crystals of the material were obtained[123]. It has not been proved, however, that this is an iridium (II) compound.

Iridium (I). The curious complex $Ir(CO)Cl(SO_2)(PPh_3)_2$ is considered on p. 280 below.

GROUP V DONORS

Like ruthenium and rhodium, iridium forms a wide range of ammine and pyridine complexes. The most distinguishing feature of the complexes with Group V ligands, however, is the very large number of hydrido phosphine and arsine complexes; ruthenium and rhodium do not seem to rival iridium in this field. It appears likely also that there may be an extensive nitrosyl chemistry of the element.

Iridium (IV)

Nitrido complexes

The mixed iridium (IV)–(III) trinuclear species $[\mathbf{NIr_3(SO_4)_6(H_2O)_3}]^{4-}$ has already been discussed (cf. p. 248).

Ammines and amine complexes

Unlike rhodium (IV), iridium (IV) does form a few complexes with this type of ligand (cf. Tables 5.4 and 5.6). Complexes of the form $IrCl_4 . L_2$ (L = pyridine, α- or β-picoline, quinoline) can be made by addition of the ligand L to solutions containing the $[IrCl_6]^{2-}$ ion or by oxidation of the corresponding iridium (III) species[111,144,159]; some iridium (IV) ammines may exist but have not been fully characterized (Table 5.4). Monopyridine[66] and β-picoline[159] salts of the type $M[IrCl_5 . L]$ can be made by oxidation of $M_2[IrCl_5 . L]$ with chlorine; the potassium salt $K[IrCl_5py]$ is dark red and is soluble to the extent of 0·7% in water at 20°. The pyridine complexes are very stable—the pyridine can only be removed by heating them with hydrochloric acid in a sealed tube at 150°.

A **diarsine** complex, probably $[Ir\ diars_2Cl_2](NO_3)_2$, is formed as a purple material when salts of $[Ir\ diars_2Cl_2]^+$ are oxidized with nitric acid[221a].

Iridium (III)

Ammines

These are summarized in Table 5.4.

Hexammines. $[\mathbf{Ir(NH_3)_6]Cl_3}$ can be made as colourless crystals by heating the halopentammines or aquopentammines with aqueous ammonia in a sealed tube at 100°[215,267]; a bromide, iodide, hydroxide and nitrate have also been prepared. The trichloride is isomorphous with $[Co(NH_3)_6]Cl_3$. The infrared (in the solid state) and Raman spectra (in aqueous solution) of the trichloride have been measured (cf. Table 3.7)[106].

The rates of proton exchange between metal hexammines $[M(NH_3)_6]^{3+}$ (M = Os, Ru, Ir, Rh, Co, Cr) and a 0·1 M acetate–acetic acid-d_1 buffer have been measured (cf. Table 5.5)[216]; the results were interpreted on the assumption that amido intermediates were involved.

Substituted ammine complexes. Many are known, and they are summarized in Table 5.4. Of particular interest are the halopentammines, the nitrito and nitro pentammines, and carboxylato pentammines.

$[Ir(NH_3)_5Cl]Cl_2$ can be made as yellow crystals by the prolonged action of ammonia solution on iridium trichloride[215] or on $Na_3[IrCl_6]$[156]; a recently recommended procedure is to pass chlorine over a mixture of iridium metal and sodium chloride and to treat the product with a mixture of ammonium chloride and ammonium carbonate[18]. Many salts of the cation are known. The solubilities in water at 15° are: chloride, 6; nitrate, 2; bromide, 0·5; iodide, 1; sulphate, 0·7 g/100 ml.

$[Ir(NH_3)_5Br]Br_2$ and **$[Ir(NH_3)_5I]I_2$** can be made from the aquopentammines with the appropriate halogen acids[156,215]. At 20° the solubility of the bromo bromide in water (g/100 ml) is 0·2, but the bromo nitrate has a solubility of 5·6.

A number of kinetic studies have been made on the halopentammines of iridium (III). The rates of aquation of $[Ir(NH_3)_5X]^{2+}$ (X = Cl, Br, I, NO_3) were found to be similar, under comparable conditions, to those of the corresponding cobalt ammines[156] (these were very early studies). The exchange between $[Ir(NH_3)_5Br]^{2+}$ and labelled bromide ion is some sixty times slower under comparable conditions than the $[Rh(NH_3)_5Br]^{2+}$–Br^- exchange[248].

Reduction of $[Ir(NH_3)_5X]^{2+}$ (X = Cl, Br, I) and $[Rh(NH_3)_5X]^{2+}$ (X = Cl, Br, I, OAc) by hexaaquo chromous ion in acid solutions has been studied[256]. For both sets of complexes, the rates decrease in the order: X = Cl > Br > I, whereas the opposite sequence is observed for cobalt (III) and chromium (III) halopentammines, and it was suggested that this reversal arises because rhodium (III) and iridium (III) are class (b) acceptors while cobalt (III) and chromium (III) are class (a) acceptors (the latter having a greater affinity for fluorine than for iodine). The X group is not transferred to the attacking chromium (in contrast to the behaviour observed with cobalt and chromium pentammines), and the mechanism

$$[(NH_3)_5Ir^{III}X] + Cr^{II} \rightarrow [(NH_3)_5Ir^{III}XCr^{II}]$$
$$[(NH_3)_5Ir^{III}XCr^{II}] \rightarrow [(NH_3)_5Ir^{II}XCr^{III}]$$
$$[(NH_3)_5Ir^{II}XCr^{III}] \rightarrow [(NH_3)_5Ir^{II}] + XCr^{III}$$

has been proposed[256].

The nitrito–nitro isomerism in iridium (III) and rhodium (III) pentammines has been studied by Basolo and Hammaker[18].

$[Ir(NH_3)_5ONO]Cl_2$ was made by the reaction between $[Ir(NH_3)_5(H_2O)]Cl_3$ and a mixture of sodium nitrite and hydrochloric acid at 0°; it forms white crystals. The infrared spectrum of the solid and electronic absorption spectrum of the aqueous solution were measured[18,49b]. The rate of formation of this nitrito complex in solution was measured (as were those for formation of the corresponding complexes of rhodium (III), cobalt (III) and chromium (III)), and the rate law was found to be of the form

$$\text{Rate} = k[\text{aquo complex}][NO_2^-][HNO_2]$$

The rates for all the complexes were of the same order of magnitude (approximately 6×10^{-4} sec^{-1} at 25° in 0·1 M nitrite), suggesting that metal–oxygen bond breaking is not involved; for the cobalt (III) reaction, experiments using ^{18}O have confirmed that there is no metal–oxygen bond rupture during the formation of the cobalt–nitrito bond[200]. The mechanism of formation of the iridium species and rhodium is probably the same as that proposed for the cobalt complex[18]:

$$[Co(NH_3)_5(H_2O)]^{3+} + H_2O \rightarrow [Co(NH_3)_5(OH)]^{2+} + H_3O^+$$
$$2\,HNO_2 \rightarrow N_2O_3 + H_2O$$
$$[(NH_3)_5Co{-}OH]^{2+} + N_2O_3 \rightarrow \left[\begin{matrix}(NH_3)_5Co{-}O\cdots H \\ \vdots \\ O{=}N\cdots NO_2\end{matrix}\right]^{2+} \rightarrow$$
$$[(NH_3)_5Co{-}ONO]^{2+} + HNO_2$$

The rates of isomerization of the nitrito complexes to give the nitro complexes were measured both in the solid state (using infrared spectra), and in aqueous solution (using electronic spectra) for the cobalt (III), iridium (III), rhodium (III), chromium (III) and platinum (IV) systems. For cobalt, iridium and platinum the rates are similar (of the order of $0{\cdot}5 \times 10^{-5}$ sec^{-1} in the solid state and somewhat higher in solution), but the rate for rhodium is an order of magnitude higher (the chromium complex does not isomerize). It was suggested that, as in the cobalt case[200], the activated complex contains a nitro group bonded to the metal through both the oxygen and the nitrogen atoms[18].

It is curious that, whereas ultraviolet irradiation of $[Ir(NH_3)_5NO_2]Cl_2$ or of $[Co(NH_3)_5NO_2]Cl_2$ yields the nitrito isomers, similar treatment of the rhodium complex produces no isomerization[18].

Acid-catalysed hydrolysis of acetato pentammines. $\mathbf{[Ir(NH_3)_5(RCOO)](ClO_4)_2}$ (R = CH_3, $C(CH_3)_3$ and CF_3) can be made from the aquopentammine and the carboxylic acid, followed by treatment with perchloric acid[198]. The rates of acid-catalysed hydrolysis ($[H^+]$ = 0·1–0·001 M) of these complexes as well as of the corresponding rhodium (III) and cobalt (III) species were measured[198]. In all cases the rates of hydrolysis increased with increasing acid concentration, and the observed pseudo first-order rate constant k_{obs} fits the expression

$$k_{obs} = k_{H_2O} + k_{H^+}[H^+]$$

where k_{H_2O} is the extrapolated rate constant for the uncatalysed rate and k_{H^+} is the acid-catalysed rate constant. This suggests that two reaction paths are involved[198]:

$$[(NH_3)_5M{-}O{-}C({=}O)R]^{2+} + H_2O \xrightarrow{k_{H_2O}} [(NH_3)_5M{-}OH_2]^{3+} + RCOO^- \quad (1)$$

$$[(NH_3)_5M{-}O{-}C({=}O)R]^{2+} + H^+ \xrightarrow{K_2} [(NH_3)_5M{-}O(H){-}C({=}O)R]^{3+} \quad (2a)$$

$$[(NH_3)_5M{-}O(H){-}C({=}O)R]^{3+} + H_2O \xrightarrow{k_3} [(NH_3)_5M{-}OH_2]^{3+} + RCOOH \quad (2b)$$

$$k_{H^+} = K_2 k_3$$

The higher the acid concentration, the greater will be the contribution of the protonated acid species to the overall rate of hydrolysis. Values of k_{H^+} are similar for the three metal systems (for the acetato complexes at 80°, k_{H^+} is of the order of 8×10^{-5} sec^{-1} M^{-1} for iridium,

3×10^{-3} for rhodium, and 3×10^{-3} for cobalt, while the corresponding k_{H_2O} values are 10^{-6}, 4×10^{-6} and 2×10^{-5} sec^{-1}). For each metal the rate decreases by a factor of about five going from the acetate to the pivalate systems (due perhaps to steric effects), and for the cobalt and rhodium systems by a factor of about twenty from the acetate to the trifluoroacetate. This may be connected with the fact that trifluoroacetate ion is a weaker base than acetate so that less of the protonated species is formed[198]. No direct evidence could be obtained as to whether hydrolysis of the complexes proceeds by metal–oxygen fission

$$[(NH_3)_5M{-}O{-}\underset{\underset{O}{\|}}{C}R]^{2+} \rightleftharpoons [(NH_3)_5M{\cdots}O{-}\underset{\underset{O}{\|}}{C}R]^{2+} \xrightleftharpoons{H_2O} [(NH_3)_5M{-}OH_2]^{3+} + RCOOH \quad (4)$$

or by acyl–oxygen bond fission

$$[(NH_3)_5M{-}O{-}\underset{\underset{O}{\|}}{C}R]^{2+} \xrightleftharpoons{H+} [(NH_3)_5M{-}\underset{\underset{H}{|}}{O}{\cdots}\underset{\underset{O}{\|}}{C}R]^{3+} \xrightleftharpoons{H_2O} [(NH_3)_5M{-}OH_2]^{3+} + RCOOH \quad (5)$$

but it seems likely that reaction (4) above involves metal–oxygen cleavage for the acetato and pivalato complexes. The trifluoroacetato complex undergoes hydrolysis by acyl–oxygen bond rupture, perhaps because the more positively charged acyl carbon atom is more susceptible to nucleophilic attack than in the acetate systems[198].

Amine complexes

[Ir en$_3$]I$_3$ can be got from $Na_3[IrCl_6]$, ethylenediamine and sodium iodide at 140°, and a bromide, nitrate and perchlorate, all colourless, are also known although no chloride has been prepared[270]. The iodide has been resolved by means of the optically active α-nitro camphor salts[270]. Electronic absorption spectra studies[174] and circular dichroism have been made on [Ir en$_3$]$^{3+}$ in aqueous solution[79,174,190], and assignments proposed. The absolute configuration of [Ir en$_3$]$^{3+}$ has been obtained by measurements of the Cotton effect[79]. Raman shifts were observed in aqueous solutions of [Ir en$_3$]$^{3+}$ at 250, 398, 560, 860, 990 and 1070 cm^{-1} and the very strong 560 cm^{-1} band was assigned to the symmetric metal–nitrogen stretch[193].

Potentiometric measurements have shown that both [Ir en$_3$]I$_3$ and [Rh en$_3$]I$_3$ are very weak acids, in aqueous solution, with an upper limit of about 10^{-12} for their dissociation constants, and such is also the case for [Co en_3]Cl_3[110]. However, the NH_2 protons in [Ir en_3]$^{3+}$ are sufficiently acidic to ionize appreciably and to permit their successive removal by a solution of potassium amide in liquid ammonia. From this reaction the complexes **[Ir(en–H)$_2$en]I** and **K_2[Ir(en–2 H)$_2$(en–H)]** (both tan coloured) were isolated, and evidence presented from potentiometric studies for the formation of the following species by the reactions below (here, as in the case of the similar osmium complexes, (en–H) represents the group $H_2N.CH_2.CH_2.NH^-$, and (en–2H) represents the group $HN.CH_2.CH_2.NH^{2-}$)[265]

$$[Ir\ en_3]^{3+} + NH_2^- \rightarrow [Ir(en{-}H)en_2]^{2+} + NH_3$$
$$[Ir(en{-}H)en_2]^{2+} + NH_2^- \rightarrow [Ir(en{-}H)_2en] + NH_3$$
$$[Ir(en{-}H)_2en]^+ + NH_2^- \rightarrow Ir(en{-}H)_3 + NH_3$$
$$Ir(en{-}H)_3 + 2\ NH_2^- \rightarrow [Ir(en{-}2\ H)_2(en{-}H)]^{2-} + 2\ NH_3$$

It was suggested that a mechanism involving reduction to iridium (II) was involved[265]:

$$[Ir^{III}en_3]^{3+} + e^- \rightarrow [Ir^{II}en_3]^{2+}$$
$$[Ir^{II}en_3]^{2+} \rightarrow [Ir^{III}(en{-}H)en_2]^{2+} + \tfrac{1}{2}H_2$$

and similarly

$$[Ir^{III}(en{-}H)en_2]^{2+} + e^- \rightarrow [Ir^{II}(en{-}H)en_2]^+$$
$$[Ir^{II}(en{-}H)en_2]^+ \rightarrow [Ir^{III}(en{-}H)_2en]^+ + \tfrac{1}{2}H_2$$

—another possibility is that iridium (I) or hydridic intermediates are involved.

The only substituted iridium ethylenediamine complex obtained so far appears to be *cis*-**[Ir en$_2$(NO$_2$)$_2$]I**, which can be got by treating $Na_3[Ir(NO_2)_4Cl_2]$ with ethylenediamine at 170°, followed by addition of potassium iodide; a bromide, nitrate and perchlorate, all colourless, were also made, and the salts were resolved by means of the optically active camphor sulphonate derivatives[270].

Other iridium (III) amine complexes which have been reported are **[Ir(EtNH$_2$)$_5$Cl]Cl$_2$**, **[Ir(EtNH$_2$)$_4$Cl$_2$]Cl** and **Ir(EtNH$_2$)$_3$Cl$_3$**, all of which are yellow crystalline materials and all made by treatment of $Ir(SEt_2)_3Cl_3$ with ethylamine at 150°[233].

[Ir(1-chxn)$_3$][IrCl$_6$] (chxn = *trans*-1,2-diaminocyclohexane, $C_6H_{10}(NH_2)_2$) can be made as a white material from the ligand and $Na_3[IrCl_6]$[130].

$\mathbf{[Ir\ dien_3]Br_3}$ (dien = diethylenetriamine) is formed as white crystals by the prolonged action of the ligand at 100° on iridium tribromide. With a solution of potassium amide in liquid ammonia it yields a pyrophoric species which is said to be **Ir(dien–H)(dien–2H)**[266].

Complexes with heterocyclic bases

Pyridine complexes are summarized in Table 5.6. Many are known but none seems to merit special attention here. As with rhodium, a pyridine:metal ratio of 4:1 is never exceeded[70]. Infrared spectra (from 4000 to 200 cm^{-1}) have been reported for a number of iridium (III) pyridine species[120a], and photochemical studies reported on $[Ir\ py\ Cl_5]^{2-}$[68a] and on other iridium pyridine species[70b].

A number of β-picoline complexes have recently been synthesized. The reaction between β-picoline and $K_2[IrCl_6]$ yields both *cis*- and *trans*-$\mathbf{K[Ir(pic)_2Cl_4]}$ (sodium, rubidium and caesium salts were also made; the most soluble in water were the sodium and potassium salts). Irradiation of the two isomers of the potassium salt with ultraviolet light gave *cis*- and *trans*-$\mathbf{Ir(pic)_2Cl_3(H_2O)}$[159]. Similarly, pyrazine (P_z) reacts with $K_2[Ir(H_2O)Cl_5]$ to give $K_2[Ir(P_z)Cl_5]$, $K[Ir(P_z)_2Cl_4]$ and $Ir(P_z)_3Cl_3$. Electronic absorption spectra were recorded[159a].

Complexes with *o*-phenanthroline and 2,2′-bipyridyl are few; the unsubstituted species are discussed below.

$\mathbf{[Ir\ bipy_3](ClO_4)_3}$ (yellow crystals) can be made by the action of the ligand on $K_3[IrCl_6]$ followed by treatment with perchloric acid[185]. The infrared spectrum of the complex has been measured from 4000 to 600 cm^{-1} (together with the spectra of bipyridyl complexes of gold, rhodium and cobalt)[186] and the electronic spectrum measured[185].

$\mathbf{[Ir\ phen_3]Cl_3}$ can be obtained by fusion of the ligand with *trans*-$[Ir\ phen_2Cl_2]Cl$. It is cream-yellow; a bromide, iodide and perchlorate are also known[47]. Treatment of $(NH_4)_3[IrX_6]$ with *o*-phenanthroline at 220° gives a mixture of *trans*-$\mathbf{[Ir\ phen_2X_2]X}$ (X = Cl, Br) and $\mathbf{[Ir\ phen_2X_2][Ir\ phenX_4]}$[47].

$\mathbf{Ir(terpy)Cl_3}$ can be got from iridium trichloride and terpyridyl[198a].

Complexes of both iridium (III) and rhodium (III) with di-2-pyridylamine (dipyram) have recently been described; the iridium species are $\mathbf{[Ir(dipyram)_3]X_3}$ (X = Cl, Br, I) and were obtained from the ligand, $K_3[IrCl_6]$ and X^-. The infrared spectra of the products from 700 to 200 cm^{-1} were measured and also the electronic absorption spectra[155b].

Nitro complexes

The nitro pentammines, $[Ir(NH_3)_5(NO_2)]^{2+}$, and their formation from the isomeric nitrito species $[Ir(NH_3)_5ONO]^{2+}$ have been considered above (p. 260).

$K_3[Ir(NO_2)_6]$ can be got by the prolonged action of excess potassium nitrite solution on $K_3[IrCl_6]$; it forms colourless crystals; sodium, rubidium, caesium, ammonium, barium and thallous salts are also known[132,199]. The infrared and Raman spectra of $[Ir(NO_2)_6]^{3-}$ have been measured[191,222]. According to a recent report, reaction of $K_3[Ir(NO_2)_6]$ with $K_3[IrCl_6]$ gives **$K_7[Ir_4(OH)_3Cl_7(NO_2)_9(H_2O)_2]$.-$4H_2O$**; a polymeric hydroxy bridged structure was proposed[199].

A few substituted nitro complexes are known (see also Tables 5.2 and 5.4): **$K_3[Ir(NO_2)_4Cl_2]$** is made by adding sodium nitrite to a solution of $Na_2[IrCl_6]$ in the presence of potassium ion. It is yellow; caesium, mercuric, lead and silver salts were also made[269]. **$K_3[Ir(NO_2)_2Cl_4]$** forms yellow crystals also, and can be made by the action of potassium nitrite on $K_2[IrCl_6]$ or by reaction of nitrogen dioxide and $(NH_4)_3[IrCl_6]$ in the presence of potassium chloride: caesium, thallous, silver, mercury and lead salts were also isolated[196]; **$K_3[Ir(NO_2)_2Cl_2ox]$** (light orange) can be made by the action of the calculated quantity of potassium nitrite on $K_3[IrCl_2ox_2]$; silver and thallous salts were also obtained[76]. **$K_3[Ir(NO_2)Cl_3ox]$** is got from $K_2[Ir(NO_2)Cl_5]$ and potassium oxalate[228]. **$K_3[Ir(NO_2)Cl_5]$** can be obtained (with difficulty) by treating the mother liquors from the preparation of $Na_3[Ir(NO_2)_4Cl_2]$ with potassium chloride[228]; its infrared spectrum has been measured[49b]. It is said that **$Cs[Ir(NO_2)$-$Br_4(H_2O)]$** can be made from $K_2[IrBr_6]$, potassium nitrite and caesium bromide; but it appears that it is a dinitro species[49b] (a potassium salt has also been prepared). **$Ir(NO_2)_3(NH_3)_3$** is got from prolonged action of aqueous ammonia on $Na_3[IrCl_2(NO_2)_4]$[269] in a sealed tube.

Nitrosyl complexes

These are listed in Table 5.7. Most of them are diamagnetic and the iridium has a formal oxidation state of three, but some of those which contain phosphine ligands are paramagnetic and may contain iridium (II) or lower oxidation states. The best known nitrosyl complex is **$K[Ir(NO)Br_5]$**, which is formed as a golden-brown crystalline solid from the reaction of potassium nitrite with $K_3[IrBr_6]$ and hydrobromic acid or from $K_2[IrBr_6]$, potassium nitrite and nitric acid[3,177].

The infrared spectrum of this complex has been measured from 80 to 4000 cm^{-1} and skeletal modes assigned[49b,93a].

Hydrazine complexes

The rose-coloured species $\mathbf{K[Ir^{III}(N_2H_5)Cl_5]}$ was made from $K_2(IrCl_6)$ and hydrazinium dichloride[259]; this complex, if it is correctly formulated, contains the positively charged monodentate hydrazinium ligand $N_2H_5^+$; it appears, however, that it may be $K[IrCl_4(N_2H_4)]$[49b]. Delepine has reported the hydrazine complex $[Ir(N_2H_4)_2Cl_2](OH)$[68], in which the hydrazine may function as a bidentate ligand.

Dimethylglyoxime complexes

These are rare for iridium. Reaction of the ligand (dimethylglyoxime = $DMGH_2$) with $(NH_4)_3[IrCl_6]$ in basic solution yields olive-brown crystals of $\mathbf{K[Ir(DMGH)_2Cl_2]}$; an ammonium salt and the free acid were also prepared[168]. Reaction of dimethylglyoxime with salts containing $[Ir(NO_2)_6]^{3-}$ gives $\mathbf{[Ir(DMGH)_2(NO_2)_2]^-}$, and $\mathbf{[Ir(DMGH)_2(NO_2)X]^-}$ (X = Cl, SCN) can be made from this and X^-. The diammine $\mathbf{[Ir(DMGH)_2(NH_3)_2]Cl}$ can be made from dimethylglyoxime and $[Ir(NH_3)_5Cl]Cl_2$[165a].

Biguanide (Bgh) complexes

Complexes of the form $[Ir\ Bgh_3]^{3+}$ have been got as the sulphate, chloride and nitrate, and are somewhat more stable than their rhodium analogues. They can be made from $K_3[IrCl_6]$ and the ligand, and the complexes have been resolved[96].

Phthalocyanine (Pc) complexes

Fusion of iridium trichloride with 1,2-dicyanobenzene gives $\mathbf{PcCl.IrCl.C_6H_4(CN)_2}$ ($PcH_2 = C_{32}H_{18}N_8$)[20,148]. The infrared (220–5000 cm^{-1}) and electronic absorption spectra were measured[148]. An iridium carbonyl porphyrin complex has been made[92a].

Phosphine, arsine and stibine complexes

These are listed in Table 5.8. Tertiary phosphines, arsines and stibines will react in alcoholic solution with hexahaloiridates (III) to give complexes of the form $\mathbf{IrX_3(LR_3)_3}$ (X = Cl, Br; L = P, As, Sb; R = alkyl or aryl)[42,81], and dipole moment measurements show that the phosphines and arsines have a symmetrical 1,2,3-structure[42]. Under certain circumstances complexes of the form $\mathbf{Ir_2Cl_6(PR_3)_6}$

and $[IrCl_4(LR_3)_2]^-$ can be obtained[42,81], and, as with the other three metals, $IrX_3(LR_3)_2$ species are sometimes obtained[4].

The action of chlorine on $IrH_3(PPh_3)_3$[184] gives the apparently pentacoordinate species **$IrCl_3(PPh_3)_2$**, which may have the distorted square-based pyramidal configuration found for the analogous ruthenium complex (cf. p. 177). Bidentate ligands such as diarsine give species of the form **[Ir diars$_2$Cl$_2$]Cl**[221a] (far infrared spectra of this have been measured[170]), while the ligand *o*-methylthiophenylarsine, *o*-$C_6H_4(AsMe_2)$.SMe, (As–S), which has both a donor arsenic and a donor sulphur-atom, reacts with iridium trihalides to give complexes of the form **Ir(As—S)$_2$X$_3$** (X = Cl, Br, I). The iodo complex is a 1:1 electrolyte in organic solvents, suggesting the formulation $[Ir(As–S)_2I_2]I$, but the chloro and bromo complexes dissociate very little in solution, and it was suggested that they were seven-coordinate species[48]; another possibility is that they are octahedrally coordinated, one of the As—S groups functioning as a monodentate ligand.

For a large number of haloiridium (III) complexes containing tertiary phosphines and arsines infrared spectra over the range 220–450 cm^{-1} have been measured and the metal–halogen stretching vibrations have been assigned. For the chloro complexes the frequency depends markedly on the nature of the *trans* ligand but very little on the *cis* ligand, and so infrared spectra may be a useful supplementary method of determining molecular configurations in such complexes. The metal–chlorine stretches are found in the range 320–303 cm^{-1} when the *trans* ligand is chloride, 278–262 cm^{-1} when it is a tertiary phosphine or arsine and 249–246 cm^{-1} when it is a hydride [130b].

The proton magnetic resonance spectrum of $IrCl_3(PEt_2Ph)_3$ has been measured[230], and a correlation for determining the stereochemistry of dimethylphenylphosphine complexes of iridium and ruthenium from their proton magnetic resonance spectra given[130a].

Catalytic activity of iridium (III) phosphines

This does not appear to be as marked as for the corresponding rhodium species. However, the tertiary phosphine complexes of iridium (III) are good catalysts for the isomerization of 1,5-C_8H_{12}-(cycloocta-1,5-diene) to 1,3-C_8H_{12} (some 1,4-isomer is also formed). It is suggested that, since the isomerization is completely inhibited by traces of free phosphines, an equilibrium is set up[203]:

$$IrCl_3(PR_3)_3 + C_8H_{12} \rightleftharpoons IrCl_3(PR_3)_2C_8H_{12} + PR_3$$

and isomerization then proceeds via a π-allylic mechanism:

$$
\begin{matrix} CH_2 \\ | \\ CH \\ \| - Ir \\ CH_2 \end{matrix} \longrightarrow \begin{matrix} CH \\ \vdots \\ CH{-}IrH \\ \vdots \\ CH \end{matrix} \longrightarrow \begin{matrix} CH \\ \| - Ir \\ CH \\ | \\ CH_2 \end{matrix}
$$

The catalytic efficiency decreases in the order: $PEt_3 > PEt_2Ph > PMe_2Ph$, although the most effective catalyst is in fact $IrHCl_2(PEt_2Ph)_3$[50, 203].

Hydrido phosphines, arsines and stibines

Iridium forms more hydrides of this type than any other element (cf. Table 5.9). The **trihydrides** take the form $\mathbf{IrH_3(LR_3)_3}$ and $\mathbf{IrH_3(LR_3)_2}$ (M = P, As): the phosphine complexes are known in symmetric and asymmetric forms[5,7,38,44a,130a,182a]. Dipole moment and proton magnetic resonance data suggest that $IrH_3(PR_3)_2$ complexes have a trigonal bipyramidal configuration in which the equatorial plane is occupied by the three hydride ligands[44a]. The main types of **dihydride** are: the octahedral $IrH_2X(LR_3)_3$ (L = P, As) and $[IrH_2(AsPh_3)_4]^+$[38,44a,262], and the five-coordinate species $[IrH_2(LPh_3)_3]^+$ (L = P, As)[7,38]. The **monohydrides**, which are all six coordinate, have the formulae $IrHX_2(LPh_3)_3$ and $IrH(PPh_3)_2X_2L$ (L = P, As, Sb)[4,44a,262] and $IrH(PPh_3)_2X_2$ is also known[4]. The comparative rarity of stibine complexes is surprising. The dipole moments, infrared spectra and proton magnetic resonance spectra of a wide range of tri-, di- and monohydrides have been measured and configurations assigned to the species[44a].

There seems little doubt that hydridic species of the above types are active intermediates in the iridium (I) catalysed hydrogenations of alkenes (cf. p. 279). It has also been shown that some of the hydrides will catalyse the isomerization of olefins such as 1-octene to a mixture of isomers; the isomerization catalysed with $IrCl_3(PPh_3)_3$ is much slower than with the corresponding hydrides, suggesting that the hydride labilizes the group *trans* to it[50]. It has already been noted that the isomerization of cycloocta-1,5-diene is readily catalysed by $IrHCl_2(PEt_2Ph)_3$[203].

Nitrosyl phosphine complexes

These have already been mentioned (pp. 265 and 295); carbonyl, alkyl and aryl phosphines, arsines and stibines are considered below (p. 274).

Phosphorus trihalide complexes

Some of these complexes have been reported for iridium (III), although the correct formulae of some of them are uncertain. They are **$IrCl_3(PCl_3)_3$** and **$IrCl_3(PCl_3)_2$** (from iridium dioxide with phosphorus trichloride and pentachloride): the initial product of the reaction is said to be 2 $IrCl_3.3PCl_3.3PCl_5$. The corresponding bromo complexes are **$IrBr_3(PBr_3)_3$** and **$IrBr_3(PBr_3)_2$**, which can be made from iridium dioxide and phosphorus tribromide. Sulphur tetrachloride reacts with $IrCl_3(PCl_3)_3$ to give **$IrCl_3(PCl_3)_2(SCl_2)$** and species such as **$IrCl_3.2PCl_3.2AsCl_3$** can be made from iridium dioxide, phosphorus pentachloride and arsenic trichloride[95].

Iridium (II)

The only established compound appears to be **$Ir(NO)Br_3(PPh_3)_2$** a maroon-coloured substance made by bromination of $[Ir(NO)_2(PPh_3)_2](ClO_4)$. It is paramagnetic with a moment of 1·34 BM at 25°[178]. The arsine complexes **$IrX_2(AsMe_2(C_7H_8))_3$**, made by the action of the arsine on iridium trihalides[81], are probably the hydrides $Ir^{III}X_2H(AsMe_2(C_7H_8))_3$.

Complexes of the form **Ir(diamine)Cl_2** are said to be formed when $K_2(IrCl_6)$ reacts with *N,N,N′,N′*-tetramethylethylenediamine or with 1,4-dimethylpyrazine: the products are yellow and crystalline[183b]. In view of the rarity of iridium (II) species, however, it seems likely that they are iridium (III) compounds with a hydroxy or even a hydride ligand. An iridium (II) phthalocyanine complex, **Pc.Ir.$C_6H_5NH_2$**, has also been claimed: it was made from *o*-cyanobenzamide, iridium trichloride and aniline[148].

Iridium (I)

Nitrogeno complexes

Treatment of the complex $Ir(CO)Cl(PPh_3)_2$ with azides yields a complex **$Ir(N_2)Cl(PPh_3)_2$**; this reacts with diethyl maleate to give **$Ir(N_2)Cl((EtOOC)_2C_2H_2)(PPh_3)_2$**. The formulation as nitrogeno complexes was based on infrared spectra and chemical properties[50b]; the mechanism of formation of the nitrogeno complex has been discussed[50d].

A number of iridium (I) *carbonyl phosphine* and *hydrido carbonyl phosphine* complexes are known (Table 5.11), and these are considered below (cf. p. 277). The only unsubstituted phosphine complex is $[Ir(diphos)_2]^+$ [122a,241a] (see Table 5.8, p. 294).

$Ir(NO)X_2(PPh_3)_2$ (X = Cl, Br, I) can be made by the action of the appropriate hydrogen halide on $[Ir(NO)_2(PPh_3)_2](ClO_4)$. These red-brown substances may well be polymeric; they have very low nitrosyl stretching frequencies (near 1560 cm^{-1}) which suggests that they may contain bridging nitrosyl groups[178].

Phosphorus trifluoride complexes

Reaction of iridium trihalides with phosphorus trifluoride under pressure yields **$HIr(PF_3)_4$**, which is a colourless liquid (m.p. −39°, b.p. 95°). It reacts with potassium amalgam in ether to give $K[Ir^{-I}(PF_3)_4]$, and this latter salt reacts with iodine at −80° to give **$IrI(PF_3)_4$**[155a].

Iridium (0)

$Ir(NH_3)_5$ has been reported; it is made by reduction of iridium (III) hexammines with potassium in liquid ammonia[267]. The substance is diamagnetic[267]: a more likely formulation is $Ir^{I}H(NH_3)_5$.

Iridium (−I)

This is the formal oxidation state of a number of nitrosyl complexes listed in Table 5.7; they are diamagnetic, and the complexes $Ir(NO)_2X(PPh_3)_2$ have low nitrosyl stretching frequencies (1490–1540 cm^{-1}) which may arise from bridging nitrosyl groups. The salt $K[Ir(PF_3)_4]$ (see above) contains iridium (−I)[155a].

Iridium (−II)

This is the formal oxidation state of the metal in $Ir(NO)_2(PPh_3)$, a violet species prepared by the action of nitric oxide on $IrH_3(PPh_3)_2$. It is paramagnetic with a moment of 1·4 BM at room temperature[178].

GROUP IV DONORS

Iridium has an extensive carbonyl chemistry, but until very recently its organometallic chemistry had been neglected. Like the corresponding rhodium species, a number of iridium carbonyl phosphine complexes show considerable catalytic powers.

Iridium (III)

Cyanide complexes

Ir(CN)$_3$, iridium cyanide, can be made by decomposition of an aqueous solution of $H_3[Ir(CN)_6]$ with hydrochloric acid[188].

$K_3[Ir(CN)_6]$ (earlier believed to be $K_4[Ir(CN)_6]$) is best prepared by fusing $(NH_4)_3[IrCl_6]$ with potassium cyanide. It forms colourless crystals; barium and lead salts were also made. The anhydrous free acid $H_3[Ir(CN)_6]$ can be made in the solid state from the potassium salt, hydrochloric acid and ether[188]; $K_3[Ir(CN)_6]$ and $K_3[Rh(CN)_6]$ are isomorphous.

The infrared spectrum of crystalline $K_3[Ir(CN)_6]$ has been measured and from this and the previously measured Raman spectra of the aqueous solution[191] assignments have been made of most of the fundamental frequencies of the $[Ir(CN)_6]^{3-}$ anion[133] (cf. Table 3.12, p. 113). Comparison with the infrared and Raman spectra of $K_3[Rh(CN)_6]$ and $K_3[Co(CN)_6]$ shows that the metal–carbon stretching force constants decrease in the order: Ir > Rh > Co, while for the three complexes the carbon–nitrogen stretching force constants remain roughly constant. These force-constant data, together with infrared intensity measurements, suggest that both the σ- and π-bond strengths in the metal–carbon linkage increase in the same order[133]. Infrared spectra (400–4000 cm^{-1}) of solid $H_3[Ir(CN)_6]$ and $D_3[Ir(CN)_6]$ suggest that they contain symmetric N—H—N and N—D—N hydrogen bonds[85]. The cyanide hydride **$[Ir(CN)_5H]^{3-}$** is believed to be present in solutions of $[Ir(CN)_6]^{3-}$ containing excess borohydride ion[104, 107]. From the observed proton chemical shift in the species it has been calculated that there is an excess negative charge of 0·2 electrons on the hydrogen atom, making the doubtful assumption that the metal–hydrogen distance is about 1·62 Å[171].

Carbonyl complexes

For iridium (I) carbonyl complexes cf. p. 277.

A wide range of carbonyl halide and carbonyl phosphine complexes of iridium is known; a summary is given in Table 5.10. The carbonyl stretching frequencies in the three complexes **$K_2[Ir(CO)X_5]$** (X = Cl, Br, I) decrease as X changes from chloride to iodide[179]. A preliminary x-ray crystal structure analysis of $K_2[Ir(CO)Br_5]$ indicates that it contains three short and two long iridium–bromine bonds[27a]. The abstract to the paper of reference 179 wrongly refers to

$K_2[Ir(CO)X_5]$ as $K[Ir(CO)X_5]$. A *p*-toluidine complex, **Ir(CO)(*p*-toluidine)$_2$Cl$_3$**, can be made by the action of the amine on $K_2[Ir_2(CO)_4Cl_5]$[8].

Carbonyl phosphine complexes*

cis-**IrX$_3$(CO)(LR$_3$)$_2$** (X = Cl, Br; L = P, As or Sb, R = alkyl or aryl) can be made from LR_3 with $H_3[IrCl_6]$ or $H_3[IrBr_6]$ in 2-methoxyethanol; dipole moment measurements were consistent with a *cis* arrangement of the (LR_3) groups[43]. Prolongation of the above reaction gives *trans*-**IrX$_3$(CO)(LR$_3$)$_2$**, and here dipole moment measurements suggest that this complex has the *trans* arrangement of the LR_3 groups. One complex was made, **IrCl$_3$(CO)(PBu$^n_3$)$_2$**, in which the dipole moment of 12·35 D suggested that two *cis*-phosphine and two *cis*-chlorine groups occupy the equatorial plane of the octahedron[43].

An interesting **peroxy carbonyl phosphine, Ir^{III}(O$_2$)Cl(CO)(PPh$_3$)$_2$,** has been made by the action of molecular oxygen on $IrCl(CO)(PPh_3)_2$; the uptake of oxygen is reversible[263], and it has been suggested that this might be a model system for haemoglobin. The x-ray crystal structure of this compound shows that the iridium atom, the two oxygen atoms and the carbonyl and chloride groups are coplanar; the two phosphine groups are above and below this plane; the complex is five or six coordinate depending on whether the oxygen molecule is considered to function as a mono- or a bidentate ligand. The two iridium–oxygen distances are the same within the limits of experimental error (Ir—O = 2·07 ± 0·03 Å) with an $O\hat{Ir}O$ angle of 36·7 ± 0·2°; and the O—O distance is 1·30 ± 0·04 Å,

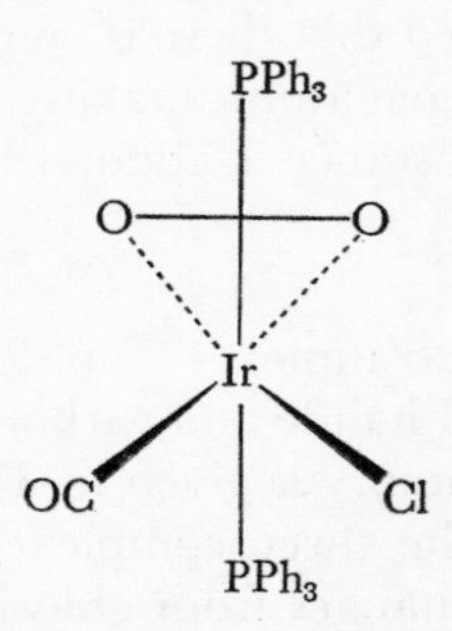

Figure 5.4 Structure of $Ir(CO)Cl(O_2)(PPh_3)_2$

* See Table 5.11.

less than that of the peroxide ion (1·45 Å) but longer than the bond length of 1·21 Å in molecular oxygen. The O—O bond length, however, is close to that found for the superoxide, O_2^-, ion (1·28 Å), but formulation of the complex as containing Ir(II) and O_2^- would presumably require it to be paramagnetic, whereas it is diamagnetic. The two Ir—P distances are 2·37 ± 0·03 Å[158].

Hydrido carbonyl phosphine complexes*

As with the hydrido phosphines (p. 268), hydrido carbonyl phosphines, arsines and stibines are known with three, two and one hydrogen atoms per iridium atom. The **trihydrides** reported are $IrH_3(CO)(PPh_3)_2$ and the arsine analogues made by the action of carbon monoxide on $IrH_3(LPh_3)_2$[5,6,38a,182a]. The **dihydrides** are of the form $[IrH_2(CO)(PPh_3)_3]^+$ (two forms of this are known)[6] $[IrH_2(CO)(PPh_3)_2]^+$[6,182a], probably pentacoordinate, and $IrH_2(CO)(PPh_3)_2Cl$, made by the action of molecular hydrogen on $Ir(CO)Cl(PPh_3)_2$. The infrared spectra of the latter chlorohydride and chlorodeuteride have been measured[260]. The **monohydrides** take the form $IrHX_2(CO)(LR_3)_2$ (X = Cl, Br; L = P, As). The geometrical configurations of some of the phosphine monohydrides have been established from dipole moment measurements. If the coordination sites on the octahedron are numbered in the following fashion:

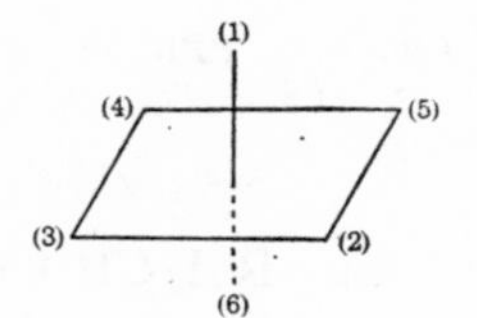

then it is found that, whereas $IrCl_{3(1,2,6)}(CO)_{(4)}(PEt_2Ph)_{2(3,5)}$ will not react with ethanolic potassium hydroxide solution, its isomer $IrCl_{3(1,2,6)}(CO)_{(3)}(PEt_2Ph)_{2(4,5)}$ will do so to give $IrCl_{2(1,6)}H_{(5)}(CO)_{(3)}(PEt_2Ph)_{2(2,4)}$, so it appears that a chlorine atom *trans* to another chlorine atom or to a carbonyl group is inert to hydrogen substitution, but is readily substituted when *trans* to the phosphine. An isomer of this latter hydride, $IrCl_{2(2,6)}H_{(1)}(CO)_{(4)}(PEt_2Ph)_{2(3,5)}$, was got by prolonged treatment of $IrCl_{3(1,2,6)}(CO)_{(3)}(PEt_2Ph)_{2(4,5)}$ with ethanolic potassium hydroxide[43]. Infrared, proton magnetic resonance spectra and dipole moments of these complexes were measured[43].

* See Table 5.11.

Carbonyl phosphine complexes containing metal–metal bonds

Iridium–mercury bonds are believed to be present in complexes of the type $\mathbf{(Ph_3P)_2(CO)ClYIr{-}HgY}$ (Y = Cl, Br, I, OAc, CN, SCN) and $\mathbf{(Ph_3P)_2(CO)Br_2Ir{-}HgBr}$, made by the reaction of the appropriate mercuric compound HgY_2 with $(Ph_3P)_2(CO)IrCl$ or $(Ph_3P)_2(CO)IrBr$. The corresponding rhodium (I) square planar species did not undergo these reactions and it was suggested that the reason for this was thermodynamic rather than kinetic[207]. The silyl species $\mathbf{R_3Si{-}IrH(CO)Cl(PPh_3)_2}$ (see p. 279) may also be included in this category of compounds[40].

Alkyl and aryl complexes

Arylsulphonyl chlorides (RSO_2Cl) will react with $Ir(CO)Cl(PPh_3)_2$ to give iridium (III) *S*-sulphinates, $\mathbf{Ir(CO)Cl_2(PPh_3)_2(RSO_2)}$, which may then lose sulphur dioxide to give aryl complexes, $\mathbf{Ir(CO)Cl_2.R.(PPh_3)_2}$. The proton magnetic resonance spectra of the sulphinates suggest that the sulphonyl group is *cis* to the carbonyl group[50a]:

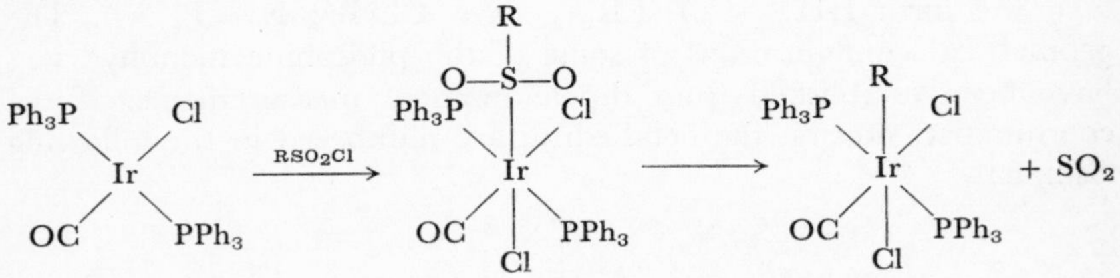

$$trans\text{-}Ir(CO)Cl(PPh_3)_2 \xrightarrow{RSO_2Cl} Ir(CO)Cl_2(PPh_3)_2(SO_2R) \longrightarrow Ir(CO)Cl_2(PPh_3)_2R + SO_2$$

$R = p\text{-}CH_3C_6H_4$

Complexes of the form $\mathbf{R.IrClI(CO)(PPh_3)_2}$ ($R = CH_3$, CH_3OCOCH_2, $CH_2{=}CH.CH_2$) can be got from the versatile complex $Ir(CO)Cl(PPh_3)_2$ and the iodide RI. The complexes are yellow, and their infrared spectra were measured[115]. Reaction of

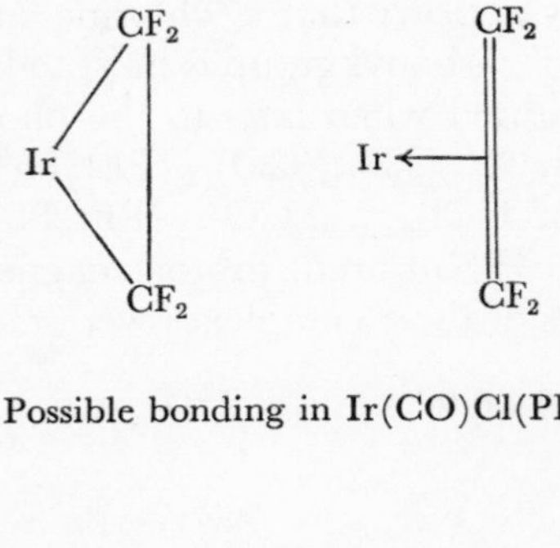

CF₂–CF₂ bridging Ir (three-membered ring); Ir ← CF₂=CF₂

Figure 5.5 Possible bonding in $Ir(CO)Cl(PPh_3)_2(C_2F_4)$

tetrafluoroethylene with $Ir(CO)Cl(PPh_3)_2$ yields **$Ir(CO)Cl(PPh_3)_2$-C_2F_4** which, from its fluorine magnetic resonance spectrum, is thought to have the alkyl-type (σ-bonded) structure rather than the π bonded form [52a,217]: in Figure 5.5.

Stable trimethyliridium complexes of the form 1,2,3-**$IrMe_3(PR_3)_3$** ($PR_3 = PEt_3$, PEt_2Ph) were made from 1,2,6-$IrCl_3(PR_3)_3$ and methylmagnesium chloride. The dipole moments of the complexes in benzene solution were 5·9 and 5·25 D (PEt_3 and PEt_2Ph, respectively) at 25° [44b].

$Ir(CO)Cl(PPh_3)_2$ will react with tetracyanoethylene (TC) to give **$Ir(CO)Cl(PPh_3)_2(TC)$**; on the basis of its infrared spectrum it is thought that it is best regarded as an iridium (III) species in which a tetracyanoethylene group forms two σ bonds to iridium (giving a three-membered ring) rather than as an iridium (I) olefin complex [13a].

Olefin complexes

These seem to be rare for iridium (III) but more are known for monovalent iridium (p. 282). The complexes **$[Ir(diene)HX_2]_2$** (diene = cycloocta-1,5-diene, X = Cl, Br, I) can be made from $H_3[IrCl_6]$, the potassium halides and the diene in ethanol. The complexes form cream-coloured crystals, and their infrared and proton magnetic resonance spectra were measured. With diethylphenylphosphine, the chloro complex yields $IrHCl_2(PEt_2Ph)_3$ [238,272]. These iridium (III) olefin complexes react with cyclopentadiene, acetylacetone and methanol to give iridium (I) derivatives (p. 282).

π-Allyl intermediates may be involved in certain iridium catalysed olefin isomerization reactions [50,203] (p. 267), and reaction of $IrCl_3(PEt_2Ph)_3$ with allyl alcohol yields a colourless allyl iridium carbonyl derivative [44].

'Sandwich' and arene complexes (Cp = π-C_5H_5)

Salts containing the **$[Cp_2Ir]^+$** cation can be made by the action of cyclopentadienyl magnesium bromide on iridium trisacetylacetonate [52] or by the oxidation of $CpIr(C_5H_6)$ [91]. No polarographic evidence could be found for the existence of the neutral species Cp_2Ir [52]. The electronic absorption spectrum of $[Cp_2Ir]^+$ was measured [52].

Duroquinone (Dqu) complexes

With iridium trichloride, duroquinone gives first of all the compounds **Dqu.$IrHCl_2$** and **Dqu_2.$IrHCl_2$**; the former will react with pyridine to give Dqu.Ir py_2Cl, and with sodium hydroxide to give

$[Dqu.Ir(OH)]_n$, while sodium cyclopentadienide yields Dqu.Ir.Cp. The electronic absorption and infrared spectra were measured, and from the latter it was concluded that the duroquinone was π bonded to the metal and that the ring was non-planar (cf. also p. 394)[250].

Stannous chloride complexes

Orange salts of $[\mathbf{Ir_2Cl_6(SnCl_3)_4}]^{4-}$ have been isolated from solutions of iridium trichloride and stannous chloride. The electronic spectra of the complexes were recorded[277].

Hydrido and carbonylhydrido complexes of iridium (III) containing $(SnCl_3)^-$ as a ligand have recently been obtained. $\mathbf{IrHX(SnCl_3)}$-$\mathbf{(PPh_3)_3}$ (X = Cl, H), was made from $[IrCl_6]^{2-}$, stannous chloride and triphenylphosphine; and $\mathbf{IrHX(SnCl_3)(CO)(PPh_3)_2}$ (X = Cl, H) was got from stannous chloride and $Ir(CO)Cl(PPh_3)_2$. The configurations of the various species were determined from proton magnetic resonance studies, and infrared spectra were recorded. It was concluded that the $[SnCl_3]^-$ group has a strong *trans* effect[256a].

Iridium (II)

Cyanide complexes

Although $K_4[Ir(CN)_6]$ is occasionally mentioned in the earlier literature and in reference 188, in fact this reference deals with $K_3[Ir(CN)_6]$ alone.

Carbonyl halides*

Three types are known: $Ir(CO)_2X_2$ (X = Cl, Br, I)[179]; $[IrX_3(CO)]^-$ (X = Br, I) which are diamagnetic and so presumably have some kind of metal–metal interaction[179]; and $[IrI_3(CO)_2)]_2{}^{2-}$ which is also diamagnetic[179]. In addition there are the species $[Ir_2(CO)_4X_4]^-$ (X = Cl, Br) and $[Ir_2(CO)_4X_5]^{2-}$ (X = Cl, Br), which formally contain iridium (1·5); they are also diamagnetic, and it has been suggested that they contain halogen bridges and involve metal–metal interaction[180]. It may be noted here that the abstract to the paper in reference 180 and the corresponding Chemical Abstract refer to $[Ir(CO)_4X_3]^-$ and to $[Ir(CO)_2X_3]^-$; however, the text of reference 180 makes it clear that the compounds in question were respectively $[Ir_2(CO)_4X_3]^-$ and $[Ir(CO)_2X_2]^-$ (both containing monovalent iridium).

* See Table 5.10.

'Sandwich' complexes

The colourless complex $\mathbf{Cp_4Ir_2}$ has been prepared by the reaction between sodium and salts of $[IrCp_2]^+$. A dimeric structure involving bridging cyclopentadiene groups was proposed, based on infrared and proton magnetic resonance spectra[91a]:

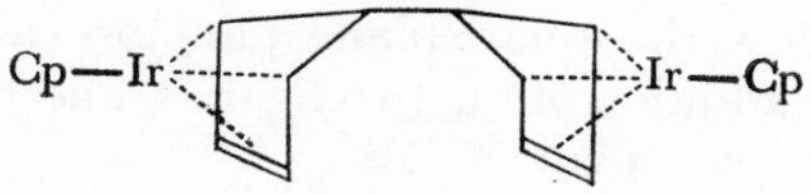

Cp—Ir ... Ir—Cp

Olefin complexes

An early reference reports that the action of ethylene on iridium trichloride gives $IrCl_2(C_2H_4)$[149,242,243].

Iridium (I)

Isocyanide complexes

Unlike rhodium trichloride, iridium trichloride does not react with isocyanides, but $Ir(CO)_2$(*p*-toluidine)Cl will react with *p*-tolylisocyanide to give the square planar species $\mathbf{[Ir(\textit{p}\text{-}MeC_6H_4NC)_4]^+}$[181].

Carbonyl complexes

There is a substantial carbonyl chemistry of iridium (I) (cf. also p. 271).

Carbonyl halides*

These take the form $\mathbf{IrX(CO)_3}$ (X = Cl, Br, I)[121]; $\mathbf{[IrX_2(CO)_2]^-}$ (X = Br, I), which are probably planar (infrared spectra suggest a *cis* configuration)[179,180]; and the dimeric species $\mathbf{[Ir_2(CO)_4Br_3]^-}$[180].

Carbonyl phosphine complexes

These are summarized in Table 5.11. The **monocarbonyls** take the forms $IrX(CO)(PR_3)_2$ (X = Cl, Br)[8,261]; $Ir(CO)Cl(PR_3)_3$[44], which is presumably five coordinate; and a few stibines[8,122b]. The **dicarbonyls** $[Ir(CO)_2(LPh_3)_2]^+$ (L = P, As) and $Ir(CO)_2(LPh_3)X$ (L = P, As and X = Cl, Br) have been made and their infrared spectra recorded in the 1900–2000 cm^{-1} region[8].

The remarkable complex $\mathbf{Ir(CO)Cl(PPh_3)_2}$ is got by the reaction of iridium trichloride in 2-methoxyethanol with the phosphine[261] (a

* See Table 5.11.

better preparation is to heat hydrated iridium trichloride with triphenylphosphine under reflux in dimethylformamide and then to add excess methanol[50b]). The dipole moment (3·9 D at 25°) suggests that it has a *trans* configuration[261]. It is 'coordinatively unsaturated' and readily takes up two extra ligands to give octahedral d^6 species[260]. It may be remarked here that it is sometimes said that this complex adds on two ligands 'across the square plane'; in most cases, however, there appears to be a *cis* addition of the two ligands, and the chloride ligand moves out of the square plane[207a].

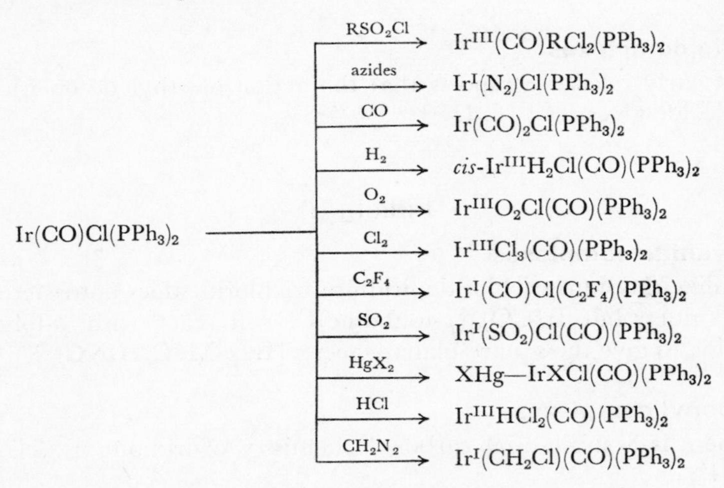

The rate of hydrogenation of $Ir(CO)Cl(PPh_3)_2$ by molecular hydrogen is first order in the complex, and the mechanism of the reaction has been discussed[207a]. It should be noted that the uptake of oxygen, hydrogen and sulphur dioxide is *reversible*.

The kinetics have been studied of the reaction

$$trans\text{-}IrX(CO)(PPh_3)_2 + YZ \rightarrow IrXYZ(CO)(PPh_3)_2$$

($X = Cl$, Br, I; $YZ = H_2$, O_2, CH_3I). The kinetics were second order and followed the rate law

$$\text{Rate} = k_2[IrX(CO)(PPh_3)_2][YZ]$$

In benzene solution the activation parameters were similar for all the reactions, lying in the range $\Delta H^{\ddagger}$ 10·8–13·1 kcal/mole and $\Delta S^{\ddagger}$ −14 to −24 e.u. for reactions with hydrogen and oxygen, while for methyl iodide $\Delta H^{\ddagger}$ was 5·6–8·8 kcal/mole and $\Delta S^{\ddagger}$ −43 to −51 e.u.[48a].

Another property of this compound is its ability to cleave a number of silicon hydrides, retaining both the silicon and hydride fragments

$$(Ph_3P)_2Ir^{I}(CO)Cl + R_3SiH \rightarrow (Ph_3P)_2Ir^{III}(SiR_3)(CO)(H)Cl$$

This reaction was observed with R_3SiH (R = Cl, EtO) and $RSiCl_2H$ (R = Et, C_6H_5), and the infrared spectra of the products were recorded[40].

Hydrido carbonyl phosphines*

Two complexes for iridium (I) are reported. **$IrH(CO)(PPh_3)_3$**, a monomeric and therefore five-coordinate complex is made from $IrCl(CO)(PPh_3)_2$ and sodium borohydride[6], or by the reaction[19]

$$IrCl(CO)(PPh_3)_2 + n\, N_2H_4 \rightarrow$$
$$IrH(CO)(PPh_3)_3 + IrCl(CO)(PPh_3)(N_2H_4)_{n-1} + N_2H_5Cl + \tfrac{1}{2} N_2$$

A tetracoordinate species, **$IrH(CO)(PPh_3)_2$**, made from $IrH(CO)(PPh_3)_3$ and carbon monoxide[6], is also known. The infrared and proton nuclear magnetic resonance spectra of $IrH(CO)(PPh_3)_3$ were measured, and x-ray measurements showed it to be isostructural with the corresponding rhodium complex[19] (cf. p. 389), so it is likely to have a trigonal bipyramidal structure, the three phosphine groups defining the equatorial plane[157]. With acids HX (X = F, Cl, Br, I), $IrH(CO)(PPh_3)_3$ gives $[IrH_2(CO)(PPh_3)_3]X$ and $[IrH_2(CO)(PPh_3)_3]HX_2$[262a].

Catalytic activity of iridium (I) hydrido carbonyl phosphine complexes. The complete $IrH(CO)(PPh_3)_3$ is an efficient catalyst for the homogeneous reduction by molecular hydrogen of acetylene (to ethane and ethylene) and of ethylene; it has also been shown that hydrogen and ethylene react *reversibly* with the complex[264]:

$$IrH(CO)(PPh_3)_3 + H_2 \rightleftharpoons IrH_3(CO)(PPh_3)_3$$

$$IrH_3(CO)(PPh_3)_3 + C_2H_4 \rightleftharpoons Ir(C_2H_4)H(CO)(PPh_3)_3 + H_2$$
$$\text{or } Ir(C_2H_5(CO)(PPh_3)_3$$

* See Table 5.11.

A suggested mechanism for the reduction involving such seven-coordinated intermediates is[264]:

$$(Ph_3P)_3(CO)IrH + C_2H_4 \rightarrow (Ph_3P)_3(CO)IrH(C_2H_4) \rightarrow$$
$$(Ph_3P)_3(CO)Ir(C_2H_5) \xrightarrow{H_2} (Ph_3P)_3(CO)Ir(C_2H_5)H_2 \rightarrow$$
$$(Ph_3P)_3(CO)IrH + C_2H_6$$

It has been proposed that $IrH(CO)(PPh_3)_3$ is more effective as a catalyst than its rhodium analogue because though both can periodically increase or decrease their coordination spheres with a concurrent change in oxidation state (the proviso being that the intermediates must be labile yet have fairly substantial equilibrium concentrations); catalytic activity of this type is therefore dependent on a balance of the relative stabilities of electronic and stereochemical factors for both the reactants and the intermediates, and it appears that in this case at least the more favourable balance is with the iridium rather than with the rhodium complex[264]. It is noteworthy that although $RhH(CO)(PPh_3)_3$ will not take up hydrogen like its iridium analogue it will act as a catalyst for the hydrogen–deuterium exchange, and also catalyses the hydrogenation of ethylene (for this purpose, however, $Rh(CO)Cl(PPh_3)_2$ is more efficient than $RhH(CO)(PPh_3)_3$ and most effective of all is the phosphine $RhCl(PPh_3)_3$). The complex also functions as a catalyst for hydroformylation[19d].

Miscellaneous carbonyl complexes

β-Diketone complexes of the form **Ir(β-diketone)(CO)**$_2$ (β-diketone = pentane-2,4-dione; 1,1,1-trifluoropentane-2,4-dione; 1,1,1,5,5,5-hexafluoropentane-2,4-dione; 1-phenylbutane-1,3-dione; 1,3-diphenylpentane-1,3-dione) were made from the ligand and $Na_2[Ir_2(CO)_4Cl_5]$; with phosphines these gave **Ir(CO)(PR**$_3$**)(β-diketone)**[28]. A similar preparative method using various Schiff bases gives complexes of the form **Ir(CO)**$_2$**Cl(base)**[29]. **Ir(amine)X(CO)**$_2$ (amine = isopropylamine, *p*-toluidine; X = Cl, Br) can be made from the amine and $K_2[Ir_2(CO)_4X_5]$; with phosphines and arsines the *p*-toluidine derivative gives $[Ir(CO)_2(LR_3)]X$ (X = Cl, Br; L = P, As)[8].

The complex **IrCl(CO)(SO**$_2$**)(PPh**$_3$**)**$_2$, made by the action of sulphur dioxide on $Ir(CO)Cl(PPh_3)_2$[263a], has been the subject of a recent x-ray structure determination. The structure is that of a tetragonal pyramid (Figure 5.6), the base being formed by the two phosphine groups (Ir—P = 2·359 ± 0·009 Å), the carbonyl group (Ir—C = 1·96 ± 0·04 Å) and the chloride (Ir—Cl = 2·37 ± 0·01 Å). The

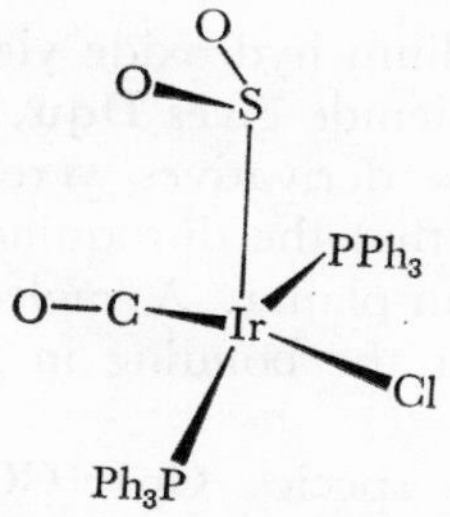

O
O—S
PPh₃
O—C—Ir
Cl
Ph₃P

Figure 5.6 Structure of $IrCl(CO)(SO_2)(PPh_3)_2$

sulphur atom of the SO_2 group forms the apex, but the Ir—SO_2 part of the molecule is not planar, the Ir—S bond making an angle of 31·6 ± 1·5° with the normal to the SO_2 plane. The iridium—sulphur distance is very long (2·49 ± 0·01 Å), and the dimensions of the SO_2 group (S—O = 1·43 ± 0·03 Å and the $O\hat{S}O$ angle is 117 ± 1·5°) do not differ significantly from those of solid sulphur dioxide. It appears that the bonding of the sulphur ligand to the iridium is very weak (compare the Ir—S bond length of 2·49 Å with the ruthenium–sulphur distance of 2·07 Å in $[RuCl(SO_2)(NH_3)_4]Cl$ (cf. p. 163): it will be recalled that the reaction between sulphur dioxide and $Ir(CO)Cl(PPh_3)_2$ is reversible [157a].

For carbonyl complexes with alkyl or aryl ligands, see p. 274 and p. 282.

Iridium (I) carbonyl phosphine complexes with metal–metal bonds

Reaction of $Ir(CO)Cl(PPh_3)_2$ with sodium amalgam in tetrahydrofuran yields $Na(Ir(CO)_3(PPh_3))$ which will in turn react with $AuCl(PPh_3)$ to give **$(Ph_3P)Au\text{–}Ir(CO)_3(PPh_3)$**; with R_3SnCl to give **$Ir(SnR_3)(CO)_3(PPh_3)$**(R = Me, Ph); with Me_2SnCl_2 to give **$Ir_2(SnMe_2)(CO)_6(PPh_3)_2$**; and with mercuric cyanide to give **$Ir_2Hg(CO)_6(PPh_3)_2$**, in the latter two complexes it is thought that the tin and mercury bridge the two iridium atoms. Infrared and proton magnetic resonance data on these species were measured [50c].

'Sandwich' and arene complexes

$CpIr(C_5H_6)$ can be made from iridium trichloride and potassium cyclopentadienide [91]. This may be regarded as an iridium (I) or (III) species (cf. p. 393). Reaction between iridium trichloride and duroquinone gives $Dqu.IrHCl_2$ which, with pyridine, gives

Dqu.Ir.py$_2$Cl, with sodium hydroxide yields [Dqu.Ir(OH)]$_n$, and with sodium cyclopentadienide gives **Dqu.Ir.Cp.** The infrared and electronic spectra of these derivatives were measured, and from the former it was concluded that the duroquinone ring was π bonded to the iridium and was non-planar. A molecular-orbital scheme was drawn up to account for the bonding in Dqu.MCp (M = Ir, Rh, Co)[250].

The cyclopentadienyl species **CpIr(CO)$_2$** is formed as yellow crystals when sodium cyclopentadienide reacts with Ir(CO)$_3$Cl. The compound is monomeric, and its infrared spectrum was measured[92]. Proton magnetic resonance studies on the π-indenyl species **π-C$_9$H$_7$Ir(CO)$_2$** have been made[92b].

Alkyl complexes

The orange, crystalline complex **Ir(CH$_2$Cl)(CO)(PPh$_3$)$_2$** is formed by the reaction between diazomethane and Ir(CO)Cl(PPh$_3$)$_2$; this formulation was favoured over the carbene alternative, Ir(CO)Cl-(PPh$_3$)$_2$(:CH$_2$), on the basis of its chemical reactions and its infrared spectrum. The complex, though it is stable in the solid state, readily decomposes in solution: in chloroform polymethylene is formed, while in styrene solutions a methylene transfer to the α carbon C—H bond of styrene takes place giving a mixture of phenylcyclopropane and α-methylstyrene. It was suggested that the carbene intermediate Ir(CO)Cl(PPh$_3$)$_2$(:CH$_2$) was involved, with an electrophilic methylene group π bonded to the metal atom[183a].

Olefin complexes

Unstable ethylene adducts, Ir(C$_2$H$_4$)(CO)X(PPh$_3$)$_2$ (X = Cl, Br) can be got from ethylene and Ir(CO)X(PPh$_3$)$_2$. The iodo complex is less stable than the chloro and can only be kept under an ethylene atmosphere[264].

The complexes **Ir(diene)(acac)** and **CpIr(diene)** can be got from acetylacetone and sodium cyclopentadienide, respectively, with Ir(diene)HCl$_2$ (diene = cycloocta-1,5-diene). With a solution of sodium carbonate in methanol the latter complex gives the methoxy species **[Ir(diene)(OCH$_3$)]$_2$**. The infrared and proton magnetic resonance spectra of all these species were measured[238]. **Ir(diene)$_2$-(SnCl$_3$)** (diene = norbornadiene and cycloocta-1,5-diene) were made by the action of stannous chloride and the diene on Na$_2$[IrCl$_6$][277]. An x-ray study of the C$_8$H$_{12}$ complex shows this to be five coordinate with an iridium distance of 2·73 Å[222a]. A curious feature of these reactions is that ligand isomerization seems to occur during the preparations; thus cycloheptatriene will react with stannous chloride and $Na_2[IrCl_6]$ to give the norbornadiene complex, and both cycloocta-1,3-diene and 4-vinyl-cyclohexene give the cycloocta-1,5-diene complex[277]. A mixture of cycloocta-1,5-diene, stannous chloride and $Na_2[IrCl_6]$ with phosphines or arsines yields $\mathbf{Ir(diene)(LPh_3)_2(SnCl_3)}$, which is presumably five coordinate[277].

Reaction of $Na_2[IrCl_6]$ with cycloocta-1,5-diene gives orange crystals of $\mathbf{[Ir(C_8H_{12})Cl]_2}$, which will react with hydrochloric acid to give $[IrHCl_2(C_8H_{12})]_2$ and with triphenylphosphine to give $\mathbf{Ir(C_8H_{12})Cl(PPh_3)}$. The reaction between $Na_2(IrCl_6)$ and norbornadiene or cyclohexa-1,3-diene gives $\mathbf{[Ir(C_7H_8)Cl]_2}$ and $\mathbf{Ir(C_6H_8)_2Cl}$, respectively, and these will in turn react with triphenylphosphine to give $\mathbf{Ir(C_7H_8)Cl(PPh_3)}$ and $\mathbf{Ir(C_6H_8)Cl(PPh_3)_2}$. With 2,3-dimethyl-1,3-butadiene, $Na_2[IrCl_6]$ gives colourless crystals of $\mathbf{Ir(Me_2C_4H_4)_2Cl}$, while with the acid $H_2[IrCl_6].aq$ the mono-olefins cycloheptene and cyclooctene yield respectively $Ir(C_7H_{12})_3(CO)Cl$ and $\mathbf{Ir(C_8H_{14})_3(CO)Cl}$; the latter dimerizes on recrystallization to $\mathbf{[Ir(C_8H_{14})_2(CO)Cl]_2}$. The infrared and proton magnetic resonance spectra of all these products were recorded[272].

Fluoro olefin complexes

These complexes of iridium (I) have recently been obtained. Hexafluorobut-2-yne reacts with $(Ir(CO)Cl(PPh_3)_2)$ to give a species $\mathbf{Ir(CO)Cl(PPh_3)_2(C_4F_6)}$. The fluorine magnetic resonance spectrum of this colourless, very stable complex suggested that it is an olefin complex of iridium (I) rather than an alkyl complex of iridium (III)[52a,217].

The reaction of tetrafluoroethylene with $Ir(CO)Cl(PPh_3)_2$, however, gives an iridium species $\mathbf{Ir(CO)Cl(PPh_3)_2(C_2F_4)}$ which is thought to contain a σ-bonded C_2F_4 group[217] (p. 274).

Iridium (0)

Carbonyls

Two carbonyls have been reported. $\mathbf{[Ir(CO)_4]_n}$, which is probably dimeric, is made by heating the water-soluble form of iridium trichloride with carbon monoxide at 180° under a pressure of 200 atmospheres in the presence of copper powder, the latter being used to take up the halogen. The product is greenish-yellow[122]. A modification of the method has been proposed for the preparation of the compound from the water-insoluble form of the trichloride[127]. It can be separated from the tricarbonyl (into which it easily decomposes) either by exploiting its greater solubility in chloroform or by sublimation. Infrared spectra have been measured for the compound and suggest that no bridging carbonyl groups are present[204].

$[Ir(CO)_3]_n$ is a canary-yellow substance made in the same way as the tetracarbonyl[122,127]. It sublimes at 210° in an atmosphere of carbon monoxide. It may well have the same structure as $Co_4(CO)_{12}$ and is said to have a very simple infrared spectrum[204]*. The use of iridium, rhodium and cobalt carbonyls for hydrogenation and hydroformylation reactions has been studied: for hydrogenation iridium seems the most effective and rhodium the least effective, but the reverse is true for hydroformylations[128]. A study of the infrared spectra of carbon monoxide adsorbed on metallic iridium has been reported[173].

$Ir(CO)_4H$ (?) may be the very volatile species formed when the reactants used for preparation of the tetra- and tricarbonyls are not completely dry[122].

$[Ir(CO)_2(P(OR)_3)]_2$ (R = Ph, Et, *p*-tolyl) can be made from iridium tricarbonyl and the phosphite; with iodine they yield $[Ir^{III}(CO)I_3(P(OR)_3)]_2$[278].

Iridium (−I)

$Ir(NO)(CO)(PPh_3)_2$ can be prepared by the action of nitric oxide on $IrH(CO)(PPh_3)_3$. It forms orange crystals and is diamagnetic. The infrared spectrum was measured[178].

HOMOGENEOUS CATALYSIS BY IRIDIUM COMPLEXES

Hydrogenation reactions

So far the only iridium catalysts reported for these are $IrH(CO)(PPh_3)_3$ and $Ir(CO)Cl(PPh_3)_2$, and in each case the proposed mechanism involves a homolytic splitting of molecular hydrogen by the complex and formation of an octahedral d^6 complex[264] (p. 280).

* A recent brief report states that the formula is $Ir_4(CO)_{12}$, and that the overall symmetry is T_d with iridium–iridium bonds[271a].

These complexes are markedly inferior to $RhCl(PPh_3)_3$ as hydrogenation catalysts, probably because in the intermediates generated by the rhodium catalyst there are vacant coordination sites which activate the olefin[212a], and also the rhodium–hydrogen bond is more labile than the iridium–hydrogen bond (see also reference 112b for hydrogenation by dimethylsulphoxide iridium III complexes).

Hydroformylation reactions

The complex $Ir(CO)Cl(PPh_3)_2$ shows mild catalytic hydroformylation properties[19d], but the rhodium analogue $Rh(CO)Cl(PPh_3)_2$ is more active in this respect (cf. p. 388).

Isomerization reactions

There have been two recent, brief reports of the isomerization of certain unconjugated dienes by hydrido chloro phosphine and chloro phosphine iridium (III) complexes[50,203]. The mechanism apparently involves π-allylic intermediates, and the hydride ligand probably labilizes the group *trans* to it to provide a readily accessible site for olefin coordination.

Table 5.1 Second-order rate constants for electron-exchange reactions of hexahaloiridates (IV)

Oxidant	Reductant[b]	T(°C)	Medium	k(M^{-1} sec^{-1})	Method[a]	Ref.
$[IrCl_6]^{2-}$	$[Fe(CN)_6]^{4-}$	25°	H_2O	$1{\cdot}2 \times 10^6$	(a)	103
	$[Fe(CN)_6]^{4-}$	25°	0·5M $HClO_4$	$4{\cdot}1 \times 10^5$	(a)	103
	$[Os\ bipy_3]^{2+}$	25°	0·5M $HClO_4$	$>10^8$	(a)	103
	$[Fe(H_2O)_6]^{2+}$	25°	0·5M $HClO_4$	$3{\cdot}2 \times 10^6$	(a)	103
	$[W(CN)_8]^{4-}$	25°	0·5M H_2SO_4	$6{\cdot}1 \times 10^7$	(a)	37
	$[Mo(CN)_8]^{4-}$	25°	0·5M H_2SO_4	$1{\cdot}9 \times 10^6$	(a)	37
	$[Fe(CN)_6]^{4-}$	25°	0·5M H_2SO_4	$3{\cdot}8 \times 10^5$	(a)	37
	$[Fe\ 4,7\text{-}DMP_3]^{2+b}$	10°	0·5M H_2SO_4	$1{\cdot}0 \times 10^9$	(b)	113
	$[Fe\ DMBPY_3]^{2+b}$	10°	0·05M NO_3^-	$1{\cdot}07 \times 10^9$	(b)	126
	$[Fe\ DMP_3]^{2+b}$	10°	0·05M NO_3^-	$2{\cdot}2 \times 10^8$	(b)	126
	$[IrCl_6]^{3-}$			$2{\cdot}3 \times 10^5$	(b)	126a
$[IrBr_6]^{2-}$	$[Fe\ DMP_3]^{2+}$	10°	0·05M NO_3^-	$1{\cdot}8 \times 10^8$	(b)	126
	$[Fe\ 4,7\text{-}DMP_3]^{2+}$	10°	0·05M NO_3^-	$1{\cdot}6 \times 10^8$	(b)	126
	$[Fe\ DMBPY_3]^{2+}$	10°	0·05M NO_3^-	$6{\cdot}8 \times 10^8$	(b)	126

[a] Method by which the rate constants have been determined are as follows:
(a) continuous flow.
(b) temperature-jump.

[b] 4,7-DMP = 4,7-dimethyl-1,10-phenanthroline, DMP = 5,6-dimethyl-1,10-phenanthroline, DMBPY = 4,4′-dimethyl-2,2′-bipyridyl.

Table 5.2 Oxalato complexes of iridium[a]

Oxidation state	Complex	Colour	Physical properties	Preparation	Ref.
IV	$Cs_2[IrCl_4\ ox]$	Red		$K_3[IrCl_4\ ox] + Cl_2 + ox^{2-}$	128a
	$K[Ir\ ox\ py\ Cl_3]$			$K_2[Ir\ ox\ py\ Cl_3] + Cl_2$	128a
III	$K_3[Ir\ ox_3]$	Orange	el[139,210], kin[210], o.r.d.[98,174]	$K_3[IrCl_6] + K_2C_2O_4$	58, 76
	cis-$K_3[Ir\ ox_2Cl_2]$	Red	i.r.[192], el[142]	$K_3[IrCl_6] + K_2C_2O_4$	58
	trans-$K_3[Ir\ ox_2Cl_2]$	Red-brown	i.r.[192], el[142]	*cis*-$K_3[Ir\ ox_2Cl_2] + H_2O$	58
	$K[Ir\ ox_2(H_2O)_2]$	Green		$K_3[Ir\ ox_3] + KOH + H_2O$	76, 77
	$Ag_3[Ir\ ox_2(OH)_2]$	Red		$K_2[Ir\ ox_2(H_2O)(OH)] + Ag^+$	76
	$K_2[Ir\ ox_2(H_2O)(OH)]$	Orange		$K_2[Ir\ ox_2(H_2O)_2] + KOH$	77
	$K_3[Ir\ ox(NO_2)_2Cl_2]$	Colourless		$K_3[Ir\ ox_2Cl_2] + KNO_2$	76
	$K_3[Ir\ ox(NO_2)Cl_3]$	Red		$K_3[Ir(NO_2)Cl_5] + K_2C_2O_4$	226
	$K_2[Ir\ ox^{4,5}py^1Cl_3{}^{2,3,6}]$	Orange		$K_3[Ir\ oxCl_4] + py$	58
	$K_2[Ir\ ox^{5,6}py^1Cl_3{}^{2,3,4}]$	Orange		$K_3[Ir\ oxCl_4] + py$	58
	$K_3[Ir\ oxCl_4]$	Brown	el[142]	$K_2[IrCl_6] + K_2C_2O_4$	76
	$K_7Ir_3Cl_4ox_6$ (?)			*cis*-$K_3[Ir\ ox_3] + H_2O + Cl^-$	58

[a] See also p. 252

Table 5.3 Iridium sulphito complexes

Oxidation state	Complex	Colour	Physical properties	Preparation	Ref.
III	$K_3[Ir(SO_3)_3]$			$Ir_2(SO_3)_3 + K_2CO_3$	23
	$Na_7[Ir(SO_3)_4Cl_2]$		i.r.[12]	$Na_3[IrCl_6] + NaHCO_3 + SO_2$	162
	$Na_3[Ir(SO_3)_3(NH_3)_3]$		i.r.[12]	$Na_7[Ir(SO_3)_4Cl_2] + NH_3$	163
	$Na_5[Ir(SO_3)_2Cl_4]$		i.r.[12]	$Na_3[IrCl_6] + NaHCO_3 + SO_2$	162
	$Na[Ir(SO_3)_2(NH_3)_3]$		i.r.[12]	$Na_5[Ir(SO_3)_2Cl_4] + NH_3$	164
	$K_4[Ir(SO_3)_2Cl_3]$		i.r.[12]	$Na_5[Ir(SO_3)_2Cl_4] + KCl$	162
	$K_4[Ir(SO_3)_2(NO_2)_2Cl]$	Orange	i.r.[12]	$K_4[Ir(SO_3)_2Cl_3] + KNO_2$	45
	$Na_2[Ir(SO_3)_2(NH_3)_3Cl]$			$Na_5[Ir(SO_3)_2Cl_4] + NH_3$	164
	$K_4[Ir(SO_3)(NO_2)_5]$	Colourless	i.r.[12]	$K_4[Ir(SO_3)_2Cl_3] + KNO_2$	45
	$K_2(NH_4)[Ir(SO_3)(NH_3)(NO_2)_4]$	Colourless		$K_4[Ir(SO_3)(NO_2)_5] + NH_3$	45
	$K_5H_3[Ir(SO_3)(HSO_3)(NO_2)_4]_2$	Colourless		$K_4[Ir(SO_3)(NO_2)_5] + NH_3 + SO_2$	45
	$H_2[Ir_4(SO_3)_7]$ (?) (also Hg, Ag and Ba salts)			$Ir_2S_3 . 3H_2S + HNO_3$	227
II	cf. p. 257				

Table 5.4 Ammine complexes of iridium[a]

Oxidation state	Complex	Colour	Physical properties	Preparation	Ref.
IV	$[Ir(NH_3)_4Cl_2]Cl_2$			$IrCl_2.2NH_3$ (?) + HNO_3	215
	$[Ir(NH_3)_2py_2Cl_2]Cl_2$			*trans*-$Irpy_2Cl_4 + NH_3$	64
III	$[Ir(NH_3)_6]Cl_3$	Colourless	kin[216], R, i.r.[159a]	$[Ir(NH_3)_5Cl]Cl_2 + NH_3$ (pressure)	215
	$[Ir(NH_3)_5Cl]Cl_2$	Yellow	kin[156]	$IrCl_3 + NH_3 + H_2O$	156, 215, 216
	$[Ir(NH_3)_5Br]Br_2$	Yellow	kin[156], el[249]	$[Ir(NH_3)_5H_2O]Br_3 + HBr$	156, 215
	$[Ir(NH_3)_5I]I_2$	Yellow	kin[156], el[249]	$[Ir(NH_3)_5H_2O]I_3$ + Heat	156, 215
	$[Ir(NH_3)_5H_2O]Cl_3$	Colourless		$[Ir(NH_3)_5Cl]Cl_2 + KOH$	215
	$[Ir(NH_3)_5OH]Cl_2$	Colourless	el[249a]	$[Ir(NH_3)_5H_2O]Cl_3 + NH_3 + H_2O$	74
	$[Ir(NH_3)_5(NO_3)](NO_3)_2$	Colourless	el[249a]	$[Ir(NH_3)_5H_2O](NO_3)_3$ + Heat (100°)	249
	$[Ir(NH_3)_5NO_2]Cl_2$	Colourless	i.r.[18,49b]	$[Ir(NH_3)_5(H_2O)]Cl_3 + H^+ + NO_2^-$	18
	$[Ir(NH_3)_5ONO]Cl_2$	Colourless	i.r.[18,49b], kin[18], el[249]	$[Ir(NH_3)_5(H_2O)]Cl_3 + H^+ + NO_2^-$	18
	$[Ir(NH_3)_5RCOO](ClO_4)_2$ (R = CH_3, CMe_3, CF_3)		kin[198], el[249]	$[Ir(NH_3)_5H_2O](ClO_4)_3 + RCOOH$	198
	$[Ir(NH_3)_5(Et_2S)]_2(SO_4)_3$			$Ir(Et_2S)_3Cl_3 + NH_3 + SO_4^{2-}$	233
	$[Ir(NH_3)_5py]$.*cis*-$[Ir\ py_2Cl_4]_3$	Orange		$Ir\ py_2Cl_4 + NH_3$	222

Table 5.4 (*continued*)

Oxidation state	Complex	Colour	Physical properties	Preparation	Ref.
III (*continued*)	$[Ir(NH_3)_5N_3](ClO_4)_2$	Yellow	el[249]	$NaN_3 + [Ir(NH_3)_5H_2O]^{3+}$	249a
	$[Ir(NH_3)_5(HCOO)](ClO_4)_2$	Yellow	el[249]	$HCOOH + [Ir(NH_3)_5OH]^{2+}$	249a
	$[Ir(NH_3)_5NCS](ClO_4)_2$		el, i.r.[249]	$NCS^- + [Ir(NH_3)_5(H_2O)]^{3+}$	249a
	$[Ir(NH_3)_5SCN](ClO_4)_2$		el, i.r.[249]	Recrystallization of above	249a
	$[Ir(NH_3)_4Cl_2]Cl$	Orange		$[Ir(NH_3)_4(NO_2)_2]Cl + HCl$	215, 269
	$[Ir(NH_3)_4py\ Cl]Cl_2$	Brown		$K_2[Ir\ py\ Cl_5] + NH_3$	63
	$[Ir(NH_3)_4(NO_2)_2]Cl$	Colourless		$Na_3[Ir(NO_2)_4Cl_2] + NH_3$ (170°)	269
	$Ir(NH_3)_3Cl_3$	Yellow		$Ir(NH_3)_3(NO_2)_3 + HCl$	269
	$IrCl_3 . 3\ NH_3$			$IrCl_3 + NH_3$	215
	$[Ir(NH_3)_3py_2Cl]Cl_2$	Colourless		$[Ir(NH_3)_3py_2(H_2O)]Cl_3 + NH_3$	63, 64
	$[Ir(NH_3)_3py_2(H_2O)]Cl_3$	Colourless		*trans*-Ir py_2Cl_4 + pyHCl + NH_3 + H_2O	63
	cis-$[Ir_2(OH)(NH_3)_6py]Cl_5$	Yellow		$K[Ir\ py_2Cl_4] + NH_3$	222
	$Ir(NH_3)_3(NO_2)_3$	Colourless		$Na_3[Ir(NO_2)_4Cl_2] + NH_3$ (140°)	269
	$[Ir(NH_3)_2py_2Cl_2]Cl$	Gold		*trans*-$K[Ir\ py_2Cl_4] + NH_3$	64
	cis-$Ir(NH_3)_2(Et_2S)Cl_3$	Yellow		*cis*-$Ir(Et_2S)_3Cl_3 + NH_3$ (140°)	232, 233
	$[Ir(NH_3)_2pyCl(H_2O)]CO_3$	Yellow		$[Ir(NH_3)_2py_2Cl_2]^+ + CO_3^{2-} + H_2O$	64
	$K_2[Ir(NH_3)Cl_5]$	Yellow		$K_3[IrCl_6] + NH_4OAc + NH_3$	167
	$Ir(NH_3)(Et_2S)_2Cl_3$	Yellow		*cis*-$Ir(Et_2S)_3Cl_3 + NH_3$ (100°)	233
O (?)	$Ir(NH_3)_5$			$[Ir(NH_3)_6]Cl_3 + K + NH_3$	267

[a] See also Table 5.5 and p. 258.

Table 5.5 Rates of hydrogen exchange[c] of metal ammines and amine complexes[d] [216]

Electronic state	Hexammine	$k \times 10^{-6}$ (M^{-1} sec^{-1})[a]	E_a (kcal/mole)	$S^{\ddagger}$ (e.u.)	Amine	$k \times 10^{-6}$ (M^{-1} sec^{-1})
t_{2g}^6	$[Ir(NH_3)_6]^{3+}$	0·015	23 ± 2	34	$[Ir\ en_3]^{3+}$	0·02[b]
t_{2g}^6	$[Rh(NH_3)_6]^{3+}$	0·21	15 ± 2	13	$[Rh\ en_3]^{3+}$	0·22
t_{2g}^6	$[Co(NH_3)_6]^{3+}$	1·6	14 ± 1	14	$[Co\ en_3]^{3+}$	2·4
t_{2g}^5	$[Os(NH_3)_6]^{3+}$	6·0				
t_{2g}^5	$[Ru(NH_3)_6]^{3+}$	600				
t_{2g}^3	$[Cr(NH_3)_6]^{3+}$	2·6	12 ± 2	8	$(Cr\ en_3)^{3+}$	3·6

[a] k is the second-order rate constant for hydrogen exchange with the complexes.
[b] Estimated value.
[c] Exchange measured in 0·1 M $DC_2H_3O_2$–$C_2H_3O_2^-$ buffer at 25°.
[d] See also p. 259.

Table 5.6 Pyridine complexes of iridium[a]

Oxidation state	Complex	Colour	Physical properties	Preparation	Ref.
IV	*cis*- and *trans*-Ir py_2Cl_4	Violet		*cis*- or *trans*-[Ir $py_2Cl_4]^-$ + HNO_3	65, 144
	Ir py_2Br_4	Brown		*trans*-[Ir $py_2Br_4]^-$ + HNO_3	72
	K[Ir $pyCl_5$]	Red		K_2[Ir $pyCl_5$] + Cl_2	66
III	*cis*- and *trans*-[Ir py_4Cl_2]Cl	Yellow	el[143], i.r.[120a]	*cis*-K[Ir py_2Cl_4] + py + EtOH (pressure)	151
	1,2,3- and 1,2,6-Ir py_3Cl_3	Red-yellow	el[143,151], i.r.[120a]	K[Ir py_2Cl_4] + py	65
	1,2,3- and 1,2,6-Ir py_3Br_3	Red-yellow	el[143,151]	$Na_3[IrBr_6]$ + py (130°)	72
	cis- and *trans*-K[Ir py_2Cl_4]	Orange	el[143], i.r.[120a]	$K_3[IrCl_6]$ + py	65, 146
	pyH[Ir py_2Br_4]	Red	el[143]	pyHBr + $K_3[IrBr_6]$	72
	cis- and *trans*-Ir $py_2Cl_3(H_2O)$		el[143]	*cis*- and *trans*-K[Ir py_2Cl_4] + H_2O (130°)	67, 70b
	cis- and *trans*-AgH[Ir $py_2Cl_3(OH)]_2$	Rose	el[143]	*cis*- and *trans*-Ir $py_2Cl_3(H_2O)$ + $AgNO_3$	67, 70b
	cis- and *trans*-K[Ir $py_2Cl_3(NO_3)$]		el[142]	*cis*- and *trans*-Ir $py_2Cl_3(H_2O)$ + HNO_3	67
	Ag_2H[Ir $py_2Br_3(OH)]_3$	Orange		Ir $py_2Br_3(H_2O)$ + $AgNO_3$	72
	Ag[Ir $py_2Br_3(NO_3)$]			Ir $py_2Br_3(H_2O)$ + HNO_3 + $AgNO_3$	72

Table 5.6 (*continued*)

Oxidation state	Complex	Colour	Physical properties	Preparation	Ref.
III (*continued*)	$[Ir\ py_3(H_2O)Cl]Cl_2$			$[Ir\ py_2Cl_4]^- + py$	70b
	$[Ir_2(OH)\ py_6Cl_4]Cl$			$[Ir\ py_3Cl(H_2O)_2]Cl + py + H_2O$	70b
	$K[Ir\ py_2Cl\ ox(H_2O)]$	Yellow		$K_3[Ir\ ox_3] + py$	65
	trans-$Ir\ py_2Cl\ ox(H_2O)$	Yellow		$Ir\ py_2Cl_3(H_2O) + ox^{2-}$	65
	$[Ir\ py_2Cl_3]_n$	Rose		*trans*-$K[Ir\ py_2Cl_4] + H_2O$ (130°)	67
	$[Ir\ py_2Cl_2(H_2O_2]Cl$			$K[Ir\ py_2ox_2] + HCl$	65
	$[Ir\ py_2Cl_2(H_2O)](OH)$	Yellow		$[Ir\ py_2Cl_2(H_2O)_2]^+ + H_2O$	65
	cis-$Ir\ py_2(Et_2S)Cl_3$	Yellow		*cis*-$Ir(Et_2S)_3Cl_3 + py$	234
	cis-$Ir\ py\ (Et_2S)_2Cl_3$	Yellow		*cis*-$Ir(Et_2S)_3Cl_3 + py$	234
	$K_2[Ir\ py^1Cl_3{}^{2,3,6}ox^{4,5}]$	Orange		$K_3[IrCl_4ox] + py$	65
	$K_2[Ir\ py^1Cl_3{}^{2,3,4}ox^{5,6}]$	Orange		$K_3[IrCl_4ox] + py$	65
	$K_2[Ir\ pyCl_5]$		el[143], i.r.[120a]	$K_3[IrCl_6] + py$	63

[a] For pyridine oxalate complexes, see Tables 5.2 and 5.4 and see also p. 264.

Table 5.7 Nitrosyl complexes of iridium

Oxidation state	Complex	Colour	Physical properties	Preparation	Ref.
III	$K[Ir(NO)Br_5]$	Gold	i.r.[49b,93a]	$K_3[IrBr_6] + KNO_2 + HBr$	177
	$[Ir(NO)Cl_3(PPh_3)_2]ClO_4$	Beige	i.r.[178]	$[Ir(NO)_2(PPh_3)_2]ClO_4 + Cl_2$	178
II	$Ir(NO)Br_3(PPh_3)_2$	Maroon	i.r.[178]	$[Ir(NO)_2(PPh_3)_2]ClO_4 + Br_2$	178
I	$Ir(NO)X_2(PPh_3)_2$ (X = Cl, Br, I)	Brown	i.r.[178]	$[Ir(NO)_2(PPh_3)_2]ClO_4 + HX$	178
−I	$[Ir(NO)_2(PPh_3)_2]ClO_4$	Violet	i.r.[178]	$[IrH_2(PPh_3)_3]ClO_4 + NO$	178
	$Ir(NO)_2X(PPh_3)_2$ (X = Cl, Br, I)	Brown	i.r.[178]	$Ir(NO)_2(PPh_3)_2 + LiX$	178
	$Ir(NO)(PPh_3)_3$	Orange	i.r.[178]	$[Ir(NO)_2(PPh_3)_2]ClO_4 + PPh_3$	178
	$Ir(NO)(CO)(PPh_3)_2$	Orange	i.r.[178]	$IrH(CO)(PPh_3)_3 + NO$	178
−II	$Ir(NO)_2(PPh_3)$	Violet	i.r.[178]	$IrH_3(PPh_3)_2 + NO$	178

Table 5.8 Phosphine, arsine and stibine complexes of iridium[a,b,c]

Oxidation state	Complex	Colour	Physical properties	Preparation	Ref.
III	1,2,6-$IrX_3(LR_3)_3$	Orange	D^{42}, i.r.,[130b] n.m.r.[130a]	$[IrX_6]^{3-}$ + EtOH + LR_3 + X^-	42, 130b
	(X = Cl, Br, I; LR_3 = PEt_3, PPr^n_3, PMe_2Ph, PPh_2Et, PEt_2Ph, $PPhPr^n_2$, $AsEt_3$, $AsEt_2Ph$)				
	$IrX_3(AsPh_2Me)_3$ (X = Cl, Br, I)	Yellow		$[IrCl_6]^{3-}$ + X^- + $AsPh_2Me$	81
	$IrCl_3(PPh_3)_2$			$IrH_3(PPh_3)_3$ + Cl_2	4
	$[IrX_4(LR_3)_2]^-$ (X = Cl, Br; LR_3 = PEt_3, PEt_2Ph, $AsPh_2Me$)	Yellow		$[IrCl_6]^{3-}$ + X^- + EtOH + LR_3	42, 81
	$Ir_2Cl_6(PEt_3)_4$			$[IrCl_6]^3$ + 2-methoxyethanol + PEt_3	42
	$IrX_3(As—S)_2$ (X = Cl, Br, I)	Yellow		$(NH_4)_3[IrX_6]$ + As—S + EtOH	48
	[Ir diars$_2Cl_2$]Cl		i.r.[170]	$IrCl_3$ + diars	221a
	$IrBr_3(SbPh_3)_3$			$[IrBr_3(SbPh_3)_2$ + $SbPh_3$	11a
	$[IrBr_3(SbPh_3)_2]_2$	Yellow		$K[IrBr_4(SbPh_3)_2]$ + MeOH	11a
	$IrBr_3(SbPh_3)_2L$ (L = CO, NH_3, py)			$[IrBr_3(SbPh_3)_2]_2$ + L	11a
	$K[IrBr_4(SbPh_3)_2]$			$K_3[IrBr_6]$ + $SbPh_3$ + EtOH	11a

Table 5.8 *(continued)*

Oxidation state	Complex	Colour	Physical properties	Preparation	Ref.
	$IrBr_3(SbPh_3)_2(MeOH)$			$K[IrBr_4(SbPh_3)_2]$ + MeOH	11a
	$IrX_2Y(PMe_2Ph)_3$ (X = Cl, Br, I; Y = Cl, Br, I, CN, SCN)		i.r.[130a], n.m.r.[130b]	$IrHX_2(PMe_2Ph)_3 + Y$	130b
	1,2,3- and 1,2,6-$IrCl_3(SbPh_3)_3$			$Na_2[IrCl_6] + SbPh_3$ + EtOH	11b
	$Na[IrCl_4(SbPh_3)_2]$			$Na_2[IrCl_6] + SbPh_3$ + EtOH	11b
	$IrCl_3(AsC_{10}H_{14}(NH_2))_3$			$K_3[IrCl_6] + (NH_2)C_{10}H_{14}As$	216a
	$[Ir(diphos)_2L_2]^+$ ($L_2 = H_2$, HCl, HBr, $(NO)_2$)			$L_2 + [Ir(diphos)_2]^+$	263b
II	$[IrCl_4(PMe_2Ph)_2]^-$		i.r.[130a], n.m.r.[130b]	$[IrCl_6]^{3-} + PMe_2Ph$	130b
	?$IrX_2(AsMe_2(C_7H_8))_3$ (X = Cl, Br, I)			$IrX_3 + AsMe_2(C_7H_8)$	81
I	$[Ir(diphos)_2]Cl$			$Ir(CO)_3Cl$ + diphos	122a, 241a
	$[Ir(diphos)_2L]^+$ (L = CO, PF_3, O_2, SO_2)		i.r.[263b]	$[Ir(diphos)]^+ + L$	263b

[a] See also Tables 5.7, 5.9 and 5.11 and pp. 266 and 272.
[b] For Tables 5.8, 5.9 and 5.10 diphos = $C_2H_4(PPh_2)_2$.
[c] (A—S) = *o*-C_6H_4(AsMe) . SMe.

Table 5.9 Hydrido phosphine, arsine and stibine complexes of iridium[a]

Oxidation state	Complex	Colour	Physical properties	Preparation	Ref.
III	1,2,3- and 1,2,6-$IrH_3(PPh_3)_3$		D[44a], i.r.[5], n.m.r.[130a]	$IrH_3(PPh_3)_2 + PPh_3$	44a, 5, 7
	1,2,3- and 1,2,6-$IrH_3(AsPh_3)_3$			$IrBr_3(AsPh_3)_3 + NaBH_4$	38
	$IrH_3(AsPh_3)_2$			$IrHBr_2(AsPh_3)_3 + NaBH_4$	38
	$IrH_3(AsPh_3)_2py$			$IrH_3(AsPh_3)_2 + py$	38
	1,2,3-$IrH_3(PMe_2Ph)_3$		n.m.r.[130a]		130a
	1,2,3- and 1,2,6-$IrH_3(PEt_2Ph)_3$		D, n.m.r.[44a], i.r.[44a]	$IrCl_3(PEt_2Ph_3) + LiAlH_4$	44a
	1,2,3-$IrH_3(AsEt_2Ph)_3$		D, n.m.r., i.r.[44a]	1,2,6-$IrCl_3(AsEt_2Ph)_3 + [AlH_4]^-$	44a
	$IrH_3(PR_3)_2$ ($PR_3 = PEt_3, PPh_3, PEt_2Ph$)		D, n.m.r., i.r.[44a]	$IrCl_3(PR_3)_3 + LiAlH_4$	44a
	$IrH_2X(PPh_3)_3$ (X = Cl, Br, I)	Colourless	i.r.[262]	$(NH_4)_2[IrX_6] + PPh_3$	262
	$[IrH_2(PPh_3)_3]ClO_4$		i.r.[7]	1,2,3- or 1,2,6-$IrH_3(PPh_3)_3 + HClO_4$	7
	$[IrH_2(AsPh_3)_3]ClO_4$			1,2,3-$IrH_3(AsPh_3)_3 + HCl + HClO_4$	38
	$IrH_2Br(AsPh_3)_3$			$IrBr_3 + EtOH + AsPh_3$	38
	$IrH_2(PPh_3)_3(SnCl_3)$		i.r., n.m.r.[256a]	$[IrCl_6]^{2-} + SnCl_2 + PPh_3$	256a
	$IrH_2(PPh_3)_3L$ (L = (CN, NO_2, OAc)			$IrH_3(PPh_3)_3 + L$	4
	$[IrH_2(PPh_3)_2L_2]ClO_4$ (L = py, PPh_3)	Colourless		$IrH_3(PPh_3)_3 + L + ClO_4^-$	4
	$[IrH_2(AsPh_3)_4]ClO_4$			$IrH_2(AsPh_3)_3 + AsPh_3$	38

Table 5.9 (*continued*)

Oxidation state	Complex	Colour	Physical properties	Preparation	Ref.
III (*continued*)	$IrH_2Cl(PMe_2Ph)$		i.r.[130b], n.m.r.[130a]	$IrCl_3(PMe_2Ph)_3 + LiCl$	130b
	$[IrH_2(diphos)_2]^+$			$H_2 + [Ir(diphos)_2]^+$	241a
	$IrH_2X(PR_3)_3$ (X = Cl, Br)		i.r.[130b], D[44a]	$IrCl_3(PR_3)_3 + OH^- + EtOH + X^-$	44a, 130b
	$IrH_2(acac)(PPh_3)_2$			$IrH_3(PPh_3)_3$ + acac	11c
	$IrH_2Cl(AsEt_2Ph)_3$		D, n.m.r., i.r.[44a]	$IrCl_3(AsEt_2Ph)_3 + EtOH + KOH$	44a
	$IrHX_2(PPH_3)_3$ (X = Cl, Br)		i.r.[11]	$[IrX_6]^{3-} + PPh_3 + EtOH$	11
	$IrHX_2(PPh_3)_2$ (X = Cl, Br, I)		i.r.[4]	$[IrX_6]^{3-} + PPh_3$	4
	$IrHX_2(PPh_3)_2Y$ (X = Cl, Br; Y = NH_3, py, MeCN, $SbPh_3$)		i.r.[11]	$IrHX_2(PPh_3)_2 + Y$	11
	$IrHX_2(AsPh_3)_3$ (X = Cl, Br)			$IrX_3 + AsPh_3 + EtOH$	38
	$IrHBr_2(SbPh_3)_3$		i.r.[10a]	$IrBr_3(SbPh_3)_3 + BH_4^-$	11a
	$IrHX_2(PR_2Ph)_3$ (X = Cl, Br, I; R = Me, Et)		i.r.[130b], n.m.r.[130a]	$IrCl_3(PR_2Ph)_3 + X^- + KOH$	130b
	$IrHX_2(LR_3)_3$ (X = Cl, Br, I; LR_3 = PEt_3, PEt_2Ph, $AsEt_3$, $AsEt_2Ph$)		D, n.m.r., i.r.[44a], i.r.[130b]	$IrCl_3(LR_3)_3 + X^- + EtOH + KOH$	44a
	$IrHCl_2(SbPh_3)_3$			$Na_2[IrCl_6] + SbPh_3$	11b
	$IrHX(PPh_3)_2(SnCl_3)$ (X = Cl, H)		i.r., n.m.r.[256a]	$[IrCl_6]^{2-} + SnCl_2 + PPh_3$	256a
	$[IrH(PPh_3)_2]^{2+}$			$IrH_3(PPh_3)_2 + HBr + Me_2CO$	11

[a] See also pp. 268 and 273.

Table 5.10 Carbonyls and carbonyl halide complexes of iridium[a]

Oxidation state	Complex	Colour	Physical properties	Preparation	Ref.
III	$K_2[Ir(CO)X_5]$ (X = Cl, Br)	Pink	i.r.[179]	$K_2[Ir(CO)I_5] + X_2$	147a, 179
	$K_2[Ir(CO)I_5]$	Red	i.r.[179]	$IrI_4 + CO + KI$ (200 atm, 240°)	179
	$K[Ir(CO)_2I_4]$	Red	i.r.[179]	$IrI_4 + CO + KI$ (200 atm, 240°)	179
	$K[Ir(CO)I_4]$	Red	i.r.[179]	$IrI_3 + KI + CO$ (200 atm, 250°)	179
	$Ir(CO)_3I_3$	Red	i.r.[179]	$IrI_3 + CO$ (250 atm, 100°)	179
	$[Ir(CO)_2I_3]_2$	Brown	i.r.[179]	$IrI_3 + CO$ (250 atm, 100°)	179
	$Ir_2(CO)_3I_6$	Red	i.r.[179]	$IrI_3 + CO$ (250 atm, 100°)	179
	?$Ir_3(CO)_4Cl_9$			$[Ir(CO)_3]_n + Cl_2$ (100°)	121
	$K[Ir(CO)_2Br_4]$	Yellow		$K_2[IrBr_6] + CO$ (50 atm, 220°)	180
II	$(AsPh_4)_2[Ir(CO)I_4]$	Brown	i.r.[179]	$K_2[Ir(CO)I_5] + Zn + AsPh_4^+$	179
	$K_2[Ir_2(CO)_4I_6]$	Orange	i.r.[179]	$IrI_3 + KI + CO$ (200 atm, 250°)	179
	$[Ir(CO)_2X_2]_n$ (X = Cl, Br, I)	Yellow		$IrX_3 + CO$ (130°)	121, 183
	$(AsPh_4)[Ir(CO)Br_3]$	Yellow			180
	$Ir(CO)X_2(p\text{-toluidine})_2$ (X = Cl, Br)			$K[Ir(CO)_2X_4] + K_2[Ir_2(CO)_4X_5]$ + *p*-toluidine	180
	$AsPh_4[Ir(CO)I_3]$	Brown	i.r.[179]	$Zn + K_2[Ir(CO)I_5] + K[Ir(CO)I_4] + AsPh_4^+$	179

Table 5.10 (*continued*)

Oxidation state	Complex	Colour	Physical properties	Preparation	Ref.
II–I	$K[Ir_2(CO)_4Cl_4]$	Gold		$(AsPh_4)[Ir_2(CO)_4Br_4]$ + KCl + HCl	180
	$(AsPh_4)[Ir_2(CO)_4Br_4]$			$K_2[IrBr_6]$ + CO (200 atm, 200°) + $AsPh_4^+$	180
	$K_2[Ir_2(CO)_4X_5]$ (X = Cl, Br)			$K_2[IrX_6]$ + CO (200 atm, 200°) + Cu	180
I	*cis*-$(AsPh_4)[Ir(CO)_2I_2]$	Yellow	i.r.[179]	$(AsPh_4)[Ir(CO)_2I_4]$ + Zn	179
	$(AsPh_4)[Ir(CO)_2Br_2]$	Yellow		$(AsPh_4)[IrBr_6]$ + CO (200 atm, 200°)	180
	$(AsPh_4)[Ir_2(CO)_4Br_3]$	Brown		$Ir(CO)_2(C_7H_7N)Br$ + $AsPh_4^+$	180
	$Ir(CO)_3X$ (X = Cl, Br, I)			IrX_3 + CO (150°)	121
	$Ir(CO)_4H$			$IrCl_3$ + CO (200 atm, 180°) + Cu + H_2O	122
O	$[Ir(CO)_4]_2$	Green	i.r.[204]	$IrCl_3$ + CO (200 atm, 180°) + Cu	122
	$[Ir(CO)_3]_n$	Yellow	i.r.[204]	$IrCl_3$ + CO (200 atm, 180°) + Cu	121, 122

[a] See also pp. 271, 276 and 277.

Table 5.11 Carbonyl and hydrido carbonyl phosphines, arsines and stibines of iridium

Oxidation state	Complex	Colour	Physical properties	Preparation	Ref.
III	*cis*- and *trans*-$IrX_3(CO)(LR_3)_2$ (X = Cl, Br; LR_3 = PEt_3, PBu^n_3, PEt_2Ph, $AsEt_3$, $AsEt_2Ph$, $SbPr^n_3$;		i.r., D[43]	$H_3[IrCl_6]$ + CO + LR_3 + 2-methoxyethanol + X^-	43
	$[Ir(CO)(P(OR)_3)I_3]_2$			$[Ir(CO)_2(P(OR)_3]_2 + I_2$	278
	$IrO_2(CO)Cl(PPh_3)_2$		X[52], i.r.[9]	$Ir(CO)(PPh_3)_2Cl + O_2$	9
	$Ir(CO)(AsPh_3)_2I_3$			$IrI_3(AsPh_3)_3$ + CO	9
	$Ir(CO)(SbPh_3)_2Cl_3$			CO + $IrCl_3(SbPh_3)_3$	11a, 11b
	$Ir(CO)_2(AsPh_3)I_3$		i.r.[9]	$K[Ir(CO)_4I_2] + AsPh_3$	9
	$Ir(CO)(PPh_3)_2X_3$ (X = Cl, Br)			$Ir(CO)Cl(PPh_3)_2 + X_2$	260
	$XHgIrXCl(CO)(PPh_3)_2$ (X = Cl, Br, I, OAc, CN, SCN)	Yellow		$Ir(CO)Cl(PPh_3)_2 + HgX_2$	207
	$BrHgIr(CO)Br_2(PPh_3)_2$	Yellow		$Ir(CO)Cl(PPh_3)_2 + HgBr_2$	207
	$IrH_3(CO)(PPh_3)_2$		i.r.[5]	$IrH_3(PPh_3)_2$ + CO	5, 6
	$IrH_3(CO)(AsPh_3)_2$		i.r.[38a]	$IrH_3(AsPh_3)_3$ + CO	38a
	$[IrH_2(CO)(PPh_3)_3]ClO_4$ (2 forms)		i.r.[6]	$IrH_2(CO)(PPh_3)_3$ + CO + ClO_4^- (150 atm)	6
	$IrH_2(CO)(PPh_3)_2(SnCl_3)$		i.r., n.m.r.[256a]	$Ir(CO)Cl(PPh_3)_2 + SnCl_2$	256a
	$[Ir(HD)(CO)(PPh_3)_3]^+$			$H^+ + IrD(CO)(PPh_3)_3$	262a
	$[IrH_2(CO)(PPh_3)_2]ClO_4$		i.r.[6]	$IrH(CO)(PPh_3)_2 + HClO_4$	6, 262a
	$IrH_2(CO)Cl(PPh_3)_2$	Yellow	i.r.[260]	$IrH(CO)(PPh_3)_2 + H_2 + Cl^-$	260

Table 5.11 *(continued)*

Oxidation state	Complex	Colour	Physical properties	Preparation	Ref.
III *(continued)*	$[IrH(CO)Cl_2(PEt_3)]_2$		i.r.[43]	$H_3[IrCl_6]$ + CO + HCl + PEt_3	43
	$IrH(CO)X(PPh_3)_2$ (X = F, Cl, Br, I; Y = Cl, Br, I, SCN)		i.r.[263c]	$Ir(CO)Y(PPh_3)_2$ + HX	263c
	$IrH(CO)X(PPh_3)_2(SnCl_3)$ (X = Cl, H)		i.r., n.m.r.[256a]	$Ir(CO)Cl(PPh_3)_2$ + $SnCl_2$	256a
	$IrH(CO)X_2(PPh_3)_2$ (X = Cl, Br, I)		i.r.[11]	$IrHX_2(PPh_3)_2$ + CO	6, 11
	$IrH(CO)X_2(PEt_2Ph)_2$ (X = Cl, Br)		i.r., n.m.r.[43]	$[IrX_6]^{2-}$ + PEt_2Ph + CO + EtOH	43
	$IrH(CO)Cl_2(AsPh_3)_2$	Yellow	i.r.[261]	$(NH_4)_2[IrCl_6]$ + $AsPh_3$ + CO	261
	$IrH(CO)Cl(PPh_3)_2SiCl_3$		i.r.[40]	$Ir(CO)Cl(PPh_3)_2$ + $HSiCl_3$	40
	$IrEt(CO)Cl(PPh_3)_2SiCl_2H$		i.r.[40]	$Ir(CO)Cl(PPh_3)_2$ + $EtSiCl_2H$	40
I	$Ir(CO)X(PPh_3)_2$ (X = Cl, Br)	Yellow	D[261]	$IrCl_3$ + X^- + PPh_3 + 2-methoxyethanol	8, 261
	$Ir(CO)Cl(PEt_3)_3$			$IrCl_3(PEt_3)_3$ + KOH + EtOH	44
	$[Ir(CO)_2(LPh_3)_2]I$ (L = P, As)		i.r.[8]	$K[Ir(CO)_2I_4]$ + LPh_3	8
	$Ir(CO)I(PPh_3)_2$		i.r.[8]	$K[Ir(CO)_2I_4]$ + PPh_3	8
	$Ir(CO)_2(LPh_3)X$ (L = P, As; X = Cl, Br)		i.r.[8]	$Ir(CO)_2$(*p*-toluidine)X + LPh_3	8
	$Ir(CO)Br(SbPh_3)_2$		i.r.[8]	$Ir(CO)_2$(*p*-toluidine)Br + $SbPh_3$	8
	$[Ir(CO_3)(PPh_2)]_2$			$Ir(CO)_3Cl$ + KPh_2	122b

Table 5.11 (*continued*)

Oxidation state	Complex	Colour	Physical properties	Preparation	Ref.
I (*continued*)	$Ir(CO)_2L_2Cl$ (L = py, *p*-tol, ½ phen, ½ bipy)		i.r.[122a]	$Ir(CO)_3Cl + L$	122a
	$Ir(CO)Cl(LPh_3)_2$ (L = P, As, Sb)			$Ir(CO)_3Cl + MPh_3$	122a
	$[Ir(CO)(diphos)_2]Cl$			$Ir(CO)_2Cl(p\text{-tol}) + diphos$	122a
	$Ir(CO)_2Cl$ diphos		X[122a]	$Ir(CO)_2Cl(p\text{-tol}) + diphos$	122a
	$[Ir(CO)_2(SbPh_3)_3]^+$			$IrCl(CO)(SbPh_3)_3 + CO + AlCl_3$	122b
	$Ir(CO)Cl(P(OPh)_3)_2$			$Ir(CO)_3Cl + P(OPh)_3$	122a
	$Ir(RCOO)(CO)(SbPh_3)_3$ (R = Me, Et)			$[Ir(CO)_2(PPh_3)_3]^+ + ROH$	122b
	$[Ir(CO)_2(L_2)_2]^+$ ($L_2 = PPh_3, P(C_6H_{11})_3$)			$Ir(CO)ClL_2 + CO + AlCl_3$	122b
	$Ir(SO_2)(CO)Cl(PPh_3)_2$	Green	X[157a]	$Ir(CO)Cl(PPh_3)_2 + SO_2$	263a
	$[Ir(CO)(diphos)_2]^+$			$Ir(CO)Cl(PPh_3)_2 + diphos$	122b, 241a
	$IrH(CO)(PPh_3)_2$	Yellow	i.r., n.m.r.[19]	$Ir(CO)Cl(PPh_3)_2 + N_2H_4$	19
	$IrH(CO)(PPh_3)_3$	Yellow		$Ir(CO)Cl(PPh_3)_2 + NaBH_4$	6
	cis-$IrH(CO)(AsPh_3)_2$		i.r.[38a]	$IrH_3(AsPh_3)_3 + CO$	38a
	$Ir(CO)(H_2S)Cl(PPh_3)_2$			$H_2S + Ir(CO)Cl(PPh_3)_2$	263c
O	$[Ir(CO)_2(P(OR)_3)]_2$ (R = Ph, Et, *p*-tolyl)			$P(OR)_3 + [Ir(CO)_3]_n$	278

Table 5.12 Magnetic measurements on iridium complexes

Complex	χ_A (× 10^6 c.g.s. units)[a]		μ_{eff} (BM)	Ref.
IrF_6	9855 (90°)	3725 (293°)	2·90 (293°)[b]	89
IrF_5	885 (75°)	727 (296°)		16
$K[IrF_6]$			1·18 (298°)	120
$Na[IrF_6]$			1·23 (298°)	120
$Cs_2[IrF_6]$			1·42 (297°)	118
$K_2[IrCl_6]$[c]	3277 (78°)	1131 (298°)	1·77 (298°)[b]	206
$(NH_4)_2[IrCl_6]$[c]	3087 (78°)	1103 (299°)	1·84 (299°)[b]	206
$(NH_4)_2[IrBr_6]$	3104 (78°)	1289 (300°)	2·09 (300°)[b]	206

[a] Temperatures (in parentheses) in °K.
[b] Approximate μ value.
[c] See also reference 51 for measurements between 1 and 298°K on these salts.

Table 5.13 Selected data on polarography of iridium complexes

Complex	Process	$E_{\frac{1}{2}}$ (versus s.c.e.)	Medium	D (cm²/sec)	Ref.
$[Ir(OH)_6]^{2-}$	IV → III	−0·60	0·5M Cl^- + OH^- (pH 12, 25°)		259a
$[IrCl_6]^{2-}$	IV → III		0·2M HCl		214a
$[IrCl_6]^{2-}$	IV → III		0·2M $HClO_4$		214a
$[IrCl_6]^{2-}$	IV → III	+0·82[a]	0·1M NaCl	8·2 × 10^{-6}[b]	228a
$[IrCl_6]^{3-}$	III → IV	+0·82	0·1M NaCl	7·6 × 10^{-6}[b]	228a

[a] Reversible; measured at a platinum electrode.
[b] Reference 154.

REFERENCES

1. Adams, D. M., and H. A. Gebbie, *Spectrochim. Acta*, **19**, 925 (1963).
2. Alcock, C. B., and G. W. Hooper, *Proc. Roy. Soc.* (*London*), *Ser. A*, **254**, 551 (1960); C. B. Alcock, *Trans. Brit. Ceram. Soc.*, **60**, 147 (1961).
3. Angoletta, M., *Ann. Chim.* (*Rome*), **53**, 1208 (1963).
4. Angoletta, M., *Gazz. Chim. Ital.*, **93**, 1343 (1963).
5. Angoletta, M., and A. Araneo, *Rend. Ist. Lombardo Sci. Lettere A*, **97**, 817 (1963).
6. Angoletta, M., and G. Caglio, *Rend. Ist. Lombardo Sci. Lettere A*, **97**, 823 (1963).
7. Angoletta, M., *Gazz. Chim. Ital.*, **92**, 811 (1962).
8. Angoletta, M., *Gazz. Chim. Ital.*, **89**, 2359 (1959).
9. Angoletta, M., *Gazz. Chim. Ital.*, **90**, 1021 (1960).
10. Anthony, U., *Gazz. Chim. Ital.*, **23**, 143, 190 (1893).
11. Araneo, A., and S. Martinengo, *Gazz. Chim. Ital.*, **95**, 61 (1965).

11a. Araneo, A., and S. Martinengo, *Gazz. Chim. Ital.*, **95**, 825 (1965).

11b. Araneo, A., S. Martinengo and F. Zingales, *Gazz. Chim. Ital.*, **12**, 1435 (1965).

11c. Araneo, A., S. Martinengo and P. Pasquale, *Rend. Ist. Lombardo. Sci., Lettre A*, **99**, 797 (1965).

12. Babaeva, A. V., Y. Y. Kharitonov and Z. M. Novozhenyuk, *Russ. J. Inorg. Chem., Eng. Transl.*, **6**, 1151 (1961).
13. Babel, D., and P. Deigner, *Z. Anorg. Allgem. Chem.*, **339**, 57 (1965).
13a. Baddley, W. H., *J. Am. Chem. Soc.*, **88**, 4545 (1966).
14. Bailey, C. A., and P. L. Smith, *Phys. Rev.*, **114**, 1010 (1959).
15. Balchan, A. S., and H. G. Drickamer, *J. Chem. Phys.*, **35**, 356 (1961).
16. Bartlett, N., and P. R. Rao, *Chem. Commun.*, **1965**, 253.
17. Bartlett, N., and D. H. Lohmann, *Chem. Commun.*, **1966**, 168; *J. Chem. Soc.*, **1962**, 5253.
18. Basolo, F., and G. S. Hammaker, *Inorg. Chem.*, **1**, 1 (1962).
19. Bath, S. S., and L. Vaska, *J. Am. Chem. Soc.*, **85**, 3500 (1963).
19a. Bell, W. E., and M. Tagami, *J. Phys. Chem.*, **70**, 640 (1966).
19b. Bell, W. E., M. Tagami and R. E. Inyard, *J. Phys. Chem.*, **70**, 2048 (1966).
19c. Bell, R., and W. Herr, Chem. Effects Nucl. Transformations, *Proc. Symp. Vienna*, **2**, 315 (1964) Chem. Abstr. **63**, 9250d (1964).
19d. Benzoni, L., A. Andretta, C. Zanzoterra and M. Camia, *Chim. Ind. (Rome)*, **48**, 1076 (1966).
20. Berezin, B. D., and G. V. Sennikova, *Dokl. Acad. Nauk. SSSR*, **159**, 117 (1964).
21. Biltz, W., *Z. Anorg. Allgem. Chem.*, **233**, 282 (1937).
22. Biltz, W., J. Laar, P. Ehrlich and K. Meisel, *Z. Anorg. Allgem. Chem.*, **233**, 257 (1937).
23. Birnbaum, C., *Ann.*, **133**, 161 (1865); **136**, 177 (1867).
24. Blasius, E., W. Preetz and R. Schmitt, *J. Inorg. Nucl. Chem.*, **19**, 115 (1961).
25. Blasius, E., and W. Preetz, *Z. Anorg. Allgem. Chem.*, **335**, 16 (1965).
26. Blasius, E., and W. Preetz, *Z. Anorg. Allgem. Chem.*, **335**, 1 (1965).
27. Bokii, G. B., and P. I. Usikov, *Compt. Rend., Acad. Sci. URSS*, **26**, 782 (1940).
27a. Bonamico, M., D. Duranti, A. Vaciago & L. Zambonelli, *Ric. Sci. Rend., Ser. A*, **7**, 613 (1964).
28. Bonati, F., and R. Ugo, *Chim. Ind. (Milan)*, **46**, 1486 (1964).
29. Bonati, F., and R. Ugo, *Chim. Ind. (Milan)*, **46**, 1339 (1964); *J. Organomet. Chem.* **7**, 167 (1967).
29a. Brauer, G., Handbook of Preparative Inorganic Chemistry, Academic Press, New York, 1965, p. 1590.
30. Brewer, L., and G. M. Rosenblatt, *Chem. Revs.*, **61**, 257 (1961).
31. Brintzinger, H., and H. Orth, *Monatsh.*, **85**, 1015 (1954).
32. Brodersen, K., F. Moers and H. G. Schnering, *Naturwissenschaften*, **52**, 205 (1965).
33. Brodensen, K., and P. Machmer, *Z. Naturforsch., Ser. B*, **17**, 127 (1962).
34. Brodersen, K., *Angew. Chem.*, **73**, 437 (1961).
35. Brown, D. R., D. R. Russell and D. W. A. Sharp, *J. Chem. Soc., Ser. A*, **1965**, 18.
36. Cady, G. H., and G. B. Hargreaves, *J. Chem. Soc.*, **1961**, 1563.
37. Campion, R. J., N. Purdie and N. Sutin, *Inorg. Chem.*, **3**, 1091 (1964).
38. Canziani, F., and E. Zingales, *Rend. Ist. Lombardo Sci. Lettere A*, **96**, 513 (1962).

38a. Canziani, F., U. Sartorelli and F. Zingales, *Rend. Ist. Lombardo Sci. Lettere A*, **96**, 21 (1965).
39. Chabrié, C., and M. A. Bouchonnet, *Compt. Rend.*, **137**, 1059 (1903).
40. Chalk, A. J., and J. F. Harrod, *J. Am. Chem. Soc.*, **87**, 16 (1965).
41. Chang, J. C., and C. S. Garner, *Inorg. Chem.*, **4**, 209 (1965).
42. Chatt, J., A. E. Field and B. L. Shaw, *J. Chem. Soc.*, **1963**, 3371.
43. Chatt, J., N. P. Johnson and B. L. Shaw, *J. Chem. Soc.*, **1964**, 1625.
44. Chatt, J., and B. L. Shaw, *Chem. Ind.* (*London*), **1960**, 931.
44a. Chatt, J., R. S. Coffey and B. L. Shaw, *J. Chem. Soc.*, **1965**, 7391.
44b. Chatt, J., and B. L. Shaw, *J. Chem. Soc.*, *Ser. A*, **1966**, 1836.
45. Chernyaev, I. I., and Z. M. Novozhenyuk, *Russ. J. Inorg. Chem.*, *Eng. Transl.*, **6**, 1247 (1961).
45a. Chernyaev, I. I., and Z. M. Novozhenyuk, *Zh. Neorgan. Khim.*, **11**, 1880 (1966).
46. Child, M. S., *Mol. Phys.*, **3**, 601, 605 (1960).
47. Chiswell, B., and S. E. Livingstone, *J. Inorg. Nucl. Chem.*, **26**, 47 (1964).
48. Chiswell, B., and S. E. Livingstone, *J. Chem. Soc.*, **1960**, 3181.
48a. Chock, P. B., and J. Halpern, *J. Am. Chem. Soc.*, **88**, 3511 (1966).
49. Claassen, H. H., and B. Weinstock, *J. Chem. Phys.*, **33**, 436 (1960).
49a. Clark, R. J. H., and C. S. Williams, *Inorg. Chem.*, **4**, 350 (1965).
49b. Cleare, M. J., and W. P. Griffith, *J. Chem. Soc.*, *in press*.
50. Coffey, R. S., *Tetrahedron Letters*, **1965**, 3809.
50a. Collman, J. P., and W. R. Roper, *J. Am. Chem. Soc.*, **88**, 180 (1966).
50b. Collmann, J. P., and J. W. Kang, *J. Am. Chem. Soc.*, **88**, 3459 (1966).
50c. Collmann, J. P., F. D. Vastine and W. R. Roper, *J. Am. Chem. Soc.*, **88**, 5035 (1966).
50d. Colman, J. P., M. Kubota, J. Y. Sun and F. Vastine, *J. Am. Chem. Soc.*, **89**, 169 (1967).
51. Cooke, A. H., R. Lazenby, F. R. McKim, J. Owen and W. P. Wolf, *Proc. Roy. Soc.* (*London*), *Ser. A*, **250**, 97 (1959).
52. Cotton, F. A., R. O. Whipple and G. Wilkinson, *J. Am. Chem. Soc.*, **75**, 3586 (1953).
52a. Cramer, R., and G. W. Parshall, *J. Am. Chem. Soc.*, **87**, 1392 (1965).
53. Delepine, M., *Compt. Rend.*, **158**, 264 (1914).
54. Delepine, M., *Ann. Chim.*, **7**, 277 (1917).
55. Delepine, M., *Compt. Rend.*, **148**, 557 (1909).
56. Delepine, M., *Bull. Soc. Chim. France*, **21** (4), 157 (1917).
57. Delepine, M., *Bull. Soc. Chim. France*, **29**, (4) 656 (1921).
58. Delepine, M., *Ann. Chim.* (*Paris*), **19** (9), 145 (1923).
59. Delepine, M., *Bull. Soc. Chim. France*, **1** (5), 1256 (1934).
60. Delepine, M., *Bull. Soc. Chim. France*, **5** (4), 364 (1909); *Compt. Rend.*, **148**, 557 (1909).
61. Delepine, M., *Compt. Rend.*, **151**, 878 (1910).
62. Delepine, M., *Compt. Rend.*, **142**, 1525 (1906).
63. Delepine, M., and J. Pineau, *Bull. Soc. Chim. France*, **45**, 228 (1929).
64. Delepine, M., *Z. Physik Chem.* (*Frankfurt*), **130**, 227 (1927).
65. Delepine, M., *Ann. Chim.* (*Paris*), **19** (9), 26, 176 (1923).
66. Delepine, M., *Compt. Rend.*, **152**, 1589 (1911).
66a. Delepine, M., *Compt. Rend.*, **251**, 2633 (1960).

67. Delepine, M., *Compt. Rend.*, **200**, 1373 (1935); *Ann. Chim.* (*Paris*), **4** (11), 292 (1935).
68. Delepine, M., in *Pascal, Traité de Chimie Minerale, Paris,* **19**, 538 (1958).
68a. Delepine, M., and F. Larèze, *Compt. Rend.*, **262**, 822 (1966).
69. Delepine, M., *Ann. Chim.* (*Paris*), **7** (9), 283 (1917).
70. Delepine, M., and F. Larèze, *Compt. Rend.*, **257**, 3772 (1963).
70a. Delepine, M., *Ann. Chim.* (*Paris*), **1959**, 1115, 1131.
70b. Delepine, M., and F. Larèze, *Compt. Rend.*, **263C**, 141 (1966).
71. Delepine-Tard, M., *Ann. Chim.* (*Paris*), **4** (11), 282, 292 (1935).
72. Delepine-Tard, M., *Compt. Rend.*, **200**, 1477 (1935).
73. Desideri, P., and F. Pantani, *Ric. Sci. Rend., Ser. A*, **1**, 265 (1961).
74. Dixon, B. E., *J. Chem. Soc.*, **1934**, 34.
75. Duffour, A., *Compt. Rend.*, **155**, 222 (1912).
76. Duffour, A., *Ann. Chim. Phys.*, **30**, 169, 433 (1913).
77. Duffour, A., *Compt. Rend.*, **152**, 1596 (1911).
78. Duffour, A., *Procès-verbal Soc. Sci. Phys. Nat. Bordeaux*, **139** (1908/9).
79. Dunlop, J. H., R. D. Gillard and G. Wilkinson, *J. Chem. Soc.*, **1964**, 3160.
80. Dwyer, F. P., and A. M. Sargeson, *J. Am. Chem. Soc.*, **75**, 984 (1953).
80a. Dwyer, F. P., and E. C. Gyarfas, *J. Proc. Roy. Soc. N. S. Wales*, **84**, 122 (1950).
81. Dwyer, F. P., and R. S. Nyholm, *J. Proc. Roy. Soc. N. S. Wales*, **79**, 121 (1945); **77**, 116 (1943).
82. Earnshaw, A., B. N. Figgis, J. Lewis and R. D. Peacock, *J. Chem. Soc.*, **1961**, 3132.
83. Emich, F., *Monatsh.*, **29**, 1077 (1908).
84. Englman, R., *Mol. Phys.*, **6**, 345 (1963).
85. Evans, D. F., D. Jones and G. Wilkinson, *J. Chem. Soc.*, **1964**, 3164.
86. von Fellenberg, L. R., *Ann.*, **24**, 207 (1838).
87. Fergusson, J. E., J. D. Karran and S. Seevaratnam, *J. Chem. Soc.*, **1965**, 2627.
88. Ferrari, A., and C. Colla, *Gazz. Chim. Ital.*, **63**, 507 (1933).
89. Figgis, B. N., J. Lewis and F. E. Mabbs, *J. Chem. Soc.*, **1961**, 3138.
90. Figgis, B. N., and G. B. Robertson, *Nature*, **205**, 694 (1965).
91. Fischer, E. O., and U. Zahn, *Ber.*, **92**, 1924 (1959).
91a. Fischer, E. O., and H. Wawersik, *J. Organomet. Chem.*, **5**, 559 (1966).
92. Fischer, E. O., and K. S. Brenner, *Z. Naturforsch., Ser. B*, **17B**, 774 (1962).
92a. Fleischer, E. B., and N. Sadasivan, *Chem. Commun.*, **1967**, 159.
92b. Fritz, H. P., and C. G. Kreiter, *J. Organomet. Chem.*, **4**, 198 (1965).
93. Fritzmann, E. K., and W. Krinitskii, *J. Appl. Chem. USSR, Eng. Transl.*, **11**, 1610 (1938).
93a. Gans, P., A. Sabatini and L. Sacconi, *Inorg. Chem.*, **5**, 1877 (1966).
94. Geisenheimer, G., *Ann. Chim. Phys.*, **23**, 231 (1891).
95. Geisenheimer, G., *Compt. Rend.*, **110**, 1004, 1336; **111**, 40 (1890).
96. Ghosh, S. P., and A. I. P. Ghosh, *J. Inorg. Nucl. Chem.*, **26**, 1703 (1964); *J. Ind. Chem. Soc.*, **41**, 330 (1964).
97. Gialdini, C., *Gazz. Chim. Ital.*, **38**, 485 (1908).
98. Gillard, R. D., *J. Chem. Soc.*, **1963**, 2092.

99. Ginzburg, S. I., M. I. Yuz'ko and L. G. Sal'skaya, *Russ. J. Inorg. Chem., Eng. Transl.*, **8**, 429 (1963).
100. Ginzburg, S. L., and M. I. Yuz'ko, *Russ. J. Inorg. Chem., Eng. Transl.*, **10**, 444 (1965).
101. Goldschmidt, W. M., T. Barth, D. Holmsen, G. Lunde and W. Zachariasen, *Skrifter Norke Videnskaps-Akad. Oslo I Mat-Natur Kl.*, **1926**, 77.
102. Goodman, G. L., M. Fred and B. Weinstock, *Proc. Intern. Symp. Mol. Struct. Spect.* (*Tokio*), **1962**, B-102.
103. Gordon, B. M., L. L. Williams and N. Sutin, *J. Am. Chem. Soc.*, **83**, 2061 (1961).
104. Green, M. L. H., *Angew. Chem.*, **72**, 719 (1960).
105. Griffith, W. P., unpublished work.
106. Griffith, W. P., *J. Chem. Soc., Ser. A*, **1966**, 899.
107. Griffith, W. P., and G. Wilkinson, unpublished work.
108. Griffiths, J. H. E., J. Owen and I. M. Ward, *Proc. Roy. Soc.* (*London*), *Ser. A*, **219**, 526 (1953).
109. Griffiths, J. H. E., J. Owen, J. G. Park and M. F. Partridge, *Proc. Roy. Soc.* (*London*), *Ser. A*, **250**, 84 (1959).
110. Grinberg, A. A., L. V. Vrublevskaya, Kh. I. Gil'dengershel' and A. I. Stetsenko, *Russ. J. Inorg. Chem., Eng. Transl.*, **4**, 462 (1959).
111. Gutbier, A., and D. Hoyermann, *Z. Anorg. Allgem. Chem.*, **89**, 340 (1914).
112. Guthrie, A. N., and L. T. Bourland, *Phys. Rev.*, **37**, 306 (1931).
112a. Haas, T. E., and E. P. Marram, *J. Chem. Phys.*, **43**, 3985 (1965).
112b. Haddad, Y. M. Y., H. B. Henbest, J. Husbands and T. R. B. Mitchell, *Proc. Chem. Soc.* (*London*), **1964**, 361.
113. Halpern, J., R. J. Legare and R. Lumry, *J. Am. Chem. Soc.*, **85**, 680 (1963).
114. Harris, C. M., and E. D. McKenzie, *J. Inorg. Nucl. Chem.*, **25**, 171 (1963).
114a. Harris, E. A., and J. Owen, *Proc. Roy. Soc.* (*London*), *Ser. A*, **289**, 122 (1965).
115. Heck, R. F., *J. Am. Chem. Soc.*, **86**, 2796 (1964).
116. Hepworth, M. A., P. L. Robinson and G. J. Westland, *J. Chem. Soc.*, **1954**, 4269.
117. Hepworth, M. A., P. L. Robinson and G. J. Westland, *Chem. Ind.* (*London*), **1955**, 1516.
118. Hepworth, M. A., P. L. Robinson and G. J. Westland, *J. Chem. Soc.*, **1958**, 611.
119. Hepworth, M. A., K. H. Jack, R. D. Peacock and G. J. Westland, *Acta Cryst.*, **10**, 63 (1957).
120. Hepworth, M. A., P. L. Robinson and G. J. Westland, *J. Chem. Soc.*, **1964**, 4269.
120a. Herbelm, F., J. D. Herbelm, J-P. Mathieu and H. Poulet, *Spectrochim. Acta*, **22**, 1515 (1966).
121. Hieber, W., H. Lagally and A. Mayr, *Z. Anorg. Allgem. Chem.*, **246**, 138 (1941).
122. Hieber, W., and H. Lagally, *Z. Anorg. Allgem. Chem.*, **245**, 321 (1940).
122a. Hieber, W., and F. Volker, *Ber.*, **99**, 2607 (1966); Jarvis, J. A. J., R. H. B. Mais, P. G. Owston and K. A. Taylor, *Chem. Commun.*, **1966**, 906.
122b. Hieber, W., and F. Volker, *Ber.*, **99**, 2614 (1966); Hieber, W., and R. Kummer, *Ber.*, **100**, 148 (1967).

123. Hofmann, K. A., and W. O. Rabe, *Z. Anorg. Allgem. Chem.*, **14**, 293 (1897).
124. Hofmann, K. A., and F. Höchtlen, *Ber.*, **37**, 245 (1904).
125. Howarth, O. W., R. E. Richards and L. M. Venanzi, *J. Chem. Soc.*, **1964**, 3335.
125a. Hulliger, F., *Nature*, **204**, 644 (1964).
126. Hurwitz, P., and K. Kustin, *Inorg. Chem.*, **3**, 823 (1964).
126a. Hurwitz, P., and K. Kustin, *Trans. Faraday Soc.*, **62**, 427 (1966).
127. Imyanitov, N. S. and D. M. Rudkovskii, *J. Gen. Chem. USSR, Eng. Transl.*, **33**, 1041 (1963).
128. Imyanitov, N. S., and D. M. Rudkovskii, *Neftekhimiya*, **3**, 198 (1963).
128a. Inamura, M., *Bull. Soc. Chim. France*, **7** (5), 750 (1940).
129. Ito, K., D. Nakamura, K. Ito and M. Kubo, *Inorg. Chem.*, **2**, 690 (1963).
130. Jaeger, F. M., and L. Bijkerk, *Z. Anorg. Allgem. Chem.*, **233**, 139 (1937).
130a. Jenkins, J. M., and B. L. Shaw, *J. Chem. Soc.*, **1966**, 1407.
130b. Jenkins, J. M., and B. L. Shaw, *J. Chem. Soc.*, **1965**, 6789.
131. Joly, A., *Compt. Rend.*, **110**, 1131 (1890).
132. Joly, A., and E. Leidie, *Compt. Rend.*, **120**, 1341 (1895).
133. Jones, L. H., *J. Chem. Phys.*, **41**, 856 (1964).
134. Jorgensen, C. K., *Mol. Phys.*, **4**, 235 (1961).
135. Jorgensen, C. K., *Mol. Phys.*, **2**, 309 (1959).
136. Jorgensen, C. K., *J. Inorg. Nucl. Chem.*, **24**, 1587 (1962).
137. Jorgensen, C. K., *Acta Chem. Scand.*, **13**, 196 (1959).
138. Jorgensen, C. K., and L. E. Orgel, *Mol. Phys.*, **4**, 215 (1961).
139. Jorgensen, C. K., *Acta Chem. Scand.*, **10**, 500 (1956).
140. Jorgensen, C. K., *J. Inorg. Nucl. Chem.*, **24**, 1571 (1962).
141. Jorgensen, C. K., *Mol. Phys.*, **5**, 485 (1962).
142. Jorgensen, C. K., *Acta Chem. Scand.*, **11**, 151 (1957).
143. Jorgensen, C. K., *Acta Chem. Scand.*, **11**, 166 (1957).
143a. Judd, B. R., *Proc. Roy. Soc. (London), Ser. A*, **250**, 110 (1959).
144. Kauffmann, G. B., *Inorg. Syn.*, **7**, 220 (1963).
145. Kauffmann, G. B., *Inorg. Syn.*, **7**, 224 (1963).
145a. Kauffmann, G. B., and L. A. Teter, *Inorg. Syn.*, **8**, 223 (1966).
146. Kauffmann, G. B., *Inorg. Syn.*, **7**, 228 (1963).
147. Kauffmann, G. B., J. H. Tsai, R. C. Fay and C. K. Jorgensen, *Inorg. Chem.*, **2**, 1233 (1963).
147a. Kharitonov, Y. Y., G. Y. Majo and Z. N. Novozhenyuk, *Izv. Akad. Nauk SSSR*, **1966**, 1114.
148. Keen, I. M., *Platinum Metals Rev.*, **8**, 143 (1964).
149. Keller, R. N., *Chem. Rev.*, **28**, 229 (1941).
150. Kemitt, R. D. W., D. R. Russell and D. W. A. Sharp, *J. Chem. Soc.*, **1963**, 4408.
151. König, E., and H. L. Schafer, *Z. Physik Chem. (Frankfurt)*, **26**, 371 (1960).
152. Krauss, F., and H. Gerlach, *Z. Anorg. Allgem. Chem.*, **147**, 268, 277 (1925).
153. Krauss, F., and H. Gerlach, *Z. Anorg. Allgem. Chem.*, **143**, 125 (1925).
153a. Krauzmann, *Compt. Rend., Ser. B*, **262**, 765 (1966).
154. Kravtsov, V. I., and G. M. Petrova, *Dokl. Phys. Chem.*, **154**, 64 (1964).
155. Kravtsov, V. I., and G. M. Petrova, *Russ. J. Inorg. Chem.*, **9**, 552 (1964).
155a. Kruck, T., A. Engelmann and W. Lang, *Ber.*, **99**, 2473 (1966); Kruck, Th., and W. Lang, *Angew. Chem.*, **4**, 871 (1965); **6**, 53 (1967).

155b. Kulasingham, G. C., and W. R. McWhinnie, *J. Chem. Soc.*, **1965**, 7145.
156. Lamb, A. B., and A. T. Fairhall, *J. Am. Chem. Soc.*, **45**, 378 (1923).
157. LaPlaca, S. J., and J. A. Ibers, *J. Am. Chem. Soc.*, **85**, 3501 (1963).
157a. LaPlaca, S. J., and J. A. Ibers, *Inorg. Chem.*, **5**, 405 (1966).
158. LaPlaca, S. J., and J. A. Ibers, *J. Am. Chem. Soc.*, **87**, 2581 (1965).
159. Larèze, F., *Compt. Rend.*, **256**, 2396 (1963).
159a. Larèze, F., *Compt. Rend.*, **261**, 3421 (1965).
160. Lassaigne, *J. Chim. Medicale*, **1**, (2) 17 (1835).
161. Lecoq de Boisbaudran, *Compt. Rend.*, **96**, 1336, 1406, 1551 (1883).
162. Lebedinskii, V. V., and M. M. Gurin, *Compt. Rend. Acad. URSS*, **36**, 22 (1942).
163. Lebedinskii, V. V., and M. M. Gurin, *Compt. Rend. Acad. URSS*, **33**, 241 (1941).
164. Lebedinskii, V. V., and Z. M. Novozhenyuk, *Russ. J. Inorg. Chem.*, **3** (2), 62 (1958).
165. Lebedinskii, W. W., E. S. Schapiro and I. P. Kassaltkina, *Izvest. Inst. Izuc. Plat.*, **12**, 101 (1935).
165a. Lebedinskii, V. V., and I. A. Fedorov, *Inst. Izuc. Plat.*, **18**, 23 (1945).
166. Lebedinskii, W. W., and W. S. Volkov, *Izvest. Inst. Izuc. Plat.*, **12**, 79 (1935).
167. Lebedinskii, W. W., and N. A. Baliskaya, *Izvest. Inst. Izuc. Plat.*, **15**, 13 (1938) (C.A. **1930**, 3515).
168. Lebedinskii, W. W., and I. A. Fedorov, *Izvest. Inst. Izuc. Plat.*, **12**, 87 (1935).
169. Lebedinskii, V. V., and P. V. Simanovskii, *Izvest. Inst. Izuc. Plat.*, **16**, 53 (1939).
170. Lewis, J., R. S. Nyholm and G. A. Rodley, *J. Chem. Soc.*, **1965**, 1483.
171. Lohr, L. L., and W. N. Lipscomb, *Inorg. Chem.*, **3**, 22 (1964).
172. Lunde, G., *Z. Anorg. Allgem. Chem.*, **163**, 350 (1927).
173. Lynds, L., *Spectrochim. Acta*, **20**, 1369 (1964).
174. McCaffery, A. J., S. F. Mason and R. E. Ballard, *J. Chem. Soc.*, **1965**, 2883.
174a. McDonald, C. G., and J. S. Shannon, *Australian J. Chem.*, **19**, 1545 (1966).
175. McDonald, J. E., and J. W. Cobble, *J. Phys. Chem.*, **66**, 791 (1962).
176. Malatesta, L., see reference 202, p. 10.
177. Malatesta, L., and M. Angoletta, *Angew. Chem.*, **2**, 155 (1963).
178. Malatesta, L., M. Angoletta and G. Caglio, *Angew. Chem.*, **2**, 739 (1963).
179. Malatesta, L., L. Naldini and F. Cariati, *J. Chem. Soc.*, **1964**, 961.
180. Malatesta, L., and F. Canziani, *J. Inorg. Nucl. Chem.*, **19**, 81 (1961).
181. Malatesta, L., *U.S. Dept. Com.*, *Tech. Service RD 262*, 065, p. 10 (1961).
182. Malatesta, L., and S. Sandroni, *Chem. Soc. Spec. Publ.*, **13**, 122 (1959).
182a. Malatesta, L., G. Caglio and M. Angoletta, *J. Chem. Soc.*, **1965**, 6974.
183. Manchot, W., and H. Gall, *Ber.*, **58**, 232 (1925).
183a. Mango, F. D., and I. Dvoretsky, *J. Am. Chem. Soc.*, **88**, 1654 (1966).
183b. Mann, F. G., and H. R. Watson, *J. Chem. Soc.*, **1958**, 2772.
184. Marino, L., *Gazz. Chim. Ital.*, **32**, 511 (1902); *Z. Anorg. Allgem. Chem.*, **42**, 213 (1904).
185. Martin, B., and G. M. Waind, *J. Chem. Soc.*, **1958**, 4284.

186. Martin, B., W. R. McWhinnie and G. M. Waind, *J. Inorg. Nucl. Chem.*, **23**, 207 (1961).
187. Martinez, M. E., see reference 195.
188. Martius, C. A., *Ann.*, **117**, 369 (1861).
189. Mathieu, J-P., *Vict. Henri Mem. Vol., Desoer, Liege 1947.*
190. Mathieu, J-P., *J. Chim. Phys.*, **33**, 78 (1936).
191. Mathieu, J-P., and S. Cornevin, *J. Chim. Phys.*, **36**, 271 (1939).
192. Mathieu, J-P., *Compt. Rend.*, **253**, 2232 (1961).
193. Mathieu, J-P., *J. Phys. Radium*, **8**, 169 (1937).
194. Mattraw, H. C., N. J. Hawkins, D. R. Carpenter and W. W. Sabol, *J. Chem. Phys.*, **23**, 985 (1955).
195. Miano, R. R., and C. S. Garner, *Inorg. Chem.*, **4**, 337 (1965).
195a. Michelotti, F. W., and W. P. Keaveney, *J. Polymer Sci., Ser. A*, **3**, 895 (1965).
196. Miolati, A., and C. Gialdini, *Gazz. Chim. Ital.*, **32**, 513 (1902).
197. Moffitt, W., G. L. Goodman, M. Fred and B. Weinstock, *Mol. Phys.*, 2, 109 (1959).
198. Monacelli, F., F. Basolo and R. G. Pearson, *J. Inorg. Nucl. Chem.*, **24**, 1241 (1962).
198a. Morgan, G., and F. H. Burstall, *J. Chem. Soc.*, **1937**, 1649.
199. Muraveiskaya, G. S., I. I. Chernyaev and V. F. Sorokina, *Russ. J. Inorg. Chem., Eng. Transl.*, **8**, 434 (1963).
200. Murmann, R. K., and H. Taube, *J. Am. Chem. Soc.*, **78**, 4886 (1956).
201. Nagami, S., *J. Chem. Soc. Japan*, **48**, 501 (1927), (cf. Gmelin, *Iridium*, **67**, 65 (1939)).
202. Naldini, L., *U.S. Dept. Com., Office Tech. Serv. AD 262*, 065, 18 (1961).
203. Nicholson, J. K., and B. L. Shaw, *Tetrahedron Letters*, **1965**, 3533.
204. Noack, K., Abstra., *8th Eur. Congress on Molec. Spectr., Copenhagen*, p. 240 (1965).
205. Norman, J. H., H. G. Staley, and W. E. Bell, *J. Chem. Phys.*, **42**, 1123 (1965).
206. Norman, V., and J. C. Morrow, *J. Phys. Chem.*, **31**, 455 (1959).
207. Nyholm, R. S., and K. Vrieze, *J. Chem. Soc.*, **1965**, 5337.
207a. Nyholm, R. S., *Congress on Catalysis* (*Amsterdam*), **1**, 74 (1965).
208. Ogawa, E., *J. Chem. Soc. Japan*, **50**, 239 (1929).
209. Ogawa, E., *J. Chem. Soc. Japan*, **51**, 1 (1930).
210. Oliff, R. W., and A. L. Odell, *J. Chem. Soc.*, **1964**, 2467.
211. Oppler, Th., *Dissert. Gottingen*, 25 (1857), (cf. Gmelin, *Iridium*, **67**, 106, 119 (1939)).
212. Orgel, L. E., *Nature*, **187**, 505 (1960).
212a. Osborn, J. A., F. H. Jardine, J. F. Young and G. Wilkinson, *J. Chem. Soc.*, **1966**, 1711.
213. Owen, J., and J. H. E. Griffiths, *Proc. Roy. Soc.* (*London*), *Ser. A*, **226**, 96 (1954).
214. Owen, J., *J. Phys. Radium*, **20**, 138 (1959).
214a. Page, J. A., *Talanta*, **9**, 365 (1962).
215. Palmaer, W., *Z. Anorg. Allgem. Chem.*, **10**, 320 (1895).
216. Palmer, J. W., and F. Basolo, *J. Inorg. Nucl. Chem.*, **15**, 279 (1960).
216a. Panattoni, G., L. Sindellari and L. Volponi, *Ric. Sci. Rend., Ser. A*, **8**, 1149 (1965).

217. Parshall, G. W., and F. N. Jones, *J. Am. Chem. Soc.*, **87**, 5356 (1965).
218. Pauling, L., *Proc. Acad. Nat. Acad. Washington*, **15**, 712 (1929).
219. Peacock, R. D., and D. W. A. Sharp, *J. Chem. Soc.*, **1959**, 2762.
220. Peacock, R. D., *J. Chem. Soc.*, **1955**, 3291.
221. Peacock, R. D., *Chem. Ind.* (*London*), **1956**, 1391.
221a. Phillips, M., *Thesis*, London, 1961.
222. Pineau, J., *Thesis*, Paris, 1923, 51 (cf. Gmelin *Iridium*, p. 152); Postollec, M., J-P. Mathieu and H. Poulet, *J. Chim. Phys.*, **60**, 1319 (1963).
222a. Pitwell, L. R., *Nature*, **207**, 1181 (1965).
222b. Porai-Koshits, M. A., S. P. Ionov and Z. M. Novozhenyuk, *J. Struct. Chem. USSR, Eng. transl.*, **6**, 161 (1965).
222c. Porta, P., H. M. Powell, R. J. Mawby and L. M. Venanzi, *J. Chem. Soc., Ser. A*, **1967**, 455.
223. Poulsen, I. A., and C. S. Garner, *J. Am. Chem. Soc.*, **84**, 2032 (1962).
224. Preetz, W., *Angew. Chem.*, **4**, 710 (1965).
225. Pshenitsyn, N. K., S. I. Ginzburg and L. G. Sal'skaya, *Russ. J. Inorg. Chem., Eng. Transl.*, **5**, 399 (1960).
226. Pshenitsyn, N. K., and S. E. Krassikov, *Izvest. Inst. Izuc. Plat.*, **11**, 17 (1933).
227. Pshenitsyn, N. K., and S. E. Krassikov, *Izvest. Inst. Izuc. Plat.*, **14**, 19 (1937).
228. Pshenitsyn, N. K., and S. E. Krassikov, *Izvest. Inst. Izuc. Plat.*, **11**, 15 (1933).
228a. Pshenitsyn, N. K., N. A. Ezerskaya and V. D. Ratnikova, *Russ. J. Inorg. Chem.*, **3**, (8), 99 (1958).
229. Puche, F., *Ann. Chim.*, **9** (11), 273 (1938).
230. Randall, E. W., and D. Shaw, *Mol. Phys.*, **10**, 41 (1965); **11**, 395 (1966).
231. Randall, J. J., and L. Katz, *Acta Cryst.*, **12**, 519 (1959).
232. Ray, P. C., and N. Adhikari, *J. Indian Chem. Soc.*, **9**, 251 (1932); **11**, 517 (1934).
233. Ray, P. C., and N. N. Ghosh, *J. Indian Chem. Soc.*, **13**, 138 (1936).
234. Ray, P. C., N. Adhikari and R. Ghosh, *J. Indian Chem. Soc.*, **10**, 275 (1933).
235. Razunas, V., G. Macur and S. Katz, *J. Chem. Phys.*, **43**, 1010 (1965).
236. Rechnitz, G. A., and J. E. McClure, *Analyt. Chem.*, **36**, 2265 (1964).
237. Rimbach, E., and F. Korten, *Z. Anorg. Allgem. Chem.*, **52**, 407 (1907).
237a. Robinson, P. L., and G. J. Westland, *J. Chem. Soc.*, **1956**, 4481.
238. Robinson, S. D., and B. L. Shaw, *J. Chem. Soc.*, **1965**, 4997.
239. Rodi, and D. Babel, *Z. Anorg. Allgem. Chem.*, **336**, 17 (1965).
240. Ruff, O., and J. Fischer, *Z. Anorg. Allgem. Chem.*, **138**, 70 (1924).
241. Ruff, O., and J. Fischer, *Z. Anorg. Allgem. Chem.*, **179**, 161 (1929).
241a. Sacco, A., M. Rossi and C. F. Nobile, *Chem. Commun.*, **1966**, 589.
242. Sadtler, *Chem. News*, **24**, 280 (1871).
243. Sadtler, *Bull. Soc. Chim. France*, **17**, 54 (1872).
244. Scavniker, S., and D. Grdenic, *Acta Cryst.*, **8**, 275 (1955).
245. Scheer, J. J., A. E. van Arkel and R. D. Heyding, *Can. J. Chem.*, **33**, 683 (1955).
246. Schlesinger, H. I., and M. W. Tapley, *J. Am. Chem. Soc.*, **46**, 276 (1924).
247. Schmidt, G., *Z. Naturforsch, Ser. A*, **16**, 748 (1961).
248. Schmidt, G. B., *Z. Phys. Chem.*, **41**, 26 (1964).

249. Schmidtke, H. H., *Z. Inorg. Chem.*, **5**, 1682 (1966).
250. Schrauzer, G. N., and K. C. Dewhirst, *J. Am. Chem. Soc.*, **86**, 3265 (1964).
251. Seubert, C., *Ber.*, **11**, 1767 (1878).
252. Sloth, E. N., and C. S. Garner, *J. Am. Chem. Soc.*, **77**, 1440 (1955).
253. Stevens, K. W. H., *Proc. Roy. Soc.* (*London*), *Ser. A*, **219**, 542 (1953).
254. Strecker, W., and M. Schurigin, *Ber.*, **42**, 1767 (1909).
255. Syrokomskii, V. S., and N. N. Proshenkova, *Zhur. Anal. Khim.*, **2**, 247 (1947).
256. Takaki, G. T., and R. T. M. Fraser, *Proc. Chem. Soc.* (*London*), *Ser. A*, **1964**, 116.
256a. Taylor, R. C., J. F. Young and G. Wilkinson, *Inorg. Chem.*, **5**, 20 (1966).
257. Taube, H., *Can. J. Chem.*, **37**, 129 (1959).
258. Taube, H., and H. Myers, *J. Am. Chem. Soc.*, **76**, 2109 (1954).
259. Tchugaev, L., *Ber.*, **56**, 2067 (1923).
259a. Van Loo, G., and J. A. Page, *Can. J. Chem.*, **44**, 515 (1966).
260. Vaska, L., and J. DiLuzio, *J. Am. Chem. Soc.*, **84**, 679 (1962).
261. Vaska, L., and J. W. diLuzio, *J. Am. Chem. Soc.*, **83**, 2784 (1961).
262. Vaska, L., *J. Am. Chem. Soc.*, **83**, 756 (1961).
262a. Vaska, L., *Chem. Commun.*, **1966**, 614.
263. Vaska, L., *Science*, **140**, 809 (1963).
263a. Vaska, L., and S. S. Bath, *J. Am. Chem. Soc.*, **88**, 1333 (1966).
263b. Vaska, L., and D. L. Catone, *J. Am. Chem. Soc.*, **88**, 5324 (1966).
263c. Vaska, L., *J. Am. Chem. Soc.*, **88**, 5325 (1966).
264. Vaska, L., *Inorg. Nucl. Chem. Letters*, **1**, 89 (1965); L. Vaska, and R. E Rhodes, *J. Am. Chem. Soc.*, **87**, 4970 (1965).
265. Watt, G. W., L. E. Sharif and E. P. Helvenston, *Inorg. Chem.*, **1**, 6 (1962).
266. Watt, G. W., and B. J. McCormick, *Inorg. Chem.*, **4**, 143 (1965).
267. Watt, G. W., E. P. Helvenston and L. E. Sharif, *J. Inorg. Nucl. Chem.*, **24**, 1067 (1962).
268. Weinstock, B., and J. G. Malm, *Proc. U.N. Intern. Conf. Peaceful Uses At. Energy, 2nd Geneva*, **28**, 125 (1958).
269. Werner, A., and O. deVries, *Ann.*, **364**, 86, 115 (1909).
270. Werner, A., and A. P. Smirnov, *Helv. Chim. Acta*, **3**, 485, 743 (1920).
271. Westland, G. J., and P. L. Robinson, *J. Chem. Soc.*, **1956**, 4481.
271a. Wilkes, G. W., and L. F. Dahl, quoted in *J. Am. Chem. Soc.*, **88**, 1821 (1966).
272. Winkhaus, G., and H. Singer, *Z. Naturforsch.*, *Ser. B*, **20**, 602 (1965); *Ber.*, **99**, 3610 (1966).
273. Wöhler, L., and S. Streicher, *Ber.*, **46**, 1583, 1721 (1913).
274. Wöhler, L., and W. Witzmann, *Z. Anorg. Allgem. Chem.*, **57**, 340 (1908).
275. Wöhler, L., K. Ewald and H. G. Krall, *Ber.*, **66**, 1638 (1933).
276. Woo, S-C., and D. M. Yost, *J. Am. Chem. Soc.*, **53**, 885 (1931).
277. Young, J. F., R. D. Gillard and G. Wilkinson, *J. Chem. Soc.*, **1964**, 5176.
278. Zingales, F., F. Canziani and U. Sartorelli, *Rend. Ist. Lombardo Sci. Lettere A*, **96**, 77 (1962).

6 RHODIUM

Of the four metals rhodium exhibits the least variety of oxidation states; almost all of its complexes involve either the tri- or monovalent states. This may partly account for the fact that more work has been done on rhodium than on any of the other three metals; the chemistry of osmium, ruthenium and (to a lesser extent) iridium is more complicated because of the greater variety of oxidation states and the consequent possibility of oxidation or reduction taking place during reactions.

In its general chemistry rhodium resembles iridium and ruthenium much more closely than cobalt; however, there are a certain number of similarities between the Group VI and Group V complexes of trivalent rhodium, cobalt and chromium. A major difference between cobalt (III) and rhodium (III) complexes, however, is that the reactions of the former sometimes involve divalent intermediates, while the corresponding reactions of rhodium (III) take different paths, and may sometimes involve hydridic species.

The property of certain phosphine, arsine and stibine complexes of rhodium in catalysing homogeneous hydrogenation and hydroformylation reactions is an interesting and important feature of its chemistry; although some cobalt and other platinum metal species also show such properties, rhodium complexes seem to be among the most active.

Rhodium (VI), (V) and (IV)

These are rare oxidation states for the metal, and are found mainly in the fluorides; iridium, while its hexa- and pentavalent complexes are equally rare, has a fairly extensive chemistry for the tetravalent state.

Rhodium (III)

The trivalent is by far the commonest oxidation state for the metal and many complexes are known with donor atoms from all four groups; almost all rhodium (III) species are octahedral.

Rhodium (II), (I) and (O)

The bivalent state is rare, though less so than with iridium; many cobalt (II) complexes are of course known, but these mostly have high spins, a very uncommon condition for any platinum metal. The monovalent state is found in many complexes involving, for the most part, π-acceptor ligands of Groups V and IV, and rhodium appears to form more species of this type than either cobalt or iridium. Most of them are square planar, and this is of importance in the catalytic reactions which a number of the compounds undergo, since there are coordination sites available above and below the square plane.

Rhodium (O) is found only in the carbonyls, as is normally the case with the zerovalent state of the platinum metals.

GROUP VII DONORS

The fluorine chemistry of rhodium resembles that of ruthenium and iridium. Amost all the rhodium complexes with the other halogens involve the element in its trivalent state, and here also there are considerable similarities of behaviour with ruthenium and iridium (but not with cobalt, which forms no unsubstituted trivalent halo species apart from $[CoF_6]^{3-}$). A peculiarity of rhodium is its formation of polynuclear chloro and bromo species, although these need closer investigation than they have yet received.

The existence of solid di- and monohalides is very doubtful, as with the other three elements.

Rhodium (VI)

Rhodium hexafluoride, RhF_6, is made by direct fluorination of the metal. It is a black solid (m.p. 70°) which exists in two forms, a low-temperature orthorhombic modification and a cubic form[53]. Infrared and Raman spectra have been measured (see Table 3.1, p. 101)[322] and as expected show none of the anomalies which would arise from the presence of a dynamic Jahn–Teller effect (cf. p. 48). The electronic absorption spectrum of the compound has been predicted[172] but not, apparently, measured.

Rhodium (V)

Rhodium pentafluoride, $[RhF_5]_4$, may be made by the action of fluorine on the trifluoride with a fluorine pressure of 6 atmospheres at 400°, and it can also be obtained together with the hexa- and trifluorides when fluorine reacts with rhodium metal. The dark red crystalline solid (m.p. 96°) is isomorphous with the pentafluorides of osmium, ruthenium and iridium ($a = 12{\cdot}28$, $b = 9{\cdot}85$, $c = 5{\cdot}48$ Å) and so the compound may be presumed to be tetrameric. The susceptibility has been measured over the range 77–293°K[156] and the magnetic moment at room temperature is 2·93 BM (Table 6.7).

$Cs[RhF_6]$ is the only fully established salt containing the $[RhF_6]^-$ anion. It can be made from equal parts of rhodium pentafluoride and caesium fluoride in iodine pentafluoride solution; it is a dark red solid, which appears to be isomorphous with $Cs[PtF_6]$[156]. It is possible that the species $Xe[RhF_6]_n$, made from xenon and rhodium hexafluoride, contains $[RhF_6]^-$ ions[20].

Rhodium (IV)

Rhodium tetrafluoride, RhF_4, can be prepared by the action of bromine trifluoride on rhodium tribromide[294]. It is a purple-red solid and has a magnetic moment of 1·1 BM at room temperature[245b]. Complexes between rhodium tetrafluoride and bromine trifluoride[294] and with selenium tetrafluoride have been reported[144].

$K_2[RhF_6]$ can be made by the action of fluorine on $K_2[RhCl_5]$; it forms yellow crystals: a rubidium and a caesium salt were also made. The potassium salt is trigonal (a = 7·53, c = 4·65 Å) as is the rubidium salt (a = 5·90, c = 4·80 Å), while the caesium salt exists in both a trigonal (a = 6·19, c = 5·00 Å) and a hexagonal (a = 6·28, c = 10·11 Å) form. The magnetic susceptibilities of these three salts have been measured at 90, 195 and 295°K (Table 6.7, p. 418)[323]. The metal–fluorine stretching frequency (ν_3) is at 589 cm^{-1} for $K_2[RhF_6]$[256], and the electronic absorption spectrum of solid $Cs_2[RhF_6]$ has been measured from 10,000 to 40,000 cm^{-1} and assignments proposed on the basis of Tanabe–Sugano diagrams[44].

Chemically, the $[RhF_6]^{2-}$ ion is less stable than the iridium, osmium and ruthenium analogues: for tetravalent platinum metal hexafluoro complexes the resistance to hydrolysis follows the order[150]: $[OsF_6]^{2-} \sim [IrF_6]^{2-} > [PtF_6]^{2-} > [RuF_6]^{2-} > [RhF_6]^{2-} > [PdF_6]^{2-}$.

$Na_3[RhF_7]$, made from fluorination of $Na_2[RhCl_6]$, is probably $NaF.Na_2[RhF_6]$[294].

Although there is no evidence for the existence of rhodium tetrachloride or even any rhodium oxychlorides with an oxidation state greater than three, one anionic chloro complex is known.

$Cs_2[RhCl_6]$ can be made by oxidation of an ice-cold solution of $Cs_3[RhCl_6]$ by chlorine gas in the presence of caesium chloride. The salt is green, and is rapidly decomposed by water to $Cs_2[RhCl_5(H_2O)]$ and chlorine. It crystallizes in the face-centred cubic system (side 10·2 Å) and is isomorphous with $(NH_4)_2[PtCl_6]$; from x-ray powder data the rhodium–chlorine distance was estimated to be 2·3 Å[84]. The magnetic susceptibility of the salt was measured over the range 78–297°K (cf. Table 6.7, p. 418), and it was deduced from this that there was probably some degree of superexchange antiferromagnetism as found in $(NH_4)_2[IrCl_6]$. The electron delocalization factor k' was calculated as 0·7, the g value 1·60 and the spin–orbit coupling constant 990 cm^{-1}[99].

Studies on the reflectance electronic spectra of the pure salt and its solid solution in $Cs_2[PtCl_6]$ show that the charge-transfer bands occur at lower frequencies than observed in any other platinum metal complexes, although the spectrum is of the type expected for a spin-paired $4d^5$ octahedron. The influence of covalent bonding on the orbital energies was discussed[173]. Attempts to prepare other salts of $[RhCl_6]^{2-}$ have failed, and Jorgensen has suggested that the stability of the caesium salt arises from its very low solubility[173].

The electron-transfer reaction in the equilibrium

$$[RhCl_6]^{2-} + [Ru\ phen_3]^{2+} \underset{k_2}{\overset{k_1}{\rightleftharpoons}} [RhCl_6]^{3-} + [Ru\ phen_3]^{3+}$$

has been studied by the temperature-jump relaxation method (starting with $[RhCl_6]^{3-}$ and $[Ru\ phen_3]^{3+}$). The lower limit of k_1 was $2{\cdot}5 \times 10^9\ \text{M}^{-1}\ \text{sec}^{-1}$ and that of k_2 $2{\cdot}7 \times 10^8\ \text{M}^{-1}\ \text{sec}^{-1}$[160] (cf. also p. 237).

The existence of rhodium (IV) chloro complexes with furildioxime ligand has been rather implausibly suggested[299a].

Rhodium (III)

Rhodium trifluoride, RhF_3, can be prepared by the action of fluorine on the triiodide at 400°. It is a red substance and has a hexagonally close-packed lattice like iridium and palladium trifluorides. The unit cell dimensions are $a = 5.330 \pm 0{\cdot}001$ Å with $\alpha = 54{\cdot}42 \pm 0{\cdot}01°$, and the rhodium–fluorine(bridge)–rhodium angle was estimated as 132° with a metal–fluorine distance of 1·98 Å[151]. It is a very stable substance, being virtually insoluble in boiling water, mineral acids or concentrated alkalis. A hexahydrate can be got by the prolonged action of hydrofluoric acid on $K_3[Rh(NO_2)_6]$. The hexahydrate is hygroscopic and very soluble in water; on heating the solid to 110° two molecules of water are lost[235]. The aqueous solution is yellow, possibly due to presence of the $[Rh(H_2O)_6]^{3+}$ ion.

Rhodium trichloride, $RhCl_3$, is the most common compound of the metal. It can be prepared in the anhydrous condition by direct chlorination of the metal at 300°, in which case it forms a red crystalline mass which can be sublimed at 800°[140]. This form is insoluble in water, and can also be made from water-soluble forms by heating them in a current of hydrogen chloride to 360° or by heating hexachlororhodates (III) to 440° in chlorine. The trichloride is isostructural with aluminium trichloride; the lattice constants are: $a = 5{\cdot}95 \pm 0{\cdot}01$ Å, $b = 10{\cdot}30 \pm 0{\cdot}02$ Å and $c = 6{\cdot}03 \pm 0{\cdot}01$ Å; $\alpha = 109{\cdot}2 \pm 0{\cdot}2°$ [18].

Thermodynamic data for the tri- and dichlorides have been obtained by studies of the rhodium–chlorine system from 700 to 1500° under chlorine pressures of 0·01–1 atmospheres. The dissociation pressure reaches one atmosphere at 970°, and the species detected in the gas phase were the tri- and dichlorides; the only stable condensed phase is the trichloride [25]. For the reaction

$$Rh(s) + \tfrac{3}{2} Cl_2 \rightarrow RhCl_3(g)$$

$\Delta H^0_{298} = 16 \pm 2$ kcal/mole and $\Delta S^0_{298} = 1{\cdot}8 \pm 2$ e.u.; and for

$$RhCl_3(s) \rightarrow RhCl_3(g)$$

$\Delta H^0_{298} = 84{\cdot}7 \pm 3$ kcal/mole and $\Delta S^0_{298} = 59{\cdot}8 \pm 3$ e.u. [25].

Electronic absorption spectra of anhydrous rhodium trichloride in fused melts of potassium chloride and of potassium nitrate have been measured; under such conditions a number of anionic chloro species were observed [246a].

Water-soluble forms of the trichloride can be got by treating basic rhodium chloride (see below) or rhodium hydroxide with hydrochloric acid [9]. These species are tri- or tetrahydrated, and an anhydrous water-soluble form can be made by heating the hydrates in a stream of hydrogen chloride to 180°. The aqueous solution chemistry of rhodium trichloride is complicated (cf. also p. 325): the brown solution first formed when the trichloride is dissolved in water contains very little free chloride ion, but on boiling the colour becomes yellow and almost all the chlorine present is then as the ion. Concentrated solutions of the trichloride behave somewhat differently and undoubtedly contain polymeric species [25a,182b,235,235a,297,299].

The powerful catalytic properties of the compound are discussed on p. 326; in addition to being a catalyst for olefin isomerization and hydrogenation reactions [276] it will catalyse the polymerization of butadiene [182a,277,305a], organic chlorination reactions [42] and also hydroformylation reactions [149a]. Chemical reactions of the hydrated form of rhodium trichloride are summarized in Figure 6.1.

Rhodium tribromide, $RhBr_3$, can be made (though with some difficulty) in the anhydrous state from the elements at 300°, although it appears that the product has not been fully characterized [140]: it is red-brown and insoluble in water. A water-soluble dihydrate can be got by treating rhodium metal with a mixture of bromine and hydrochloric acid, which gives dark red crystals of the compound [128].

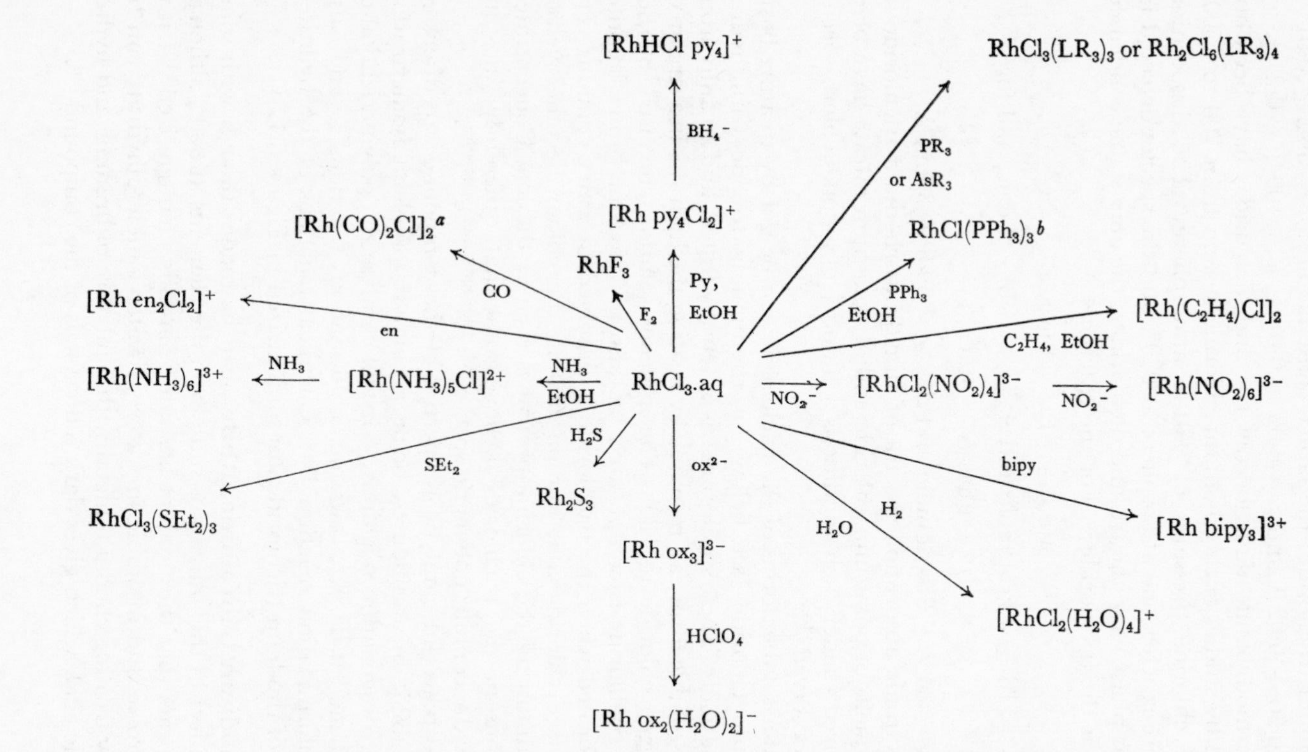

Figure 6.1 Reactions of rhodium trichloride [a] cf. p. 387; [b] cf. p. 366

Rhodium triiodide, RhI_3, apparently exists only in the anhydrous form, and can be made by the action of a solution of potassium iodide on the tribromide[128].

Oxy and hydroxy halides. 'Basic rhodium chloride', of unknown formula, can be made by the action of hydrochloric acid on hydrated rhodium (III) oxide[136], or by prolonged heating of $Na_3[RhCl_6]$ with concentrated sulphuric acid[75]. By analogy with $Ir(OH)_2Cl$ and $Rh(OH)_2Br$ it is probably best formulated as $Rh(OH)_2Cl$.aq. **$Rh(OH)_2F$** can be made by heating $K_3[RhF_6]$ with hydrofluoric acid[257].

$Rh(OH)_2Br.2H_2O$ is formed as a yellow precipitate when a solution of rhodium tribromide is treated with potassium hydroxide[128].

The halorhodates (III). **$K_3[RhF_6]$** is best made by fusion of potassium hexanitrorhodate (III) with potassium hydrogen difluoride. At 300° the compound $KHF_2.K_3[RhF_6]$ is formed, and if this is heated to 500° for a long time the pure compound $K_3[RhF_6]$ is obtained as a buff-coloured solid[257] which is insoluble in water and is unaffected by it. The electronic absorption spectrum of the solid has been measured and assignments proposed[287].

$K_2[RhF_5]$ is got by repeated fusion of $K_3[RhF_6]$ with potassium hydrogen difluoride[257]. The compound is insoluble in water, and is likely to have a polymeric structure like the other halo complexes of the form $[MCl_5]_2^{4-}$, which have already been discussed (p. 139).

$K_3[RhCl_6]$ can be made by warming a solution of $K_2[RhCl_5(H_2O)]$ (see p. 328) with potassium chloride, or from the sesquioxide and concentrated potassium chloride solution. It forms red crystals, and sodium, ammonium and barium salts have also been prepared[75,183a]. A method for the preparation of $[RhCl_6]^{3-}$ salts in high yield has been given recently, in which chlorine is passed over a heated mixture of the metal and alkali metal chloride, and the hexachloro complex extracted with water[183]. There is some evidence that $[RhCl_6]^{3-}$ dissolved in hydrochloric acid or in water polymerizes to other chloro or chlorohydroxy species[192a,206a]. The infrared spectrum of the caesium salt has a band at 306 cm^{-1} ascribed to ν_3[151a], and incomplete Raman spectra have been measured of the aqueous solution (Table 3.3, p. 103)[191a].

The decomposition equilibrium

$$2\,Na_3[RhCl_6] \rightleftharpoons 2\,Rh + 6\,NaCl + 3\,Cl_2$$

has been studied from 676 to 993°[271]. Polarographic reduction of $[RhCl_6]^{3-}$ and of rhodium (III) chloro-aquo species have been interpreted to indicate that there is a reversible three-electron reduction step[68], but more recent studies suggest that in fact only two electrons are involved[112] so that the reduction product may be a rhodium (I) species or a rhodium (III) hydridochloro complex (see also p. 326). Electronic absorption spectra of $[RhCl_6]^{3-}$ have been measured[174] and band assignments proposed[94,174].

The kinetics of the aquation of $[RhCl_6]^{3-}$ and of the water replacement of $[RhCl_5(H_2O)]^{2-}$ have been studied by spectrophotometric and isotopic tracer techniques in perchloric–hydrochloric acid media:

$$[RhCl_6]^{3-} + H_2O \underset{k_2}{\overset{k_1}{\rightleftharpoons}} [RhCl_5(H_2O)]^{2-} + Cl^-$$

Both processes are described by the rate law

$$-\,d[RhCl_6{}^{3-}]/dt = k_1[RhCl_6{}^{3-}] - k_2[RhCl_5H_2O^{2-}][Cl^-]$$

At 25°, $k_1 = 0{\cdot}11$ min^{-1} and $k_2 = 0{\cdot}013$ min^{-1} M^{-1}, and the Arrhenius activation energies are respectively 25 and 17 kcal/mole. The reaction is essentially independent of acid concentration up to 4 M[278] (see also reference 25c). The effect of mercuric ion on the aquation of $[RhCl_6]^{3-}$ has been studied kinetically. The rates are considerably increased, and the formation of an intermediate metal–metal bonded species, $[Hg.RhCl_6]^-$, was proposed to account for this[25a].

The kinetics of the isotopic exchange process

$$[RhCl_6]^{3-} + {}^{36}Cl^- \rightleftharpoons [RhCl_5{}^{36}Cl]^{3-} + {}^{35}Cl^-$$

were studied and it was found that, as is the case for the $[OsCl_6]^{2-}$–Cl^- exchange, they could be accounted for entirely by an aquation mechanism involving $[RhCl_5(H_2O)]^{2-}$ and (to a small extent only) $[RhCl_4(H_2O)_2]^-$[278].

Chemical properties of $[RhCl_6]^{3-}$ are summarized in Figure 6.2.

$K_2[RhCl_5]$ can be made by prolonged heating of $K_2[RhCl_5(H_2O)]$ to 250°[75]. It is slightly soluble in water, in which it slowly reforms the aquo complex. It is probably dimeric with two chloro bridges, like the analogous ruthenium salt (see p. 139).

Polymeric halo complexes

There is evidence, from the electronic spectra of anhydrous rhodium trichloride in alkali metal chloride melts[246a] and from ion-exchange

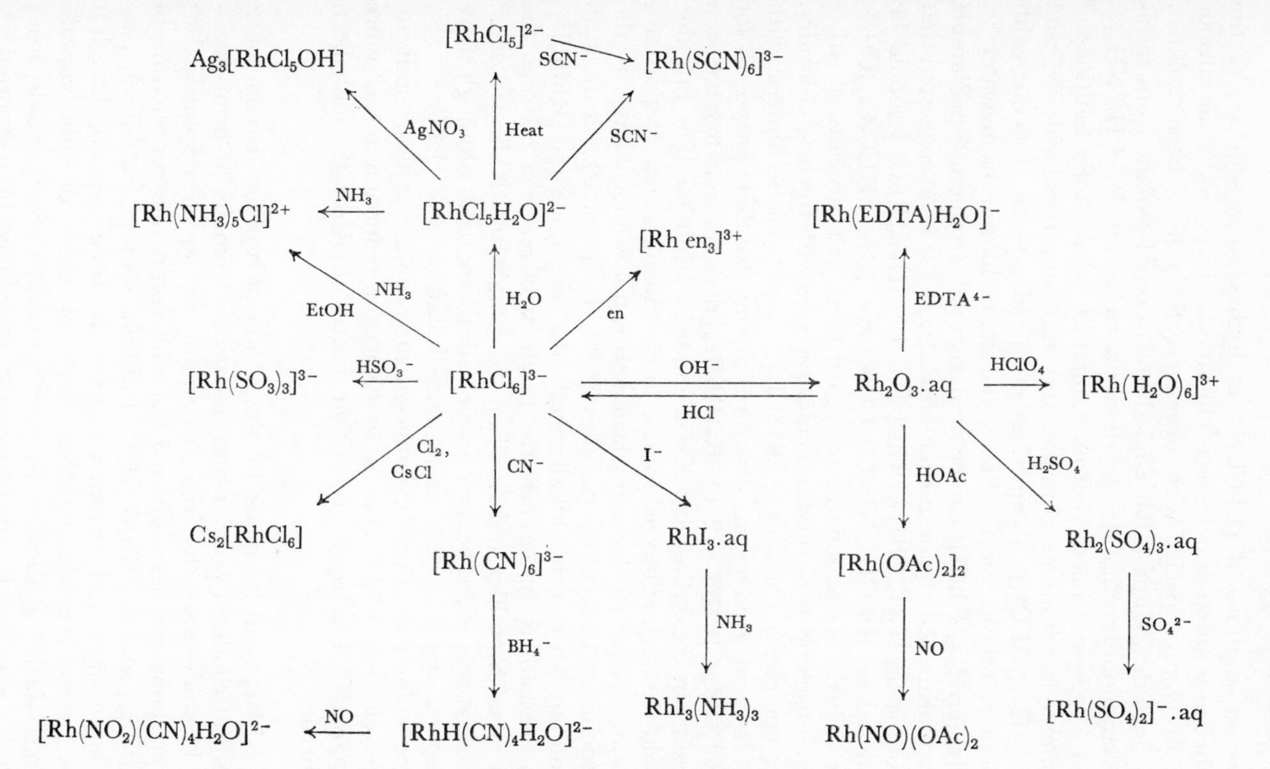

Figure 6.2 Reactions of $[RhCl_6]^{3-}$

studies on solutions of $[RhCl_6]^{3-}$ in hydrochloric acid[192a], of the existence in solution of polymeric chloro complexes, and some curious rhodium chloro species with organic cations have been isolated. These include $\mathbf{(Me_4N)_3[Rh_2Cl_9]}$ (brown crystals) made from tetramethylammonium chloride and rhodium trichloride[141], $\mathbf{(CH_3.NH_3)_2[RhCl_5]}$ (rose-red needles) from a mixture of alcoholic solutions of monomethylammonium chloride and rhodium trichloride[106], and $\mathbf{(CH_3.NH_3)_4[RhCl_7]}$, obtained as deep red crystals (together with rhodium metal) by recrystallizing the pentachloride from water[106]. Finally, $\mathbf{(enH_2)_2[RhCl_7]}$ can be similarly made from ethylenediamine hydrochloride and rhodium trichloride[141]. It has been suggested that the complexes $(CH_3.NH_3)_4[RhCl_7]$ and $(enH_2)_2[RhCl_7]$ should be formulated as $[Rh(CH_3.NH_3Cl)_4Cl_2]Cl$ and $[Rh(enHCl)_2Cl_4]Cl$[141], but it seems more reasonable to regard them as aggregates of either rhodium trichloride or rhodium chloro species with the base chlorides.

The complexes containing $[Rh_2Cl_9]^{3-}$ may well be dimeric with three halogen bridges, a structure similar to that proposed for $[Ru_2Cl_3(PR_3)_6]Cl$ (cf. p. 206). $\mathbf{K_3[RhBr_6]}$ does not seem to have been reported, but the sodium salt can be made by adding sodium bromide to a solution of rhodium tribromide in the stoichiometric proportions. This sodium salt is a dodecahydrate and is not isomorphous with the corresponding hexachloro complex[128,267]. It is remarkable that no ammonium salt or other alkali metal salts containing the $[RhBr_6]^{3-}$ anion are known; apparently the products of reaction between the alkali metal bromides and rhodium tribromide are $[RhBr_5]^{2-}$ salts; the same is true when heavy organic cations are used, although there are reports of pyridinium and guanadinium salts of $[RhBr_6]^{3-}$[267]. Polarographic reductions of rhodium (III) bromo complexes indicate a three-electron step[69], but a two-electron reduction seems more reasonable[112]. Electronic absorption spectra of $[RhBr_6]^{3-}$ have been measured[174].

$\mathbf{K_2[RhBr_5]}$ can be made by the action of bromine vapour on a mixture of rhodium powder and potassium bromide, or from potassium bromide and rhodium tribromide in aqueous solutions[142]; Poulenc, however, has suggested that this compound is a mixture of $K_3[Rh_2Br_9]$ and $K_4[Rh_2Br_{10}]$[267]. Lithium, sodium, rubidium, caesium, ammonium and barium salts have also been claimed, though it is not always certain whether some of these do not contain $[RhBr_5(H_2O)]^{2-}$ as they are frequently hydrated. Salts of anhydrous $[RhBr_5]^{2-}$ with a wide range of organic cations have been reported[234].

$K_3[Rh_2Br_9]$ (red-brown crystals with a green reflex) is made from potassium bromide and rhodium tribromide; caesium and ammonium salts were also made as well as a pyridinium salt[267]. **$K_4[Rh_2Br_{10}]$-$6H_2O$** (deep red octahedra) is made from hydrobromic acid, rhodium tribromide and potassium bromide (this complex is less stable in solution than $K_3[Rh_2Br_9]$, and caesium, ammonium and pyridinium salts were also claimed)[267]. **$K_5[Rh_2Br_{11}].6H_2O$** (deep red crystals, very unstable in solution) is made from the reaction of a large excess of potassium bromide on rhodium tribromide; caesium and ammonium salts were also isolated[267] (these latter salts could be impure forms of the hexabromo species). Salts of **$[RhBr_7]^{4-}$** with organic cations have been got from rhodium trichloride, hydrobromic acid and the organic base[128].

Mixed chlorobromo complexes

Complexes with the following dubious formulae have been claimed: **$K_3[RhCl_{4½}Br_{1½}].H_2O$** (violet; made from rhodium tribromide, potassium chloride and hydrochloric acid) and **$K_5[Rh_2Cl_{1½}Br_{9½}]$-$6H_2O$** (from $K_2[RhCl_5(H_2O)]$ and hydrobromic acid); the first compound is isomorphous with $K_3[RhCl_6].H_2O$ and the second with $K_5[Rh_2Br_{11}].6H_2O$[267].

No rhodium (III) iodo complexes seem to be known apart from **3(enHI).4RhI$_3$**, which can be obtained from rhodium trichloride, ethylenediamine hydriodide and hydriodic acid[234].

It is clear that the rhodium–chloro and rhodium–bromo systems need further investigation.

The rhodium (III) chloro-aquo system

Dissolution of hydrated rhodium trichloride in water gives a red-brown solution from which only part of the chlorine present can be precipitated with silver nitrate, and it is clear that in such solutions there exist species in which the chlorine is coordinated to the metal. By the use of ion-exchange techniques similar to those used to investigate the ruthenium (III)–chloro-aquo system, solutions of rhodium (III) hexaquo perchlorate dissolved in hydrochloric acid were shown to contain $[RhCl(H_2O)_5]^{2+}$, $[RhCl_2(H_2O)_4]^+$, 1,2,3- and 1,2,6-$RhCl_3(H_2O)_3$, $[RhCl_4(H_2O)_2]^-$, $[RhCl_5(H_2O)]^{2-}$, $[RhCl_6]^{3-}$ (the presence of coordinated water molecules is inferred: only the charge and the rhodium : chlorine ratio were determined). Qualitatively the results obtained were similar to those for the analogous ruthenium system (cf. p. 140), but the *cis* and *trans* isomers of

$[RhCl_4(H_2O)_2]^-$ and of $[RhCl_2(H_2O)_4]^+$ could not be distinguished* [331]. The formation constants of the above-mentioned ions were (at 0·6 M and 120°) $k_1 > 10^3$, $k_2 > 10^3$, $k_3 \sim 10^3$, $k_4 = 250 \pm 120$, $k_5 = 28 \pm 8$, $k_6 = 0{\cdot}56 \pm 0{\cdot}18$ [331]. These chloro-aquo species were also separated by high-voltage ionophoresis, and the spectra of the individual species measured from 200 to 600 mμ. Again, the geometrical isomers were not distinguished [32].

The disparity reported by different workers for the number of electrons involved in the irreversible polarographic reduction of rhodium chloro-aquo complexes has been mentioned above; early reports suggested a three-electron process [68] but later work indicates a two-electron reduction [112], while polarography on a solution of rhodium trichloride in perchloric acid also indicated a two-electron irreversible process [318].

As with ruthenium (III) and iridium (III) chloro-aquo systems the substitutional lability of coordinated water groups in $[RhCl_n(H_2O)_{6-n}]^{(3-n)+}$ increases sharply with n: the chief difference between the three systems is the marked decrease in the rate of a given ligand substitution in the sequence: Ru > Rh > Ir [278].

Catalytic activity of rhodium (III) chloro complexes. Solutions of rhodium trichloride in hydrochloric acid will homogeneously activate molecular hydrogen. Hydrogen is absorbed by a solution containing rhodium trichloride, ferric chloride and 3–6 M hydrochloric acid, and the quantity consumed is that necessary to reduce the iron (III) to iron (II). The rate law is

$$-\,d[H_2]/dt = k[H_2][Rh^{III}]$$

At 80° in 3 M hydrochloric acid $k = 0{\cdot}6$ l/M sec; $\Delta H^\ddagger = 24{\cdot}1$ kcal/mole and $\Delta S^\ddagger = 9$ e.u.; these three values are close to those found for the analogous reaction with ruthenium chloro complexes (cf. p. 141). It was suggested that the rate-determining step is the heterolytic splitting of hydrogen with formation of $[HRhCl_5]^{3-}$ which is then reoxidized by ferric ion [147]:

$$[RhCl_6]^{3-} + H_2 \underset{k_2}{\overset{k_1}{\rightleftharpoons}} [HRhCl_5]^{3-} + Cl^- + H^+$$

$$[HRhCl_5]^{3-} + Cl^- + 2\,Fe^{3+} \rightarrow [RhCl_6]^{3-} + H^+ + 2\,Fe^{2+} \text{ (Fast)}$$

It appears that $[RhCl_6]^{3-}$ is the species mainly responsible [166] but

* Recently, however, the *cis* and *trans* isomers of $[RhCl_4(H_2O)_2]^-$ have been isolated by ion-exchange methods [41a].

$[RhCl_5H_2O]^{2-}$ and $[RhCl_4(H_2O)_2]^-$ are also catalytically active. The activity increases with the number of coordinated chloride ions up to six: at 80° neutral and cationic chlororhodates (III) are reduced to the metal by molecular hydrogen whether ferric ion is present or not[166]. (See also the similar ruthenium (III) chloride hydrogenation catalysis, p. 141.)

In neutral aqueous solutions of $RhCl_3$ (which undoubtedly contain polymeric species) the aquation of the chloro complexes is catalysed by molecular hydrogen at room temperature to give the yellow *trans*-$[Rh(H_2O)_4Cl_2]^+$, but there is no net uptake of hydrogen. A hydridic mechanism similar to that for the formation of *trans*-$[Rh\,py_4Cl_2]^+$ has been proposed for this (cf. p. 354)[124]. Ethanolic solutions of rhodium trichloride containing hex-1-ene will take up molecular hydrogen to give n-hexane at room temperatures (a similar result is observed with 1,2,6-$Rh\,py_3Cl_3$ as a catalyst); there is also a catalysed isomerization of hex-1-ene to *trans*-hex-2-ene[124]. Isomerization of 1-hexene to the *cis*-2- and *trans*-2-isomer has been observed with ethanolic solutions of rhodium trichloride, both with and without cocatalysts. The general type of reaction, presumed to proceed *via* a rhodium (III) hydridic intermediate, is envisaged as

$$\begin{array}{lcl} \mid & & \mid & & \\ CH & & CH_2 & & CH_3 \\ \| \;\text{—RhH} & & \mid & & \mid \\ CH & \longrightarrow & CH\text{—}Rh & \longrightarrow & CH \\ \mid & & \mid & & \| \;\text{—RhH} \\ CH_2 & & CH_2 & & CH \\ \mid & & \mid & & \end{array}$$

but the reaction is undoubtedly more complicated than this[48,73a,73b,146,146a]. The isomerization of deuterated vinyl- and allyl-l-olefins by rhodium trichloride has been studied, and it was found that the isomerization was accompanied by a redistribution of deuterium over the allylic system. There was also rapid intramolecular deuterium exchange. A reaction mechanism was proposed involving a rapid and reversible addition of the olefin to a rhodium (III) hydridic species[146a].

Further information on rhodium (III) catalysis of olefin isomerization and polymerization is given below, p. 353, 367, 375, 403.

In aqueous solutions anionic chloro complexes of rhodium (III) are reduced by molecular hydrogen in the presence of maleic acid to form rhodium (I) maleate complexes; however, in dimethylacetamide solutions rhodium trichloride is an effective homogeneous catalyst for the reduction of maleic to succinic acid by hydrogen, the reaction proceeding via a rhodium (I) maleate complex[166].

The dimerization of ethylene is catalysed by rhodium trichloride hydrate in alcoholic solution: a mixture of 1- and 2-butenes is produced, but the initial product is probably 1-butene[7,71]. The trichloride is rapidly converted by the ethylene into $[Rh^{I}Cl_2(C_2H_4)_2]^-$ which is believed to be the active intermediate[73] (see p. 395).

Stereospecific polymerization of butadiene in the presence of aqueous solutions of rhodium trichloride or rhodium nitrate has been interpreted in terms of a free-radical propagation mechanism[28a].

Solid aquo- and hydroxyhalo complexes

A few of these have been isolated and are given below.

$\mathbf{K_2[RhCl_5(H_2O)]}$ can be made by heating a 1:2 mixture of rhodium metal with potassium chloride in a current of chlorine[142], by adding potassium chloride to a solution of $Na_3[RhCl_6].12H_2O$ in water[75], or by recrystallization of $K_3[RhCl_6]$ from water. It forms deep red crystals, and rubidium, caesium and ammonium salts are also known. A hydrated form of the free acid can be made by evaporation of a solution of rhodium trichloride in hydrochloric acid over sulphuric acid[136].

The kinetics of the water replacement reaction for $[RhCl_5H_2O]^{2-}$ have been studied (p. 324)[278] and also the kinetics of the equilibrium[278a]

$$[RhCl_5(H_2O)]^{2-} \rightleftharpoons [RhCl_4(H_2O)_2]^- + H_2O$$

$\mathbf{Ag_3[RhCl_5(OH)]}$ seems to be the only reported hydroxychloro rhodium (III) complex, and can be made by adding silver nitrate to a solution of $(NH_4)_2[RhCl_5(H_2O)]$. It is a deep red powder, insoluble in water[75].

$\mathbf{Cs_2[RhBr_5(H_2O)]}$ is got by addition of caesium bromide to a solution of $(pyH)_3[RhBr_6]$[267]. It forms green crystals, and a lithium salt is also known.

Rhodium (II)

It is said that **rhodium dichloride, $RhCl_2$**, can be made from the elements at 948°, or by heating the trichloride in a current of chlorine to this temperature[327]; thermodynamic data have been obtained for the compound in the gas phase[25]. For

$$Rh(s) + Cl_2 \rightarrow RhCl_2(g)$$

$\Delta H^0_{298} = 30{\cdot}3 \pm 3$ kcal/mole and $\Delta S^0_{298} = 8{\cdot}1 \pm 3$ e.u.[25]. The colour of the dichloride may vary from a coppery red to deep brown, according to the conditions of preparation; like the reported iridium dihalides it is insoluble in water and in acids. A compound **Rh_2Cl_5** was claimed by Berzelius in 1828 from the action of chlorine on the metal, but it seems likely that this was a mixture of the metal and the trichloride. Dwyer and Nyholm prepared a hygroscopic black solid which they believed to be the dichloride by adding hydrochloric acid to 'rhodium (II) hydroxide', prepared by a sodium stannite reduction of sodium rhodite. The black solid reacted quickly with water to give an orange basic compound which, when dissolved in hydrochloric acid, gave a strongly reducing solution[85]. It is quite possible that these species contain coordinated $(SnCl_3)^-$ groups. The dichloride prepared by chlorination of the metal is said to be isomorphous with the iridium, rhodium and platinum dichlorides[255]. It has been rather implausibly suggested that the dichloride has a structure involving a metal cluster, Rh_6Cl_{16}[185].

$RhBr_2$ and **RhI_2** are both claimed to be formed by the action of the appropriate halogen acids on 'rhodium (II) hydroxide'[85].

$(pyH)_6[Rh_2Br_{10}]$ has been reported[86], but later work, however, suggests that this is in fact *trans*-$[Rh\,py_4Br_2]Br$[101].

Rhodium (I)

Chlorination of rhodium above 965° gives the monochloride as a very stable solid, insoluble in water and in acids[327]. It has been suggested, however, that the product was simply a mixture of the metal and the trichloride[25].

The products of the polarographic reduction of rhodium (III) chloro species may, as already mentioned, be rhodium (I) chloro species or rhodium (III) hydrido chlorides[112].

GROUP VI DONORS

No oxy complexes have been characterized. On the whole it appears that rhodium (III) has a somewhat greater affinity for oxygen, and possibly a lesser affinity for sulphur, than has iridium (III).

It is curious that most of the carboxylates of rhodium are formally of the divalent state, but the corresponding iridium (II) species have not been reported.

Rhodium (VI)

No trioxide has been isolated, but there is some evidence for its existence in the gas phase, and an ionization potential of 11·4 ev has been determined for it[244]. Potassium rhodate, presumed to be $\mathbf{K_2[RhO_4]}$, is said to be formed when chlorine is passed into a solution of rhodium dioxide or sesquioxide dissolved in a concentrated solution of potassium hydroxide; the compound forms blue crystals[61]. A blue barium salt has been prepared which appeared to contain hexavalent rhodium and had a magnetic moment corresponding to one unpaired spin per metal atom[47a]. Grube reports the presence of $[RhO_4]^{2-}$ in solutions of rhodium sesquioxide in perchloric acid which have been oxidized anodically or with hypochlorites[137,139] and violet rhodium (VI) species are said to be formed by oxidation of rhodium (III) with hypobromite[253a].

RhS_3, $RhSe_3$ and $RhTe_3$, made by sintering processes, are semiconductors.

Rhodium (V)

Rhodium (V) oxy species such as RhO^{3+}, RhO_2^+ and $[RhO_3]^-$ are said to be present in solutions of rhodium (III) aquo complexes after oxidation of these with hypochlorite[11]. Rhodium (V) may be present in the violet solutions obtained by the action of sodium bismuthate on rhodium sulphate[300b], and blue solutions of rhodium (V) are said to result from similar oxidation with hypobromite[253a].

$\mathbf{Rh_2S_5}$ can be made by heating the water-insoluble form of rhodium trichloride with an excess of sulphur to over 600°. The product is chemically inert and is not attacked by concentrated mineral acids. The dissociation pressure of the compound has been measured from 715 to 830°[182].

Although $\mathbf{Rh_2Se_5}$ and $\mathbf{Rh_2Te_5}$ have been claimed[30], it has been shown that the only tellurides formed in the Rh—Te system are $RhTe_2$ (which exists in two forms), RhTe[109a] and Rh_3Te_2[334a], and the selenide system is probably similar. They are all got by heating rhodium trichloride with the elements to 600° in an atmosphere of carbon dioxide. The compounds are insoluble in most acids but are attacked by aqua regia[30].

Rhodium (IV)

Rhodium dioxide, $\mathbf{RhO_2}$, has not apparently been made in the pure anhydrous state: all attempts at dehydration of RhO_2 hydrates give the sesquioxide, Rh_2O_3. The dihydrate can be made by anodic oxidation of rhodium (III) solutions followed by addition of alkali, or by oxidation of rhodium (III) species with chlorine[328]. The hydrate is green, giving a green solution in alkali and a blue solution in acetic acid. It is possible, however, that the hydrate is a peroxide of rhodium (III) since its oxygen analyses are variable. The existence of gaseous rhodium dioxide at high temperatures has been demonstrated by transpiration methods and an estimate made of its dissociation energy[5,36,241], and additional evidence for its existence has been obtained from mass spectroscopy[243]. The ionization potential of the gaseous species is found to be 10·0 ev by electron-impact measurements[243].

The rhodites (IV)

Like sodium iridite, **Na_2RhO_3** can be made by heating sodium carbonate with the metal in air, and it has been shown that its lattice is of the sodium stannite type[283]. **$Sr_4[RhO_6]$** (no preparative data given) is said to have a triply primitive hexagonal lattice, as have $Sr_4[IrO_6]$ and $Sr_4[PtO_6]$[273]. A number of uncharacterized 'rhodites' such as $Na_2O.8RhO_2$ and $K_2O.6RhO_2$ are said to be formed on heating $Na_3[Rh(NO_2)_6]$ and $K_3[Rh(NO_2)_6]$ to 440° in air[208].

Rhodium disulphide, RhS_2. Although there has been some doubt cast on the existence of the disulphide[182], its preparation by direct union of the elements has been reported and a value of a = 5·574 ± 0·005 Å given for the cell of its pyrites structure[306]. Thermodynamic data have been given for the mono-, sesqui- and disulphides[216]. The ditelluride **$RhTe_2$**, which can be made from the elements, exists in a high-temperature $Cd(OH)_2$-type form and a low temperature pyrites form[109a]. The latter is a superconductor at 1·51°K[109a], and this is also so for RhSSe and $RhSe_2$, made by sintering processes[157a].

Rhodium (III)

Rhodium sesquioxide, Rh_2O_3, is the most stable oxide of rhodium, and can be made in the anhydrous form as a dark grey powder by heating the metal or the trichloride in a stream of oxygen to 600°[211]. It can also be made as a pentahydrate by the action of alkalis on solutions of rhodium trichloride[189]; tri- and monohydrates are also reported. It is said that it is reduced to the metal when fused with potassium cyanide[208], a rather surprising result. It is also supposed to decompose to RhO and Rh_2O on heating[329], but later work suggests that these latter oxides do not exist and that the metal only is obtained[284]. Magnetic susceptibility measurements have been made on the anhydrous oxide over the range 298–623°K and show a slight temperature-independent paramagnetism[143]. The heat of formation of the compound has been determined[329].

Rhodium hydroxide, $Rh(OH)_3$, has been reported (mostly in a series of patent references) as being formed by the addition of alkalis to rhodium trichloride, and the solubility product of $Rh(OH)_3 . aq$ in water has been given as $4{\cdot}8 \times 10^{-23}$ [10,107]. The compound is probably identical with the hydrated sesquioxide.

The rhodites (III)

Oxy complexes of both rhodium (IV) and rhodium (III) are indiscriminately referred to in the literature as 'rhodites'. **MRh_2O_4** (M = Mg, Zn, Cd, Mn, Cu) can be made by heating rhodium with the appropriate carbonate: these have spinel structures (the cupric salt is a tetragonal spinel) and the lattice constants have been determined; **$MRhO_3$** (M = Fe^{III}, Cr^{III}) have ilmenite structures[186]. The MRh_2O_4 compounds become antiferromagnetic at low temperatures[33].

Aquo and hydroxy complexes

The aqueous solution chemistry of trivalent rhodium is very complicated. Hexaaquo rhodium perchlorate (see below) dissolves in water to give a light yellow solution which on boiling turns dark brown, and from this latter solution it is not possible to precipitate the hexaaquo species, $[Rh(H_2O)_6](ClO_4)_3$; since the perchlorate group is unlikely to enter the first coordination sphere of the metal, either hydroxyaquo and/or polynuclear complexes have been formed.

Hexaaquo rhodium (III) perchlorate, $[Rh(H_2O)_6](ClO_4)_3$, ('rhodium perchlorate') can be made in the form of yellow needles by the action of excess perchloric acid on rhodium trichloride (there was evidence for the intermediate formation of a dark red chloro-aquo perchlorate)[12,296]. X-ray powder photographs showed that the solid has a face-centred cubic structure (a = 11·16 ± 0·02 Å) and is isomorphous with $[Co(NH_3)_6](ClO_4)_3$[12]. An aqueous solution of the compound was studied by potentiometric, conductimetric and spectrophotometric methods. Potentiometric studies on the OH^-–$[Rh(H_2O)_6]^{3+}$ system indicated a sequence of reactions such as

$$[Rh(H_2O)_6]^{3+} \xrightarrow{OH^-} [Rh(OH)(H_2O)_5]^{2+} + H_2O$$

$$2\,[Rh(OH)(H_2O)_5]^{2+} \longrightarrow [Rh_2(OH)_2(H_2O)_8]^{4+} \text{ (diol bridged dimer) } + 2\,H_2O$$

$$[Rh_2(OH)_2(H_2O)_8]^{4+} \longrightarrow [Rh_2O_2(H_2O)_8]^{2+} \text{ (dioxo bridged dimer) } + 2H^+$$

although the results were not claimed to be conclusive[107]. Thus the behaviour of rhodium (III) in aqueous solution seems to be similar to that of iron (III). A recent study of the exchange reaction between a freshly prepared solution of rhodium (III) perchlorate and ^{18}O-labelled water using the isotope dilution technique gave a hydration number for the rhodium of 5·9 ± 0·4, thus establishing the presence of the hexaaquo species. The rate of exchange was given by[262]

$$\text{Rate} = k_1[[Rh(H_2O)_6]^{3+}] + \frac{k_2K_a[[Rh(H_2O)_6]^{3+}]}{[H^+]}$$

where k_1 and k_2 are the first-order rate constants for the reactions

$$[Rh(H_2O)_6]^{3+} \underset{k_{-1}}{\overset{k_1}{\rightleftharpoons}} [Rh(H_2O)_5]^{3+} + H_2O$$

and

$$[Rh(H_2O)_5(OH)]^{2+} \underset{k_{-2}}{\overset{k_2}{\rightleftharpoons}} [Rh(H_2O)_4(OH)]^{2+} + H_2O$$

and K_a the first acid dissociation constant ($pK_a = 3{\cdot}3$ at 25°):

$$[Rh(H_2O)_6]^{3+} \rightleftharpoons [Rh(H_2O)_5(OH)]^{2+} + H^+$$

The dependence of the exchange rate on concentration, acidity, temperature and ionic strength was measured[262] and the results compared with those found for the exchange of water with $[Cr(H_2O)_6]^{3+}$[158,159]. Differences in rate (at the same temperature) between the rhodium and chromic complexes were ascribed to mechanistic differences: for the (d_6) rhodium the exchange appears to proceed through a dissociative separation of water from the first coordination sphere, while for the (d_3) chromium some bimolecular 'outer'-sphere ligand participation may be an important factor[262].

The reaction of chloride ion with $[Rh(H_2O)_6]^{3+}$ was studied as a function of temperature, pH and chloride ion concentration. The proposed mechanism involves a rate-determining dissociation followed by a rapid addition of chloride:

$$[Rh(H_2O)_6]^{3+} \rightleftharpoons [Rh(H_2O)_5OH]^{2+} + H^+ \quad K_a$$
$$[Rh(H_2O)_5OH]^{2+} + Cl^- \rightleftharpoons [Rh(H_2O)_5OH]^{2+}Cl^- \quad K_1$$
$$[Rh(H_2O)_5OH]^{2+}Cl^- \rightleftharpoons [Rh(H_2O)_4(OH)Cl]^+ + H_2O \quad k_1$$
$$[Rh(H_2O)_6]^{3+} + Cl^- \rightleftharpoons [Rh(H_2O)_6]^{3+}Cl^- \quad K_2$$
$$[Rh(H_2O)_6]^{3+}Cl^- \rightarrow [Rh(H_2O)_5Cl]^{2+} + H_2O \quad k_2$$
$$[Rh(H_2O)_5Cl]^{2+} + Cl^- \rightarrow [Rh(H_2O)_4Cl_2]^+ + H_2O \quad \text{Fast}$$
$$[Rh(H_2O)_4(OH)Cl]^+ + Cl^- \rightarrow Rh(H_2O)_3(OH)Cl_2 + H_2O \quad \text{Fast}$$

The speed of the last two reactions is ascribed to the *trans* effect of the chloride ligand opposite to water, leading to *trans*-$[Rh(H_2O)_4Cl_2]^+$ or *trans*- $Rh(H_2O)_3(OH)Cl_2$[300a].

The suggestion that $[Rh(OH)_2(H_2O)_4]^+$ was present in solutions of rhodium hydroxide in perchloric acid has been made as a result of titration studies on such solutions[138] but other work did not succeed in identifying this ion as a major constituent of the solutions[12,62,107,295]. There is a review of the various species believed to be present in aqueous rhodium (III) solutions in the presence of perchlorate, nitrate, sulphate, oxalate and chloride ions[297]. Polarographic reduction of the hexaaquo rhodate (III) ion is said to involve a three-electron step[210].

Peroxy complexes

$K_4[Rh_2O_2(CN)_8(H_2O)]$ is considered on p. 372[196].

$RhCl(O_2)(PPh_3)_2 . \frac{1}{2} CH_2Cl_2$ has been got by the action of molecular oxygen on a dichloromethane solution of $RhCl(PPh_3)_3$[16], and **$RhCl(O_2)(AsPh_3)_2$** when the preparation of $RhCl(AsPh_3)_3$ was attempted in the air[216c]. As with the analogous iridium peroxyphosphine complex it is uncertain whether these should be considered as true peroxide complexes or as oxygen adducts with rhodium (I).

Acetylacetone complexes

Rh acac$_3$ can be made from rhodium nitrate and acetylacetone at pH 4 under reflux. The compound forms orange-yellow crystals (m.p. 260°)[87]. Like the iridium complex it is insoluble in water, slightly soluble in alcohol and ether, and very soluble in benzene and chloroform. The trisacetylacetonates of rhodium (III), cobalt (III) and chromium (III) have been resolved by chromatography on a 16 foot column of *d*-lactose hydrate, and the optically active forms were chlorinated, brominated, nitrated and acetylated. In each case the substituted rhodium chelates retained their original optical configurations, suggesting that the chelate rings are not ruptured during such electrophilic substitutions. The optical stability of the 'parent' rhodium complex was particularly marked, while the cobalt complex readily racemized during recrystallization[63,65]. The distribution of Rh $acac_3$ between water and a number of organic solvents was measured and the results interpreted in terms of the hydration of the complex by water[156a]. The mass spectrum of Rh $acac_3$ has been recorded[215a].

Nitration and formylation of Rh $acac_3$, Co $acac_3$ and Cr $acac_3$ have been carried out, and proton magnetic resonance spectra of the products recorded[64]. Tristrifluoroacetylacetonates of rhodium (III) were made from rhodium nitrate and 1,1,1-trifluoro-2,4-pentanedione, and the *cis* and *trans* isomers separated by chromatography on alumina. The proton and fluorine magnetic resonance spectra, electronic absorption spectra and x-ray powder diagrams of these were measured (the proton and fluorine magnetic resonance spectra clearly distinguish the isomers) and of the corresponding cobalt (III) species[97]. The rates of isomerization for these complexes were measured at various temperatures, and it was found that, although the *cis* cobalt complex isomerized rapidly at 66–99°, the *cis* rhodium species was stable in this respect up to 165°[98]. Other fluoroacetyl acetonates have recently been prepared[52a].

The β-diketone complexes $\mathbf{Rh(C_{15}H_{11}O_2)_3}$ and $\mathbf{Rh(C_{15}H_9O_6N_2)_3}$ were got from dibenzoylmethine and from *p,p'*-dinitrodibenzoylmethine with $Rh(acac)_3$[330a].

Carboxylic acid complexes

Acetates. Apart from salts of $[\mathbf{Rh(NH_3)_5(OAc)}]^{2+}$ (cf. p. 261), the known acetates of rhodium are all likely to involve the metal in the divalent state. It seems likely that the $\mathbf{Rh(OAc)_3.2\frac{1}{2}H_2O}$ made by Claus in 1860 by addition of acetic acid to rhodium sesquioxide[61] is in fact the dimeric rhodium (II) acetate considered on p. 345.

EDTA complexes. EDTA is taken here to mean the fully ionized anion, so that ethylenediamine tetraacetic acid itself would be written H_4EDTA.

$\mathbf{K[Rh(EDTA)(H_2O)]}$ can be made from freshly prepared rhodium hydroxide and $H_4.EDTA$, a procedure which gives firstly $\mathbf{Rh(H.EDTA)(H_2O)}$, which then is reacted with potassium hydroxide;

a sodium and an ammonium salt were also made. The potassium and ammonium salts were resolved by using optically active *cis*-$[Co(NO_2)_2 en_2]^+$, and the rates of racemization measured[88]. It was suggested that the rhodium complex has the equatorial [Co(EDTA)-$(H_2O)]^-$ structure, in which the water molecule is *cis* to one coordinated nitrogen and *trans* to the other (rather than the polar alternative in which the water is *cis* to both nitrogen atoms). (The metal is of course still octahedrally coordinated and is likely to be so in all the complexes discussed in this section.) For the equilibria

$$Rh(H.EDTA)(H_2O) \rightleftharpoons [Rh(EDTA)(H_2O)]^- + H^+$$

$pK_1 = 2{\cdot}32 \pm 0{\cdot}08$, and for

$$H_2O + [Rh(EDTA)(H_2O)]^- \rightleftharpoons [Rh(EDTA)(OH)(H_2O)]^{2-} + H^+$$

$pK_1 = 9{\cdot}12 \pm 0{\cdot}02$ (the aquo group is thus much less acidic than in $[Cr(EDTA)(H_2O)]^-$, for which $pK_1 = 7{\cdot}52$)[88].

Other EDTA complexes which have been reported are: $\mathbf{[RhCl_2(H_2.EDTA)]^-}$ and $\mathbf{[RhBr_2(H_2.EDTA)]^-}$ (from RhH-(EDTA)(H_2O) and the appropriate halogen acids), both prepared in optically active forms[88]; $\mathbf{[Rh(H.EDTA)Cl]^-}$ (from sodium EDTA and rhodium trichloride) and $\mathbf{Na[Rh(EDTA)].2\,H_2O}$, made from the previous complex, silver oxide and sodium hydroxide[332].

Polarographic, spectrophotometric and potentiometric measurements have been carried out on solutions containing the [Rh(EDTA)-$(H_2O)]^-$ anion, and at high pH (>8) evidence was obtained for the formation of $\mathbf{[Rh(EDTA)(OH)(H_2O)]^{2-}}$ and the polymeric species $\mathbf{[Rh(EDTA)(OH)]_n^{2n-}}$; the polarographic data suggest a three-electron reduction of the rhodium[96], but this has been disputed and a two-electron reduction proposed[112].

Infrared spectra have been studied of $Rh(H.EDTA)(H_2O)$, $K[Rh(H_2.EDTA)Cl_2]$ and $K[Rh(H_2.EDTA)Br_2]$ in both the solid state and in aqueous solution, and in the first case it was shown that the areas of the bands due to coordinated and free carboxylate bands are in a 3:1 ratio, suggesting that the postulated pentadentate bonding of EDTA in this complex (coordination from two nitrogen and three oxygen atoms) is correct[114]. Electronic absorption spectra have been measured of solutions of $[Rh(EDTA)(H_2O)]^-$, $[Rh(EDTA)]^-$, $[Rh(EDTA)(OH)]^{2-}$, $Rh(H.EDTA)(H_2O)$, $[Rh(H.EDTA)Cl]^-$, $[Rh(H_2.EDTA)Cl_2]^-$, $[Rh(H_2.EDTA)Br_2]^-$ and [Rh(PDTA)-$(H_2O)]^-$ (H_4PDTA = 1,2-propylenediaminetetraacetic acid). The circular dichroism of the latter complex was also measured, and these measurements reveal splittings of energy levels arising from the low symmetry of the complexes; it was shown that both the rhodium (III) and corresponding cobalt (III) complexes have the same relative splitting of energy levels[115]. Retention of configuration during the interconversions of L-(−)-Rh(H.EDTA)(H_2O), (−)-[Rh(H_2.EDTA)Cl_2]$^-$ and (−)-[Rh(H_2.EDTA)Br_2]$^-$ has been demonstrated[113].

Formate complexes. Although brief mention has been made of a rhodium (III) formate made from rhodium sesquioxide and formic acid[40] it is likely that this is a rhodium (II) derivative (cf. p. 346).

Heptanoates. Rhodium (III) heptanoate, **Rh($C_7H_{15}COO)_3$**, can be made from sodium heptanoate and rhodium trichloride; unlike rhodium trichloride, the substance is inactive as an isomerization catalyst for olefins unless cocatalysts are added[146].

Malonate complexes. **K_3[Rh($C_3H_2O_4)_3$]** can be made from freshly-prepared rhodium sesquioxide and potassium malonate; it has been resolved by use of the optically active cinchonium salts[162].

Oxalates. **K_3[Rh ox$_3$].4½H_2O** can be made by the action of potassium oxalate on rhodium trichloride or on K_2[RhCl_5(H_2O)]. It forms red crystals, and a monohydrate and the anhydrous form are also reported; sodium, ammonium and rubidium salts are also known[162]. The potassium salt has been resolved by using the optically active strychnine base[162].

The electronic spectrum of [Rh ox$_3$]$^{3-}$ has been measured in aqueous solution and assignments proposed[116,177]. Circular dichroism studies on the complex have been reported[212,231], and measurements of the Cotton effect in aqueous solutions[230]. The magnetic dipole allowed transitions were identified[122]. Rotatory dispersion curves and electronic absorption spectra of a large number of salts containing the *d*- and *l*-[Rh ox$_3$]$^{3-}$ anions were recorded, and a correlation found between changes in absorption maxima and in intensities of rotation and absorption with both the ionic potential and polarizabilities of the cations. The changes in optical rotation were ascribed to ion-pair effects between the optically active and optically inactive ions[4].

The proton magnetic resonance of a polycrystalline sample of K_3[Rh ox$_3$].4½H_2O has been measured over the range 77–343°K, and it was demonstrated that some of the protons were in an environment which differed from that of the protons in hydrate water. From this it appears that at least some of the ions were in the *cis* or *trans*

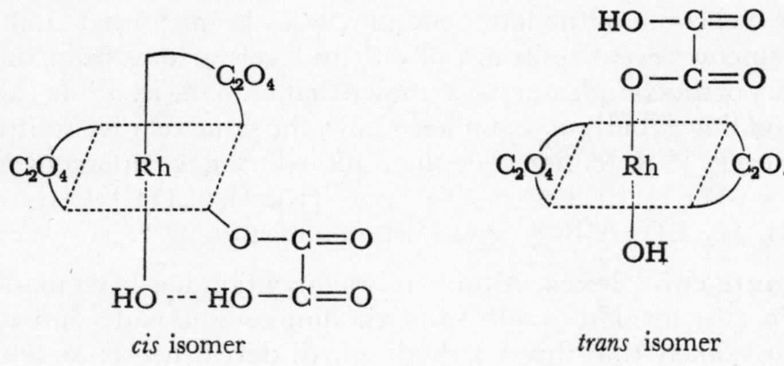

Figure 6.3

hydroxy form (Figure 6.3). Since the anhydrous salt can be made from the hydrate and since the complex is readily resolvable into *d* and *l* forms, the *trans* isomer can be excluded. The final conclusion from this study was that the solid compound should be formulated as[266b]

$$K_6[Rh\,ox_2(Hox)(OH)][Rh\,ox_3]\,.\,8H_2O$$

with an internal HO—Hox hydrogen bond in which the proton–proton distance in the HO····H—O—C system is 2·43 Å (in the water molecules in the complex the proton–proton distance is 1·53 ± 0·03 Å)[266b]. The existence of hemihydrates of trisoxalato complexes of iridium and ruthenium suggests that these too may have similar structures.

It is likely that in solution the $[Rh\,ox_3]^{3-}$ and $[Rh\,ox_2(Hox)(OH)]^{3-}$ species are in equilibrium. For the exchange of labelled oxalate ion with aqueous solutions of '$[Rh\,ox_3]^{3-}$' in the pH range 2–8 the pseudo first-order rate constant k_{ex} is given by

$$k_{ex} = k_{H_2O} + k_{H^+}[H^+] + k_{OH^-}[OH^-] \quad (2 < pH < 8)$$

The pseudo first-order rate constant of aquation k_{aq} is given at low acidities by

$$k_{aq} = k_{H^+}[H^+]$$

The process is very slow; at 130° the half-time for oxalate exchange is between 4 and 16 hours, according to conditions. At 133°, k_{H_2O} = 6×10^{-6} sec^{-1}; k_{H^+} = $1·5 \times 10^{-2}$ M^{-1} sec^{-1}; k_{OH^-} = $1·3 \times 10^{2}$ M^{-1} sec^{-1}. The product of aquation is $[Rh\,ox_2(H_2O)_2]^-$ (above pH 8, oxalate ion and sesquioxide form). The proposed mechanism[21] involves two rapid 'pre-equilibria'

$$(k_1) \quad [Rh\,ox_3]^{3-} + H_2O \rightleftharpoons [Rh\,ox_2.ox^*(H_2O)]^{3-} \quad (1)$$

$$(k_2) \quad [Rh\ ox_3]^{3-} + H_3O^+ \rightleftharpoons [Rh\ ox_2(Hox)(H_2O)]^{2-} \quad (2)$$

(ox* represents monodentate oxalate, i.e. OC_2O_3; Hox represents protonated monodentate oxalate, i.e. OC_2O_3H).

This is followed by the rate-determining steps[21]

$$(k_3) \quad [Rh\ ox_2 . ox^*(H_2O)]^{3-} + H_2O \rightleftharpoons [Rh\ ox_2(H_2O)_2]^- + ox^{2-} \quad (3)$$

$$(k_4) \quad [Rh\ ox_2(Hox)(H_2O)]^{2-} + H_2O \rightleftharpoons [Rh\ ox_2(H_2O)_2]^- + Hox^- \quad (4)$$

$$(k_5) \quad [Rh\ ox_2 . ox^*(H_2O)]^{3-} + OH^- \rightarrow [Rh\ ox_2(H_2O)(OH)]^{2-} + ox^{2-} \quad (5)$$

The kinetics of aquation of $[Rh\ ox_3]^{3-}$ have been measured in solvent mixtures of normal and heavy water, and rate constants obtained. The reaction is slow; in molar acid, the half-time for aquation in water at 50° is 47 hours. The rate is accelerated slightly in heavy water, and from this the solvent deuterium isotope effect can be evaluated ($k_D/k_H = 3{\cdot}68$)[192]. These results support the 'pre-equilibrium' mechanism described above[21,192].

Studies on the acid-catalysed racemization of $[Rh\ ox_3]^{3-}$ show that the rate is very slow from pH 2–6, but below pH 2 there is a marked acid catalysis as there is with $[Cr\ ox_3]^{3-}$ [246].

Polarographic reduction of a solution of rhodium trichloride in excess oxalic acid show two irreversible two-electron cathodic waves at $-0{\cdot}43$ and $-0{\cdot}83$ v (versus S.C.E.) ascribed to $[Rh\ ox_2(H_2O)_2]^-$ and $[Rh\ ox_3]^{3-}$, respectively[318]; polarographic data on these systems have also been presented by Pantani[253].

Aquooxalates. Both *cis*- and *trans*-**K[Rh ox$_2$(H$_2$O)$_2$]** have recently been made: the monohydrate of the potassium trisoxalato rhodate (III) was treated with perchloric acid and the two isomers of the diaquo product separated on an anion-exchange column. The potassium salts are both yellow, and their infrared and electronic absorption spectra were measured[116]. The *cis* form can be converted into the *trans* by boiling its aqueous solution.

cis-**K$_3$[Rh ox$_2$Cl$_2$]** (green crystals) can be made from potassium chloride and the *cis* diaquo complex, and *trans*-**K$_3$[Rh ox$_2$Cl$_2$]** by boiling the *cis* isomer in aqueous solution: it forms orange crystals. The electronic absorption and infrared spectra were measured[116]. The *cis* and *trans* forms can be distinguished by their infrared spectra in the 1600 cm^{-1} region[232].

Absorption spectra and polarographic reduction of *citrate* and *tartrate* complexes of rhodium (III) have been studied[253].

Nitrato and nitrito complexes

'Rhodium nitrate', $Rh(NO_3)_3.2H_2O$, (red) can be made from hydrated rhodium sesquioxide and nitric acid[61], and is often used for reactions in place of the trichloride because of its good solubility in water. It has been used in the catalytic preparation of *trans*-1,4-polybutadienes. A basic nitrate of unknown formula can also be made[139].

$[Rh(NH_3)_5(NO_3)]^{2+}$ salts are known (cf. Table 6.1), and salts of $[Rh(NH_3)_5ONO]^{2+}$ are dealt with on p. 260 and in Table 6.1.

Phosphato and phosphito complexes

Unlike iridium, rhodium does not seem to form complexes with phosphates (or at least none has been definitely established). However, **'rhodium phosphate',** of unknown composition, has been made by the action of sodium phosphate on a solution of rhodium trichloride, and also by dissolving the hydrated sesquioxide in phosphoric acid[61]. Evidence has been presented for the existence of a complex phosphato anion in the red solution obtained by adding ammonium hydrogen phosphate and ammonium chloride to a solution of rhodium trichloride[138], and polynuclear complexes with phosphite ligands are also reported[307].

Sulphato complexes

'Rhodium sulphate', $Rh_2(SO_4)_3.nH_2O$, can be made as one of a number of hydrates or in the anhydrous form by treating the hydrated sesquioxide with excess sulphuric acid. The hydrates are red or yellow while the anhydrous form (made by heating the hydrates to 440°) is red[127,127a,189,207]. It is not certain whether the sulphate groups are coordinated in the hydrates; both rhodium trichloride and rhodium perchlorate hydrates exist in yellow and red forms, and in the latter case at least this arises from formation of polynuclear hydroxy- and oxy-bridged complexes (cf. p. 334)[107,299]. An acid sulphate, $Rh_2(SO_4)_3.H_2SO_4.16\,H_2O$, has also been reported[190]. As with iridium, alums such as $K_2SO_4.Rh_2(SO_4)_3.24\,H_2O$ can be made from rhodium sulphate and potassium sulphate, and these are also known with caesium, rubidium, ammonium and thallium (I) in place of potassium[261]. Repeated evaporation of the caesium alum yields $Cs[Rh(SO_4)_2].H_2O$, probably a true sulphato complex[190]. Studies have been made of the rhodium sulphate system in aqueous solution[297,298].

Selenates

These also exist in red and yellow forms, and can be made from hydrated rhodium sesquioxide and selenic acid[189].

Miscellaneous oxygen donor complexes

Rhodium trichloride reacts with tropolone to give $Rh(O_2C_7H_5)_3$[237].

Dimethylsulphoxide complexes, $RhX_3(DMSO)_3$, (X = Cl, I) can be got from rhodium trichloride X^- and the ligand. The chloride is orange and the iodide brown. Far infrared spectra were measured[166c] for organometallic DMSO complexes. (See p. 400.)

The heterometallic chelate complex tris(bis(pyridine-2-aldoxime) (platinum (II)) (rhodium perchlorate), $[(Pt(C_6H_5N_2O)_2)_3Rh]$-$(ClO_4)_3$, was made from aqueous solutions of rhodium trichloride and monohydrogen bis(pyridine-2-aldoxime) platinum (II) chloride as brown crystals[208d].

Sulphur, selenium and tellurium donors

Rh_2S_3 can be made as a black powder by the action of hydrogen sulphide on solutions of rhodium trichloride; like Ir_2S_3 it is chemically quite inert, being unaffected by mineral acids. The dissociation pressure has been measured from 953 to 1083°[182]. A phase rule study of the rhodium–sulphur system together with x-ray powder measurements suggested that the only definite sulphides formed were Rh_2S_5, Rh_2S_3, Rh_3S_4 and Rh_9S_8, and no evidence could be found for the previously reported RhS_2 and RhS[182]. Thermodynamic data have been obtained for Rh_2S_3[216]. For rhodium selenides and tellurides see p. 331.

$Rh(SH)_3$ is said to be formed by the action of hydrogen sulphide on aqueous solutions of rhodium trichloride. It is a black solid, and will not dissolve in excess sulphide.

Sulphito complexes

'Rhodium sulphite', $Rh_2(SO_3)_3.6H_2O$, can be made by dissolving hydrated rhodium sesquioxide in sulphurous acid solutions. It is colourless, and forms double salts with potassium sulphite (no formula was proposed[61]).

$K_3[Rh(SO_3)_3].nH_2O$ (n = 2 and $3\frac{1}{2}$) can be made by the action of potassium hydrogen sulphite on $K_3[RhCl_6]$[198]. Infrared spectra of this and of other complexes which appear to contain bidentate sulphite groups have been studied with a view to distinguishing between the four likely possibilities[240]:

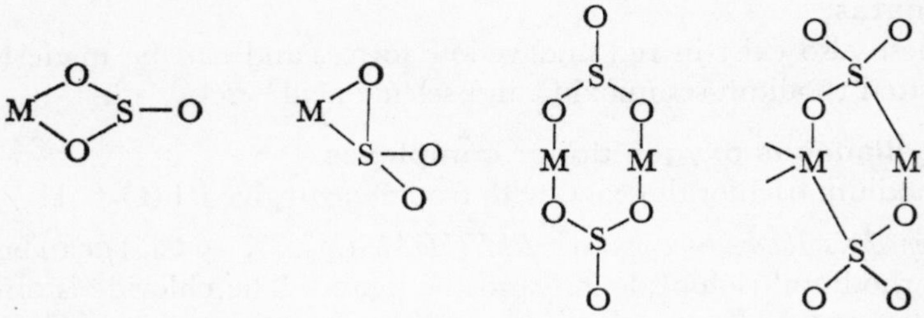

Structure **2** is the least likely as it involves a three-membered ring with angles close to 60°, but it was considered that no definite conclusions could be drawn from the results[240]. As already mentioned, studies on iridium (III) species containing a single bidentate sulphite group suggested that **1** was the most likely, but the evidence was far from conclusive (cf. p. 255)[13]. Earlier infrared studies on $K_3[Rh(SO_3)_3]$ had been interpreted in terms of structure **4** with bridging sulphite groups, but, again, later work suggested that no clear conclusions could be drawn from the spectra[14,15]. There was agreement, however, that monodentate sulphite groups in both iridium (III) and rhodium (III) sulphito complexes involve a metal–sulphur rather than a metal–oxygen bond[13,15,240].

Three sulphito ammine complexes of rhodium (III) have been prepared. Sodium sulphite reacts with $[Rh(NH_3)_5Cl]Cl_2$ to give *trans*-$Na[Rh(SO_3)_2(NH_3)_4]$[198a] and with $Rh(NH_3)_3Cl_3$ to give $\mathbf{Na_3[Rh(SO_3)_3(NH_3)_3]}$ and $\mathbf{Na_5[Rh(SO_3)_4(NH_3)_2]}$[206]. Ammonium and potassium salts were also prepared and their infrared spectra measured[15].

Thiourea complexes

$\mathbf{[Rh(thiourea)_6]Cl_3}$ can be made by heating a solution of $Na_3[RhCl_6]$ with an excess of thiourea; it forms golden-yellow crystals, and the same reaction gives $\mathbf{[Rh(thiourea)_5Cl]Cl_2}$ and $\mathbf{Rh(thiourea)_3Cl_3}$[199]. The electronic absorption spectrum of the hexathiourea complex has been measured and assignments proposed[287].

Dithiocarbamato complexes

$\mathbf{Rh(R_2NCS_2)_3}$ (R = Me, Et, Bu) can be made from an acetone solution of the sodium salt of the ligand and rhodium trichloride[67a,218]. The electronic absorption spectrum of the diethyldithiocarbamate complex has been measured and assignments proposed[175], and infrared spectra of the methyl and ethyl complexes were recorded[67a]. Carbonyl dithiocarbamates of rhodium (I) are also known (see p. 391).

Thiocyanato complexes

Rhodium thiocyanate, $Rh(SCN)_3.xH_2O$, is slowly precipitated as an orange solid from aqueous solutions of sulphuric acid, rhodium trichloride and potassium thiocyanate. It dissolves in excess thiocyanate[191].

$K_3[Rh(SCN)_6]$ can be made from $K_3[RhCl_6]$ or $K_2[RhCl_5]$ and a solution of potassium thiocyanate. It forms red crystals, and a silver salt is also known[17]. ^{14}N magnetic resonance studies suggest that, as in the iridium salt, there are metal–sulphur rather than metal–nitrogen bonds[157], and this was also the conclusion reached from infrared studies[208a]. An x-ray study of the potassium salt indicated that the anion has a distorted octahedral structure with metal–sulphur bonds, the thiocyanate groups forming two parallel sets with metal–sulphur–carbon angles of 120°[335].

Polarographic studies on the $[Rh(SCN)_6]^{3-}$ ion are said to show a well-defined three-electron irreversible reduction step[70] but more recent work suggests that only two electrons are involved[112] (see Table 6.8). In solutions of pH between 7 and 10, evidence was obtained for the existence of hydroxy complexes of the form $[Rh(SCN)_x(OH)_{6-x}]^{3-}$ and $[Rh(SCN)_y(H_2O)_{6-y}]^{(3-y)+}$ ($y < 3$), and the absorption spectra of these were reported as well as their polarograms[70]. Electronic spectra of $[Rh(SCN)_6]^{3-}$ have been measured and assignments proposed[287].

The free acid $H_3[Rh(SCN)_6]$ can be made by treatment of $K_3[Rh(SCN)_6]$ with sulphuric acid followed by extraction with amyl alcohol[17], but it is not clear whether the product was hydrated or not.

Alkyl sulphide complexes

$RhX_3(SEt_2)_3$ (X = Cl, Br, I) can be made from the appropriate rhodium trihalides and diethyl sulphide. Electronic absorption spectra were measured and assigned, and dissociation pressure measurements made; the complexes are isomorphous with the corresponding iridium species. The thermal stability of the three rhodium complexes with halogen decreases from chloride to iodide, an effect attributed to the *trans* effect of the halide groups[100].

The bromo species $\mathbf{RhBr_3(SEt_2)_3}$ and $\mathbf{Rh_2Br_6(SEt_2)_4}$ were made by Dwyer and Nyholm from rhodium tribromide and diethyl sulphide; and $\mathbf{RhI_3(SEt_2)_3}$ was got from the chloro species with iodide[91].

$\mathbf{RhCl_3(SMe_2)_3}$ is obtained as orange crystals from rhodium trichloride trihydrate and dimethyl sulphide (m.p. 109°). With methyl magnesium iodide it yields $Rh_2I_2Me_4(SMe_2)_4$: this and other dimethyl sulphide alkyl complexes are discussed on p. 374.

Reaction between diethyl selenide and $(NH_4)_3[RhCl_6]$ yields $\mathbf{RhCl_3(SeEt_2)_3}$; the corresponding dimethyl complex can be similarly obtained[106b].

Miscellaneous sulphur complexes

$\mathbf{KCa[Rh(C_2S_2O_2)_3]}$ ($C_2S_2O_2^{2-}$ is the thiooxalate ion) can be made by heating rhodium trichloride with potassium thioxalate and calcium ion. The salt was resolved by using optically active $[Co\ en_2(NO_2)_2]Cl$ and, like the trisoxalato rhodate (III) complex, it is optically stable[89]. Optical and circular dichroism measurements have been made and assignments for the ion have been given[212].

Complexes of rhodium (III) with dialkyl and diaryl **dithiophosphates** have been made with a view to using these for analytical purposes[45], and Jorgensen has measured and assigned the electronic spectra of diethyldithiophosphate, thiosemicarbazide and 2,2′-di(aminoethyl)sulphide rhodium (III) complexes[175]; these studies have been extended to cover the diethyldiselenophosphate complex[176].

Thiadiazole complexes have been made by reacting rhodium trichloride with the ligands 2,5-bis-*t*-octyldithiadiazole and with 2,5-bismethythia-1,3,4-thiadiazole. The infrared and electronic spectra of the products were recorded[263].

Thiosulphato complexes result from the reaction of sodium thiosulphate and ethylenediamine with $(NH_4)_3[RhCl_6]$; products such as $Na_3[Rh(S_2O_3)_3en_2]$, $Na_5[Rh(S_2O_3)_3en_2]$ (this formally contains rhodium (I)) and $Na_{10}[Rh_4(S_2O_3)_{15}(SO_3)_2en_8]$ have been claimed[55]. The well-defined species $\mathbf{Na[Rh\ en_2(S_2O_3)_2]}$ can be got from *trans*-$[Rh\ en_2Cl_2]^+$ and thiosulphate[38].

Ammine thiosulphates are also known: $\mathbf{Na_3[Rh(S_2O_3)_3(NH_3)_3]}$ can be got from $[RhCl_6]^{3-}$, thiosulphate and ammonia[55]. **8-Quinolinethiol** reacts with rhodium dichloride to give $\mathbf{Rh(C_9H_6NS)_3}$ as a crystalline solid[16b].

A **disulphamide complex,** *cis*-$\mathbf{Na_3[Rh(SO_2(NH_2)_2)_2(H_2O)_2]}$, has been made from sulphamide, sodium carbonate and $Na_3[RhCl_6]$[223]. That this has a *cis* configuration was shown by resolution of the complex with the α-phenylethylamine salt; the active salt does not racemize in cold aqueous solution at all, and in boiling solution does so only at the rate of some 30% per hour[223]. Infrared studies on the complex indicate that there are metal–oxygen rather than metal–nitrogen bonds[306a].

Rhodium (II)

Rhodium oxide, RhO, has been claimed as a product of the thermal decomposition of the sesquioxide and a heat of formation calculated[329], but its existence as a solid has not been thoroughly substantiated; its existence in the gas phase has, however, been demonstrated[5,243]. The band spectrum of the gas has been measured[274] and the ionization potential found to be 9·3 ev[243].

$\mathbf{Rh(OH)_2}$ is said to be formed as a black solid when sodium rhodate $Na_2[RhO_3]$ is reduced by sodium stannite[85]: it is possible that this compound contains coordinated $(SnCl_3)^-$.

Oxy complexes

The existence of rhodium (II) in glasses has recently been demonstrated by electron spin resonance methods[306b] (see also p. 307).

Carboxylic acid complexes

The reaction of glacial acetic acid with $(NH_4)_3[RhCl_6]$ gives a compound which was first formulated as a rhodium (I) hydride, $RhH(OAc)_2.H_2O$[54], but later work showed it to be a dimer, $\mathbf{Rh_2(OAc)_4(H_2O)_2}$, and this was confirmed by the x-ray crystal structure. The two rhodium atoms are bridged by four coordinated acetate groups, the rhodium–rhodium distance being very short (2·45 Å); there is a water molecule coordinated to each rhodium atom[265]. The complex is diamagnetic[54] suggesting strong metal–metal interaction, as in dimeric copper (II) acetate, which although not diamagnetic has a low magnetic moment.

Rhodium acetate, $\mathbf{[Rh(OAc)_2]_2}$, can be made from glacial acetic acid and rhodium hydroxide. Like the previous compound it is diamagnetic and it forms large green crystals. It will give a large number of adducts (1 molecule dimer : 2 molecules of ligand); those with water, acetic acid and tetrahydrofuran are green, with pyridine and ammonia red and with nitric oxide red—this latter adduct will formally contain rhodium (I). A 1:1 *o*-phenanthroline complex was also made. Infrared spectra of these and of the anhydrous acetate were measured[167,239]. Rhodium (II) trifluoroacetate (dimeric like the acetate) has been made, and this too reacts with donors such as pyridine and triphenylphosphine[300].

Formates. Reaction of formic acid with $H_3[RhCl_6]aq$ gives a dark green product which was first formulated as $RhH(HCOO)_2 \frac{1}{2}H_2O$[56], but it now seems certain[57,265] that this is $\mathbf{[Rh(HCOO)_2]_2 \cdot \frac{1}{2}H_2O}$; adducts with donor groups such as pyridine and triphenylphosphine can be obtained[56,57,300].

Rhodium (II) propionates can be made from rhodium sesquioxide and propionic acid; the hydrate is $[Rh(EtCOO)_2(H_2O)]_2$ and ionizes in aqueous solution[300]:

$$[Rh(EtCOO)_2(H_2O)]_2 \rightleftharpoons [Rh(EtCOO)_2(OH)]_2 + 2\,H^+$$

Sulphur and tellurium containing compounds

Rhodium sulphide, RhS, has been claimed[99a], but its existence is uncertain. The telluride **RhTe**, made from the elements, has the nickel arsenide structure[109a]; $\mathbf{Rh_3Te_2}$ has an orthorhombic structure with a rhodium–tellurium distance of 2·61 Å[334a]. Rhodium (II) sulphito complexes such as $\mathbf{[Rh(SO_3)_2(SO_4)]^{4-}}$ and $\mathbf{[Rh(SO_3)_2]^{2-}}$ have been claimed as the products of reaction between bisulphites and rhodium (III) compounds[275], but the view that these contain rhodium (II) has been justly criticized since they are not oxidized by iodine, which suggests that they contain rhodium (III)[90].

Salts of $\mathbf{[Rh^{II}(MNT)_2]^{2-}}$ (MNT is the maleonitriledithiolate dianion, $C_4N_2S_2^{\,2-}$) have been isolated from the reaction between anhydrous rhodium (II) acetate and the disodium salt of the ligand. The salts form green crystals and have a magnetic moment of 1·91 BM at room temperatures[29]. The electronic absorption spectra have been measured and also the electron spin resonance spectrum of the tetra-n-butyl-ammonium salt; it was concluded from the latter that the rhodium has a spin-doublet ground state[29,217a]. It appears to be isostructural with the corresponding nickel (II) complex and so, like the latter, is probably square planar:

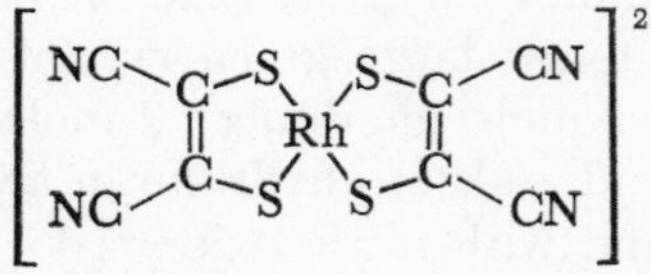

```
 ┌                                   ┐ 2−
 │ NC        S       S        CN     │
 │   \C—   /   \   /   —C/           │
 │     ‖        Rh        ‖          │
 │   /C—   \   /   \   —C\           │
 │ NC        S       S        CN     │
 └                                   ┘
```

Zinc tungstate crystals containing a small percentage of rhodium have been prepared and electron spin resonance used to show that the rhodium is in the divalent state; total rhodium was present in these crystals to the extent of about 0·009 mole per cent. It was concluded that the unpaired electron of rhodium (II) spends some 16% of its time on the neighbouring oxygen ions[306b].

Rhodium (I)

Rh_2O, has been claimed as a thermal degradation product of the sesquioxide and a heat of formation given[329], but there is no convincing evidence for its existence.

'Rhodium (I)' formates and acetates are discussed above (p. 345) and 'rhodium (I)' thiosulphato complexes on p. 344.

GROUP V DONORS

Rhodium forms a large number of ammines and amine complexes, and there have recently been studies on various monohydrido ammines and amine complexes of rhodium (III). There is an extensive phosphine chemistry of the element, although it appears at present that there are fewer hydrido phosphine complexes of rhodium (III) than of iridium (III). Many of the rhodium (I) phosphine complexes exhibit remarkable catalytic properties, especially the compound $Rh(PPh_3)_3Cl$.

Rhodium (III)

Ammines

These are summarized in Table 6.1. A number of soluble ammines of rhodium (III) will catalyse the reduction of quinone by molecular hydrogen, but rapid deposition of metal occurs[161a].

Hexammines. $\mathbf{[Rh(NH_3)_6]Cl_3}$ can be made in a similar way to the iridium hexammine chloride, by the prolonged action of hot aqueous ammonia in a sealed tube on $[Rh(NH_3)_5Cl]Cl_2$[179]. The chloride forms colourless crystals (solubility 13 g/100 ml at 80°), and a nitrate (2 at 20°), bromide, iodide, perchlorate and sulphate (2 at 20°) have also been made. The infrared spectrum of the solid chloride has been measured from 200 to 4000 cm^{-1} and the Raman spectrum of the aqueous solution has been recorded[108,134] (cf. Table

3.7, p. 106). The electronic absorption spectrum has been measured in aqueous solution[287].

The exchange of protons in $[Rh(NH_3)_6]^{3+}$ with deuterium in a 0·1 M solution of an acetic acid-d_1 acetate buffer has been studied[251] (cf. also p. 290, Table 5.5). Thermal degradation reactions of rhodium (III) hexammines and other substituted rhodium (III) ammines have been reported; in the case of the hexammine decomposition to the sesquioxide and rhodium trichloride occurs above 300°[324].

Substituted ammines. These are summarized in Table 6.1.

$[Rh(NH_3)_5Cl]Cl_2$. The simplest preparation is that recently given by Johnson and Basolo: rhodium trichloride is heated for 3 hours with a solution of ammonium chloride and ammonium carbonate. This procedure gives a mixture of the yellow chloropentammine chloride and the dichloro tetrammine chloride, which can be separated by recrystallization[168]. The solubility of the chloride is 0·83 g/100 ml at 20°. A wide range of salts containing the $[Rh(NH_3)_5Cl]^{2+}$ cation is known, including the bromide, iodide, sulphate and perchlorate[180]. An x-ray crystal structure analysis of $[Rh(NH_3)_5Cl]Cl_2$ shows that the rhodium–chlorine bond length is 2·40 Å and the rhodium–nitrogen distance 2·23 Å (errors uncertain)[326].

Other substituted ammines. The acid-catalysed hydrolysis of $[Rh(NH_3)_5X]^{2+}$ (X = Cl, Br) was studied by Lamb, who showed that the observed rate constant k_{obs} was given by

$$k_{obs} = k_1 + k_2[X]$$

[X] being the average value of halide concentration[194]:

$$H_2O + [Rh(NH_3)_5X]^{2+} \underset{k_2}{\overset{k_1}{\rightleftharpoons}} [Rh(NH_3)_5(H_2O)]^{3+} + X^-$$

A more recent study gave a value of $k_{obs} = 6{\cdot}2 \times 10^{-5}\ sec^{-1}$ for the hydrolysis of the chloropentammine in 0·1 M nitric acid at 80°; the rate constant of base hydrolysis was also measured at various pH values (at pH 9·9 it was $26 \times 10^{-5}\ sec^{-1}$ at 80°)[169]. The significance of these and related results is discussed below (p. 355). Kinetics of the reaction

$$[Rh(NH_3)_5X]^{2+} + OH^- \rightarrow [Rh(NH_3)_5OH]^{2+} + X^- (X = Cl, Br, I)$$

were studied; the second-order rate constants fell in the order: Cl > Br > I, the reverse of the sequence for the corresponding cobalt (III) species[45a]. The kinetics of the radiolytic reduction of $[Rh(NH_3)_5Cl]Cl_2$ have been investigated by studying the electronic absorption spectra of the radiolysed solutions[18a]. The $[Rh(NH_3)_5Br]^{2+}$–Br^- exchange has been studied[285].

The pentammine hydride species **$[Rh(NH_3)_5H](SO_4)$** was isolated from the reaction between $[Rh(NH_3)_5Cl]Cl_2$ and zinc dust in ammoniacal solution, and its electronic, proton magnetic resonance and infrared spectra were measured; a tetrammine, *trans*-$[Rh(NH_3)_4(H_2O)H]SO_4$, can also be made[249a]. On the basis of comparisons of the electronic absorption spectra of $[Rh(NH_3)_5X]^{2+}$ ($X = Cl, Br, I, H, OH, NO_2$) with other rhodium (III) complexes the hydride ion was assigned a position in the spectrochemical series between water and ammonia[247]: $NO_2^- > NH_3 > NCS^- \sim H^- > H_2O > OH^- > Cl^- > Br^- > I^-$; however, the hydride group may have a higher or lower position in the series depending on the other ligands present in the complex.

$[Rh(NH_3)_5(ONO)]Cl_2$ can be got from the aquopentammine and nitrous acid at 0°; both it and the nitro complex $[Rh(NH_3)_5NO_2]Cl_2$ to which it isomerizes are colourless. The kinetics of formation of the nitrito complex and of the nitrito–nitro isomerization for both the iridium (III) and rhodium (III) complexes have already been considered (p. 260)[22]. The infrared spectrum of this and the ^{15}N substituted product have been measured from 200 to 4000 cm^{-1} (as have the spectra of the nitro isomers)[61a].

Enthalpy data have been obtained for the reaction

$$[Rh(NH_3)_5H_2O]^{3+} + X^- \rightarrow [Rh(NH_3)_5X]^{2+} + H_2O$$
$$(X = Cl, Br, I)$$

and for the reverse aquation reaction, and related to the *trans* effect of the halide ligands[263a].

$[Rh(NH_3)_5(RCOO)](ClO_4)_2$ ($R = CH_3, (CH_3)_3C$ and CF_3) can be prepared from the aquopentammine, the carboxylic acid and perchloric acid. The rates of acid hydrolysis of these species and of the corresponding iridium (III) and cobalt (III) species were measured (cf. p. 261)[236].

trans-**$[Rh(NH_3)_4Cl_2]Cl$** can be made in the same way as the chloropentammine[168]. Studies on the rates of acid and base hydrolysis of this species and of other rhodium dihalo complexes have been made[169], and are considered below (cf. p. 355).

Amine complexes*

[Rh en$_3$]Cl$_3$ can be made by heating together ethanolic solutions of $Na_3[RhCl_6]$ and ethylenediamine[119]. It forms white crystals; a bromide, iodide, thiocyanate and nitrate were also made. The complex has been resolved into the optical antimers[325].

Infrared spectra have been measured for [Rh en$_3$]Cl$_3$ between 400 and 4000 cm^{-1}, and the rhodium–nitrogen stretch assigned to a band at 580 cm^{-1}; from similar results on a number of other tris-ethylenediamine complexes an attempt was made to correlate the metal–nitrogen stretching and the NH_2 rocking vibrations with the stability constants of the complexes[135a,270]. The Raman spectrum of an aqueous solution of [Rh en$_3$]$^{3+}$ gave shifts at 219, 388, 500 and 1000 cm^{-1} in addition to other bands arising from the ethylenediamine groups[228]. The electronic absorption spectrum of [Rh en$_3$]$^{3+}$ has been measured and compared with that of the iridium complex[177,227a], circular dichroism measurements have been made[82,212,230] and magnetic dipole allowed transitions identified[122]. The effect of association in aqueous solution between a number of anions and [Rh en$_3$]$^{3+}$ on the circular dichroism bands of the latter has been studied, and also on the propylenediamine complex [Rh pn$_3$]$^{3+}$ [227a].

There is no catalytic racemization of optically active isomers of either [Rh en$_3$]$^{3+}$ or [Pt en$_3$]$^{4+}$ in the presence of active carbon, platinum black or silica gel, nor is there any substantial exchange of labelled ethylenediamine with these complex ions in the presence of activated charcoal[292]—in contrast the cobalt (III) complex is quickly racemized in the presence of these catalysts. A very slow exchange between [Ir en$_3$]$^{3+}$, [Rh en$_3$]$^{3+}$ and their respective radioactive metals (derived from Szilard–Chalmers reactions) is observed[299b].

Potentiometric measurements on [Rh en$_3$]$^{3+}$ show that, like the analogous iridium and cobalt complexes, it is only very weakly acidic[135]. The exchange rate of NH_2 protons in [Rh en$_3$]$^{3+}$ with deuterium oxide in a buffered solution has been measured and shown to be very similar to that for $[Rh(NH_3)_6]^{3+}$ in aqueous solutions; as with the hexammines the proton exchange rates for [M en$_3$]$^{3+}$ decrease in the sequence: M = Co(III) > Rh(III) > Ir(III)[251] (see Table 5.5, p. 290).

Deprotonation of [Rh en$_3$]I$_3$ by reaction with potassium amide in liquid ammonia (cf. p. 263) yields the diamagnetic rhodium (III)

* See Table 6.2.

species **[Rh en$_2$(en–H)]I$_2$**, **[Rh en(en–H)$_2$]I** and **Rh(en–H)$_3$**. A paramagnetic complex **K[Rh(en–H)$_2$(en–2H)]** was claimed to be the product of still further deprotonation (μ_{eff} = 1·5 ± 0·1 BM at room temperatures) and it was suggested that this was a case of a paramagnetic rhodium (III) compound; this seems, however, highly unlikely, and the possibility that the paramagnetism arises from some rhodium (II) or mixed oxidation state species was not excluded[321] (another possibility is that the unpaired electron is associated with the ligands rather than with the metal atom). Infrared spectra of these deprotonated species were measured over the range 250–4000 cm^{-1} but showed few differences from the spectrum of [Rh en$_3$]Cl$_3$[321].

cis- and *trans*-**[Rh en$_2$Cl$_2$]Cl** can be made by refluxing rhodium trichloride in aqueous solution with ethylenediamine hydrochloride in the presence of base, or from ethylenediamine and [Rh-py$_4$Cl$_2$]Cl[126a]. The isomers can be separated by fractional crystallization, and a method has been described for the estimation of each[168]. The exchange rate of ^{36}Cl with *trans*-[Rh en$_2$Cl$_2$]$^+$ was studied[286] and also its polarographic reduction[112]. A number of other amine complexes of rhodium (III), [Rh(AA)$_2$Cl$_2$]$^+$ (AA = diamine), were made by similar methods (cf. also Table 6.2).

General properties of rhodium (III) tetramine complexes are considered together below (p. 353).

[Rh dien$_2$]I$_3$ (dien = diethylenetriamine) can be made from the ligand, rhodium trichloride and sodium iodide. Deprotonation reactions have been carried out on this substance (and its iridium analogue) with potassium amide in liquid ammonia to give **[Rh (dien–H)$_2$]I** and **Rh(dien–H)(dien–2H)**. These diamagnetic species were studied by x-ray powder photographs and by infrared spectra; the latter were said to indicate that the protons were removed from the NH$_2$ groups of the amine. The reactions involved are believed to be[320]

$$[\text{Rh dien}_2]^{3+} + \text{NH}_2^- \rightarrow [\text{Rh(dien–H)dien}]^{2+} + \text{NH}_3$$

$$[\text{Rh(dien–H)dien}]^{2+} + \text{NH}_2^- \rightarrow [\text{Rh(dien–H)}_2]^+ + \text{NH}_3$$

$$[\text{Rh(dien–H)}_2]^+ + \text{NH}_2^- \rightarrow \text{Rh(dien–H)(dien–2 H)} + \text{NH}_3$$

Amino acid complexes

α-Alanine complexes, (+)-**Rh(L–ala)$_3$** and (−)-**Rh(L–ala)$_3$** have recently been made from the acid and rhodium hydroxide; optical rotatory dispersion curves as well as electronic and infrared spectra were measured, and the results compared with those obtained for the corresponding cobalt (III) species[83].

The reaction between *cis*- or *trans*-[Rh en_2Cl_2]$^+$ and amino acids in the presence of ethanol and sodium iodide yields **[Rh en_2L]I_2** (L = glycine, alanine, leucine, methionine, valine, tyrosine, phenylalanine); these compounds have the *cis* or *trans* configuration[319].

Complexes of rhodium (III) with glycine acid have been made[336], and some obscure **rhodium hydrazine amino** acid complexes have been claimed[47].

Complexes with heterocyclic bases

Pyridine complexes are summarized in Table 6.3. Despite extensive attempts, no hexa- or pentapyridine derivatives of rhodium (III) could be isolated[118] (the [Rh py_6]Br_3 reported[86] is in fact 1,2,6-Rh py_3Br_3[101]), and as with iridium it seems that a maximum of four pyridine groups can be accommodated by a rhodium atom, due perhaps to steric reasons. Photochemical studies on rhodium (III) pyridine complexes have been reported[76].

trans-**[Rh py_4Cl_2]Cl** can be produced as yellow crystals by the action of pyridine on rhodium trichloride[118,125]; efforts to prepare the *cis* isomer failed, and it was suggested that this form did not exist because of steric factors. A hydroxide, nitrate, perchlorate, iodide and sulphate are also reported[180], and infrared[118] and electronic absorption spectra for the chloride have been measured[118,288]. Polarographic and coulometric studies on *trans*-[Rh py_4Cl_2]$^+$ showed that a two-electron reduction was involved[252]; the rates of acid and base hydrolysis of the complex have been measured[169] (cf. p. 355).

The complex is a useful starting material for other rhodium complexes since it readily undergoes the reaction.

$$trans\text{-}[\mathrm{Rh\ py_4Cl_2}]^+ + 4\,\mathrm{L} \rightarrow trans\text{-}[\mathrm{RhL_4Cl_2}]^+ + 4\,\mathrm{py}$$

where L is an amine, ammonia or $\frac{1}{2}$-oxalate[126a].

Addition of an alkaline solution of potassium perosmate to [Rh py_4Cl_2]Cl gives a species claimed to be [Rh py_4Cl_2]OH-$2OsO_4$[304].

[Rh py_4HX]$^+$ (X = Cl, Br) is formed by reaction of borohydride ion with *trans*-[Rh py_4X_2]$^+$, and it is possible that in the presence of excess pyridine [Rh py_5H]$^{2+}$ is formed[101]:

$$\underset{\text{(Yellow)}}{trans\text{-}[\mathrm{Rh\ py_4Cl_2}]^+} \xrightarrow{\mathrm{H^-}} \underset{\text{(Pale brown)}}{[\mathrm{Rh\ py_4HCl}]^+} \xrightarrow{\mathrm{py}} \underset{\text{(Colourless)}}{[\mathrm{Rh\ py_5H}]^{2+}}$$

1,2,6-Rh py_3Cl_3 can be made by treating *trans*-[Rh py_4Cl_2]Cl with pyridine in a sealed tube at 150° for 3 days; it forms deep orange crystals[118]. The infrared[60b,151a] and electronic absorption spectra[118,288] were measured. The **1,2,3-Rh py_3Cl_3** isomer is also formed in this reaction[118]—Poulenc's observation that the 1,2,6-isomer was converted into the 1,2,3-form by the action of sunlight[268] could not be confirmed[118].

1,2,3-(yellow)- and 1,2,6-(orange)-**Rh $py_3(SCN)_3$** were prepared from pyridine and $[Rh(SCN)_6]^{3-}$: the infrared and electronic spectra of the products suggest that the thiocyanate groups are bonded through sulphur[119]. No tetrapyridine thiocyanate complexes could be prepared[119], possibly because of steric hindrance between the bent Rh—SCN groups and the pyridine molecules.

Rh py_3Br_3 can be made by the action of an excess of pyridine on $K_3[Rh_2Br_9]$; it was said to exist in *three* forms, none of which is identical to [Rh py_4Br_2][Rh py_2Br_4][269]. Later work, however, showed that the three forms are the 1,2,3- and 1,2,6-isomers and *trans*-[Rh py_4Br_2]-Br.HBr.$2H_2O$[81].

Studies of reaction kinetics of a number of rhodium (III) complexes with pyridine have been very briefly reported; the reactants were *cis*-pyH[$RhCl_4(NH_3)$py] and $[Rh(NO_2)_4py_2]^-$ and the products $RhCl_3py_2(NH_3)$ and Rh $py_3(NO_2)_3$, respectively. The reactions were second order, and it was observed that the nitro complex was some nine times more reactive than the chloro, presumably due to the greater *trans* effect of NO_2^-.

Formation and reactions of tetramines

A great deal of work has been reported recently concerning complexes of the forms *trans*-$[Rh(AA)_2X_2]^+$ where AA is a bidentate nitrogen donor such as ethylenediamine, bipyridyl, dimethylglyoxime and X is a halogen ligand, and *trans*-$[RhA_4X_2]^+$ (where A is ammonia or pyridine). The preparations of most of these complexes are listed in Tables 6.1, 6.2 and 6.3. It should be noted that in most cases the only evidence for the *trans* configuration in these complexes is their electronic spectra.

Formation. It was observed by Delepine in 1929[77,78] that the addition of ethanol to an aqueous solution of $[RhCl_6]^{3-}$ and pyridine gave an immediate and quantitative yield of *trans*-[Rh py_4Cl_2]Cl, whereas without ethanol Rh py_3Cl_3 was produced, which would only with difficulty take up more pyridine to give the tetra complex. Later observations[119,280] showed that other tetramines could be made in a similar way, and that instead of ethanol other reducing agents such as hypophosphorous acid, stannous salts, hydrazine and borohydrides would catalyse the formation of the compounds.

Basolo and coworkers studied the kinetics of formation of *trans*-$[Rh\,py_4Cl_2]^+$ from pyridine and $[RhCl_5(H_2O)]^{2-}$ in the presence of a catalyst solution which was made by the action of hydrazine on aqueous chlororhodate (III) solutions. The reaction was found to be first order in $[RhCl_5(H_2O)]^{2-}$ and in the catalyst and zero order in pyridine, provided the latter was in excess. They suggested a mechanism similar to that proposed for catalysis of platinum (IV) reactions by platinum (II), in which a small amount of rhodium (I) (thought to be present as planar $[Rh\,py_4]^+$) is generated from rhodium (III), pyridine and the reducing agent[280].

Later work, however, suggests that the catalytic intermediate might be a rhodium (III) hydride rather than rhodium (I). All the reagents so far used to expedite the rhodium (III)–pyridine reactions are capable of giving rise to transition metal hydrides, and if such a species were formed the hydride in it would be labile to substitution by other groups[119,124]. A remarkable observation which supports this hypothesis is that the reaction of pyridine with aqueous rhodium trichloride solutions or with $Rh\,py_3Cl_3$ is efficiently catalysed by molecular hydrogen at room temperatures and pressures—no net uptake of hydrogen is observed. The suggested mechanism is[124]

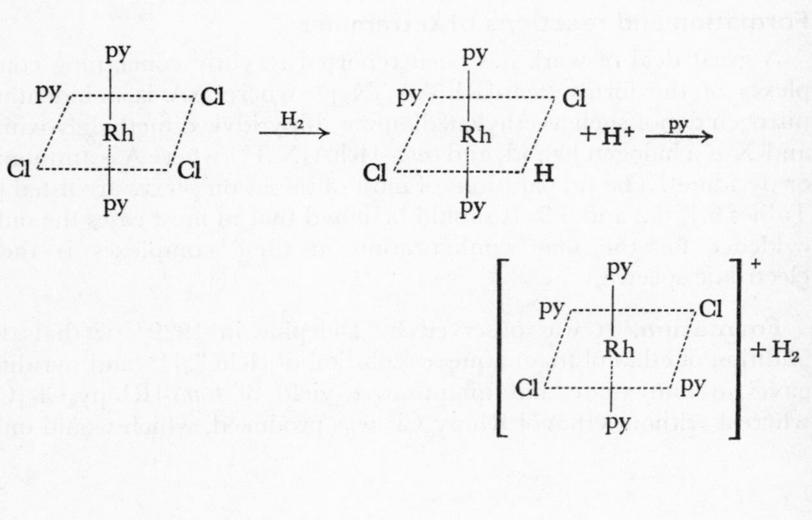

py
py Cl
Rh $\xrightarrow{H_2}$
Cl Cl
py

py
py Cl
Rh $+ H^+ \xrightarrow{py}$
Cl H
py

$\Big[$ py
py Cl
Rh
Cl py
py $\Big]^+$ $+ H_2$

Similarly, homogeneous catalysis is observed in the aquation of rhodium trichloride in the presence of hydrogen: the red aqueous solution of the trichloride solution becomes yellow when molecular hydrogen is passed through it at room temperatures, and the absorption spectrum shows that *trans*-$[Rh(H_2O)_4Cl_2]^+$ has been formed; again no net uptake of hydrogen is observed[124].

Hydrido tetramine complexes. Reaction of borohydride ion with aqueous solutions of rhodium tetramine complexes gives mono- or even dihydrido species, most of which have not been isolated. The evidence for their existence in solution derives from infrared and proton magnetic resonance measurements. The known hydrides include $[Rh\,py_4HX]^+$ (X = Cl, Br)[101]; $[Rh(NH_3)_4HCl]^+$[247]; $[Rh(NH_3)_4(H_2O)H]^{2+}$[249a]; $[Rh\,en_2HX]^+$ (X = Cl, Br, I)[117,247]; and $[Rh(DMGH)_2HCl]^-$[117,247]. The electronic absorption spectra of these have been measured and on the basis of the results (and of similar measurements on a series of pentammine rhodium (III) complexes) it was suggested that, in these compounds, the hydride group should be placed between water and ammonia in the spectrochemical series[247]. This does not necessarily conflict with studies on platinum (II) phosphine hydrides which have placed the hydride ligand at the strong-field end of the spectrochemical series, since it is likely that the ligand-field strength of the highly polarizable hydride ion is very much affected by the nature of the other ligands present.

The monohydrides mentioned above are presumed to have the *trans* configuration[247]. There is, however, some evidence for the existence of *cis*-$[Rh\,en_2HCl]^+$ (made from the corresponding dichloride and sodium borohydride[247]), and *cis*-$[Rh\,trienHCl]^+$ has been isolated as a tetraphenylboronate: the latter appears to be the most stable tetramine complex as regards hydride replacement in solution[117,247]. Prolonged treatment of either *cis*- or *trans*-$[Rh\,en_2Cl_2]^+$ with borohydride yields $[Rh\,en_2H_2]^+$, isolated as a tetraphenylboronate. This probably has a *trans* configuration, and it was suggested that, in its parent species *trans*-$[Rh\,en_2HCl]^+$ the chloride ion is labilized by the hydride[117].

Acid and base hydrolyses. The rates of hydrolysis in acid solution (usually 0·1 M nitric acid) and in basic solution (buffers of pH 8·9, 9·9, 11·9, 12·7) were measured for complexes *trans*-$[RhA_4Cl_2]^+$ (A = NH_3, $\frac{1}{2}$en, $\frac{1}{4}$trien, $\frac{1}{2}$*meso*-butylene diamine (*m*-bn), $\frac{1}{2}$*d,l*-butylenediamine (*d,l*-bn), $\frac{1}{2}$bipy, $\frac{1}{2}$tetramethylethylenediamine (tetrameen)) and for *cis*-$[RhA_4Cl_2]^+$ (A = $\frac{1}{2}$en, $\frac{1}{4}$trien, $\frac{1}{2}$tetrameen); and

$[Rh(NH_3)_5Cl]Cl_2$; *cis*- and *trans*-$[Rh\ ox_2Cl_2]^{3-}$ were similarly studied[169]. For the *acid hydrolyses*, first-order kinetics were found in each case. The observed rate constant is a composite of the four constants k_1 to k_4 in the reactions

$$[RhA_4Cl_2]^+ + H_2O \underset{k_2}{\overset{k_1}{\rightleftharpoons}} [RhA_4Cl(H_2O)]^{2+} + Cl^-$$

$$[RhA_4Cl(H_2O)]^{2+} + H_2O \underset{k_4}{\overset{k_3}{\rightleftharpoons}} [RhA_4(H_2O)_2]^{3+} + Cl^-$$

and from these an overall rate constant 'k_1'' was derived; at 80° for solutions in 0·1 M nitric acid, this had the value of $4{\cdot}7 \times 10^{-5}$ sec^{-1} for *trans*-$[Rh(NH_3)_4Cl_2]^+$ and $2{\cdot}7 \times 10^{-5}$ sec^{-1} for *trans*-$[Rh\ en_2Cl_2]^+$. Values for all the other complexes studied did not differ greatly from these, so the rate of reaction is insensitive to the charge on the complex, in contrast to the analogous cobalt (III) systems where, for example, the rate of acid hydrolysis of $[Co(NH_3)_5Cl]^{2+}$ is some thousand times slower than that for *trans*-$[Co(NH_3)_4Cl_2]^+$.

The rates of *base hydrolyses* of these rhodium amines are again of the same order of magnitude for all the complexes ($8{\cdot}9 \times 10^{-5}$ sec^{-1} for *trans*-$[Rh(NH_3)_4Cl_2]^+$ at 80° and pH 9·9, $4{\cdot}4 \times 10^{-5}$ sec^{-1} for *trans*-$[Rh\ en_2Cl_2]^+$ at 80° and pH 9·9). During acid or base hydrolysis of the rhodium (III) species there was almost complete retention of both geometrical configuration (in the case of *cis*- and *trans*-$[Rh\ en_2Cl_2]^+$) and optical configuration (in the case of *l-cis*-$[Rh\ en_2Cl_2]^+$). For cobalt ammines, base hydrolysis is some million times faster than acid hydrolysis, and base hydrolysis is usually accompanied by a large degree of isomerization and racemization[169].

It has been suggested that these differences between analogous rhodium (III) and cobalt (III) systems arise from a contribution of π bonding from chloro or amido ligands in the cobalt complexes and the absence of such bonding in the rhodium complexes. For both acid and base hydrolysis of cobalt (III) it has been postulated that the reaction proceeds by a dissociative mechanism, yielding a five-coordinate intermediate which can undergo a geometrical rearrangement to a trigonal bipyramidal structure, in which there is more effective ligand-to-metal π bonding. This intermediate is optically inactive and the original complex can be reformed from it, thus explaining the racemization and isomerization effects. For rhodium (III), a transition state is proposed in which five inert ligands retain their original positions, forming a square-based pyramid, while the entering and leaving groups occupy almost equivalent positions above the basal plane of the pyramid in the transition state:

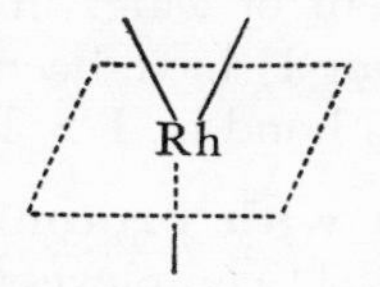

In this *cis*-attack mechanism (S_N2) optical and geometrical configurations will of course remain the same[169].

The rate constant for exchange of labelled chloride with *trans*-$[Rh\ en_2Cl_2]^+$ was found to be $4{\cdot}0 \times 10^{-5}$ sec^{-1} at 80° and the rate constant of hydrogen–deuterium exchange in *cis*- and *trans*-$[Rh\ en_2Cl_2]^+$ was found to be $4{\cdot}5 \times 10^5$ M^{-1} sec^{-1} and $2{\cdot}4 \times 10^6$ M^{-1} sec^{-1}, respectively[169]. The rates of the reactions

$$trans\text{-}[Rh\ en_2Cl_2]^+ + 2\,X \rightarrow trans\text{-}[Rh\ en_2X_2]^{n+} + 2\,Cl^-$$

($X = OH^-$, NO_2^-, I^-, thiourea, NH_3) were measured at 80° and were found to be comparable in magnitude[169].

***Trans*-effect studies.** The relative enthalpies of bonding of *trans*-dihalogeno bisethylenediamine rhodium (III) complexes in aqueous solution decrease in the sequence[37,38]: $I_2 > IBr > ICl > Br_2 > BrCl > Cl_2$. These enthalpy data give a measure of the class (b) character[3] or 'softness'[258] of rhodium in these complexes; thus, for the Lewis acid $[Rh\ en_2X\text{–}]^{2+}$ the class (b) character increases from X = Cl to X = I. The results can be accounted for on the assumption that the halide ion weakens the bond *trans* to it, and that this effect increases as follows: Cl < Br < I. This is supported by infrared spectra of the metal–halogen stretching modes in the complexes[38], and it is found that the thermodynamic data are paralleled by kinetic effects, the labilizing effect of the halides decreasing from iodide to chloride[37,37a]. The rates of replacement of X^- from *trans*-$(Rh\ en_2XY)^+$ (where X and Y are Cl or Br) are independent of the nature or concentration of the incoming nucleophile. The mechanisms were discussed in terms of the class (b) character of the reactant complexes, but it was concluded that no distinction could be made in these cases between a S_N1 or S_N2 type of reaction. When X = Cl or Br the *trans* effect of L is in the order: I > Br > Cl (either in terms of rate constants or of activation enthalpies). The high *trans* effect of iodide is thought to arise from its polarizability and relatively weak bond strength, so that it can compensate for either an increase or a decrease in the electron density at the rhodium[37a].

Kinetics of the replacement of water in *trans*-[Rh $en_2L(H_2O)]^{2+}$ by X^- (L and X = Cl, Br or I) have been studied; the kinetic *trans* effect of L on the Rh—OH_2 bond is: I > Br > Cl[37].

Formation of adducts with protonic acids. It is a curious property of *trans*-$[Rh(AA)_2X_2]^+$ complexes that they will form adducts with the halogen acids (HX) of the type $[Rh(AA)_2X_2]X.HX.2H_2O$ (a similar property is shared by the analogous cobalt (III) tetramines). Indeed it has been suggested that the formation of such adducts, which are made by simple recrystallization of $[Rh(AA)_2X_2]X$ from the concentrated aqueous acid HX, can be used as evidence of the *trans* configuration of the complexes. Compounds of this type which have been reported include *trans*-[Rh $en_2X_2]X.HX.2H_2O$ (X = Cl, Br)[123]; *trans*-[Rh $py_4X_2]X.HX.H_2O$ (X = Cl, Br)[81,123]; *trans*-[Rh $bipy_2Cl_2]Cl.HCl.2H_2O$[81], *trans*-[Rh $phen_2Cl_2]Cl.HCl.2H_2O$[81] and *trans*-[Rh $pn_2Cl_2]Cl.HCl.2\,H_2O$[81]. Infrared spectra of these complexes indicate that they contain the $(H_5O_2)^+$ ion, so they should be reformulated as *trans*-$[Rh(AA)_2X_2]X_2(H_5O_2)$[81,123]. The preparation of $[Rh\,A_4X_2](O_2NO.H.ONO_2)$ (X = Cl, Br; A = py or $\frac{1}{2}$ bipy), where the anion is the dinitrate group, has recently been described[126].

Complexes with bipyridyl, terpyridyl and *o*-phenanthroline

Curiously, no *o*-phenanthroline rhodium complexes apart from the very stable [Rh $phen_2Cl_2]Cl$ seem to have been reported, but a number of bipyridyl compounds are known, including some which appear to involve rhodium (II) and rhodium (I) (for these latter species see p. 365 and 366).

[Rh bipy$_3$](ClO$_4$)$_3$ was made as colourless crystals by fusing the ligand with rhodium trichloride at 270°. The electronic absorption and infrared spectra were recorded[225]. A chloride, bromide, iodide and thiocyanate are also known[145].

[Rh terpy$_2$]Cl$_3$ can be made by fusion of the ligand with rhodium trichloride: a bromide, iodide, thiocyanate and perchlorate were also made, the colours varying from white (perchlorate) to orange (iodide), changing apparently with the polarizability of the anion[145].

trans-**[Rh bipy$_2$Cl$_2$]Cl** can be made by reaction of an alcoholic solution of bipyridyl with an aqueous solution of $Na_3[RhCl_6]$ or rhodium trichloride[119,163], and its infrared spectrum was measured from 600 to 4000 cm^{-1} [119]. The complexes Rh bipy $Cl_3(H_2O)$, [Rh bipy-$(H_2O)_2Cl_2$]Cl, [Rh bipy$(H_2O)_3Cl$]Cl_2 and [Rh bipy$(H_2O)_4$]Cl_3 have all been claimed as by-products during the preparation of [Rh bipy$_2Cl_2$]$^+$ [163].

trans-[Rh bipy$_2$ Cl_2]$^+$ is very resistant to either acid or base hydrolysis, in contrast with *trans*-[Rh en$_2Cl_2$]$^+$, *trans*-[Rh$(NH_3)_4Cl_2$]$^+$ or *trans*-[Co bipy$_2Cl_2$]$^+$. It has been suggested that the enhanced reactivity of the cobalt complex may arise because there is a greater strain in the bipyridyl rings than in the analogous rhodium compound, the rhodium 'ion' being larger than that of cobalt; but it is not clear, however, why the *trans*-[Rh bipy$_2Cl_2$]$^+$ cation should be so much more resistant to hydrolysis than the other rhodium tetramines quoted above[169].

[Rh bipy$_2$Br$_2$]Br and a polymeric species analysing as [Rh$_2$bipy$_3$Br]$_n$ can be made from bipyridyl and $[RhBr_6]^{3-}$ in aqueous solution in the presence of hydrazine, and [Rh bipy$_2I_2$]I from rhodium triiodide and bipyridyl; the infrared and electronic absorption spectra of the two dihalo complexes were measured[119].

[Rh phen$_2$Cl$_2$]Cl was made from *o*-phenanthroline and $[RhCl_6]^{3-}$: the infrared spectrum was measured from 400 to 4000 cm^{-1}, and a *trans* configuration assigned to the cation on the basis of the electronic spectrum[119].

Dipyridylamine complexes

Complexes of the form [Rh dipyram$_3$]X_3 and [Rh dipyram$_2X_2$]X (dipyram = di-2-pyridylamine; X = Cl, Br, I) have been got from the ligand, rhodium trichloride and alkali metal halides. The infrared spectra from 200 to 750 cm^{-1} and the electronic spectra of these species (and of their iridium analogues) were reported[193a].

Nitro complexes

The nitro pentammines $[Rh(NH_3)_5(NO_2)]^{2+}$ and their formation from the isomeric nitrito species $[Rh(NH_3)_5ONO]^{2+}$ have already been considered (p. 260), cf. also Table 6.1[22].

K$_3$[Rh(NO$_2$)$_6$] is best produced by the reaction of a hot solution of potassium nitrite with $K_3[RhCl_6]$ or an acid solution of rhodium trichloride[208]. It forms colourless crystals; sodium, rubidium, caesium, ammonium, thallous and barium salts are also known. The solubility of the sodium salt in water is 40 g/100 ml at 17° and 100 g/100 ml at 100°, but the potassium salt is far less soluble. The x-ray crystal structure shows that the rhodium–nitrogen bond length is 2·10 Å (errors uncertain)[34]. The electronic absorption spectrum of $[Rh(NO_2)_6]^{3-}$ has been measured and assignments proposed[287], and the infrared and Raman spectra have also been measured[266c].

A few substituted nitro complexes are known (see Tables 6.1, 6.2 and 6.3), and there is a nitropentacyano complex (see p. 372).

No **nitrosyl complexes** of rhodium (III) seem to be definitely established, although cyanide ion reacts with $[Rh(NO)_2Cl]_n$ to give a species believed to be $K_3[Rh(NO)(CN)_5]$[131].

Hydrazine complexes

A series of very ill-defined rhodium hydrazine complexes has been claimed by Cambi and coworkers[46,47]. Addition of hydrazine hydrate to rhodium trichloride gives a series of yellow diamagnetic solids, apparently polymeric, of non-stoichiometric formulae, which react with cyanide ion to give diamagnetic polymeric cyano hydrazine and hydrazide species. Some paramagnetic rhodium (II) and rhodium (IV) species were also claimed but most of this work is difficult to accept without supporting evidence for the various formulations given.

Hydrazine complexes of the form $\mathbf{Rh_2Cl_6(PR_3)_4\ N_2H_4}$ (R = Et, Pr^n, Bu^n) have been made from $RhCl_3(PR_3)_3$ and hydrazinium chloride[49].

Alkyl cyanide (RCN) complexes

Although no such complexes are reported for osmium, ruthenium or iridium, treatment of a mixture of $Na_3[RhCl_6]$ and ammonium chloride with acetonitrile yields $\mathbf{(NH_4)_2[Rh(CH_3CN)Cl_5]}$ (rubidium, caesium and silver salts were also prepared). The complexes form red needles[205]. Complexes of the form $\mathbf{RhCl_3.3RCN}$ (R = Me, Et, Ph, 3-MeO$(CH_2)_2$) can be got from rhodium trichloride and the ligand. With glutaronitrile, $RhCl_3.1\frac{1}{2}(RCN)$ was formed, and it was suggested that this was polymeric and contained nitrile bridges. The infrared and electronic spectra of these complexes were measured; the C≡N stretching frequency rises some 70 cm^{-1} on coordination[166b,319a].

Dimethylglyoxime complexes (Dimethylglyoxime = $DMGH_2$)

$\mathbf{(NH_4)[RhX_2(DMGH)_2]}$ (X = Cl, Br, I) can be made from an alcoholic solution of rhodium trichloride, the ammonium halide and dimethylglyoxime[92,119] or from the ligand and rhodium tetrapyridine complexes[126a]. The infrared spectrum of the dichloro complex and its electronic absorption spectrum have been measured[119]. Potassium and silver salts are also known of the $[RhX_2(DMGH)_2]^-$ anion and also a 'free acid' $H[RhX_2(DMGH)_2]$, made from acid solutions of the rhodium trihalides with the ligand (X = Cl, Br, I)[92]. Later infrared and electronic spectral studies suggest that these acids indeed have the $[RhX_2(DMGH)_2]^-$ formulation in aqueous solution, but in the solid state the proton is associated with one of the dimethylglyoxime groups to give **$Rh(DMGH_2)(DMGH)X_2$**[119].

$[Rh(DMGH)_2XCl]^-$ (X = Br, SCN) salts are said to be formed by the reaction of the appropriate ammonium salts with $[RhCl_2(DMGH)_2]^-$[206], but these results could not be reproduced[119]. It was also claimed that **$Rh(DMGH)_2pyCl$** could be made from dimethylglyoxime and *trans*-$[Rh\ py_4Cl_2]Cl$[206], but in fact the product of this reaction is $[Rh(DMGH)_2Cl_2]^-$; the pyridine derivative can, however, be made from $pyH[Rh(DMGH)_2Cl_2]$ and pyridine in the presence of hypophosphorous acid, and its infrared and proton magnetic resonance spectra were measured[119].

$[Rh(DMGH)_2HCl]^-$ is believed to be the product of the reaction between borohydride ion and $[Rh(DMGH)_2Cl_2]^-$; the proton magnetic resonance spectrum was measured[117]. Other dimethylglyoxime complexes include $[RhS_6(DMGH)_2]^-$ (presumably a polysulphide S_6^{2-} group is involved here)[219] and $[Rh(NO_2)_2(DMGH)_2]^-$[219].

The complex $Rh(DMGH)_2(thiourea)Cl$ is reported[206], and there is crystallographic information on $Rh(DMGH)_2(NH_3)Cl$[264].

$Rh(DMGH)_3$ was made from rhodium sulphate and the ligand in ethanol[92]; and *cis*-$[RhCl_2(DMGH)_2]^-$ was claimed to be the oxidation product of $H_2[RhCl_2(DMGH)_2]$[92].

All these bisdimethylglyoxime complexes are likely to have the other two ligands in the *trans* positions, the two DMG groups being held in a plane by hydrogen bonding. This is not of course possible for $Rh(DMGH)_3$ and it would be desirable to have confirmatory evidence for the existence of this species.

Phthalocyanine (Pc) complexes

RhPc.Cl can be made from rhodium trichloride and *o*-cyanobenzamide[151b,184] and the infrared (220–5000 cm^{-1}) and electronic absorption spectra were recorded[184]. **$Rh.Pc.HSO_4$** has been made as deep blue crystals by fusing rhodium trichloride with phthalonitrile[184]. Rate constants for the dissociation of the latter complex in sulphuric acid were determined, and the electronic absorption spectrum measured[28].

Biguanide complexes

[Rh Bgh$_3$]Cl$_3$ (Bgh = $C_2H_7N_2$) can be got from the action of the ligand on the trichloride; the salt was resolved[111].

Phosphine, arsine and stibine complexes

These are summarized in Table 6.4. Tertiary phosphines and arsines give complexes of the form 1,2,6-$RhX_3(LR_3)_3$ (X = Cl, Br; L = P, As; R = alkyl and aryl)—the symmetrical configuration is suggested by the dipole moments of approximately 7 D[49]. There is also some evidence for the existence of 1,2,3-$RhCl_3(PR_3)_3$ species[148], made with the less sterically hindered ligands PPh_2H and PEt_2H. No stibine complexes have been so far reported. Under appropriate conditions triethyl arsine will react with rhodium trihalides to give dimeric species $Rh_2X_6(AsEt_3)_4$ and $Rh_2X_6(AsEt_3)_3$ of uncertain structures[49]. The reaction of arsines with rhodium trihalides is said to give hexakis species of the form $[Rh(AsR_3)_6][RhX_6]$[93]. If this formulation is correct these are the only hexakisarsines reported for any of the platinum metals, but it seems likely that there would be steric difficulty in arranging six bulky arsine groups around rhodium, and these complexes may in fact be $[Rh_2X_3(AsR_3)_6]X_3$. A complex with chelating diphosphines is found in [RhHCl(diphosphine)$_2$]cl only[282], but the ligand 'diarsine' reacts with rhodium trichloride to give $[Rh(diars)_2Cl_2]Cl$[245a], believed to have a *trans* configuration as only one metal–chlorine stretching mode was observed[208b].

Proton magnetic resonance spectra of $RhCl_3(PEt_2Ph)_3$ have recently been measured[272]. This species will react with saturated carboxylic acids to give olefins; thus hexanoic acid yields pent-2-ene—a carboxylato complex is apparently formed as an intermediate. The final rhodium complex is $RhCl(CO)(PEt_2Ph)_2$[270c].

Catalytic activity of phosphines and arsines. These are not so effective as catalysts as rhodium (I) phosphines, arsines and stibines (cf. p. 367), but $Rh(LR_3)_3Cl_3$ (LR_3 = PPh_3, $AsMe_2Ph$) in ethanolic solution will catalyse the reduction of hex-1-ene to n-hexane by molecular hydrogen, and in its presence n-heptaldehyde is reduced to n-heptyl alcohol by hydrogen at 50 atmospheres[249] (see also p. 367).

It is very probable that some of the hydrido species mentioned below are involved. $RhCl_3(PEt_2Ph)_3$ is a good catalyst for isomerization of 1,5-C_8H_{12} to 1,3-C_8H_{12} (p. 267)[242].

Hydrido phosphines and arsines

These complexes of rhodium (III) seem to be much less common than for iridium (III).

Monohydrides. The action of hydrogen chloride on solutions of $RhCl(PPh_3)_3$ yields $\mathbf{RhHCl_2(PPh_3)_2}$[16,282a] and on $RhCl(LPh_3)_3$ (L = As, Sb) $\mathbf{RhHCl_2(LPh_3)_2}$[216a]. The compound will undergo hydrogen transfer reactions with ethylene, acetylene and tetrafluoroethylene to give $RhClR(PPh_3)_2$ (see p. 366)[16]; infrared and proton magnetic resonance studies were also reported[16,216c]. Treatment of $RhX_3(AsPh_2Me)_3$ with hypophosphorous acid yields $\mathbf{RhHX_2(AsPh_2Me)}$ (X = Cl, Br, I), and the formulation was confirmed by their infrared spectra[208c]. This observation suggests that many if not all of the so-called 'rhodium (II)' complexes made by hypophosphorous acid reductions may be hydrides of trivalent rhodium. **[RhHCl(diphosphine)$_2$]Cl** can be made from hydrogen chloride and RhH(diphosphine)$_2$[282].

Dihydrides. Species of the form $\mathbf{RhH_2X(PPh_3)_2}$ (X = Cl, Br, I) are got when molecular hydrogen is passed into solutions of $RhX(PPh_3)_3$ in benzene or chloroform[248,282a]. The reactions are reversible. The chloro species has received the most study: it is pale yellow and the infrared and proton resonance spectra suggest a *cis* arrangement of hydride ligands and of phosphines

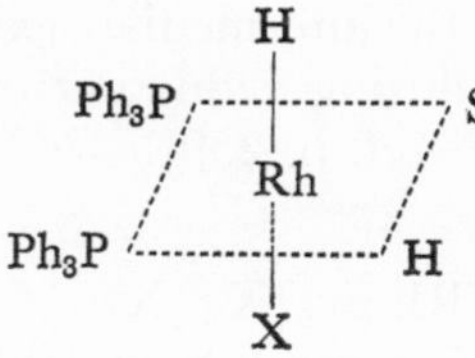

H
Ph_3P S
Rh
Ph_3P H
X

S is a solvent group; the species is probably always octahedral in solution and even as a solid may sometimes be obtained as a solvate; thus from dichloromethane the yellow complex $[RhClH_2(PPh_3)_2]$-$\frac{1}{2}CH_2Cl_2$ may be crystallized[248]. Analogous complexes of the form $RhH_2Cl(LPh_3)_2$ (L = As, Sb) can be got by the action of molecular hydrogen on solutions of $RhCl(LPh_3)_3$ in dichloromethane[216a]. Another dihydrido species is $[RhH_2Cl(PPh_3)_2]_2$, got from a solution of $Rh_2Cl_2(PPh_3)_4$ in dichloromethane with molecular hydrogen. It is thought to have the structure[248]

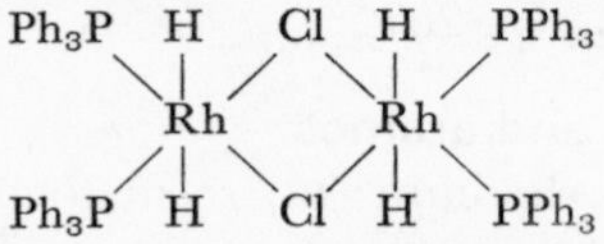

```
Ph3P  H    Cl   H    PPh3
    \ |  /   \  |  /
      Rh        Rh
    / |  \   /  |  \
Ph3P  H    Cl   H    PPh3
```

Complexes containing metal–metal bonds

Complexes of the form $(Ph_2MeAs)_3X_2Rh—HgY$ (X = Cl, Br; Y = F, Cl, Br, I, OAc) can be made from $(Ph_2MeAs)_3X_2RhH$ with the appropriate mercuric salt HgY_2; complexes with Y = CN and CNS were similarly made and it was shown that they were likely to be dimeric with cyano or thiocyanato bridges. The complexes are stable towards air and moisture in air. With halogens, hydrogen chloride or oxidizing agents the rhodium–mercury bond is broken[245]. The species $RhX_2(HgX)(PEt_2Ph)_3$ are also known[282a].

The electronic absorption spectra of the complexes in dichloromethane solution were measured, and on the basis of these results it was suggested that the 'ligands' $HgBr^-$, $HgCl^-$, HgF^- and $HgOAc^-$ exert a higher ligand-field effect than the hydride group, due perhaps to some degree of double bonding in the rhodium–mercury link[245].

Other complexes containing rhodium–metal bonds are the $SnCl_3^-$ complexes (cf. p. 398 and 401), and there are also species with rhodium–boron bonds (p. 390).

Carbonyl, alkyl and aryl phosphine complexes are considered below (p. 386).

Rhodium (II)

There is some evidence for the intermediate existence of $[\mathbf{Rh(NH_3)_5}]^{2+}$ or $[\mathbf{Rh(NH_3)_5(H_2O)}]^{2+}$ during reduction of $[Rh(NH_3)_5X]^{2+}$ with chromous hexaaquo ion[301] (cf. p. 259).

Pyridine complexes

Complexes of the form $[Rh\ py_6]X_2$ (X = Cl, Br) and $[Rh\ py_5X]X_2$ (X = Cl, Br) were claimed to result from the reaction of rhodium (III) halides with pyridine and hypophosphorous acid[86], but these have recently been shown to be, respectively, *trans*-$[Rh\ py_4X_2]X$ and (in the chloro case) *trans*-$[Rh\ py_4Cl_2](H_5O_2)Cl_2$[101]. Several other compounds were reformulated: $Rh\ py_4Br_2$ is *trans*-$[Rh\ py_4Br_2]^+$-*trans*-$[Rh\ py_2Br_4]^-$; $(pyH)_2[Rh_2\ py_4Cl_6]$ is *trans*-$[Rh\ py_4Cl_2]^+$-*trans*-$[Rh\ py_2Cl_4]^-$, and $(pyH)_4[Rh_2py_2X_8]$ is *trans*-$(pyH)[Rh\ py_2X_4]$ (X = Cl, Br)[101]. All these reformulations involve rhodium (III).

[Rh bipy$_2$Cl]NO$_3$ and **[Rh bipy$_2$Cl]ClO$_4$** (both form red crystals) can be made by the action of sodium amalgam on the appropriate [Rh bipy$_2$Cl$_2$]$^+$ salts; they are diamagnetic and it was suggested that they might contain a rhodium (III) hydride cation, [Rh bipy$_2$-HCl]$^+$ [226]. Reduction of [Rh bipy$_3$](ClO$_4$)$_3$ with sodium borohydride gave a paramagnetic species [Rh bipy$_2$]NO$_3$ which had a magnetic moment of 1·86 BM at 10°, and it was suggested that this was also a hydridic species, [Rh^{II}bipy$_2$H]NO$_3$ [226]. Rhodium (II) **cyanohydrazine** complexes have been claimed (cf. p. 360)[46,47].

Dimethylglyoxime complexes

A few complexes said to contain rhodium (II) have been reported. Sodium formate reacts with [RhCl$_2$(DMGH)$_2$]$^-$ to give a black, strongly reducing species said to be H[Rh^{II}(DMGH)$_3$], which with hydrochloric acid gave a very unstable purple-red compound which was not isolated but was thought to be H$_2$[Rh^{II}Cl$_2$(DMGH)$_2$]. On oxidation this gave yellow crystals of *trans*-H[RhCl$_2$(DMGH)$_2$] and red crystals which were thought to be *cis*-H[RhCl$_2$(DMGH)$_2$][92]. It is possible that these are rhodium (I) complexes or hydrides of rhodium (III) though the former is perhaps more likely since, although no high-field proton resonance could be detected in solutions of the 'rhodium II' species, they did not contain paramagnetic complexes[112]. For [Rh(DMGH)$_2$HCl]$^-$ see p. 355[117].

Phosphine complexes

Reaction of the phosphine (*o*-Me.C$_6$H$_4$)$_3$P (abbreviated as OP) with an ethanolic solution of rhodium trichloride at room temperatures yields the blue-green paramagnetic species *trans*-**RhCl$_2$(OP)$_2$**, isomorphous with the known square-planar palladium species. The magnetic moment at room temperatures is 2·3 BM and the electron spin resonance spectrum of the compound was measured[27a]. The species reported as RhX$_2$(AsPh$_2$Me)$_3$ (X = Cl, Br, I)[90] are in fact hydrides of rhodium (III), RhHX$_2$(AsPh$_2$Me)$_3$[208c].

Rhodium (I)

Amine complexes

The complex Rh(C$_2$H$_5$N)$_3$I was made from Rh(C$_2$H$_5$N)$_3$Cl$_3$ (cf. Table 6.2), silver oxide and iodide ion[283a].

Bipyridyl complexes

Reduction of [Rh $bipy_2Cl_2$](NO_3) with sodium borohydride gives the paramagnetic [Rh $bipy_2$](NO_3)[226] (see also p. 365); a species [Rh $bipy_2$]ClO_4 is also known[226] and may be a hydride[117].

Phosphine, arsine and stibine complexes

These are summarized in Table 6.4. The remarkable planar complexes of the form **RhX(PPh$_3$)$_3$** (X = Cl, Br, I) can be made from an ethanolic solution of the trihalide and triphenylphosphine[16,26,248], and **RhCl(LPh$_3$)$_3$** (L = As, Sb) can be got from [Rh(C_2H_4)$_2$-Cl]$_2$ and excess ligand in the absence of air[216c]. The complexes dissociate in solution:

$$RhCl(LPh_3)_3 \rightleftharpoons RhCl(LPh_3)_2 + LPh_3$$

The resulting species in solution is likely to have a weakly bound solvent molecule in the fourth coordination site. Dimeric species of the form **Rh$_2$Cl$_2$(LPh$_3$)$_4$** can be isolated from the solution.

$$2\ RhCl(PPh_3)_2(S) \rightleftharpoons [RhCl(PPh_3)_2]_2 + 2\ S$$

The dimer is pink and can be readily reconverted into RhCl(PPh$_3$)$_3$ by treatment with triphenylphosphine in ethanol[248].

Chemical reactions of RhCl(PPh$_3$)$_3$. The species undergoes a number of electrophilic addition reactions; in addition, because of the vacant coordination site available in the solvated species, nucleophilic attack may also occur on the rhodium.

Reaction with carbon monoxide and carbonyl abstraction reactions.

$$RhCl(PPh_3)_2(S) + CO \rightarrow RhCl(CO)(PPh_3)_2 + S$$

The reaction is irreversible; the phosphine complex will also form the same product by abstracting carbon monoxide from aldehydes, allyl alcohol, acetic acid and dimethylformamide at room temperature[16,308], and will catalyse the decarbonylation of aroyl chlorides to aryl chlorides at higher temperatures (200°)[33a]. Kinetic studies using n-valeraldehyde indicate that the abstraction reaction is first order in both complex and aldehyde[16]. The mechanism is discussed on p. 378[16]. The complex will also abstract a thiocarbonyl group from carbon disulphide to give RhCl(CS)(PPh$_3$)$_2$[16a] (cf. p. 390).

Reaction with ethylene.

$$RhCl(PPh_3)_2(S) + C_2H_4 \rightleftharpoons RhCl(PPh_3)_2(C_2H_4) + S$$

This reaction is reversible, but the ethylene complex is stable in the solid state (cf. p. 396).

Reaction with molecular hydrogen. There is a reversible reaction[248,249]:

$$RhCl(PPh_3)_2(S) + H_2 \rightleftharpoons RhClH_2(PPh_3)_2(S)$$

and proton magnetic resonance studies show that the two hydride ligands are *cis* to each other[248].

Other reactions of this complex are summarized in the scheme below, with page references indicating fuller discussion of the products[248]

$$RhCl(PPh_3)_3 \xrightarrow{CH_3I} RhMe.I.Cl(PPh_3)_2(MeI) \text{ (p. 373)}$$

$$RhCl(PPh_3)_3 \xrightarrow{\text{Allyl chloride}} RhCl_2(C_3H_5)(PPh_3)_2 \text{ (two forms) (p. 380)}$$

$$RhCl(PPh_3)_3 \xrightarrow{HCl} RhHCl_2(PPh_3)_2 \text{ (p. 363)}$$

$$RhCl(PPh_3)_3 \xrightarrow{O_2,\ CH_2Cl_2} RhO_2Cl(PPh_3)_2.\tfrac{1}{2}CH_2Cl_2 \text{ (p. 334)}$$

$$RhCl(PPh_3)_3 \xrightarrow{Ph_2C_2} RhCl(Ph_2C_2)(PPh_3)_2$$

$$RhCl(PPh_3)_3 \xrightarrow{L} Rh(PPh_3)_2LCl$$

(L = py, DMSO, CH_3CN)

Catalytic activity of $RhCl(PPh_3)_3$[248]

Hydrogenation reactions. In benzene or similar solvents $RhCl(PPh_3)_3$ is an efficient catalyst for the homogeneous hydrogenation by molecular hydrogen of non-conjugated olefins and acetylenes under ambient conditions, although ethylene is not hydrogenated. This catalytic activity is general for the range of complexes $RhX(PPh_3)_3$ and increases in efficiency from X = Cl to X = I, but the arsine complex $RhCl(AsPh_3)_3$ is less efficient than $RhCl(PPh_3)_3$. It is the latter which has been the most extensively investigated.

It has been shown by studies using molecular deuterium that in the catalysed reduction of maleic and fumaric acids, and of hex-2-yne to hex-2-ene, there is preferential *cis* addition; it was also found that the rate of hydrogen–deuterium exchange in the presence of the complex is slow compared with the rates of olefin hydrogenation. From quantitative studies on the rates of hydrogenation of hept-1-ene, cyclohexene and hex-1-yne the rate expression

$$\text{Rate} = \frac{k'K_1[H_2][\text{olefin}][\text{Rh catalyst}]}{1 + K_1[H_2] + K_2[\text{olefin}]}$$

was derived[248]. In this expression $[H_2]$ is the concentration of hydrogen in solution, and the rate constant k' and equilibrium constants K_1 and K_2 are thus defined:

$$\begin{array}{ccc} RhCl(PPh_3)_2(S) + H_2 & \overset{K_1}{\rightleftharpoons} & cis\text{-}RhH_2Cl(PPh_3)_2(S) \\ K_2 \text{ Olefin} \updownarrow & & \downarrow k' \text{ Olefin} \\ RhCl(PPh_3)_2(\text{olefin}) & \xrightarrow[H_2]{k''} & RhCl(PPh_3)_2(S) + \text{paraffin} \end{array}$$

For cyclohexene the values $E_a = 22{\cdot}9$ kcal/mole, $\Delta H^{\ddagger} = 22{\cdot}3$ kcal/mole, $\Delta S^{\ddagger} = 12.9$ e.u. were found for the rate-determining step.

The proposed mechanism for the hydrogenation supposes the prior formation of the *cis*-dihydro complex $RhH_2Cl(PPh_3)_2(S)$ (the existence of such a species in solutions of $RhCl(PPh_3)_3$ in the presence of molecular hydrogen alone was demonstrated by proton magnetic resonance); this is the hydrogen activation step. There is then a competitive displacement of the weakly held solvent molecule S by the olefin (substrate activation step) and finally a *cis* transfer of bound hydrogen to the olefin (hydrogen transfer step) (Figure 6.4).

The conditions necessary for the hydrogen activation step to take place are very critical: thus for systems of the type $RhCl(PPh_3)_2L$, hydrogen activation proceeds readily if L is a poor π acceptor (benzene, chloroform, pyridine, acetonitrile) but not if L is a good acceptor (carbon monoxide, tetrafluoroethylene, ethylene)—hence the failure of the complex to hydrogenate ethylene[248].

The existence of the intermediate $RhClH_2(PPh_3)_2(\text{olefin})$ has not been proved directly, but there is strong evidence that, in olefin attack on the *cis*-dihydrido species, there must be a vacant coordination site on the dihydride at which the olefin can be activated. Furthermore, as there is a rapid stereospecific *cis* reduction of the olefin it is reasonable to assume that this vacant site is *cis* to the two metal–hydrogen bonds. This then partly explains why such complexes as $Ir(CO)Cl(PPh_3)_2$ will not effectively catalyse the hydrogenation of olefins although they will readily activate molecular hydrogen—there is no vacant site for olefin coordination.

It is thought likely that the final hydrogen transfer step occurs without the formation of an alkyl intermediate but that there is a simultaneous transfer of both hydride ligands to the olefin. Thus in going through the transition state there is a simultaneous breaking of rhodium–hydrogen bonds and making of carbon–hydrogen bonds, giving two simultaneous three-centre interactions as shown in the

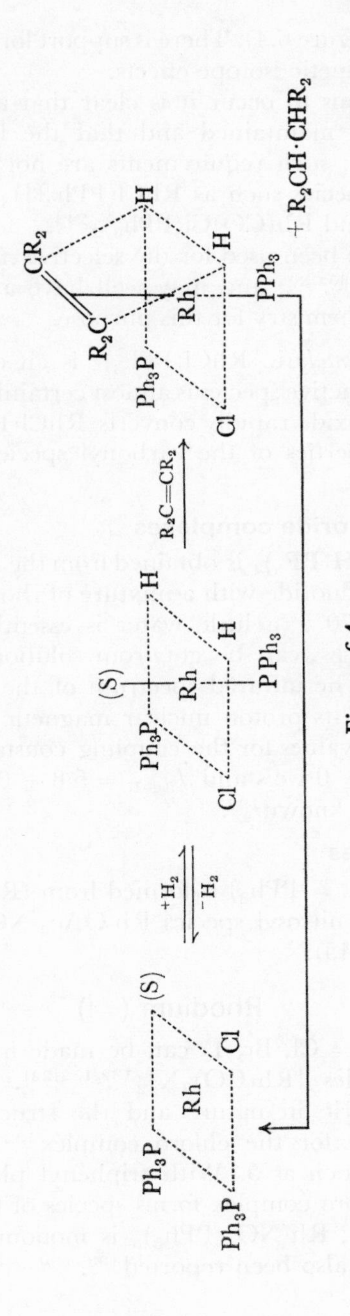
Ph$_3$P
Ph$_3$P
Rh
(S)
Cl
$^+$H$_2$
$^-$H$_2$
Ph$_3$P
Rh
(S)
H
Cl
H
PPh$_3$
R$_2$C=CR$_2$
Ph$_3$P
R$_2$C
CR$_2$
Rh
H
H
Cl
PPh$_3$
+ R$_2$CH·CHR$_2$

Figure 6.4

reaction scheme (Figure 6.4). There is support for this view from quantitative studies of kinetic isotope effects.

For these reactions to occur it is clear that a delicate balance of equilibria must be maintained and that the lability of the intermediates is critical; such requirements are not fulfilled or are only partially met by species such as $RhCl(PPh_2H)_3$, $Rh(SnCl_3)(PPh_3)_3$, $RhCl(P(OPh)_3)_3$ and $Rh(CO)Cl(PPh_3)_2$[248].

The complex has been used for the selective *cis* hydrogenation in a number of steroids[30a,80a] and may well have a promising future in synthetic organic chemistry for this purpose.

Hydroformylation catalysis. $RhCl(PPh_3)_3$ is an efficient hydroformylation catalyst; the active species is almost certainly $Rh(CO)Cl(PPh_3)_2$ since carbon monoxide rapidly converts $RhCl(PPh_3)_3$ into this[16,248]. The catalytic properties of the carbonyl species are considered on p. 388.

Phosphorus trifluoride complexes

The hydride $\mathbf{RhH(PF_3)_4}$ is obtained from the reaction of hydrogen and phosphorus trifluoride with a mixture of rhodium trichloride and copper metal at 170°; (a little water is essential to the reaction). Salts of $[\mathbf{Rh(PF_3)_4}]^-$, can be got from solutions of the hydride in aqueous acetone. The infrared spectrum of the hydride was measured, and study of its proton nuclear magnetic resonance spectrum gave the following values for the coupling constants: $J_{P-H} = 57{\cdot}4 \pm 2$ c/s, $J_{F-H} = 16{\cdot}6 \pm 0{\cdot}1$ c/s and $J_{Rh-H} = 5{\cdot}8 \pm 0{\cdot}1$ c/s[193]. The dimer $[Ph(PF_3)_4]_2$ is also known[193].

Nitrosyl complexes

$Rh(NO)L_2Cl_2$ ($L = PPh_3$) is formed from $(Rh(NO)_2Cl)_n$ and the phosphine[153]. The nitrosyl species Rh $OAc_2(NO)$ has already been mentioned[167] (p. 345).

Rhodium (–I)

$[\mathbf{Rh(NO)_2X}]_n$ (X = Cl, Br, I) can be made from nitric oxide and the carbonyl halides $[Rh(CO)_2X]_2$[132,152,221]. The complexes are black and polymeric in nature and the structure **6** (Figure 6.5) has been proposed for the chloro complex[132] although there are other possibilities such as **5**. With triphenyl phosphine, arsine and stibine (L) the chloro complex forms species of the form $\mathbf{Rh(NO)L_3}$ and $Rh(NO)L_2Cl_2$; $Rh(NO)(PPh_3)_3$ is monomeric[153]. The species $Rh(NO)(PF_3)$ has also been reported[193].

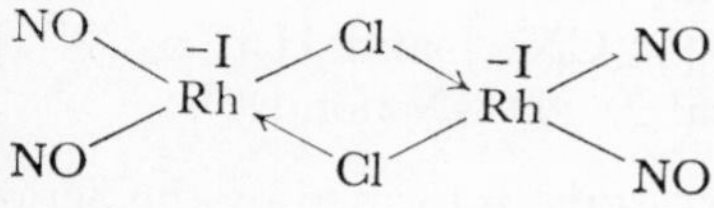

(5) 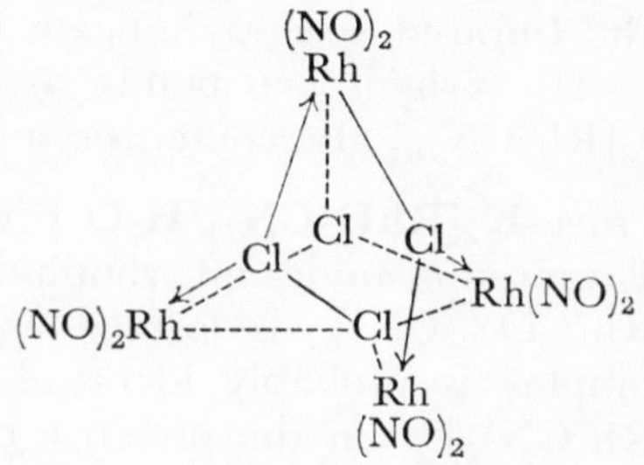 (6)

Figure 6.5 Possible structures for $[Rh(NO)_2Cl]_n$

GROUP IV DONORS

The organometallic chemistry of rhodium has been more extensively investigated than that of the other three metals. Most of the complexes involve rhodium (I), though there is a substantial carbon chemistry of rhodium (III).

Rhodium (III)

Cyanide complexes

$Rh(CN)_3$, rhodium cyanide, is formed as a brown powder by the action of concentrated sulphuric acid on solid $K_3[Rh(CN)_6]$ above 100° [191] or from cyanide ion and a solution of rhodium trichloride [196]. It will dissolve in an excess of hot potassium cyanide solution [196] and will react with aqueous ammonia to give a species thought to be $4\,Rh(CN)_3.7NH_3.7H_2O$ [191]. Its infrared spectrum has been recorded [196].

$K_3[Rh(CN)_6]$ can be made by fusion of potassium cyanide with $(NH_4)_3[RhCl_6]$; it forms pale yellow crystals, and sodium and barium salts are also known [191,227,287]. The aqueous solution is not destroyed by boiling with dilute sulphuric acid. The infrared spectra of the solid [171] and Raman spectra [229] of the aqueous solution have been measured and assignments proposed for the $[Rh(CN)_6]^{3-}$ ion (cf. Table 3.12, p. 113) (see also p. 271 for a discussion of results). The electronic absorption spectra were also measured and assigned [287]. Polarographic reduction of $[Rh(CN)_6]^{3-}$ shows a micro-electron reduction [133].

The anhydrous free acid $H_3[Rh(CN)_6]$ can be made as a white solid by the action of hydrochloric acid and ether on the potassium salt. Infrared spectra indicate that the solid contains symmetrical N—H—N hydrogen bonds, as do $H_3[Ir(CN)_6]$ and $H_3[Co(CN)_6]$: $D_3[Rh(CN)_6]$ also contains symmetrical N—D—N bonds[95].

trans-$\mathbf{K_2[RhH(CN)_4(H_2O)]}$ (white crystals) is formed by the action of excess cyanide on rhodium carbonyl chloride; the complex $[Rh(CO)_2(CN)]_n$ is formed as an intermediate[196]. This hydridic complex is probably identical with that detected in solutions of $[Rh(CN)_6]^{3-}$ in the presence of borohydride ion[133]. The infrared, electronic absorption and proton magnetic resonance spectra of $K_2[RhH(CN)_4H_2O]$ were measured, and it was concluded that the water was *trans* to the hydride[196].

Some evidence was found for the existence of $[RhH(CN)_5]^{3-}$ in solution, but no solid could be isolated[133]; it may be that the *trans* effect of the hydride group is sufficiently strong to labilize the *trans* cyanide group[196]. A theoretical interpretation of the value of the proton chemical shift in this complex has been given[209]. The tetracyano hydride reacts with oxygen to give the binuclear bridged peroxo species $\mathbf{K_4[Rh_2O_2(CN)_8(H_2O)_8]}$ and with nitric oxide to give $\mathbf{K_2[Rh(CN)_4(NO_2)(H_2O)]}$: the infrared spectra of these were recorded. A pentacyano nitro complex, $\mathbf{K_3[Rh(CN)_5NO_2]}$, was also made, and evidence obtained for a bishydroxycyano species $\mathbf{K_3[RhH(OH)_2(CN)_3]}$. A curious reaction was observed between tetrafluoroethylene and $K_2[RhH(CN)_4(H_2O)]$ in aqueous solution: the pentacyano derivative $\mathbf{K_3[Rh(CN)_5(C_2F_4H)]}$ was formed together with some rhodium metal. The fluorine and proton magnetic resonance spectra of this suggest that there is a rhodium–carbon σ bond, and the infrared spectrum was also consistent with such a formulation[196]. Another alkyl complex is *trans*-$\mathbf{K_2[Rh(CN)_5CH_3]}$, prepared from rhodium carbonyl chloride and sodium cyanide in methanol[216d].

Carbonyl complexes

See Table 6.5.

Carbonyl halides*

$\mathbf{[Rh(CO)_2F_3]_2}$ can be made by the reaction between rhodium tetrafluoride and carbon monoxide, and is the only carbonyl fluoride complex known apart from $Pt(CO)_2F_8$[293]. Salts of $\mathbf{[Rh(CO)_4I]^-}$ were prepared by the action of iodine on $[Rh(CO)_2I_2]^-$; the infrared spectrum showed only one carbonyl stretching frequency, so it was

* See also Table 6.5

concluded that the compound was probably binuclear with iodine bridges[312] (however, even a symmetrical bridged structure would be expected to show more than one carbonyl stretching mode).

Carbonyl phosphines, arsines and stibines*

The action of halogens in carbon tetrachloride on $Rh(CO)Cl(LR_3)_2$ yields $Rh(CO)Cl(LR_3)_2X_2$ (L = P, As, Sb; R = aryl; X = Cl, Br, I)[51a,274a,313]; infrared spectra were reported. The exchange rate of carbon monoxide (labelled) with $Rh(CO)Cl_3(PPh_3)_2$ was measured and found to be slow (at 25° the rate constant was $3{\cdot}6 \times 10^{-5}$ sec^{-1})[39]. For comparison, the rate of exchange of carbon monoxide with *trans*-$RhCl(CO)(PPh_3)_2$ is extremely fast at this temperature[129,330], but this latter reaction probably proceeds via a low-energy S_N2 mechanism[39]. For the trivalent complex, the slow rate is independent of carbon monoxide concentration and an S_N1 dissociation mechanism was suggested[39]:

$$Rh(CO)Cl_3(PPh_3)_2 \rightleftharpoons RhCl_3(PPh_3)_2 + CO$$

The only **hydrido carbonyl phosphine** of rhodium (III) so far reported is $RhHCl_2(CO)(PPh_3)_2$, obtained by addition of hydrogen chloride to $RhCl(CO)(PPh_3)_2$[249a]; it is stable only in the solid state and readily loses hydrogen chloride[16]. The stibine analogue has been made[154a].

Thiocarbonyl complexes

Oxidation of $RhX(CS)(PPh_3)_2$ with the halogen X_2 yields $\mathbf{RhX_3(CS)(PPh_3)_2}$ (X = Cl, Br); infrared spectra of the products were reported[16a]. A further discussion of these interesting complexes is given on p. 390. A carbonyl disulphide complex, $Rh^{III}(CS_2)_2Cl(PPh_3)$, has also been made[16a].

Alkyl and aryl complexes

Until recently no rhodium complexes of this type were known, but there has lately been a spate of work on the topic.

Alkyls

Methyl complexes. The species $RhCl(PPh_3)_3$ reacts readily with methyl iodide to give green crystals of $RhCl(MeI)_2(PPh_3)_2$, and the proton magnetic resonance spectra of the solution in deutero-chloroform suggests that the formulation should be $Rh^{III}IMeCl(PPh_3)_2$-(MeI), with a coordinated methyl iodide ligand[197a] (Figure 6.6).

* See Table 6.6.

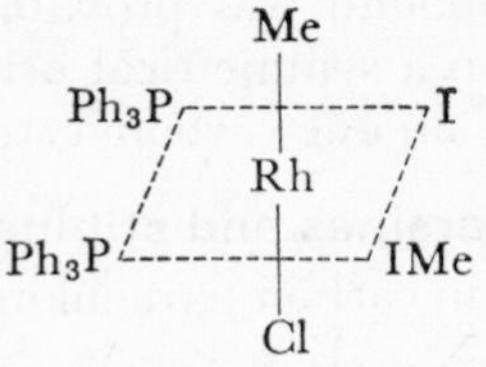

Me
Ph_3P I
Rh
Ph_3P IMe
Cl

Figure 6.6 Structure of $Rh^{III}ClIMe(Ph_3)(MeI)$

Similar complexes could not be made with MeX (X = Cl, Br), due perhaps to higher carbon–halogen bond strength in methyl chloride and bromide compared with the iodide[197a]. The methyl iodide complex reacts with carbon monoxide in the presence of methyl iodide or triphenylphosphine to give an orange product which may be **$RhClIMe(CO)(PPh_3)_2$**[197a]. The species **$RhClIMe(CO)(P(n\text{-}C_4H_9)_3)_2$** has been isolated; it forms golden-yellow crystals and will absorb carbon monoxide to give the acetyl derivative **$Rh(CH_3CO)ClI(CO)(P(n\text{-}C_4H_9)_3)_2$**; the infrared spectra of these products were recorded[149]. Similar species result from reaction of acetyl chloride with $RhCl(PPh_3)_3$: firstly **$Rh(MeCO)Cl_2(PPh_3)_2$** is formed and then **$RhMeCl_2(CO)(PPh_3)_2$**[16]. Addition of methyl iodide to Rh(fulvene)-$(CO)_2Cl$ yields the octahedral species **$RhClIMe(CO)_2$(fulvene)**[8] (cf. (**17**) of Figure 6.13). For *trans*-$K_2[Rh(CN)_5CH_3]$ see also p. 372[216d].

The reaction of a solution of $RhCl_3(SMe_2)_3$ in benzene with methyl magnesium iodide solution yields deep-red crystals of **$Rh_2I_2Me_4(SMe_2)_3$** which, from its proton magnetic resonance spectrum, is thought to contain two bridging iodide and one bridging dimethyl sulphide groups. The species will react with sodium cyclopentadienide to give **$CpRhMe_2(SMe_2)$** (Cp = $\pi\text{-}C_5H_5$); the reaction also gives a binuclear species which was not obtained in a pure state but was believed to be **$Cp_2Rh_2Me_4(SMe_2)$**, the dimethyl sulphide bridging the two metal atoms. The proton magnetic resonances of these two cyclopentadienyl complexes were measured and ^{103}Rh–proton coupling constants reported[106b].

Ethyl complexes. **$Cs[RhEtCl_3(H_2O)_2]$** can be isolated as red crystals from an acid solution of $[RhCl(C_2H_4)_2]_2$, caesium chloride and methanol; it decomposes on warming with hydrochloric acid to give ethane. There is evidence for the intermediate formation of

$[\mathbf{RhEtCl_3(C_2H_4)(S)}]^-$ and $[\mathbf{Rh(CH_2.CH_2.CH_2.CH_3)Cl_3S}]^-$ (S = solvent) during the rhodium (I) catalysed dimerization of ethylene[73] (cf. p. 395).

The hydride complex $RhHCl_2(PPh_3)_2$ will react in solution with ethylene to give $\mathbf{RhCl_2Et(PPh_3)_2}$. The reaction is very fast and its efficiency has been rationalized in terms of steric and electronic factors. The mechanism for ethylene addition is thought to involve a four-centre intermediate:

$$(Ph_3P)_2Rh(H)(S)Cl_2 \underset{}{\overset{C_2H_4}{\rightleftharpoons}} (Ph_3P)_2Rh(H)(CH_2{=}CH_2)Cl_2 \longrightarrow$$

$$(Ph_3P)_2Rh(H\cdots CH_2\cdots CH_2)Cl_2 \longrightarrow (Ph_3P)_2Rh(S)(CH_2{-}CH_3)Cl_2$$

(S) = Solvent

The complex reacts with carbon monoxide to give $\mathbf{RhCl_2Et(CO)}$-$\mathbf{(PPh_3)_2}$ at low temperatures[16]; this isomerizes to an acyl complex at $-30°$[16]. Although $RhHCl_2(PPh_3)_2$ will react with tetrafluoroethylene to give $RhCl_2(C_2F_4H)(PPh_3)_2$ the reaction is much slower than with ethylene, and this has been ascribed to the much lower σ basicity of the fluoro ligand which makes competitive displacement of solvent molecules much slower[16].

Miscellaneous alkyl and σ-allyl complexes. The phosphine complex $RhCl(PPh_3)_3$ reacts with acetylene and hydrogen chloride in solution to give $\mathbf{RhCl_2(CH{=}CH_2)(PPh_3)_2}$[16], and the carbonyl phosphine $Rh(CO)Cl(P(n\text{-}C_4H_9)_3)_2$ reacts with CH_3OCOCH_2Cl to give $\mathbf{Rh(CO)Cl_2(CH_2COOCH_3)(P(n\text{-}C_4H_9)_3)_n}$[149].

Reaction of allyl chloride or 2-methylallyl chloride with $RhCl(PPh_3)_3$ yields, in addition to π-allylic complexes, species which are believed to contain allyl groups both σ and π bonded to the rhodium (cf. Figure 6.8, p. 381); with allyl chloride and $RhCl(PPh_3)_3$, there is proton magnetic resonance evidence for the existence in solution of a complex containing a σ-bonded allyl group[197].

A vinyl complex $\mathbf{RhCl_2(CH{=}CH_2)(PPh_3)_2}$ can be got from the reaction of acetylene with a solution of $RhHCl_2(PPh_3)_3$. At low temperatures this will react with carbon monoxide to give the yellow crystalline carbonyl complex $\mathbf{RhCl_2(CH{=}CH_2)(CO)(PPh_3)_2}$, but

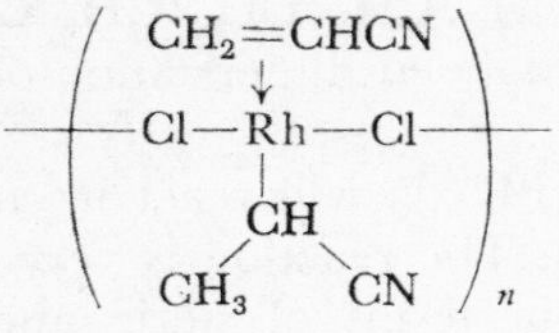

$$\left(\begin{array}{c} CH_2{=}CHCN \\ \downarrow \\ -Cl{-}Rh{-}Cl- \\ | \\ CH \\ CH_3 \quad CN \end{array}\right)_n \qquad \begin{array}{c} (py)_3RhCl_2 \\ | \\ CH \\ CH_3 \quad CN \end{array}$$

(7) 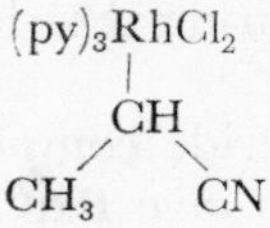 (8)

Figure 6.7

at higher temperatures there is an insertion reaction and $\mathbf{RhCl_2(COC_2H_3)(PPh_3)_2}$ results[16].

Treatment of an ethanolic solution of rhodium trichloride with acrylonitrile yields a yellow insoluble species $\mathbf{RhCl_2(CH_2{=}CHCN)_2}$ thought to have structure **7**; this reacts with pyridine to give the complex **8** (Figure 6.7). The evidence for these structures derives from infrared and some proton magnetic resonance measurements. It was suggested that the mechanism of formation of these species involves prior formation of a rhodium (III) monohydride which is then followed by a Michael addition to acrylonitrile[78a].

The reaction of an ethanolic solution of rhodium trichloride with $(o\text{-}MeC_6H_4)_3P$ (abbreviated as OP) gives the rhodium (II) species *trans*-$RhCl_2(OP)_2$ (cf. p. 365) and also a compound which analyses as $RhCl(OP)_2$ (the bromo analogue can also be made). Infrared and proton magnetic resonance measurements show this latter complex to be a rhodium (III) species in which there has been a chemical change in the ligand[27a]:

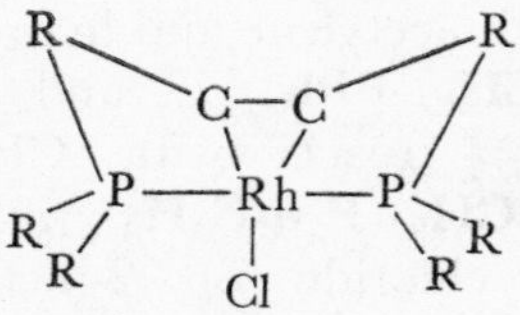

$$\begin{array}{c} R \qquad\qquad\qquad R \\ C{-}C \\ P{-}Rh{-}P \\ R\;\;R \qquad | \qquad R\;\;R \\ Cl \end{array}$$

(for clarity the hydrogen atoms and *o*-methyl groups are omitted; R represents a phenyl ring).

Reaction of tetracyanoethylene (TC) with $Rh(CO)X(PPh_3)_2$ (X = Cl, Br, NCS) in benzene leads to the stable species $\mathbf{Rh(CO)X(PPh_3)_2(TC)}$. Consideration of the infrared spectra of the products suggest that they are best regarded as rhodium (III) σ-bonded species with a three-membered rhodium–TC ring rather than rhodium (I) olefin complexes (cf. p. 399) for the analogous case of perfluoroalkyls). The thiocarbonyl complexes **Rh(CS)X(PPh$_3$)$_2$(TC)** (X = Cl, Br) were similarly prepared from Rh(CS)X(PPh$_3$)$_2$[16a].

Perfluoroalkyl complexes. Perfluoroalkyl complexes of the type **CpRh(CO)RI** (R = CF_3, C_2F_5, C_3F_7; Cp = π-C_5H_5) can be made from the perfluoroalkyl iodide and CpRh(CO)$_2$. The complexes form red crystals, and their proton and fluorine magnetic resonances were recorded[214]. X-ray crystal studies on the perfluoroethyl compound show that the metal has octahedral coordination (taking the cyclopentadienyl ligand as being formally tridentate); the rhodium–carbon (carbonyl) bond length is $1{\cdot}97 \pm 0{\cdot}03$ Å while the rhodium–carbon (alkyl) distance is $2{\cdot}08 \pm 0{\cdot}03$ Å; this small difference between the two may be taken as some evidence of double-bonding in the metal–alkyl–carbon bond. The rhodium–carbon distance to the cyclopentadienyl group is $2{\cdot}24 \pm 0{\cdot}03$ Å and the rhodium–iodine distance is 2·653 Å[59].

Reaction of Rh^{I}(acac)(C_2H_4)(C_2F_4) with a variety of donors L (phosphines, amines, nitriles) yields species of the form **Rh(acac)L$_2$-(C_2F_4)** and **[Rh(acac)L(C_2F_4)]$_2$**. The infrared and fluorine magnetic resonance spectra of these suggests that the structures involve a σ- rather than a π-bonded C_2F_4 group[254]. These species are further discussed on p. 399 (cf. Figure 5.5, p. 274).

The complex K_3[Rh(CN)$_5$(C_2F_4H)] has already been discussed[196] (p. 372). Reaction of RhHCl$_2$(PPh$_3$)$_2$ with tetrafluoroethylene gives RhCl$_2$(C_2F_4H)(PPh$_3$)$_2$.

Aryl and perfluoroaryl complexes. Treatment of RhBr$_3$(PR$_3$)$_3$ (PR$_3$ = PPr$_3$, PEt$_2$Ph) with 1-naphthyl magnesium bromide gives cream coloured crystals of **RhBr(1-naphthyl)$_2$(PR$_3$)$_2$**. These are monomeric in benzene solution and have dipole moments just over 3 D. A pentacoordinate structure was suggested in which the phosphines are in *trans* positions and produce an approximately spherical structure with a deep surrounding groove (like a yo-yo); the bromine atom and aryl groups then fill the groove to give a pentacoordinate structure[50].

The reaction of benzoyl chloride with RhCl(PPh$_3$)$_3$ gives the stable species **RhPhCl$_2$(CO)(PPh$_3$)$_2$**[16], and reaction of $C_6H_5CH_2X$ (X = Cl, I) with RhCl(CO)(P(n-C_4H_9)$_3$)$_2$ gives **Rh(CO)XCl-($C_6H_5CH_2$)(P(n-C_4H_9)$_3$)$_2$** as golden yellow crystals; the infrared spectrum was recorded[149].

Certain cyclopentadienyl rhodium complexes with aromatic perfluoro ligands can be regarded as containing metal–perfluoroaryl σ bonds (cf. p. 392).

Acyl and aroyl complexes

Reactions between solutions of $RhCl(PPh_3)_3$ in dichloromethane and acetyl, propionyl or benzoyl chlorides are complex and yield a variety of products, the nature of which depend on the conditions of preparation. The acyl or aroyl derivatives $\mathbf{RhCl_2(COR)(PPh_3)_2}$ ($R = Me, Et, Ph$) may be obtained, often with 'solvent of crystallization'. In the case of the benzoyl complex aryl migration to the thermodynamically more stable $RhCl_2Ph(CO)(PPh_3)_2$ easily occurs and appears to be irreversible, whereas the isomerization of the acetyl complex to $RhCl_2Me(CO)(PPh_3)_2$ is reversible; no evidence was obtained, however, for the existence of $RhCl_2Et(CO)(PPh_3)_2$ in the reaction leading to the propionyl complex $RhCl_2(COEt)(PPh_3)_2$. Reaction of the latter with carbon monoxide or ethanol gave $RhCl_2(COEt)(CO)(PPh_3)_2$ and $RhCl_2(COEt)(EtOH)(PPh_3)_2$. Infrared and proton magnetic resonance spectra of these products were measured[16]. Other acyl complexes have recently been reported[308].

The reaction of $RhCl(PPh_3)_3$ with acyl or aroyl chlorides is thought to involve an initial *cis*-addition process giving a pentacoordinate species which is coordinatively unsaturated; alkyl or aryl migration leads to an octahedral complex. The second stage illustrated below is that of decarbonylation: thus the aldehyde decarbonylation reactions of $RhCl(PPh_3)_3$ to give *trans*-$RhCl(CO)(PPh_3)_2$ (p. 388) probably take such a path.

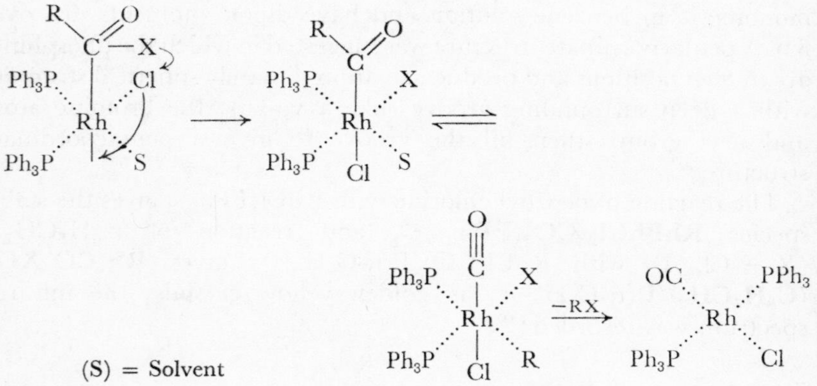

(S) = Solvent

Addition of Me(CO)X to $RhX(CO)(PEt_2Ph)_2$ (X = Cl, Br) yields $\mathbf{RhX_2(COMe)(CO)(PEt_2Ph)_2}$[51a] and RhClIMe(CO)(P(n-$C_4H_9)_3)_2$ absorbs carbon monoxide to give **RhClI(COMe)(CO)-**$\mathbf{(P(C_4H_9)_3)_2}$[149].

'Sandwich' complexes*

Salts of the 'rhodicinium' cation $\mathbf{Cp_2Rh^+}$ can be got by treating rhodium trisacetylacetonate with cyclopentadienyl magnesium bromide[67,105]. The salts were isolated as the nitrate and perchlorate and their electronic absorption spectra recorded. The infrared and proton magnetic resonance spectra of Cp_2Rh^+ salts have been recorded[105]. Polarographic reduction of the perchlorate showed a one-electron wave ($E_{1/2} = -1{\cdot}53$ v versus s.c.e.), the product of reduction being, presumably, neutral rhodocene, Cp_2Rh[67].

A few other cyclopentadienyl derivatives of rhodium (III) have been prepared. The species $\mathbf{[CpRh(C_6H_5.C_5H_4)]^+}$ (π-cyclopentadienyl π-phenylcyclopentadienyl rhodium (III)) can be got by the action of hydrochloric acid on CpRh(1-*exo*-$C_6H_5.C_5H_4$) (the latter is compound (C) of p. 393); the action of halogens on (C) yields $\mathbf{[CpRhX_2]_n}$ (X = Br, I). Pyridine reacts with $[CpRhBr_2]_n$ to give $\mathbf{CpRhBr_2Py}$, a typical 'bridge-splitting' reaction. The infrared spectra of all these complexes are consistent with the formulations given[10a]. There are a few cyclopentadienyl complexes containing methyl groups (cf. p. 374)[106b] and a number of cyclopentadienyl rhodium (III) complexes with π-allyl ligands (p. 381)[270a].

Reaction of $CpRh(CO)_2$ with a solution of iodine in ether gives $\mathbf{CpRh(CO)_2I_2}$[188a], and of $CpRh(C_3H_5)_2$ with hydrochloric acid gives $\mathbf{[CpRhCl_2]_n}$[270a].

The compound $\mathbf{Cp_6Rh_2}$ is formed as a by-product of the reaction between sodium cyclopentadienide and rhodicinium salts. Because of its insolubility it was not possible to measure its proton magnetic resonance spectrum; it was suggested that it might be a Diels–Alder adduct type of molecule, formed by the condensation of two cyclopentadienyl rings from the species CpRh(1-exo-$C_5H_5.C_5H_5$)[10a].

Assignment of the fundamental modes in the infrared spectrum of $[(\pi\text{-}C_6H_6)RhCp]^{2+}$ has been made[106a].

A large number of rhodium (I) monocyclopentadienyl complexes are known (cf. p. 391). That no rhodium (III) hexamethylbenzene species have been reported, is unexpected since such compounds are found for rhodium (II) and rhodium (I).

* In this section Cp denotes (π-C_5H_5).

Olefin complexes

Only a few rhodium (III) olefin complexes are known, though a large number of rhodium (I) species are known (cf. p. 394). Ruthenium (II), which is isoelectronic with rhodium (III), does form numerous olefin complexes (p. 188), and it has been suggested that the reluctance of rhodium (III) to do so arises from its greater charge and consequently smaller size, which prevents a good overlap of ligand and metal orbitals[27].

The species $[\mathbf{Rh}(\mathbf{C_2H_5})\mathbf{Cl_3}(\mathbf{C_2H_4})]_2^{2-}$ is believed to be formed as a product of the reaction between $[Rh^{I}(C_2H_4)_2Cl_2]^-$ and hydrogen chloride; a diethylene species, $[Rh(C_2H_4)_2HCl_3]^-$, is probably also involved in this process. Equilibrium constants for the reaction

$$[Rh(C_2H_5)Cl_3(C_2H_4)S]^- \rightleftharpoons [Rh(C_2H_5)Cl_3S]^- + C_2H_4$$

(S = solvent) have been measured[73] (cf. also p. 395).

A number of monocyclopentadienyl complexes with four-electron donors L of the form **CpRhL** are known, which may be regarded as diene complexes of rhodium (I) or monoolefin complexes of rhodium (III). For convenience these have been grouped together and are dealt with on p. 392.

Fulvene complexes of the form Rh(fulvene)$(CO)_2Cl_2H$ and $[RhCl_3(\text{fulvene})]_2$ have been made from Rh(fulvene)$(CO)_2Cl$ and hydrogen chloride; the fulvenes (di-*p*-tolyl and diphenylfulvene) function as olefin donors (cf. p. 396 and Figure 6.13) (**16**)[8].

Allyl complexes

Trisallyl rhodium (III), $\mathbf{Rh(C_3H_5)_3}$, can be made by the action of allyl magnesium chloride on $[RhCl(C_3H_5)_2]_2$: it forms yellow crystals (m.p. 80–85°)[270a]. The proton magnetic resonance spectra of this complex over a temperature range suggest that there are three π-allylic ligands symetrically bonded (though non-equivalent) per rhodium atom. The mass spectrum of the complex has also been recorded[24a].

Reaction of $Rh^{I}(PPh_3)_3Cl$ with allyl or 2-methylallyl chloride yields $Rh(PPh_3)_2(RC_3H_4)Cl_2$ (R = H, Me), each compound existing in two forms (Figure 6.8). The proton magnetic resonance spectra of these suggest that in one case the allyl group forms both a σ and a π bond to the metal (**9**) and in the other it is fully π bonded to the metal (**10**)[197a]; other n.m.r. data are also reported on the methyl allyl

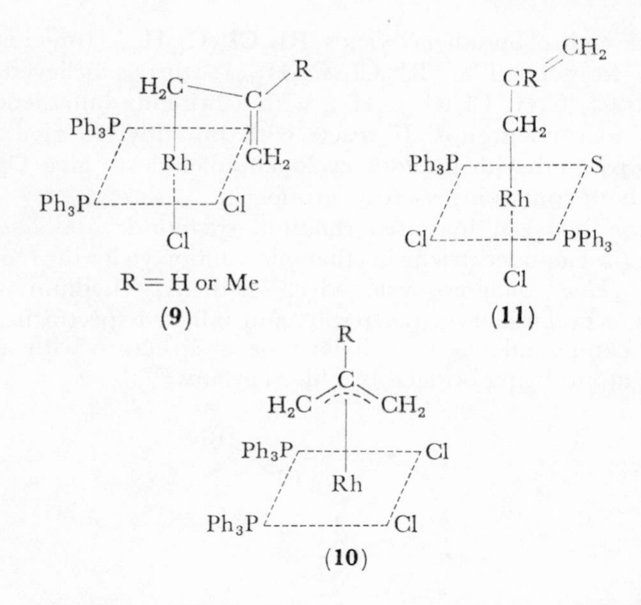

Figure 6.8 Possible structures of $Rh(PPh_3)_2(RC_3H_4)Cl_2$

species[317c]. One of the forms of $Rh(PPh_3)_2(C_3H_5)Cl_2$, while it has structure **9** in the solid state, is thought to be a σ-allyl complex in solution (**11**). A carbonyl complex, $\mathbf{Rh(PPh_3)_2(CO)(C_3H_5)Cl_2}$ can be made from $Rh(PPh_3)_2(C_3H_5)Cl_2$ and carbon monoxide[197a].

Reaction of allyl chloride with methanolic solutions of rhodium carbonyl chloride yields $\mathbf{[RhCl(C_3H_5)_2]_2}$, and it was found that water is essential to the reaction which may be summarized as

$$[Rh(CO)_2Cl]_2 + 6\,C_3H_5Cl + 4\,H_2O \rightarrow [RhCl(C_3H_5)_2]_2 + 4\,CO_2 + 2\,C_3H_6 + 6\,HCl$$

With 2-methylallyl chloride the analogous species $\mathbf{(RhCl(C_4H_7)_2)_2}$ is formed, but at 40° the main product is $\mathbf{[RhCl(C_8H_{14})]_2}$, this being di-$\mu$-chloro-bis-(2,5-dimethylhexa-1,5-diene). With pyridine, $[RhCl(C_3H_5)_2]_2$ gave $\mathbf{RhCl\,py(C_3H_5)}$ and $\mathbf{[Rh\,py_2(C_3H_5)_2]^+}$, and with thallous cyclopentadienide it gives $\mathbf{CpRh(C_3H_5)_2}$; this latter compound reacts with hydrochloric acid to give $\mathbf{CpRhCl(C_3H_5)}$ (which appears to contain a σ- and a π-bonded allyl) and $[CpRhCl_2]_n$[270a]. The reaction of an ethanolic solution of rhodium trichloride with butadiene yields $\mathbf{Rh_2Cl_4(C_{12}H_{20})}$ (previously incorrectly formulated as $Rh_2Cl_4(C_{12}H_{18})$); this is believed to be $(C_4H_7)RhCl_2(C_4H_6)Cl_2Rh(C_4H_7)$, with a bridging butadiene group and two π-crotyl groups. It reacts with bipyridyl to give $\mathbf{RhCl_2(C_4H_7)bipy}$ and with thallous cyclopentadienide to give $\mathbf{CpRhCl(C_4H_7)}$, both containing π-crotyl groups[270a].

Reaction between hydrated rhodium trichloride and *trans,trans,-trans*-1,5,9-cyclododecatriene in ethanolic solution yields the red species $\mathbf{RhCl_2(C_{12}H_{19})}$, dichloro(cyclododeca-1,5-dienyl) rhodium (III). On the basis of preliminary x-ray results and infrared spectra it appears that the compound has a π-allylic type of structure with adjacent rhodium atoms being bridged by chloro groups[250]:

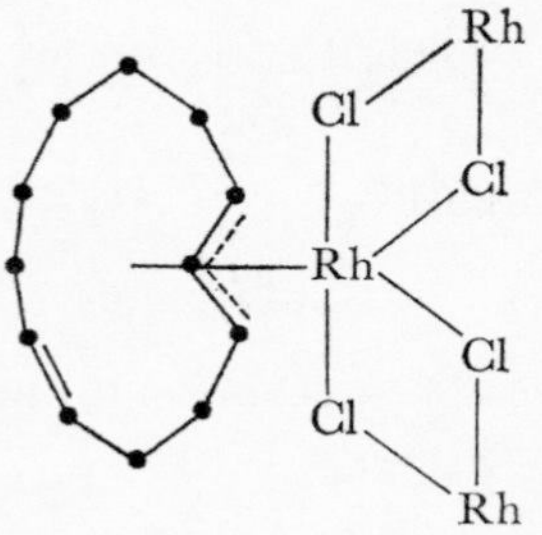

Figure 6.9 Structure of $RhCl_2(C_{12}H_{19})$

It was supposed that the ethanol functions as a reducing agent and that a rhodium (III) hydride complex is first formed; this isomerizes the ligand by means of a reversible nucleophilic attack on the olefinic double bond by the hydride, and a π-allyl–metal bond is then formed. The compound will react with a number of bidentate ligands to give orange or yellow products $\mathbf{RhCl_2(C_{12}H_{19})}$ (L = en, bipy, *p*-toluidine, 1,3-butadiene), and will react with carbon monoxide to give $\mathbf{Rh(CO)_2Cl_2(C_{12}H_{19})}$ (the proton magnetic resonance spectrum of this was measured) and with ammonia to give $\mathbf{RhCl_2(C_{12}H_{19})(NH_3)_2}$[250].

Rhodium allyl complexes probably function as intermediates in rhodium chloride catalysed reactions[242] (cf. p. 267), and there is a report of an uncharacterized species obtained by reaction of allyl alcohol with rhodium trichloride; on reaction with more allyl alcohol, $Rh_2Cl_2(C_3H_5OH)_4$ is formed (p. 400)[241] (these may, however, be olefinic species[197a]).

Rhodium (II)

The only rhodium (II) organometallic complexes so far reported involve π-bonding ligands where extensive delocalization of the unpaired electron on to the ligand is possible.

Rhodocene, Cp_2Rh, has been ingeniously prepared by the bombardment of ^{104}ruthenocene with neutrons[24]:

$$Cp_2{}^{104}Ru \xrightarrow{n,\gamma} Cp_2{}^{105}Ru \xrightarrow{\beta^-,\gamma} Cp_2{}^{105}Rh \xrightarrow{\beta^-} \text{rhodocene}(^{104}Rh)$$

There is no real evidence, however, that a rhodium (III) hydride was not formed. Recently, however, rhodocene has been prepared by a more straightforward chemical method, by the action of sodium on rhodicinium salts. The first product is dimeric, $\mathbf{Cp_4Rh_2}$; the infrared and proton magnetic resonance spectra of solutions of this yellow crystalline material suggest that it contains linked cyclopentadiene groups (see p. 277). The same preparation also yields a dark coloured sublimate which changes in the course of a few minutes to the dimer. Its paramagnetism and electron spin resonance spectrum (it has two g values, $g_{\parallel}$ 2·033 and $g_{\perp}$ 2·002) indicate that it is rhodocene, $\mathbf{Cp_2Rh}$, and this can also be made by direct sublimation of Cp_4Rh_2[105a]. Bishexamethyl benzene rhodium (II) salts, $[(\pi\text{-}C_6Me_6)_2Rh]^{2+}$, can be made from rhodium trichloride, aluminium, hexamethylbenzene and aluminium tribromide: red salts with $[PtCl_6]^{2-}$ and $[PF_6]^-$ were isolated. The infrared spectrum was measured from 400 to 4000 cm^{-1} and the magnetic susceptibility determined over the range 90 to 291°K (cf. Table 6.7, p. 418) (μ_{eff} = 1·32 BM at room temperature)[105]. The stability of this rhodium (II) species is remarkable. On reduction with zinc in hydrochloric acid it gives salts of $[(\pi\text{-}C_6Me_6)_2Rh]^+$[105] (cf. p. 394).

Rhodium (I)

There is an extensive organometallic chemistry of rhodium (I).

Cyanide complexes

The apparently monovalent rhodium cyano complex prepared by reduction of $[Rh(CN)_6]^{3-}$ with hypophosphorous acid[222] is almost certainly identical with the rhodium (III) hydrido cyano complexes described above, and the same is likely to be true of the two-electron polarographic reduction product of $[Rh(CN)_6]^{3-}$[133]. Two genuine rhodium (I) cyanides have, however, been made: $[\mathbf{Rh(CO)_2(CN)}]_n$, a blue species made by addition of a methanolic solution of potassium cyanide to rhodium carbonyl chloride, and **[Rh(PPh$_3$)$_2$(CN)]$_n$**, made by addition of triphenyl phosphine to [Rh(CO)$_2$(CN)]$_n$. The infrared spectra of these complexes were measured[196]. A possible structure for the latter is [Rh(PPh$_3$)$_2$(CN)]$_4$, in which four rhodium (I) atoms at the corners of a square are linked by four linear cyanide bridges; this is consistent with the infrared spectra which suggest that linear cyanide bridges are present. The structure then would be similar to that established for [R$_2$Au^{III}(CN)]$_4$[187,260].

Isocyanide complexes

[Rh(CNR)$_4$]$^+$ salts can be made by refluxing the appropriate isocyanides with rhodium trichloride (R = *p*-ClC$_6$H$_4$, C$_6$H$_5$, C$_7$H$_7$O); the complexes were isolated as chlorides, perchlorates and hexafluorophosphates. Curiously, the colour of the solutions varies with the solvent; thus [Rh(*p*-MeC$_6$H$_4$NC)$_4$]$^+$ is yellow in benzene, blue in methanol, violet in ethanol, red in aqueous ethanol and violet in chloroform, while the solid perchlorate is yellow. This behaviour is suggestive of solvent interaction, and in some cases addition products with the solvents were isolated[220]. Treatment of RhX(CO)(LR$_3$)$_2$ with isocyanides yields **[Rh(RNC)$_2$(LR$_3$)$_2$]X** (X = Cl, Br; X = P, As, Sb; R = aryl)[314]. All these rhodium (I) isocyanide complexes are diamagnetic and are likely to be square planar. For carbonyl isocyanide complexes see p. 390.

Carbonyl complexes

See Table 6.5.

Carbonyl halides

These are of the form **[Rh(CO)$_2$X]$_2$** (X = Cl, Br, I) (made by the action of carbon monoxide on rhodium trihalides)[197,312] and **[Rh(CO)$_2$X$_2$]$^-$** (X = Cl, Br, I), made from [Rh(CO)$_2$Cl]$_2$ and the halogen acid. The tetrabutylammonium salts were isolated and the infrared spectra measured[312]. The binuclear species **[Rh$_2$(CO)$_2$X$_4$]$^{2-}$** (X = Br, I) have also been made, the infrared spectra were measured and a halogen-bridged structure proposed[312].

[Rh(CO)$_2$Cl]$_2$ has proved in recent years to be one of the most important compounds of rhodium, in particular as a starting material for the preparation of other rhodium (I) species. It may be prepared by passing carbon monoxide over rhodium trichloride at 105°[213], and forms red crystals. The x-ray crystal structure shows that the solid has an unusual structure (Figure 6.10). Two essentially planar

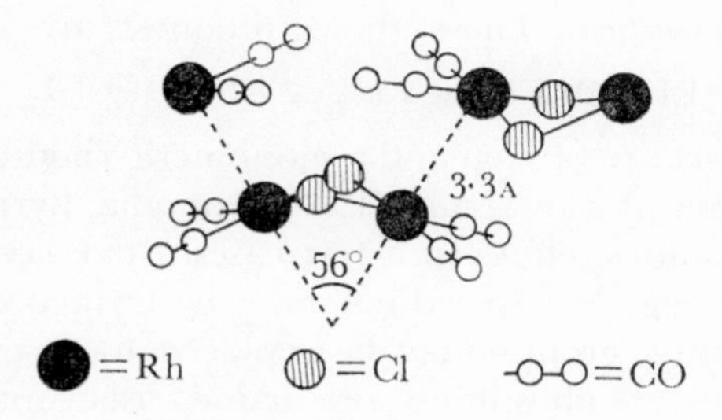

Figure 6.10 Rhodium carbonyl chloride

$Rh(CO)_2Cl$ groups are joined by two chloride bridges, the planes of the two groups being inclined at an angle of about 124°: the rhodium–carbon distance is 1·77 ± 0·05 Å, the carbon–oxygen distance is 1·21 ± 0·05 Å, and the rhodium–(bridge) chlorine distance is 2·38 ± 0·05 Å. The rhodium–rhodium distance is only 3·31 Å, and it appears that in the solid the dimers are held together in an infinite chain by weaker metal–metal bonds which are broken in solution. It is suggested that the stronger metal–metal bond within the dimer arises through 'bent bonding', i.e. overlap of metal orbitals which do not point directly at each other but make an angle of about 56° [74]. (The formation of such bent metal–metal bonds has also been postulated for osmium dodecacarbonyl, cf. p. 100). It is possible that these bent metal–metal bonds persist in solutions of rhodium carbonyl chloride, since the dipole moment of the species in solution is 1·64 ± 0·3 D (and of the bromide 2·23 ± 0·3 D); for a coplanar structure a zero dipole moment would be expected[109], but large atom polarization effects in complexes of heavy metals make such arguments dubious.

There is a very fast exchange of labelled carbon monoxide with rhodium carbonyl chloride at room temperatures, and it was suggested that a singly bridged intermediate was involved[330]:

$$(CO)_2Rh\begin{matrix} Cl \\ \diagup\;\diagdown \\ \diagdown\;\diagup \\ Cl \end{matrix}Rh(CO)_2 \rightleftharpoons (CO)_2Rh{-}Cl{-}Rh(CO)_2Cl$$

$$\underset{-CO}{\overset{+CO}{\rightleftharpoons}} (CO)_3Rh{-}Cl{-}Rh(CO)_2Cl$$

Reactions of the carbonyl chloride (cf. also Figure 6.11)

These are of the following three main types.

Bridge-splitting reactions. These, the commonest, are of the form

$$[Rh(CO)_2Cl]_2 + 2\,L \rightarrow 2\,Rh(CO)_2Cl.L$$

The chloro bridges are broken and a monomeric rhodium (I) complex, presumably square planar, results (L = ammonia, pyridine, hydroxylamine, alkyl cyanides, etc.). In a few cases a five coordinate species $Rh(CO)_2Cl.L_2$ (e.g. L = pyridine) may be formed, and sometimes one of the carbonyl groups may be replaced to give $Rh(CO)Cl.L_2$ (e.g. L = triphenyl phosphine or arsine, isocyanides, dimethylsulphoxide)[152,197]. In one case an octahedral rhodium (I) complex (a rare coordination for this oxidation state), $Rh(CO)Cl.L_4$ (L = triphenyl stibine) was formed[309].

Bridge replacement. These may be effected by silver salts in non-aqueous media:

$$[Rh(CO)_2Cl]_2 + 2\,AgX \rightarrow [Rh(CO)_2X]_2 + 2\,AgCl$$

and the X groups (e.g. acetate, phthalate, nitrate, sulphate) function as bridging groups: it has even been suggested that in $[Rh(CO)_2]_2SO_4$ the sulphate is tetradentate[197].

Carbonyl replacement. This takes place without bridge-splitting with dienes:

$$[Rh(CO)_2Cl]_2 + 2\,\text{diene} \rightarrow [Rh\ \text{diene}\ Cl]_2 + 4\,CO$$

but in some cases the carbonyl groups are displaced and the bridge destroyed[35]:

$$[Rh(CO)_2Cl]_2 + 2\,\text{diene} + 2\beta\text{-diketone} \rightarrow 2\,Rh(\text{diene})(\beta\text{-diketone}) + 2\,HCl + 4\,CO$$

and[282]:

$$[Rh(CO)_2Cl]_2 + 4\,\text{diphosphine} \rightarrow 2[Rh(\text{diphosphine})_2]Cl + 4\,CO$$

Adducts. Crystalline addition complexes of rhodium carbonyl chloride with dienes of the form $[Rh(CO)_2Cl]_2$.diene (diene = cyclohexa-1,5-diene, 2,3-dimethyl-1,3-butadiene) can be made from the carbonyl chloride and the dienes. Infrared and proton magnetic resonance spectra were recorded[326b].

Carbonyl phosphine, arsine and stibine complexes

These are summarized in Table 6.6. They are of the form $\mathbf{Rh(LR_3)_2(CO)X}$ (L = P, As, Sb; X = Cl, Br; R = alkyl or aryl), made by the action of LR_3 on rhodium carbonyl chloride or, in some cases, from the ligand and alcoholic solutions of rhodium trichloride:

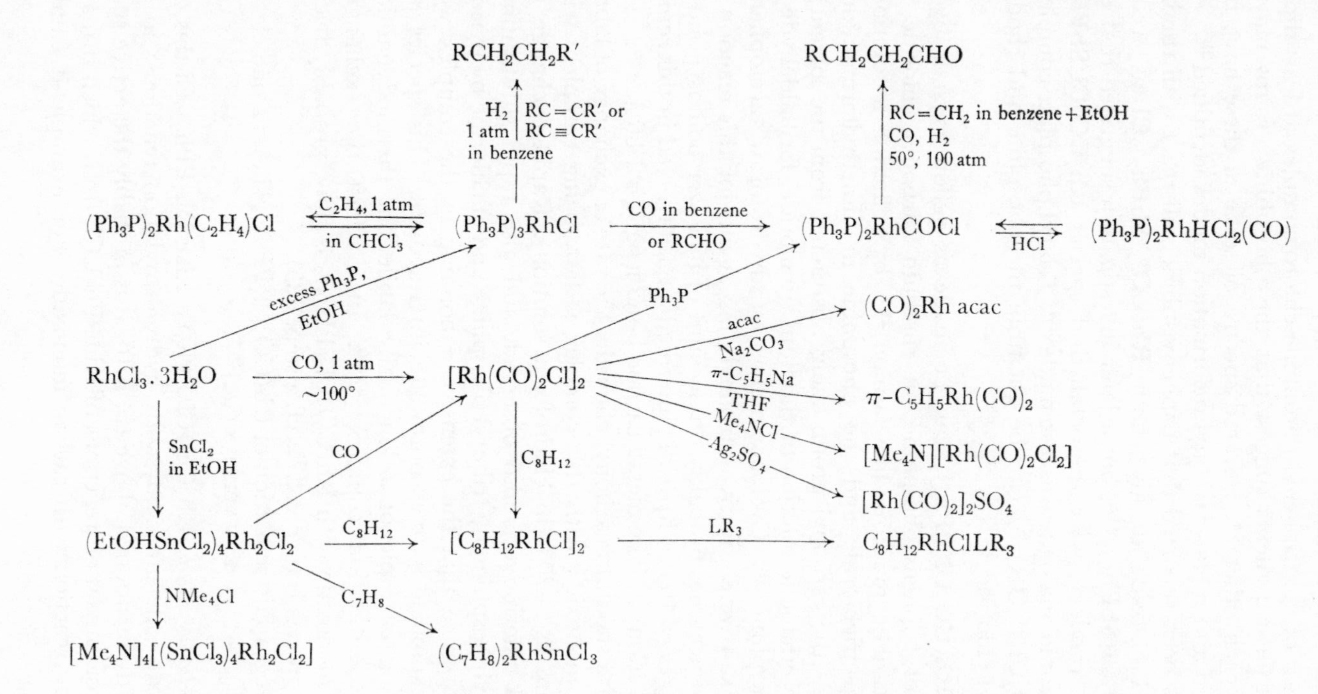

Figure 6.11 Reactions of rhodium carbonyl chloride

in the case of the triphenyl phosphine chloro complex at least dipole-moment measurements suggest that the phosphine groups may be *trans* to each other[315]. Infrared spectra of some of these have been measured and metal–carbonyl deformation modes identified[2b].

It has been reported that triphenylstibine will react with rhodium carbonyl chloride to give both $\mathbf{Rh(CO)_2(SbPh_3)_3Cl}$ as well as $\mathbf{Rh(CO)Cl(SbPh_3)_2}$[155], but a later investigation suggested that both reaction products were the octahedral species $\mathbf{Rh(CO)Cl(SbPh_3)_4}$, and a bromo analogue was also made[309]. Triaryl phosphite complexes, $\mathbf{Rh(CO)Cl(P(OR)_3)_2}$, can be got from the phosphite and rhodium carbonyl chloride[311].

trans-$\mathbf{Rh(CO)Cl(PPh_3)_2}$ can be made as yellow crystals by the action of triphenylphosphine on rhodium carbonyl chloride (the arsine can be made in like fashion)[215], by refluxing a solution of rhodium trichloride and the phosphine in dimethylformamide or alcohols, (the carbonyl group being abstracted from the solvent), or from an ethanolic solution of rhodium trichloride, formaldehyde and the phosphine[248]. Cyclohexanone, tetrahydrofuran, acetophenone and dioxan were effective carbonylating agents for this reaction also (but not acetone, probably on account of its lower boiling point). It was suggested that a hydridic intermediate is involved in this remarkable reaction[281]. The metal–carbon bond length is 1·86 Å[319b].

As with rhodium carbonyl chloride, the rate of exchange of labelled carbon monoxide with this complex is fast, being complete within a minute at $-20°$ (in chloroform solution). Rapid exchange with labelled chlorine was also observed, and also rapid substitution of triphenylphosphine by tributyl phosphine and of chlorine by pyridine. It was argued that the extensive π bonding in the complex would greatly stabilize a five coordinate intermediate. This species is an interesting example of a kinetically labile but thermodynamically stable coordination complex[129,330]. In contrast the exchange of carbon monoxide with $Rh(CO)Cl_3(PPh_3)_2$ is slow, probably because an S_N1 process is involved[39] (cf. also p. 385).

Polarographic reduction of $Rh(CO)Cl(PPh_3)_2$ shows a one-electron wave ($E_{1/2} = -1{\cdot}43$ v versus s.c.e.)[281].

Catalytic activity of $Rh(CO)Cl(PPh_3)_2$. Like $Rh(PPh_3)_3Cl$ this complex is an efficient catalyst for hydroformylation reactions; in fact, as already mentioned above (p. 370), it is probably the active species in hydroformylation reactions of $Rh(PPh_3)_3Cl$, from which it may be made by reaction with carbon monoxide. For example it catalyses the reaction of hex-1-yne with a 1:4 hydrogen–carbon monoxide mixture at 110° and 120 atmospheres pressure to give n-heptaldehyde and 2-methylhexaldehyde[166a]. The mechanism is likely to be similar to that postulated for cobalt carbonyl catalysed hydroformylations; a hydridic intermediate is formed which adds on to the olefinic double bond, and the carbonyl group is inserted into the metal–carbon bond formed in the resulting metal–alkyl intermediate[249].

$Rh(SO_2)Cl(CO)(PPh_3)_2$ is formed by the action of sulphur dioxide on $Rh(CO)Cl(PPh_3)_2$: it is isomorphous with the analogous iridium complex (p. 280)[317a].

Hydrido carbonyl phosphine complexes*

The only example reported seems to be **$RhH(CO)(PPh_3)_3$**, made by treating $Rh(CO)Cl(PPh_3)_2$ with hydrazine and triphenylphosphine; the infrared and proton magnetic resonance spectra were measured[23]. The x-ray crystal structure of the complex showed that it has a trigonal bipyramidal structure: in the trigonal plane there are the three phosphorus atoms of the phosphine groups (rhodium–phosphorus 2·32 ± 0·01 Å) and the two axial groups are hydrogen (Rh—H 1·60 ± 0·12 Å) and carbonyl (Rh—C = 1·83 ± 0·03 and C—O = 1·18 ± 0·02 Å). The rhodium atom is displaced 0·355 Å below the equatorial plane towards the carbonyl group, and there is no apparent bond-lengthening of the metal–carbon bond *trans* to the hydride. The rhodium–hydrogen distance is 'normal' as judged by the sum of 'covalent radii'[195].

This determination is of considerable interest as it indicates that in this complex at least, the metal–hydrogen distance is close to that expected from the sum of covalent radii of rhodium and hydrogen (for a list of such calculated bond distances, see footnote (15) in reference 144a). It appears that some metal–hydrogen bonds may be much shorter, however, as in the case of $HMn(CO)_5$ which has a metal–hydrogen distance of 1·28 Å[144a].

Catalytic activity of $RhH(CO)(PPh_3)_3$. This complex, in ethanolic solution, will catalyse the exchange of molecular hydrogen and deuterium and will also function as a catalyst for the homogeneous reduction of ethylene by molecular hydrogen. It is less efficient in this respect than $IrH(CO)(PPh_3)_3$ which, unlike the rhodium complex, will take up molecular hydrogen to give $IrH_3(CO)(PPh_3)_3$—possible reasons for this have already been proposed (p. 279)[317].

* See Table 6.6.

Complexes containing metal–metal bonds. Reaction of $Rh(CO)Cl(PPh_3)_2$ with sodium amalgam solution in a carbon monoxide atmosphere yields $Na[Rh(CO)_2(PPh_3)_2]$, which will react with Me_3SnCl to give $\mathbf{Me_3Sn{-}Rh(CO)_2(PPh_3)_2}$[63a].

Thiocarbonyl complexes

The compound $RhCl(PPh_3)_3$ will abstract a carbonyl group from an aldehyde to give *trans*-$RhCl(CO)(PPh_3)_2$; similarly, it will react with carbon disulphide to give the monomeric $\mathbf{RhCl(CS)(PPh_3)_2}$ as bright orange crystals (m.p. 250°). The infrared spectrum of this remarkable species suggests that it has a metal–carbon bond and that there is metal–carbon π bonding. An x-ray crystal structure analysis of the chloro complex shows that the Rh—C—S system is linear (Rh—C $= 1{\cdot}787 \pm 0{\cdot}01$ Å and C—S $= 1{\cdot}536 \pm 0{\cdot}01$ Å and that the rhodium has square-planar coordination (Rh—Cl $= 2{\cdot}386 \pm 0{\cdot}003$ Å, Rh—P $= 2{\cdot}335 \pm 0{\cdot}002$ Å). The C—S distance in the complex is only slightly shorter than in carbon disulphide[33b]. This square planar complex is less reactive than $RhCl(CO)(PPh_3)_2$, e.g. it will not add on hydrogen chloride, but it can be oxidized by chlorine or bromine to $RhX_3(CS)(PPh_3)_2$ (X = Cl, Br)[16a].

Miscellaneous carbonyl complexes*

β-Diketone complexes of the form $\mathbf{Rh(\beta\text{-diketone})(CO)_2}$ (β-diketone = 1,1,1-trifluoropentane-2,4-dione, 1,1,1,5,5,5-hexafluoropentane-2,4-dione, 4-phenylbutane-1,4-dione, 3-allylpentane-2,4-dione) were made from rhodium carbonyl chloride and the ligand; infrared and fluorine magnetic resonance spectra were recorded. The complexes are monomeric and will react with phosphines and arsines to give $Rh(CO)(LPh_3)(\beta\text{-diketone})$ (L = P, As); with L = Sb, the octahedral $\mathbf{Rh(CO)(\beta\text{-diketone})(SbPh_3)_3}$ is formed. Olefins will replace the carbonyl group to give Rh(olefin)(β-diketone) (olefin = cycloocta-1,5-diene and norbornadiene)[35].

Schiff bases will react with rhodium carbonyl chloride to give $\mathbf{Rh(CO)_2Cl(base)}$[36].

Boron trihalides BY_3 (Y = Cl, Br) and $Rh(CO)X(LPh_3)_2$ (X = Cl, Br; L = P, As) give $\mathbf{Rh(CO)X(LPh_3)_2.BY_3}$ complexes containing a rhodium–boron bond[270b].

Isocyanides react with rhodium carbonyl chloride to give $\mathbf{[Rh(CO)X(RNC)]_2}$ (R = aryl, X = Cl, Br); excess isocyanide

* Table 6.6.

yields $(Rh(RNC)_4)^+$[314]. A similar reaction can also be made to yield $[\mathbf{Rh(CO)_2(RNC)_2}]^+$ (X = Cl, Br; R = C_6H_5, *p*-ClC_6H_4, *m*-MeC_6H_4, *o*-MeC_6H_4, α-$C_{10}H_7$, β-$C_{10}H_7$, $C_6H_5CH_2$)[310].

$[\mathbf{Rh(CO)_2X}]_2$ (X = NO_3, SCN, $\frac{1}{2}SO_4$, RCOO) can be made from the appropriate silver salts and rhodium carbonyl chloride; unlike the other reactions described above these preparations do not appear to involve bridge-splitting, and in each case the X group replaces chlorine as the bridging ligand; the sulphate is claimed to be tetradentate in $[Rh(CO)_2]SO_4$. Infrared spectra were reported[197].

Amine carbonyl complexes of the form $Rh(CO)_2Cl$(amine) (amine = aniline, methylamine, hydroxylamine, pyridine, *p*-toluidine, α-picoline) are made from the amines and rhodium carbonyl chloride[197]. Infrared spectra were recorded.

Dithiocarbamato carbonyl complexes, $Rh(CO)_2(S_2NCR_2)_2$,(R = Me, Et) can be got from the ligands and rhodium carbonyl chloride[67a].

'Sandwich' and arene complexes

Carbonyl cyclopentadienyl complexes. $\mathbf{CpRh(CO)_2}$ can be made by the reaction between sodium cyclopentadienide and rhodium carbonyl chloride. The product is a deep orange diamagnetic liquid (m.p. $-11°$). Its infrared spectrum was measured[102] and was consistent with the presence of two *cis* carbonyl groups and a π-bonded (C_5H_5) ring[102]. Exposure of this compound to air gives red crystals of $[CpRh(CO)_2]_2$ (decomposes at 123°); the infrared spectrum was measured and was said to support the formulation given[103], but there is still some doubt about the structure of the compound.

Irradiation of $CpRh(CO)_2$ gives the trimer $\mathbf{Cp_3Rh_3(CO)_3}$, and an x-ray crystal structure analysis of this shows that the three metal atoms form an equilateral triangle (Rh—Rh = 2·62 Å) with three bridging carbonyl groups (Rh—C = 2·01 Å); the carbonyl groups are all on one side of the triangle and the Cp groups on the other side (Rh—C (ring) = 2·24 Å)[235b].

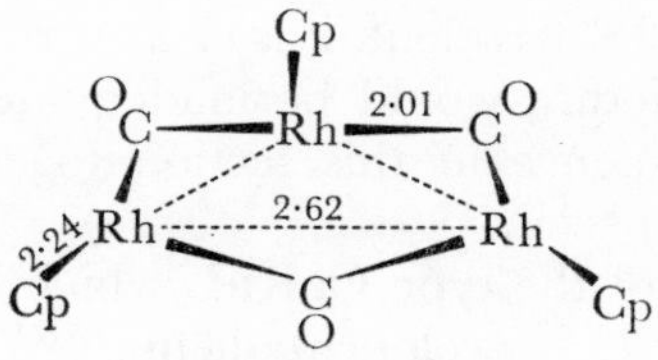

Irradiation of $CpRh(CO)_2$ also yields $\mathbf{Cp_2Rh_2(CO)_3}$ which contains two terminal and one bridging carbonyl groups[235b].

Ethylene cyclopentadienyl complexes. $\mathbf{CpRh(C_2H_4)_2}$ was prepared from sodium cyclopentadienide and $[(C_2H_4)_2RhCl]_2$[188]. Proton magnetic resonance studies on solutions of the complex at low temperatures were interpreted as showing that the ethylene rotates about the coordination bond axis, the barrier to such rotation being of the order of 6 kcal/mole. If the conventional $(\sigma + \pi)$ picture of coordination is accepted for the metal–olefin linkage in this complex, this rotation would not rupture the π bond; since as the ethylene rotates from a position perpendicular to the rhodium coordination plane, in which the d_{xz} orbital is involved in the π bond, to the coplanar orientation (π bonding to d_{xy}) it passes through a stage where both d_{xy} and d_{xz} are involved in the metal–olefin π bond. There is no exchange between free ethylene and the coordinated ethylene in $CpRh(C_2H_4)_2$ but there is a rapid bimolecular exchange between $Rh(acac)(C_2H_4)_2$ and C_2D_4: it is suggested that the difference arises from the fact that, whereas in the cyclopentadienyl complex the rhodium has formally inert-gas configuration, the acetylacetone complex is one electron-pair short of this state, so it can accept two more electrons from an olefin group to give an activated complex for S_N2 exchange[71].

Diene cyclopentadienyl complexes. $\mathbf{CpRh(CH_2{=}CH(CH_2)_2\text{-}CH{=}CH_2)}$ was got by treatment of $[Rh(C_2H_4)_2Cl]_2$ with 1,5-hexadiene followed by addition of sodium cyclopentadienide. The proton magnetic resonance spectrum of the complex was measured and interpreted[71].

Cyclopentadienyl complexes with other four-electron donors. There exist a number of complexes of the form **CpRhL**, where L is a four-electron donor of such a type that it could function either as a chelating di-olefin, as above, or as a '$\pi + 2\sigma$' ligand, in which an electron pair is donated from one double bond and two more electrons form a pair of metal–carbon σ bonds. Although in the former (2π) case the metal atom would formally be monovalent and in the latter ($\pi + 2\sigma$) trivalent, it is clear that for these complexes any simple bonding picture would be inadequate, and so they are considered for convenience in this section together with other monocyclopentadienyl species.

The complexes of the type CpRhL which have been reported are $\mathbf{CpRh(C_5H_6)}$ (A)(L = cyclopentadiene)[104,130]; $\mathbf{CpRh(C_5H_5.C_5H_5)}$

(B) (L = cyclopentadienylcyclopentadiene)[10a]; **CpRh($C_6H_5.C_5H_5$)** (C) (L = phenylcyclopentadiene)[10a]; and the fluorinated species **CpRh($C_5(CF_3)_4O$)** (D) (L = tetrakistrifluoromethyl cyclopentadienone)[79] and **CpRh($C_6(CF_3)_6$)** (E) (L = hexakistrifluoromethylbenzene)[79]. The first three can be made from rhodicinium salts with sodium borohydride (A), sodium cyclopentadienide (B) or lithium phenyl (C), while the fluoro species (D) and (E) are both got by the reaction between CpRh$(CO)_2$ and hexafluoro-but-2-yne; this reaction also yields the hitherto unknown tetrakis(trifluoromethyl) cyclopentadienone, $C_9F_{12}O$[79].

The structures of these species have been investigated by a variety of methods. CpRh(C_5H_6), on the basis of its infrared spectrum was first thought to be a (2π) type of complex[130], but in view of the structures of the chemically similar (B) and (C) it is probably better to regard it as being primarily of the ($\pi + 2\sigma$) type. CpRh(C_5H_5. C_5H_5) (B) is thought on the basis of its proton magnetic resonance spectrum to have an *exo*-cyclopentadienyl group and to be of the ($\pi + 2\sigma$) type (structure **12**, Figure 6.12)[10a]; and CpRh($C_6H_5.C_2H_5$) (C) is isomorphous with the corresponding cobalt complex, which has been shown by the x-ray methods to have structure (**12**) with an *exo*-phenyl group[60]. The fluoro complex CpRh($C_5(CF_3)_4O$) (D) and CpRh($C_6(CF_3)_6$) (E) were thought, on the basis of their infrared and fluorine magnetic resonance spectra to have structures (**13**) and (**14**), respectively[79]. In the case of (E) this was subsequently confirmed by x-ray studies, which shows that the benzene ring is 'hinged' as

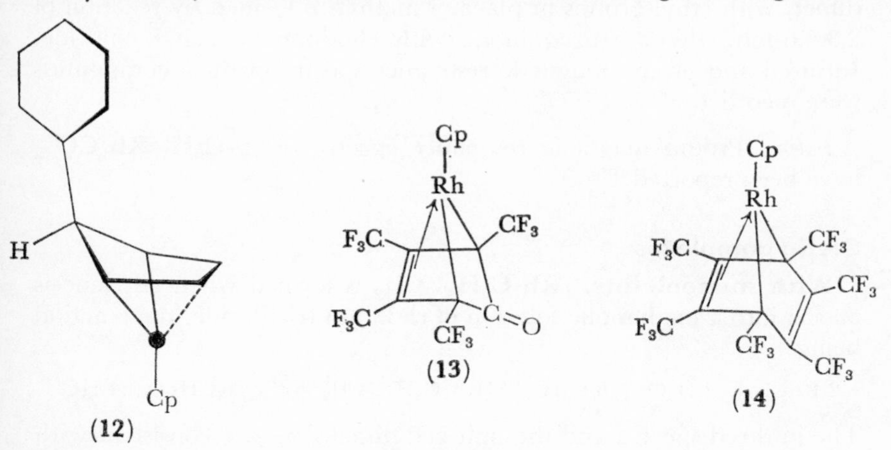

Figure 6.12 Substituted rhodium cyclopentadienyl complexes

shown; this clearly implies that for the benzene ring formally acting as a four-electron donor, the (2π) type of bonding is less likely in this case than the $(\pi + 2\sigma)$. The two (Rh—C)σ-bond distances are each $2{\cdot}15 \pm 0{\cdot}03$ Å, the coordinated C=C distance is $1{\cdot}45 \pm 0{\cdot}05$ Å while the uncoordinated distance is $1{\cdot}32 \pm 0{\cdot}05$ Å[60a]. The complex (D) is isostructural with the corresponding cobalt species, which has been shown by x-ray analysis to have structure (**13**)[110].

Arene and other sandwich complexes

Hexamethyl benzene. Salts containing the $[\pi\text{-}(\mathbf{C_6Me_6})_2\mathbf{Rh}]^+$ cation have been isolated by reducing $(C_6Me_6)_2Rh^{2+}$ salts with zinc and hydrochloric acid. They are yellow, and infrared spectra over the range 400–4000 cm^{-1} were recorded[105].

Duroquinone. Reaction of duroquinone and an ethanolic solution of rhodium trichloride yields the red polymeric species $(\mathbf{Dqu.RhCl})_n$; this reacts with pyridine to give $\mathbf{Dqu.Rh\,py_2Cl}$ as orange crystals, and with sodium cyclopentadienide to give CpRh.Dqu (m.p. 195°). Both the infrared and proton magnetic resonance spectra of these species suggest that the duroquinone is π bonded to the metal, and that the ring is not planar. A molecular orbital bonding scheme was proposed for complexes of the form CpM.Dqu (M = Ir, Rh, Co)[291]. Reaction of rhodium carbonyl chloride with duroquinone gives the dimeric chloro-bridged species $[Dqu.RhCl]_2$, which has different properties from the polymer mentioned above. A similar type of dimer, with ethyl groups in place of methyl, is formed by reaction of 2,3,5,6-tetraethyl-*p*-benzoquinone with rhodium carbonyl chloride. Infrared and proton magnetic resonance spectra of these compounds were recorded[216b].

Indene. Proton magnetic resonance spectra of $(\pi\text{-}\mathbf{C_9H_7})\mathbf{Rh}(\mathbf{CO})_2$ have been reported[106c].

Olefin complexes

With monoolefins. $[\mathbf{Rh}(\mathbf{C_2H_4})_2\mathbf{Cl}]_2$ is formed when ethylene is passed into a methanolic solution of rhodium trichloride, the reaction being:

$$2\,RhCl_3 + 2\,H_2O + 6\,C_2H_4 \rightarrow [Rh(C_2H_4)_2Cl]_2 + 2\,CH_3CHO + 4\,HCl$$

The infrared spectra and the unit cell dimensions are consistent with the complex being a chloro bridged dimer[72]. The complex acts as a catalyst for the addition of silanes to olefins, and it has been suggested that the processes involved in such catalysis are closely related to those for the metal-catalysed hydrogenation of olefins[48]; the complex does not, however, catalyse isomerization of olefins, either with or without cocatalysts[146].

$[Rh(C_3H_6)_2Cl]_2$ was made in a similar way to the ethylene complex[72].

$Rh(C_2H_4)_2(acac)$ is formed as orange-yellow crystals from the reaction between acetylacetone and $[Rh(C_2H_4)_2Cl]_2$; its proton magnetic resonance spectrum was measured. The complex exchanges its coordinated ethylene with free ethylene rapidly (as measured by proton magnetic resonance), whereas no such exchange is observed with $CpRh(C_2H_4)_2$. This difference of behaviour, it was suggested, arises because the rhodium in the acac complex is two electrons short of an inert-gas configuration and is able to accept two electrons from another ethylene molecule, giving a trisethylene species $Rh(C_2H_4)_3$-(acac) as an intermediate for a S_N2 exchange process. This is less likely for $CpRh(C_2H_4)_2$ since in this the rhodium has achieved an inert-gas configuration[71].

Ethylene dimerization reactions. Both $[Rh(C_2H_4)_2Cl]_2$ and $Rh(C_2H_4)_2$-acac in alcoholic hydrochloric acid solutions will catalyse the dimerization of ethylene to 1- and 2-butenes. It has been suggested that in both cases the active catalyst is $[Rh(C_2H_4)_2Cl_2]^-$, and this species is also thought to be formed by the direct action of ethylene on an ethanolic solution of rhodium trichloride[73].

The ethylene dimerization is believed to take the following path

$$[Rh(C_2H_4)_2Cl_2]^- \xrightarrow[(S\,=\,\text{solvent})]{HCl\,+\,S} [C_2H_5Rh^{III}Cl_3(C_2H_4)S]^-$$

The presence of this alkyl species was demonstrated by proton magnetic resonance studies. Its formation may involve an intermediate hydridic species from which the alkyl is formed by an insertion reaction:

$$[Rh^I(C_2H_4)_2Cl_2]^- + HCl \rightarrow [Rh(C_2H_4)_2HCl_3]^- \xrightarrow{S} [Rh(C_2H_5)Cl_3(C_2H_4)S]^-$$

The second step is a second insertion reaction

$$[Rh(C_2H_5)Cl_3(C_2H_4)S]^- \rightarrow [Rh(C_2H_5CH_2CH_2)Cl_3S]^-$$

This is the rate-determining step for the ethylene dimerization and rate constants were measured. The butyl rhodium (III) species then decomposes to butene and $[RhCl_2S]^-$, which combines with two moles of ethylene to regenerate $[Rh(C_2H_4)_2Cl_2]^-$ [73,73a,73b]. Olefin isomerization and polymerization catalysed by rhodium trichloride is discussed on p. 404.

$RhCl(C_2H_4)(PPh_3)_2$ can be made as a bright yellow crystalline solid by the interaction of ethylene with a benzene solution of $RhCl(PPh_3)_3$. The reaction is reversible, and there is rapid exchange between free and coordinated ethylene in solution even at $-50°$ (the mean lifetime for residence of ethylene on the metal atom under such circumstances is less than 10^{-2} sec)[248]. In contrast there is no ligand exchange with tetrafluoroethylene and $RhCl(C_2F_4)(PPh_3)_2$. For the reaction

$$RhCl(PPh_3)_2 + C_2H_4 \overset{K}{\rightleftharpoons} RhCl(PPh_3)_2(C_2H_4)$$

K is approximately 100 l/mole at room temperature; it is some 2000 times lower for the corresponding complex with propylene, due probably to a lowering of the 'π acidity' of the olefin by hyperconjugation effects. It is noteworthy that there is no evidence of isomerization of olefins when they interact with solutions of $RhCl(PPh_3)_3$ [248].

An analogous arsine complex **$RhCl(C_2H_4)(AsPh_3)_2$** can be made from $RhCl(AsPh_3)_3$ [216c].

Fulvene complexes of the form **Rh(fulvene)$(CO)_2$Cl** (fulvene = di-*p*-tolyl- and diphenylfulvene) are made from the ligand and rhodium carbonyl chloride. With hydrogen chloride they give Rh(fulvene)-

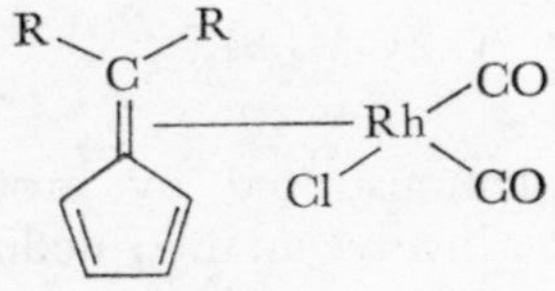

(15)

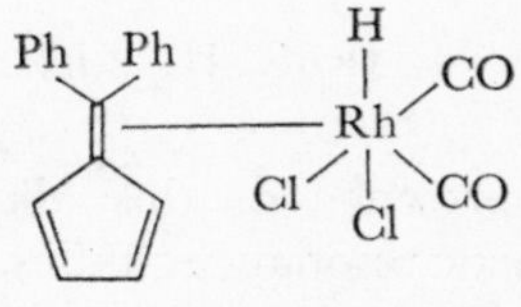

(16) (p. 380)

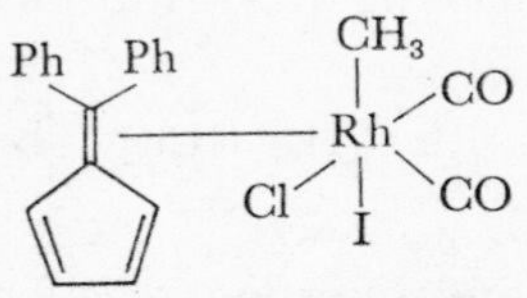

(17) (p. 380)

Figure 6.13 Fulvene complexes of rhodium

$(CO)_2Cl_2H$ and $[RhCl_3(fulvene)]_2$[8]. Infrared and proton magnetic resonance studies suggest that the ligand functions as a mono olefin (**15**) (Figure 6.13). Complexes with cycloheptene and norbornene are also known[326b].

Diolefins. Complexes of the form $[Rh(diene)Cl]_2$ can be made by refluxing hydrated rhodium trichloride with the diene (cycloocta-1,5-diene[52], norbornadiene[1], cyclooctatetraene[1], dicyclopentadiene[52], 1,5-hexadiene[71], cyclohexa-1,3-diene[326b], 2,5-dimethylhexa-1,5-diene[326b].

The complex with cycloocta-1,5-diene (C_8H_{12}) is typical of these.

$\mathbf{[Rh(C_8H_{12})Cl]_2}$ is formed as orange crystals (m.p. 256°), and from this the bromo and iodo complexes can also be got[52]. X-ray studies on $[Rh(C_8H_{12})Cl]_2$ show that the structure is

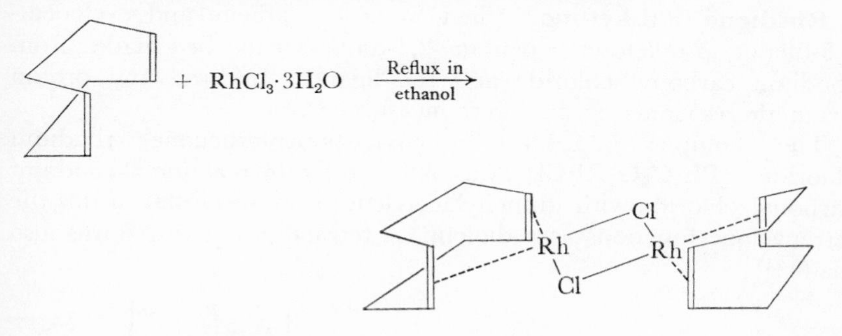

Figure 6.14 Structure of $[Rh(C_8H_{12})Cl]_2$

with Rh—Cl = 2·38 ± 0·01 Å, C—C (ring) = 1·52 ± 0·09 Å, and C═C = 1·44 ± 0·07 Å (in the free ligand, C═C is 1·34 Å); the $Rh\widehat{Cl}Rh$ angle is 94°. The structure differs from that of rhodium carbonyl chloride since the latter has (effectively) octahedral co-ordination and 'bent' metal–metal bonds, whereas here the rhodium has square-planar coordination[161]. The metal–halogen bridging vibrations of the RhX_2Rh system in $[RhX(diene)]_2$ occur near 280 and 265 cm^{-1} (X = Cl), and near 195 and 180 cm^{-1} (X = Br)[2a]. The chloro complex will react with several ligands and, like rhodium carbonyl chloride, undergo bridge-splitting reactions to give $\mathbf{Rh(C_8HI_2)(Cp)}$, $\mathbf{Rh(C_8H_{12})(acac)}$, $\mathbf{[Rh(C_8H_{12})(diamine)]^+}$ and $\mathbf{[Rh(C_8H_{12})(amine)]^+}$ as well as $\mathbf{[Rh(C_8H_{12})(OAc)]_2}$ and $\mathbf{[Rh(C_8H_{12})(MeOH)]_2}$[52].

Other olefin complexes such as $\mathbf{Rh(C_7H_8)_2(SnCl_3)}$ (C_7H_8 = norbornadiene) can be made from rhodium trichloride, stannous chloride and the diene. In water this complex dissociates to $[\mathbf{Rh(C_7H_8)_2}]^+$, and with phosphines, arsines and stibines gives $\mathbf{Rh(C_7H_8)(LPh_3)_2(SnCl_3)}$ (L = P, As, Sb)[333]. Reaction of $(C_8H_{14})_2RhCl$ with other conjugated dienes or other olefins containing activated double bonds leads to a partial or total replacement of cyclooctene; complexes produced by such methods were of the form $\mathbf{L^1L^2RhCl}$ ($L^1 = L^2$ = pentadiene, isoprene, methyl sorbate, methyl maleate, acrylonitrile, 2,3-dimethylbutadiene; L^1 = isoprene with L^2 = cyclooctene, or *p*-toluidine; L^1 = 2,3-dimethylbutadiene with L^2 = *p*-toluidine). The infrared spectra of these products were briefly reported, and from these it was deduced that in all cases bonding from the olefinic double bonds to the metal was involved[266a].

Rh(diene)(β-diketone) (diene = norbornadiene and cycloocta-1,5-diene; β-diketone = pentane-2,4-dione) can be made from rhodium carbonyl chloride and the ligands. Infrared and proton magnetic resonance spectra were measured[35].

The complex 2,3,4,5-tetraphenylcyclopentadienone rhodium chloride, $[\mathbf{(Ph_4C_5O)RhCl}]_2$, was obtained by the reaction of rhodium carbonyl chloride with diphenylacetylene; it appears that in this the tetracyclone functions as a diolefin. A tetraethyl derivative was also made[217]:

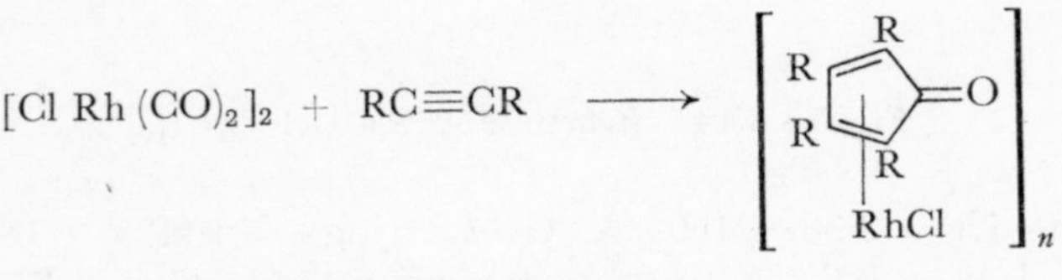

$$[\mathrm{Cl\,Rh(CO)_2}]_2 + \mathrm{RC{\equiv}CR} \longrightarrow [(\mathrm{R_4C_5O})\mathrm{RhCl}]_n$$

Figure 6.15

The reaction with phenylacetylene also gives a polymeric tetracyclone complex, $[\mathbf{(Ph_4C_5O)RhCl(CO)}]_n$. The reaction of the phenyl complex with pyridine yields $\mathbf{(Ph_4C_5O)RhClpy_2}$, with thallous acetylacetonate $\mathbf{(Ph_4C_5O)Rh(acac)}$ and with triphenylphosphine $\mathbf{(Ph_4C_5O)RhCl(PPh_3)}$[217].

Conjugated olefin complexes. Dibutadiene rhodium (I) chloride, $\mathbf{Rh(C_4H_6)_2Cl}$ complexes can be made from rhodium trichloride and butadiene in ethanolic solution, or by treatment of $(C_8H_{14})_2RhCl$ (see below) with butadiene[266]. A preliminary x-ray analysis gave a rhodium–chlorine distance of 2·45 ± 0·03 Å and the rhodium–carbon distance is 2·20 ± 0·05 Å[266].

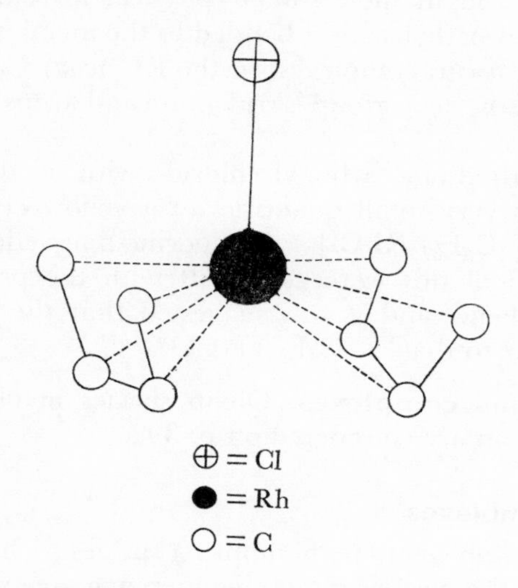

Figure 6.16 Structure of $Rh(C_4H_6)_2Cl$

It appears that each butadiene molecule functions as a diolefin, but more definite information should be available when there are more precise details of the structure.

Dicyclooctene rhodium (I) **chloride, $Rh(C_8H_{14})_2Cl$,** can be made from cyclooctene and rhodium trichloride in ethanolic solution[266].

Fluoro olefin complexes. $RhCl(C_2F_4)(PPh_3)_2$ and **$RhCl(C_2F_3Cl)(PPh_3)_2$** were made from the fluoro olefins and $RhCl(PPh_3)_3$. The infrared spectra and fluorine magnetic resonance spectra were consistent with these being olefin complexes, although the σ-bonded rhodium (III) structure involving a three-membered ring could not be excluded[233]. The analogous arsine species were made from $RhCl(AsPh_3)_3$ and tetrafluoroethylene[216c].

The reaction of tetrafluoroethylene with $Rh(acac)(C_2H_4)_2$ yields **$Rh(acac)(C_2F_4)(C_2H_4)$**; infrared and fluorine magnetic resonance experiments suggest that the C_2F_4 group is bonded as an olefin to the rhodium. However, treatment of this species with a variety of ligands

L^1 and L^2 yields **Rh(acac)(C_2F_4)L′$_2$** (L^1 = PPh_3, PBu^n_3, amines, dimethylsulphoxide) and **[Rh(acac)(C_2F_4)L^2]$_2$** (L^2 = dimethylformamide, nitriles), and in these similar physical measurements suggest that the tetrafluoroethylene is σ bonded to the metal, so that these are formally rhodium (III) complexes; in the Rh(acac)(C_2F_4)L^2 species it is probable that the acac group is tridentate and forms a metal–carbon σ bond[254].

Reaction of rhodium carbonyl chloride with octafluorocyclohexa-1,3-diene yields very small quantities of a yellow crystalline species believed to be **[(C_6F_8)$_2$RhCl]$_2$**; the fluorine magnetic resonance and infrared spectra of this were consistent with the presence of a co-ordinated 1,3-diene, and it was suggested that the complex had a structure similar to that of (C_6F_8)Fe(CO)$_3$[159a].

Miscellaneous complexes. Olefin species involving the cyclopentadienyl group are considered on p. 392.

Acetylene complexes

In general it appears that rhodium (I) species such as the carbonyl chloride have the property of oligomerizing acetylenes[79,217], but reaction of [Rh(CO)$_2$Cl]$_2$ with diethyl- and diphenylacetylene gives, in addition to cyclopentadienone derivatives of rhodium (I) (cf. p. 393), the acetylenic species **(RC≡CR)Rh(CO)Cl**[217].

The complexes RhCl(LPh_3)$_3$ (L = P, As) react with diphenylacetylene to give the stable species RhCl(Ph_2C_2)(LPh_3)$_2$; their infrared spectra suggest that these involve acetylene acting as a simple donor ligand in a square-planar rhodium (I) complex. Some evidence was also obtained for the existence of an analogous stibine species[216c].

Fluoroacetylene species. The only one so far reported for these metals appears to be **RhCl(C_4F_6)(PPh_3)$_2$**, got from hexafluorobut-2-yne and RhCl(PPh_3)$_3$. The infrared and fluorine magnetic resonance spectra suggest that this is a true acetylenic complex[233].

Allyl complexes

Rhodium trichloride is reduced by an excess of allyl alcohol to **Rh_2Cl_2(C_3H_5OH)$_4$**; this species, which may simply be an alcoholate or an olefin complex[197a] rather than a π-allyl complex, will catalyse the decomposition of allyl alcohol to propene, acraldehyde and propionaldehyde[241]. A number of rhodium (III) allyl complexes are known and are discussed on p. 380.

Stannous chloride complexes

Tetraethyl- and tetramethylammonium salts of $[\mathbf{Rh_2Cl_2(SnCl_3)_4}]^{4-}$ have been isolated from solutions of stannous chloride together with hydrochloric acid, rhodium trichloride and the tetraalkyl ammonium chloride. These yellow complexes are probably those involved in the colorimetric determination of rhodium by the stannous chloride method. The structure proposed is[333]:

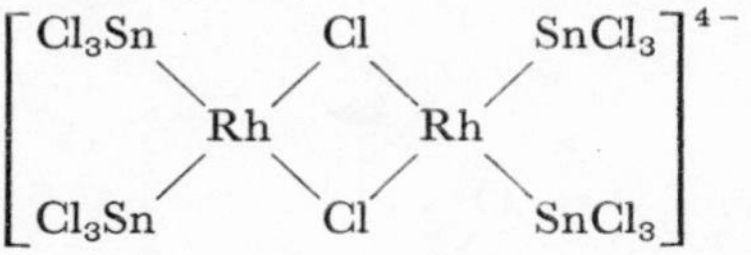

$$\left[\begin{array}{ccccc} Cl_3Sn & & Cl & & SnCl_3 \\ & \diagdown\ \diagup & & \diagdown\ \diagup & \\ & Rh & & Rh & \\ & \diagup\ \diagdown & & \diagup\ \diagdown & \\ Cl_3Sn & & Cl & & SnCl_3 \end{array}\right]^{4-}$$

and this is in agreement with infrared measurements which show typical $(SnCl_3)^-$ vibrations (near 360 and 340 cm^{-1}), bridged metal–chlorine modes, and strong metal–tin stretches near 210 cm^{-1}[2].

Other stannous chloride complexes have already been discussed (cf. pp. 398 and 415).

Rhodium (0)

Three rhodium carbonyls, and possibly a carbonyl hydride, are known.

$[\mathbf{Rh(CO)_4}]_n$, probably dimeric, forms light orange crystals (m.p. 76°) and is made by the action of carbon monoxide at 200° and 280 atmospheres for 15 hours on the metal[154].

$[\mathbf{Rh(CO)_3}]_4$ forms brick-red crystals and is made by heating a mixture of rhodium trichloride and copper powder at 80° with 200 atmospheres pressure of carbon monoxide. It is more stable than the tetracarbonyl, decomposing at 150°[154]. A preliminary x-ray study shows the complex to have a similar structure to $Co_4(CO)_{12}$—the metal atoms are at the apices of a tetrahedron with two terminal carbonyl groups per metal atom, the latter being joined by symmetric metal–metal bonds and carbonyl bridges[321a]. The infrared spectrum has been measured in the 2000 cm^{-1} region[24b].

$\mathbf{Rh_6(CO)_{16}}$, originally formulated as $Rh_4(CO)_{11}$, is made by heating the tricarbonyl to 150° under a carbon monoxide atmosphere. It is very stable and does not decompose until 220°[154]. An x-ray crystal structure analysis shows that the six metal atoms lie at the corners of an octahedron; there are twelve terminal carbonyl groups

(Rh—C = 1·864 ± 0·015 Å, C—O = 1·155 ± 0·015 Å) and four carbonyl groups on trigonal axes through alternate octahedral faces (Rh—C = 2·168 ± 0·001 Å and C—O = 1·201 ± 0·022 Å)[66]. A molecular-orbital description of the bonding based on a localized tetragonal antiprismatic D_{4d} disposition of orbitals about each rhodium atom was proposed. The infrared spectrum is consistent with this structure[66]. The bonding has also been considered on the basis of the equivalent orbital method[185]. Mass spectra are reported for the compound[166d].

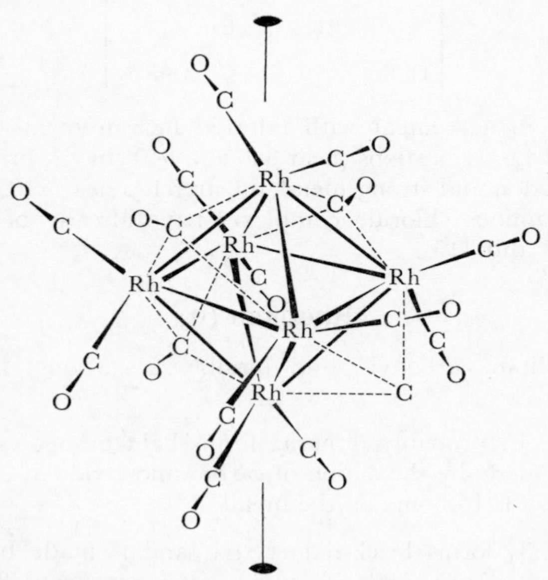

Figure 6.17 Molecular structure of $Rh_6(CO)_{16}$. (Reproduced by permission from E. R. Corey, W. Beck and L. F. Dahl, *J. Am. Chem. Soc.*, **85**, 1202 (1965))

Rh(CO)$_4$H. A volatile compound (m.p. −11°) formed in small quantities during rhodium carbonyl preparations and may well be the hydride[154].

Rhodium (−I)

Reaction of $Rh(CO)Cl(PPh_3)_2$ with a solution of sodium amalgam gives the sodium salt **Na[Rh^{-I}(CO)$_2$(PPh$_3$)$_2$]**. This will react with Me_3SnCl to give $Me_3Sn–Rh(CO)_2(PPh_3)_2$[63a].

HOMOGENEOUS CATALYSIS BY RHODIUM COMPLEXES

Of the four metals, the compounds of rhodium show the most varied catalytic properties, although they have been the most extensively investigated.

Homogeneous hydrogenation reactions

The catalysis of the hydrogenation of olefins with molecular hydrogen has been the subject of recent and extensive investigation. Two general mechanisms have been described.

Heterolytic splitting of hydrogen

Solutions of rhodium trichloride in hydrochloric acid will activate molecular hydrogen to reduce iron (III) to iron (II). The catalytically active species are $[RhCl_6]^{3-}$, $[RhCl_5(H_2O)]^{2-}$ and $[RhCl_4(H_2O)_2]^-$; of these the most active appears to be $[RhCl_6]^{3-}$. The mechanism is likely to be closely related to that proposed for similar catalysis by ruthenium (III) chloro species[147,166]:

$$[RhCl_5(H_2O)]^{2-} + H_2 \rightleftharpoons [RhHCl_4(H_2O)]^{2-} + Cl^- + H^+$$

$$Cl^- + [RhHCl_4(H_2O)]^{2-} + 2\,Fe^{3+} \rightarrow [RhCl_5(H_2O)]^{2-} + H^+ + 2\,Fe^{2+}$$

A similar type of mechanism is probably involved in the catalysis of olefin hydrogenation by ethanolic solutions of 1,2,6-Rh py_3Cl_3[124] (p. 354) and $RhCl_3(LR_3)_3$ (LR_3 = tertiary phosphines and arsines)[124]. The reactions of these species with molecular hydrogen under mild conditions give rise to monohydrido complexes which can be isolated[124].

Homolytic splitting of hydrogen

By far the most efficient catalyst for the homogeneous hydrogenation of olefins or acetylenes is $RhCl(PPh_3)_3$. The mechanism of catalysis by this species is discussed above (p. 367)[248]. In essence its activity depends on the fact that it will dissociate in solution to a species $RhCl(PPh_3)_2$ which is associated with one or more solvent molecules; this will then take up molecular hydrogen to give a *cis*-dihydride, $RhH_2Cl(PPh_3)_2$, which still has a 'vacant' coordination site (probably occupied by a weakly bound solvent molecule) for activation and coordination of the olefin. Other species such as $Rh(CO)Cl(PPh_3)_2$,

$Ir(CO)Cl(PPh_3)_2$ and $IrH(CO)(PPh_3)_3$ are unlikely to have such sites after dihydride formation (unless they become seven or eight coordinate, as has been suggested for $OsH(CO)Cl(PPh_3)_3$).

Hydroformylation reactions

The complex $RhCl(CO)(PPh_3)_2$ is the most effective hydroformylation catalyst yet discovered amongst this group of metals, and is superior in activity to cobalt carbonyl at low temperatures (ca. 70°). The mechanism of hydroformylation with the complex is not yet clear but presumably in some respects it is similar to the cobalt carbonyl process; one significant difference, however, is that it is likely that a rhodium (III) dihydride is an intermediate, whereas in the cobalt catalysis a monohydride is involved[95a,166a]. Rhodium (III) species of the form $RhCl_3(LR_3)_3$ (LR_3 = tertiary phosphine or arsine) have mild hydroformylation catalysis properties, but it is probable that they are partially reduced in the course of the reaction to rhodium (I) species which are the catalytically active species[249].

Isomerization reactions

Ethanolic solutions of rhodium trichloride are potent catalysts for olefin isomerization reactions[124,146]. The mechanism may involve attack by the olefin on a rhodium (III) hydride species with the subsequent formation of an alkyl intermediate, which then splits to give the isomer[73a,73b,146a]. Some rhodium (III) phosphine species, e.g. $RhCl_3(PEt_2Ph)_3$, will isomerize certain unconjugated dienes, and it is thought that π-allylic intermediates may be involved[242] (p. 267).

Polymerization reactions

The ability of acidic ethanolic solutions of rhodium trichloride to catalyse the dimerization of ethylene to butene has recently been the subject of a detailed study[73] (cf. p. 395).

Table 6.1 Ammine complexes of rhodium[a]

Oxidation state	Complex	Colour	Physical properties	Preparation	Ref.
III	$[Rh(NH_3)_6]Cl_3$	Colourless	R, i.r., kin., el. (p. 347)	$RhCl_3 + EtOH + NH_3$ or $[Rh(NH_3)_5Cl]Cl_2 + NH_3$	249b 179
	$[Rh(NH_3)_5Cl]Cl_2$	Yellow	X, i.r., kin., el. (p. 348)	$RhCl_3 + EtOH + NH_3$	126a, 168, 249b
	$[Rh(NH_3)_5Br]Br_2$	Yellow	kin.[194], el.[249]	$[Rh(NH_3)_5H_2O]Br_3 + HBr$	180
	$[Rh(NH_3)_5I]I_2$	Orange	el.[247]	$[Rh(NH_3)_5H_2O]I_3 + HI$	180, 201
	$[Rh(NH_3)_5H_2O]Cl_3$	Colourless	el.[247]	$[Rh(NH_3)_5Cl]Cl_2 + NH_3$	169
	$[Rh(NH_3)_5OH]Cl_2$	Colourless	el.[247]	$[Rh(NH_3)_5Cl]Cl_2 + KOH$	169
	$[Rh(NH_3)_5NO_3](NO_3)_2$		el.[247]	$[Rh(NH_3)_5H_2O](NO_3)_3$ + Heat	181
	$[Rh(NH_3)_5ONO]Cl_2$	Colourless	kin., i.r.[61a], el.[289]	$[Rh(NH_3)_5H_2O)Cl_3 + HNO_2$	22
	$[Rh(NH_3)_5NO_2]Cl_2$	Colourless	i.r.[61a], el.[247]	$[Rh(NH_3)_5ONO]Cl_2$ + Heat	22
	?$[Rh(NH_3)_5(SO_4)]_2(SO_4)$			$[Rh(NH_3)_5H_2O]_2(SO_4)_3$ + Heat	181
	$[Rh(NH_3)_5RCOO](ClO_4)_2$ ($R = CH_3, CMe_3, CF_3$)		kin.[236], el.[289]	$[Rh(NH_3)_5H_2O](ClO_4)_3$ + RCOOH	236
	$[Rh(NH_3)_5NCS](ClO_4)_2$		el.[289]	$[Rh(NH_3)_5H_2O](ClO_4)_3$ + NaSCN	289
	$[Rh(NH_3)_5SCN](ClO_4)_2$		el.[289]	$[Rh(NH_3)_5H_2O](ClO_4)_3$ + NaSCN	289
	$[Rh(NH_3)_5N_3](ClO_4)_2$		el.[289]	$[Rh(NH_3)_5H_2O](ClO_4)_3 + NaN_3$	289
	$[Rh(NH_3)_5H]SO_4$	Colourless	el., i.r., n.m.r.[117,247]	$[Rh(NH_3)_5Cl]Cl_2 + BH_4^-$	249a

Table 6.1 (*continued*)

Oxidation state	Complex	Colour	Physical properties	Preparation	Ref.
III (*continued*)	*trans*-$[Rh(NH_3)_4Cl_2]Cl$	Yellow	kin.[169], el.[169]	$RhCl_3 + (NH_4)_2CO_3$; HCl	168
	$RhCl_3 . 4\,NH_3$			$RhCl_3 + NH_3$	259
	1,2,6-$Rh(NH_3)_3Cl_3$	Yellow	el.[290]	$Na_3[RhCl_6] + NH_4OAc + NH_4Cl$	201, 290
	$RhCl_3 . 3\,NH_3$			$RhCl_3 + NH_3$	259
	$Rh(NH_3)_3Br_3$	Brown		$[Rh(NH_3)_6]Br_3$ + Heat	31
	$Rh(NH_3)_3I_3$	Red	el.[290]	$RhI_3 + NH_3 + H_2O$	302
	$Rh(NH_3)_3(NO_2)_3$				201
	$[Rh(NH_3)_2(DMGH)_2]Cl$			$[Rh(NH_3)_5Cl]Cl_2 + DMGH_2$ (150°)	303
	$Na_3[Rh(NH_3)_2(S_2O_3)_3]$			$[RhCl_6]^{3-} + Na_2S_2O_3 + NH_4OH$	55
	$K_2[Rh(NH_3)Cl_5]$	Red		$Na_3[RhCl_6] + NH_4Cl$	202
	cis- and *trans*-$[Rh(NH_3)en_2Cl](NO_3)_2$	Yellow	el.[120], kin.[169]	*cis*- and *trans*-$[Rh\,en_2Cl_2](NO_3) + NH_3$	168
	$RhBr_3 . NH_3$	Brown		$[Rh(NH_3)_6]Br_3$ + Heat	31

[a] See also p. 347.

Table 6.2 Rhodium amine complexes[a]

Oxidation state	Complex	Colour	Physical properties	Preparation	Ref.
(a) Ethylenediamine (en) complexes					
III	[Rh en_3]Cl_3	Colourless	el., kin., i.r., R, o.r.d., cf. p. 350	Na_3[RhCl_6] + en + EtOH	119
	cis-[Rh en_2Cl_2]Cl	Yellow	el.[247], kin.[169]	$RhCl_3$ + enHCl	168
	trans-[Rh en_2Cl_2]Cl	Yellow	el.[247], kin.[169], Pol.[112]	$RhCl_3$ + enHCl	126a, 168
	cis- and *trans*-[Rh en_2XH]$^+$ (X = Cl, Br, I)		el.[117,247]	*cis*- or *trans*-[Rh en_2X_2]$^+$ + BH_4^-	117, 247
	cis-[Rh en_2H_2](BPh_4)		el.[117,247]	*trans*-[Rh en_2ClH]$^+$ + BH_4^- + BPh_4^-	117
	cis-[Rh en_2X_2]Cl (X = Br, I, NO_2)	Orange	el.[247], kin.[169]	*cis*-[Rh en_2Cl_2]Cl + X^-	168
	trans-[Rh en_2X_2]Cl (X = Br, I, SCN, N_3, NO_2)	Yellow	el.[247], kin.[169]	*trans*-[Rh en_2Cl_2]Cl + X^-	168
	cis- or *trans*-[Rh en_2(NH_3)Cl]$(NO_3)_2$	Yellow	el.[247], kin.[169]	*cis*- or *trans*-[Rh en_2Cl_2](NO_3) + NH_3	168
	trans-[Rh en_2ClX](ClO_4) (X = I, NO_2, SCN, N_3)	Yellow	el.[38]	*trans*-[Rh en_2Cl_2]$^+$ + X^-	38
	trans-[Rh en_2BrX](ClO_4) (X = I, N_3)	Yellow	el.[38]	*trans*-[Rh en_2Br_2]$^+$ + X^-	38
	trans-[Rh $en_2(S_2O_3)_2$]Na		el.[38]	*trans*-[Rh en_2Cl_2](NO_3) + $S_2O_3^{2-}$	38
	Na_3[Rh $en_2(S_2O_3)_3$]			[Rh Cl_6]$^{3-}$ + en + $S_2O_3^{2-}$	55
	[Rh en_2(en—H)]I_2		i.r.[321]	KNH_2 + [Rh en_3]I_3	321

Table 6.2 (*continued*)

Oxidation state	Complex	Colour	Physical properties	Preparation	Ref.
III (*continued*)	[Rh en(en—H)$_2$]I		i.r.[321]	KNH_2 + [Rh en$_3$]I$_3$	321
	Rh(en—H)$_3$		i.r.[321]	KNH_2 + [Rh en$_3$]I$_3$	321
	K[Rh(en—H)$_2$(en—2 H)]		i.r.[321]	KNH_2 + [Rh en$_3$]I$_3$	321
(b) Miscellaneous monoamines					
	$RhCl_3(RNH_2)_3$ (R = Et, Ph)			$RhCl_3$ + RNH_2	235
	$RhAz_3X_3$ (X = Cl, Br)		el.[283a]	$RhCl_3$ + Az + X^-	283a
	[Rh Az_4X_2]$^+$ (X = Cl, Br, I)		el.[283a]	$RhCl_3$ + Az + X^-	283a
	[Rh Az_6]Cl_3		el.[283a]	$RhCl_3$ + Az + X^-	283a
	[Rh Az_5Cl]Cl_2 (Az = ethyleneimine, C_2H_5N)		el.[283a]	$RhCl_3$ + Az + X^-	283a
(c) Miscellaneous diamines					
	[Rh (diamine)$_3$]Cl_3 (diamine = $C_5H_{10}(NH_2)_2$,2,4-n-diaminopentane and 2,4-n-*meso*-diaminopentane)	Colourless		$Na_3[RhCl_6]$ + diamine	80
	[Rh (cptn)$_3$]I_3 (cptn = $C_5H_8(NH_2)_2$, *trans*-1,2-n-diaminocyclopentane)	Colourless		$Na_3[RhCl_6]$ + cptn + I^-	164
	[Rh (chxn)$_3$]I_3 (chxn = $C_6H_{10}(NH_2)_2$, *trans*-1,2-diaminocyclohexane)	Colourless		$Na_3[RhCl_6]$ + chxn + I^-	165
	[Rh pn$_3$]Cl_3 (pn = MeCH(NH$_2$)CH$_2$NH$_2$, 1,2-propanediamine)		o.r.d.[212], el.[290a]	$RhCl_3$ + pn	212, 290a

Table 6.2 (*continued*)

Oxidation state	Complex	Colour	Physical properties	Preparation	Ref.
(d) Miscellaneous triamines					
III (*continued*)	$[Rh(tpn_2)]Cl_3$			$[Rh(NH_3)_5Cl]Cl_2$ + tpn + NaOH	224, 305
	(tpn = $C_3H_5(NH_2)_3$, 1,2,3-triaminopropane)				
	$[Rh\,dien_2]I_3$		i.r.[320], el.[290a]	$RhCl_3$ + dien + I^-	290a, 320
	$[Rh(dien{-}H)_2]I$		i.r.[320]	$[Rh\,dien_2]I_3 + KNH_2$	320
	Rh(dien—H)(dien—2 H)		i.r.[320]	$[Rh\,dien_2]I_3 + KNH_2$	320
	1,2,6-Rh dienX_3		el.[259,290]	$[RhX_6]^{3-}$ + dien	290
	1,2,3-Rh dienCl_3		el.[259,290]	$RhCl_3$ + HCl + dien	290
	(X = Cl, Br, I)				
	(dien = $(NH_2C_2H_4)_2NH$, diethylenetriamine)				
(e) Tetradentate amines					
	cis-$[Rh(cyclen)_2Cl_2]^+$		el.[64a]	$RhCl_3$ + cyclen	64a
	(cyclen = 1,4,7,10-tetrazacyclododecane)				
	cis-$[Rh\,trien\,Cl_2]^+$		el.[120], i.r.[120]	$[RhCl_6]^{3-}$ + trien	120
	cis-$[Rh\,trien\,ClH]^+$		el.[117]	*cis*-$[Rh\,trien\,Cl_2]^+ + BH_4^-$	117
	(trien = triethylenetetramine $(CH_2NH_2(CH_2)_2NH_2)_2$)				
	trans-$[Rh\,tet\,Cl_2]^+$	Yellow	el.[36a]	$[Rh\,py_4Cl_2]^+$ + tet	36a
	(tet = 1,4,8,11-tetraazaundecane)				

[a] See also Table 6.3 and p. 350.

Table 6.3 Pyridine complexes of rhodium[a]

Oxidation state	Complex	Colour	Physical properties	Preparation	Ref.
III	*trans*-[Rh py_4Cl_2]Cl	Yellow	i.r.[151a], el.[118,288] Pol.[112]	$RhCl_3$ + py + EtOH	125, 126
	[Rh py_4Br_2]Br	Yellow	el.[288], Pol.[112]	$RhBr_3$ + py	268
	[Rh py_4Br_2][Rh py_2Br_4]			K[Rh py_2Br_4] + [Rh py_4Br_2]Br	268
	[Rh $py_4HX]^+$; [Rh $py_5H]^{2+}$ (soln. only)		n.m.r.[101]	*t*-[Rh $py_4X_2]^+$ + BH_4^-	101
	[Rh $py_4Br(NO_3)](NO_3)$	Orange		[Rh py_4Br_2]Br + $AgNO_3$	268
	1,2,3- and 1,2,6-Rh py_3Cl_3		i.r.[60b], el.[118,178,288]	*t*-[Rh py_4Cl_2]Cl + py (150°)	118
	Rh py_3Br_3 (3 forms claimed)		el.[288]	$K_3[Rh_2Br_9]$ + py	269
	Rh py_3I_3		i.r.[101]	$RhCl_3$ + py + KI + H_3PO_2	101
	Rh $py_3(NO_3)_3$	Orange		[Rh py_4Br_2]Br + $AgNO_3$	268
	Rh $py_3(NO_2)_3$	Colourless		$Na_3[Rh(NO_2)_6]$ + py	203
	1,2,3- and 1,2,6-Rh $py_3(SCN)_3$		i.r., el.[119]	$[Rh(SCN)_6]^{3-}$ + py + H_3PO_2	119
	Rh py_3X ox (X = Cl, Br)			[Rh py_4X_2]X + ox^{2-}	268
	cis- and *trans*-pyH[Rh py_2Cl_4]	Orange	i.r., el.[118,178]	$Na_3[RhCl_6]$ + HCl + py	77
	pyH[Rh py_2Br_4]	Red		$RhBr_3$ + py + HBr	268

Table 6.3 (*continued*)

Oxidation state	Complex	Colour	Physical properties	Preparation	Ref.
III (*continued*)	*cis*- and *trans*-$Rh\ py_2Cl_3(H_2O)$	Orange		$pyH[Rh\ py_2Cl_4] + H_2O$	77
	$[Rh\ py_2Cl_3]_2$	Rose	i.r., el.[118]	1,2,6-$Rh\ py_3Cl_3 + CHCl_3$	118
	$(NH_4)[Rh\ py_2(NO_2)_4]$			$Na_3[Rh(NO_2)_6] + py + NH_4Cl$	203
	cis- and *trans*- $Ag[Rh\ py_2Cl_3(NO_3)]$	Orange		$Rh\ py_2Cl_3(H_2O) + HNO_3 + Ag^+$	77
	$[Rh\ py_2\ en\ X_2]X$ (X = Cl, Br)	Yellow		$[Rh\ py_4X_2]X$ + en	235
	$[Rh\ py\ en_2X]X_2$ (X = Cl, Br)	Yellow		$[Rh\ py_4X_2]X$ + en	235
	$Rh\ py(DMGH)_2Cl$			$[Rh\ py_4Cl_2]Cl + DMGH_2$	204
	$(pyH)_2[Rh\ py\ Br_5]$	Red		$RhBr_3 + py + HBr$	268
	$[Rh\ py_2(CN)_2Cl]_n$		i.r.[121]	*trans*-$[Rh\ py_4Cl_2]Cl + CN^-$	121
	$Rh_2py_4Cl_6(H_2O)$	Red		*trans*-$K[Rh\ py_2Cl_4] + H_2O$	77
	$RhHCl_2(PPh_3)_2py$	White		$RhCl(PPh_3)_3 + py + H_2$	248

[a] See also p. 352.

Table 6.4 Phosphine, arsine and stibine complexes of rhodium[a]

Oxidation state	Complex	Colour	Physical properties	Preparation	Ref.
III	*trans*-$RhCl_3(PR_3)_3$ (PR = PEt_3, PPr^n_3, PBu^n_3, PEt_2Ph, PMe_2Ph, $PEtPh_2$)	Yellow	D[49]	$RhCl_3 + PR_3 + EtOH$	49
	trans-$RhBr_3(PPr^n_3)_3$		D[49]	$RhCl_3(PPr^n_3)_3 + LiBr + EtOH$	49
	$Rh_2(PR_3)_4Cl_6$ (R = Et, Pr^n, Bu^n, pentyl^n)		D[49]	$RhCl_3 + PR_3$	49
	cis- and *trans*-$RhCl_3(PR_3)_3$ (PR_3 = PPh_2H, PEt_2H)	Yellow		$RhCl_3 + PR_3$	148
	trans-$RhCl_3(AsR_3)_3$ (AsR_3 = $AsEt_3$, $AsBu^n_3$, $AsMe_2Ph$, $AsPh_2Me$)		D[49]	$RhCl_3 + AsR_3 + EtOH$	49, 93
	$Rh_2Cl_6(AsEt_3)_4$		D[49]	$RhCl_3 + AsEt_3$	49
	$Rh_2X_6(AsEt_3)_3$ (X = Cl, Br)		D[49]	$RhCl_3 + AsEt_3 + X^-$	49
	$[Rh(AsR_3)_6][RhX_6]$ (X = Cl, Br, I; AsR_3 = $AsPh_2Me$, $AsMe_2(C_6H_4Me)$)			$RhX_3 + AsR_3$	93
	$[Rh\ diars_2Cl_2]Cl$		i.r.[208b]	$RhCl_3$ + diars	245b
	$[Rh(As—S)_2X_2][Rh(As—S)X_4]$ (X = Cl, Br, I)	Orange		RhX_3 + As—S + EtOH	58
	$[Rh(As—S)_2I_2]^+$			$[RhCl_6]^{3-}$ + HI + As—S + EtOH	58
	$(Ph_2MeAs)_3X_2Rh—HgY)$ (X = Cl, Br; Y = F, Cl, Br, I, OAc, CN, CNS)	Yellow	el.[245]	$(Ph_2MeAs)_3X_2RhH + HgY_2$	245

Table 6.4 *(continued)*

Oxidation state	Complex	Colour	Physical properties	Preparation	Ref.
III (*continued*)	$RhHX_2(AsPh_2Me)_3$ (X = Cl, Br, I)		i.r.[208c]	$RhX_3(AsPh_2Me)_3 + H_3PO_2$	90, 208c
	$RhHX_2(LR_3)_2$ (X = Cl, Br, I; $LR_3 = PPh_3, PEtPh_2, PEt_2Ph$)		i.r.[208c]	$RhX_3(AsPh_2Me)_3 + H_3PO_2$	90, 208c
	$RhH_2Cl(PR_3)_3$ ($PR_3 = PPh_3, PEtPh_2$)			$RhCl_3 + PR_3 + H_2$	248, 282a
	$Rh\ X_3(CS)(PPh_3)_2$ (X = Cl, Br)			$RhX(CS)(PPh_3)_2 + X_2$	16a
	$Rh(LPh_3)_2XH_2$ (X = Cl, Br; L = P, As, Sb)		i.r., n.m.r.[248]	$RhX(LPh_3)_3 + H_2$	249
	$Rh_2(PPh_3)_4H_4Cl_2$		n.m.r.[248], i.r.[248]	$Rh_2(PPh_3)_4Cl_2 + H_2$	248
	$[RhHCl(diphosphine)_2]Cl$	Yellow		$RhH(diphosphine)_2 + HCl$	282
	$[RhX_2(QAS)]X$ [b] (X = Cl, Br, I)			$[RhX(QAS)] + X_2$	232a
	$[RhCl_3(TAS)]$ [b]			$RhCl_3 + TAS$	232a
	$RhH_2X(PPh_3)_2py$ (X = Cl, Br)	White		$RhX(PPh_3)_3 + py + H_2$	248
	$[RhCl_2(P(OCH_2)_3C.CH_3)_4]Cl$	Pink		$RhCl_3 + P(OCH_2)_3C.CH_3 + EtOH$	317b
	$Rh(CH_3)ClI(PPh_3)_2(CH_3I)$			$RhCl(PPh_3)_3 + CH_3I$	197a
	$RhCl_2Et(PPh_3)_2$			$RhCl(PPh_3)_3 + C_2H_4 + HCl$	16
	$RhCl_2(CH{=}CH_2)(PPh_3)_2$			$RhCl(PPh_3)_3 + C_2H_2 + HCl$	16
II	*trans*-$RhCl_2(P(o\text{-}MeC_6H_4)_3)_2$	Blue	e.s.r., i.r.,[27a]	$RhCl_3 + EtOH + P(o\text{-}MeC_6H_4)_3$	27a
	$Rh_2Cl_4(PEtPh_2)_4$	Yellow		$RhHCl_2(PEtPh_2)_3 + air$	282a

Table 6.4 (*continued*)

Oxidation state	Complex	Colour	Physical properties	Preparation	Ref.
I	$Rh(PPh_2H)_3Cl$	Yellow		$[Rh(C_2H_4)_2Cl]_2 + PPh_2H$	148
	$Rh(LR_3)_3X$ ($X = Cl, Br, I$; $LR_3 = PPh_3, AsPh_3, SbPh_3$)			$RhCl_3 + EtOH + LR_3 + X^-$	216c, 248
	$Rh(P(OR)_3)_3X$ ($R = MeC_6H_4$, p-ClC_6H_4)			$[Rh(CO)_2Cl]_2 + P(OR)_3 + X^-$	311
	$Rh_2(P(OR)_3)_4(SCN)_2$			$Rh(P(OR)_3)_2(CO)Cl + SCN^-$	311
	$Rh(PR_3)_2Br(1\text{-naphthyl})_2$ ($PR_3 = PPr^n_3, PEt_2Ph$)	Cream	D[50]	$Rh(PR_3)Br_3$ + 1-naphthyl MgBr	50
	$Rh(PPh_3)_3(SnCl_3)$	Red		$RhCl_3 + SnCl_2 + PPh_3$	333
	[Rh(diphosphine)$_2$]Cl (diphosphine $= C_2H_4(PPh_2)_2$)	Yellow		$[Rh(CO)_2Cl]_2$ + diphosphine	282
	RhH(diphosphine)$_2$	Orange	D, i.r.[282]	[Rh(diphosphine)$_2$]X + $LiAlH_4$	282
	$Rh(NO)(PPh_3)_2Cl_2$			$PPh_3 + [Rh(NO)_2Cl]_n$	153
	RhX(QAS) ($X = Cl, Br, I$) [b]			$Rh_2X_2(C_8H_{12})_2$ + QAS	232a
	$RhCl(PPh_3)_2(S)$			$RhCl(PPh_3)_3$ in solution (S)	248
	$[RhCl(PPh_3)_2]_2$	Pink		$RhCl(PPh_3)_3$ refluxed in benzene	248
	$RhCl(PPh_3)_2(C_2H_4)$	Yellow		$RhCl(PPh_3)_3 + C_2H_4$	248
	$RhCl(PPh_3)_2L$ (L = py, DMSO, CH_3CN)			$RhCl(PPh_3)_3 + L$	248

[a] See also pp. 362 and 366.
[b] QAS = tris (*o*-diphenylarsinophenyl)arsine; TAS = bis (*o*-diphenylarsinophenyl)phenylarsine.

Table 6.5 Carbonyls and carbonyl halides of rhodium[a]

Oxidation state	Complex	Colour	Physical properties	Preparation	Ref.
III	$[Rh(CO)_2F_3]_2$			$RhF_4 + CO$	293
	$[Rh(CO)_4I]_2{}^{4-}$		i.r.[312]	$[Rh(CO)_2I_2] + I_2$	312
	$Rh(CO)_2Cl_2H(fulvene)$			$Rh(CO)_2Cl(fulvene) + HCl$	8
I	$[Rh(CO)_2Cl]_2$	Red	X[74], Kin.[330], D[109]	$RhCl_3 + CO$ (105°)	213
	$[Rh(CO)_2X]_2$ (X = Br, I)	Red	D[109]	$RhX_3 + CO$	154
	$[Rh(CO)_2X]_2$ (X = NO_3, SCN, RCOO, $\frac{1}{2}SO_4$)		i.r.[197]	$AgX + [Rh(CO)_2Cl]_2$	197
	$[Rh(CO)_2X_2]^-$ (X = Cl, Br, I)		i.r.[312]	$[Rh(CO)_2Cl]_2 + HX$	197, 312
	$[Rh(CO)X_2]_2^{2-}$ (X = Br, I)		i.r.[312]	$[Rh(CO)_2X_2]^- + HX$	312
	$Rh(CO)_2L.Cl$ (L = py, picoline, aniline, CH_3NH_2, NH_2OH, *p*-toluidine)		i.r.[197]	$[Rh(CO)_2Cl]_2 + L$	197
	$Rh(CO)_2$(β-diketone)			$[Rh(CO)_2Cl]_2$ + β-diketone	35
	$Rh(CO)X(RNC)_2$ (X = Cl, Br; R = aryl)			$[Rh(CO)_2X]_2 + RNC$	310
	$[Rh(CO)Cl(SnCl_3)_2]^{2-}$			$[Rh(CO)_2Cl]_2 + HCl + SnCl_2$	333
	$[Rh(CO)_2(SR)]_2$ (R = Et, Ph)			$[Rh(CO)_2Cl]_2 + RSH$	152
	$[Rh(CO)(QAS)]Cl$			$[Rh(CO)_2Cl]_2$ + QAS	232a
	$Rh(CO)_2Cl(fulvene)$			fulvene + $[Rh(CO)_2Cl]_2$	8
	$Rh(CO)Cl(RC{\equiv}CR)$ (R = Et, Ph)			$[Rh(CO)_2Cl]_2 + RC{\equiv}CR$	217
	?$Rh(CO)_4H$			Rh + CO (280 atm, 200°)	154
0	$[Rh(CO)_4]_2$	Orange		Rh + CO (280 atm, 200°)	154
	$[Rh(CO)_3]_n$	Red		$RhCl_3$ + CO (200 atm, 80°) +	154
	$Rh_6(CO)_{16}$		X[66]	$Cu[Rh(CO)_3]_n$ + CO (150°)	154

[a] See also Table 6.6, see also pp. 372 and 384.

Table 6.6 Carbonyl and hydrido carbonyl phosphine, arsine and stibine complexes of rhodium[a]

Oxidation state	Complex	Colour	Physical properties	Preparation	Ref.
III	$Rh(CO)Cl_3(LR_3)_2$ (L = P, As, Sb; R = Ph, p-MeC_6H_4, p-ClC_6H_4)		i.r.[313], kin.[39]	$Rh(CO)Cl(LR_3)_2 + Cl_2$	313
	$Rh(CO)X_3(LR_3)_2$ (X = Cl, Br; $LR_3 = PEt_2Ph, AsEt_2Ph$)		D[51a], i.r.[51a]	$RhX_3 + CO + EtOH + LR_3$	51a, 282a
	$Rh(CO)ClI_2(LR_3)_2$ (L = P, As)		i.r.[313]	$Rh(CO)Cl(LR_3)_2 + I_2$	313
	$Rh(CO)ClRX(P(n\text{-}C_4H_9)_3)_2$ (X = Cl, I; R = Me, $MeOCOCH_2$, $C_6H_5CH_2$)		i.r.[149]	$Rh(CO)Cl(P(n\text{-}C_4H_9)_3)_2 + RX$	149
	$Rh(CO)ClI(CH_3CO)(P(n\text{-}C_4H_9)_3)_2$		i.r.[149]	$Rh(CO)Cl(CH_3)I(P(n\text{-}C_4H_9)_3)_2 + CO$	149
	$Rh(CO)Br_2(CH_3CO)(PEt_2Ph)_2$		i.r.[51a], D[51a]	$Rh(CO)Br(PEt_2Ph)_2 + CH_3COBr$	51a
	$RhHCl_2(CO)(SbPh_3)_2$			$RhCl(CO)(SbPh_3)_3 + HCl$	154a
	$Rh(CO)I_2Me(PPh_3)_2$	Orange		$RhClIMe(PPh_3)_2(MeI) + CO$	197a
	$Rh(CO)Br_3(PPh_3)_2$			$Br_2 + Rh(CO)Br(PPh_3)_2$	274a
	$RhHCl_2(CO)(PPh_3)_2$			$HCl + Rh(CO)Cl(PPh_3)_3$	16
I	*trans*-$Rh(CO)X(LR_3)_2$ (X = Cl, Br, I; $LR_3 = PPh_3, PEtPh_2, AsPh_3$)	Yellow	kin.[129,330], D[315]	$[Rh(CO)Cl]_2 + MPh_3$	51, 215, 282a, 316
	$Rh(CO)Cl(LPh_3)_2$ (L = As, Sb)	Yellow		$RhCl(LPh_3)_3 + CO$	216c
	$Rh(CO)I(PPh_3)_2$	Orange		$RhMeClI(PPh_3)_2(MeI) + CO$	197a
	$Rh(CO)X(LR_3)_2$ (X = Cl, Br, I, SCN; $LR_3 = LEt_3, LPh_3, LMe_2Ph$; L = P, As)		D[51a], i.r.[51a]	$RhCl_3 + LR_3 + X^- + CO + EtOH$	51a

Table 6.6 (*continued*)

Oxidation state	Complex	Colour	Physical properties	Preparation	Ref.
I (*continued*)	$Rh(CO)X(SbPh_3)_4$ (X = Cl, Br)			$[Rh(CO)_2X]_2 + SbPh_3$	309
	$Rh(CO)Cl(P(C_6H_{11})_3)_2$			$[Rh(CO)_2Cl]_2 + P(C_6H_{11})_3$	155
	$Rh(CO)Cl(P(OR)_3)_2$ (R = Ph, *p*-C_6H_4Me, *p*-C_6H_4Cl)	Yellow		$[Rh(CO)_2Cl]_2 + P(OR)_3$	311
	$Rh(CO)(SR)(PPh_3)_2$ (R = Et,Ph)			$[Rh(CO)_2SR]_2 + PPh_3$	152
	trans-$Rh(CO)X.(LPH_3)_2$ (X = Cl, I, SCN; $LPh_3 = AsPh_3, SbPh_3$)		D[315]	$[Rh(CO)_2Cl]_2 + L + X^-$	315
	$Rh(CO)H(PPh_3)_3$		i.r.[23], X[195]	$Rh(CO)Cl(PPh_3)_2 + N_2H_4 + PPh_3$	23
	Rh(CO)Cl(diphosphine)	Yellow		$[Rh(CO)_2Cl]_2$ + diphosphine	154a
	$Rh(CO)Cl(SO_2)(PPh_3)_2$	Yellow		$Rh(CO)Cl(PPh_3)_2 + SO_2$	317a
	$Rh[(CO)_2(SbPh_3)_3]^+$			$Rh(CO)Cl(SbPh_3)_3 + AlCl_3 + CO$	154a
	$Rh(CO)(SbPh_3)_3(MeCOO)$			$[Rh(CO)_2(SbPh_3)_3]^+ + KOH$	154a
				+ MeOH	154a
	$[Rh(CO)_2(PR_3)_2]^+$ ($Ph_3 = PPh_3, P(C_6H_{11})_3$)			$Rh(CO)Cl.(PR_3)_2 + CO + AlCl_3$	154a
	$Rh(CO)Cl(SbPh_3)_3$			$SbPh_3 + [Rh(CO)_2Cl]_2$	155
	$Rh(CO)X(LPh_3)_2.BY_3$ (X = Cl, Br; Y = Cl, Br; L = P, As)	Yellow	i.r., n.m.r.[270b]	$Rh(CO)X(LPh_3)_2 + BY_3$	270b
	$Rh(CO)(SbPh_3)_3$(β-diketone)		i.r., n.m.r.[35]	$Rh(CO)_2$(β-diketone) + $SbPh_3$	35
	$[Rh(CO)_2(PPh_2)]_n$	Yellow	i.r.[154a]	$[Rh(CO)_2Cl]_2 + KPh_2$	154a
	cis- and *trans*-$[Rh(MR_2)Cl(CO)]_2$ ($MR_2 = PPh_2, AsPh_2$)	Orange	i.r.[154a]	$[Rh(CO)_2Cl]_2 + M_2R_4$	154a

[a] See also pp. 373 and 386.

Table 6.7. Magnetic measurements on rhodium complexes

	Complex	χ_a(× 10^6 c.g.s units)		μ_{eff}(BM)		Ref.
t_{2g}^4	$[RhF_5]_4$	5895 (77°)	3669 (293°)		2·93 (293°)	156
t_{2g}^3	$K_2[RhF_6]$	4072 (90°)	1505 (295°)	1·73 (90°)	1·95 (295°)	323
	$Rb_2[RhF_6]$	4074 (90°)	1513 (295°)	1·75 (90°)	1·96 (295°)	323
	$Cs_2[RhF_6]$	4153 (90°)	1594 (295°)	1·76 (90°)	2·01 (295°)	323
	$Cs_2[RhCl_6]$			1·4 (78°)	1·7 (293°)	99
d^7	$[\pi\text{-}C_6H_3Me_3]_2Rh$	2460 (90°)	739 (291°)		1·32 (291°)	105

Table 6.8. Selected data on polarography of rhodium complexes

Complex	Process[a]	$E_{\frac{1}{2}}$ (versus s.c.e.)	Medium	D (cm^2/sec)	Ref.
$RhCl_3$.aq	III → h	−0·39	0.5M HCl		318
trans-$[Rh\ py_4Cl_2]^+$	III → h	−0·39	0.1M KCl		112
trans-$[Rh\ py_4Br_2]^+$	III → h	−0·28	0·1M KCl		112
trans-$[Rh\ en_2Cl_2]^+$	III → h	−0·79	0·1M KCl		112
$[Rh(H_2EDTA)Cl_2]^-$	III → h	−0·73	0.1M KCl	$2{\cdot}3 \times 10^{-6}$[b]	112
	h → h_2?	−0·97			
$[Rh\ ox_3]^{3-}$	III → I?	−0·83	0·5M H_2ox		318
$[Rh\ ox_2H_2O]^{3-}$	III → I?	−0·43	0.5M H_2ox		318
$[Rh(CN)_6]^{3-}$	III → h	−1·54	M KCN		133
$[Rh(SCN)_6]^{3-}$	III → I?	−0·39	0·9M KSCN		326a
$[Rh(NH_3)_5Cl]^{2+}$	III → h	−0·93	M NH_4Cl		326a

[a] All reductions irreversible at dropping mercury electrode. h = monohydridic species of rhodium (III), h_2 = dihydride of rhodium (III).
[b] From value for corresponding cobalt complex.

REFERENCES

1. Abel, E. W., M. A. Bennett and G. Wilkinson, *J. Chem. Soc.*, **1959**, 3178.
2. Adams, D. M., and P. J. Chandler, *Chem. Ind.* (*London*), **1965**, 269.
2a. Adams, D. M., and P. J. Chandler, *Chem. Commun.*, 1966, 69.
2b. Adams, D. M., *J. Chem. Soc.*, **1964**, 1771.
3. Ahrland, S., J. Chatt and N. R. Davies, *Quart. Revs.*, **12**, 265 (1958).
4. Albinak, M. J., D. H. Bhatnagar, S. Kirschnov and A. J. Sonnessa, *Can. J. Chem.*, **39**, 2360 (1961).
5. Alcock, C. B., and G. W. Hooper, *Proc. Roy. Soc. London, Ser. A*, **254**, 551 (1960).
6. Alcock, C. B., *Trans. Brit. Ceram. Soc.*, **60**, 147 (1961).
7. Alderson, T., E. L. Jenner and R. V. Lindsey, *J. Am. Chem. Soc.*, **87**, 5638 (1965).
8. Altman, J., and G. Wilkinson, *J. Chem. Soc.*, **1964**, 5654.
9. Anderson, S. N., and F. Basolo, *Inorg. Syn.*, **7**, 214, 216 (1963).
10. Andrikides, A., *Prakt. Akad. Athenen*, **12**, 32 (1937).
10a. Angelici, R. J., and E. O. Fischer, *J. Am. Chem. Soc.*, **85**, 3733 (1963).
11. Ayres, G. N., *Anal. Chem.*, **25**, 1622 (1953).

12. Ayres, G. H., and J. S. Forrester, *J. Inorg. Nucl. Chem.*, **3**, 365 (1957).
13. Babaeva, A. V., Y. Y. Khartitonov and Z. M. Novozhenyuk, *Russ. J. Inorg. Chem. Eng. Transl.*, **6**, 1151 (1961).
14. Babaeva, A. V., and Y. Y. Kharitonov, *Proc. Acad. Sci. USSR Chem. Sect., Eng. Transl.*, **144**, 448 (1962).
15. Babaeva, A. V., Y. Y. Kharitonov and E. V. Shenderetskaya, *Russ. J. Inorg. Chem., Eng. Transl.*, **7**, 790 (1962).
15a. Baddley, W. H., *J. Am. Chem. Soc.*, **88**, 4545 (1966).
16. Baird, M., D. N. Lawson, J. T. Mague, J. A. Osborn and G. Wilkinson, *Chem. Commun.*, **1966**, 129; M. C. Baird, J. T. Mague, J. A. Osborn and G. Wilkinson, *J. Chem. Soc.*, *in press*.
16a. Baird, M., and G. Wilkinson, *Chem. Commun.*, **1966**, 514, 267; **1967**, 92.
16b. Bankovskis, J., G. Mezarups and A. Ievins, *Zh. Analit. Khim.*, **17**, 721 (1962); *Chem. Abstr.*, **58**, 13123b (1962).
17. Barbieri, G. A., *Atti Accad. Naz. Lincei Mem. Classe Sci. Fis. Mat. Nat. Sez. II*, **13**, 433 (1931).
18. Barnighausen, H., and K. B. Handa, *J. Less-Common Metals*, **6**, 226 (1964).
18a. Barsova, L. I., A. K. Pikaev, V. I. Spitsyn and A. A. Balandin, *Proc. Acad. Sci. USSR*, **144**, 417 (1962).
19. Bartlett, N., and N. K. Jha, 'Xenon-platinum hexafluoride and Related Reactions' in *Noble Gas Compounds* (Ed. H. H. Hyman), Chicago, 1963.
20. Bartlett, N., in *Noble Gas Compounds*, Chicago, 1963.
21. Barton, D., and G. M. Harris, *Inorg. Chem.*, **1**, 251 (1962).
22. Basolo, F., and G. S. Hammaker, *Inorg. Chem.*, **1**, 1 (1962).
23. Bath, S. S., and L. Vaska, *J. Am. Chem. Soc.*, **85**, 3500 (1963).
24. Baumgartner, F., E. O. Fischer and U. Zahn, *Ber.*, **91**, 2336 (1958).
24a. Becconsall, J. K., and S. O'Brien, *Chem. Commun.*, **1966**, 720.
24b. Beck, W., and K. Lottes, *Ber.*, **94**, 2578 (1961).
25. Bell, W. E., M. Tagami and U. Merten, *J. Phys. Chem.*, **66**, 490 (1962).
25a. Belyaev, A. V., and B. V. Ptitsyn, *J. Gen. Chem. USSR Eng. Transl.*, **35**, 1881 (1965).
25b. Belyaev, A. V., and B. V. Ptitsyn, *Russ. J. Inorg. Chem.* (*Eng. Transl.*) **11**, 836 (1966).
25c. Belyaev, A. V., and B. V. Ptitsyn, *Russ. J. Inorg. Chem.* (*Eng. Transl.*) **11**, 417, 717 (1966).
26. Bennett, M. A., and P. A. Longstaff, *Chem. Ind.* (*London*), **1965**, 846.
27. Bennett, M. A., *Chem. Rev.*, **62**, 611 (1962).
27a. Bennett, M. A., R. Bramley and P. A. Longstaff, *Chem. Commun.*, **1966**, 806.
28. Berezin, B. D., *Proc. Acad. Sci. USSR Chem. Sect. Eng. Transl.*, **150**, 478 (1963).
28a. Berger, R. S., and E. A. Youngman, *J. Polymer Sci.*, *Ser. A*, **2**, 357 (1964); Biellmann, J-F., and H. Liesenfelt, *Compt. Rend.*, *Ser. C*, **263**, 251 (1966).
29. Billig, E., S. I. Shupack, J. H. Waters, R. Williams and H. B. Gray, *J. Am. Chem. Soc.*, **86**, 926 (1964).
30. Biltz, W., and P. Ehrlich, *Z. Anorg. Allgem. Chem.*, **233**, 282 (1937).
30a. Birch, A. J., and K. A. M. Walker, *J. Chem. Soc.*, *Ser. C*, **1966**, 1894.
31. Birk, E., and F. Kamm, *Festschrift zum funfzigjahrigen Bestehen der Platinschmelze G. Siebert G.m.b.H., Hanau*, **1931**, 15 (Gmelin, 'Rhodium', p. 148).

32. Blasius, E., and W. Preetz, *Z. Anorg. Allgem. Chem.*, **335**, 1 (1965).
33. Blasse, G., *Phillips Res. Rep.*, **18**, 383 (1963).
33a. Blum, J., *Tetrahedron Letters*, **1966**, 1605.
33b. de Boer, J. L., D. Rogers, A. C. Skapski and T. G. H. Troughton, *Chem. Commun.*, **1966**, 756.
34. Bokii, G. B., and L. A. Popova, *Izvest. Akad. Nauk. SSSR Otd. Khim. Nauk*, **1945**, 89.
35. Bonati, F., and G. Wilkinson, *J. Chem. Soc.*, **1964**, 3156.
36. Bonati, F., and R. Ugo, *J. Organomet. Chem.*, **7**, 167 (1967).
36a. Bosnich, B., R. D. Gillard, E. D. McKenzie and G. A. Webb, *J. Chem. Soc., Ser. A*, **1966**, 1331.
37. Bott, H. L., and A. J. Poë, *J. Chem. Soc.*, **1965**, 5931; *J. Chem. Soc., Ser. A*, **1967**, 205.
37a. Bott, H. L., E. J. Bounsall and A. J. Poë, *J. Chem. Soc.*, **1966**, 1275.
38. Bounsall, E. J., and A. J. Poë, *J. Chem. Soc.*, **1966**, 286.
39. Brault, A. T., E. M. Thorsteinson and F. Basolo, *Inorg. Chem.*, **3**, 770 (1964).
40. Bredig, G., and Th. Blackadder, *Z. Physik, Chem. (Frankfurt)*, **81**, 389 (1913) (footnote).
41. Brewer, L., and G. M. Rosenblatt, *Chem. Rev.*, **61**, 257 (1961).
41a. Bridges, K. L., and J. C. Chang, *Inorg. Chem.*, **6**, 619 (1967).
42. Brintzinger, H., and H. Orth, *Monatsh.*, **85**, 1015 (1954).
43. Brisi, C., *Ann. Chim. (Rome)*, **53**, 325 (1963).
44. Brown, D. H., D. R. Russell, and D. W. A. Sharp, *J. Chem. Soc.*, **1966**, *Ser. A*, 18.
45. Buseev, A. I., and M. I. Ivanyutin, *Tr. Komis. po Analit. Khim. Akad. Nauk. SSSR, Inst. Geokhim. i Analit. Khim.*, **11**, 172 (1960); *Chem. Abstr.*, **55**, 24381b (1961).
45a. Bushnell, G. W., G. C. Lalor and E. A. Moelwyn-Hughes, *J. Chem. Soc.*, **1966**, 719.
46. Cambi, L., and E. Paglia, *Atti Accad. Naz. Lincei Mem. Classe Sci. Fis. Mat. Nat. Sez. I*, **29**, 15 (1960); **30**, 429 (1961).
47. Cambi, L., E. Paglia, and G. Bargigia, *Atti Accad. Naz. Lincei Mem. Classe Sci. Fis. Mat. Nat. Sez. I*, **30**, 636 (1961).
47a. Carrington, A., and M. C. R. Symons, *Chem. Revs.*, **63**, 445 (1963).
48. Chalk, A. J., and J. F. Harrod, *J. Am. Chem. Soc.*, **87**, 16 (1965).
49. Chatt, J., N. P. Johnson and B. L. Shaw, *J. Chem. Soc.*, **1964**, 2508.
50. Chatt, J., and A. E. Underhill, *J. Chem. Soc.*, **1963**, 2088.
51. Chatt, J., and B. L. Shaw, *Chem. Ind. (London)*, **1961**, 290.
51a. Chatt, J., and B. L. Shaw, *J. Chem. Soc., Ser. A*, **1966**, 1437.
52. Chatt, J., and L. M. Venanzi, *J. Chem. Soc.*, **1957**, 4735.
52a. Chattoraj, S. C., and R. E. Sievers, *Inorg. Chem.*, **6**, 408 (1967).
53. Chernick, C. L., H. H. Claassen and B. Weinstock, *J. Am. Chem. Soc.*, **83**, 3165 (1961).
54. Chernyaev, I. I., E. V. Shenderetskaya, L. A. Nazarova and A. S. Antsyshkina, *Proc. VII Int. Conf. on Co-ord. Chem. Stockholm* 260 (1962).
55. Chernyaev, I. I., and A. G. Maiorova, *Russ. J. Inorg. Chem. Eng. Transl.*, 5, 517, 583 (1960).

56. Chernyaev, I. I., E. V. Shenderetskaya and A. A. Karyagina, *Russ. J. Inorg. Chem. Eng. Transl.*, **5**, 559 (1960).
57. Chernyaev, I. I., E. V. Shenderetskaya, A. G. Maiorova and A. A. Karyagina, *Russ. J. Inorg. Chem., Eng. Transl.*, **10**, 537 (1965).
58. Chiswell, B., and S. E. Livingstone, *J. Chem. Soc.*, **1960**, 3181.
59. Churchill, M. V., *Chem. Commun.*, **1**, 86 (1965); *Inorg. Chem.*, **4**, 1734 (1965).
60. Churchill, M. R., and R. Mason, *Proc. Chem. Soc.* (*London*), **1963**, 112.
60a. Churchill, M. R., and R. Mason, *Proc. Chem. Soc.* (*London*), **1963**, 365.
60b. Clark, R. J. H., and C. S. Williams, *Inorg. Chem.*, **4**, 350 (1965).
61. Claus, C., *Bull. Acad. Petersburg*, **2** (3), 187 (1860).
61a. Cleare, M. J., and W. P. Griffith, *J. Chem. Soc.*, in press.
62. Cola, M., and A. Perotti, *Gazz. Chim. Ital.*, **94**, 191 (1964).
63. Collman, J. P., R. P. Blair, R. L. Marshall and L. Slade, *Inorg. Chem.*, **2**, 577 (1963).
63a. Collmann, J. P., F. D. Vastine and W. R. Roper, *J. Am. Chem. Soc.*, **88**, 5035 (1966).
64. Collman, J. P., R. L. Marshall, W. L. Young and S. D. Goldby, *Inorg. Chem.*, **1**, 704 (1962).
64a. Collmann, J. P., and P. W. Schneider, *Inorg. Chem.*, **5**, 1380 (1966).
65. Collman, J. P., R. L. Marshall, W. L. Young, and C. T. Sears, *J. Org. Chem.*, **28**, 1449 (1963).
66. Corey, E. R., L. F. Dahl and W. Beck, *J. Am. Chem. Soc.*, **85**, 1202 (1963).
67. Cotton, F. A., R. O. Whipple and G. Wilkinson, *J. Am. Chem. Soc.*, **75**, 3586 (1953).
67a. Cotton, F. A., and J. A. McCleverty, *Inorg. Chem.*, **4**, 1398 (1964).
68. Cozzi, D., and F. Pantani, *J. Inorg. Nucl. Chem.*, **8**, 385 (1958).
69. Cozzi, D., and F. Pantani, *J. Electroanal. Chem.*, **2**, 72 (1961).
70. Cozzi, D., and F. Pantani, *J. Electroanal. Chem.*, **2**, 230 (1961).
71. Cramer, R., *J. Am. Chem. Soc.*, **86**, 217 (1964).
72. Cramer, R., *Inorg. Chem.*, **1**, 722 (1962).
73. Cramer, R., *J. Am. Chem. Soc.*, **87**, 4717 (1965).
73a. Cramer, R., *J. Am. Chem. Soc.*, **88**, 2272 (1966).
73b. Cramer, R., and R. V. Lindsey, *J. Am. Chem. Soc.*, **88**, 3534 (1966).
74. Dahl, L. F., C. Martell and D. S. Wampler, *J. Am. Chem. Soc.*, **83**, 1761 (1961).
75. Delepine, M., *Bull. Soc. Chim. Belges*, **36**, 108 (1927).
76. Delepine, M., *Compt. Rend.*, **242**, 27 (1956); **240**, 2468 (1955).
77. Delepine, M., *Bull. Soc. Chim. France*, **45**, 235 (1929).
78. Delepine, M., *Compt. Rend.*, **236**, 559 (1953).
78a. Dewhirst, K. C., *Inorg. Chem.*, **5**, 319 (1966).
79. Dickson, R. S., and G. Wilkinson, *J. Chem. Soc.*, **1964**, 2699; *Chem. Ind.* (*London*), **1963**, 1432.
80. Dippel, C. J., and F. M. Jaeger, *Rec. Trav. Chim.*, **50**, 547 (1931).
80a. Djerassi, C., and J. Guttwiller, *J. Am. Chem. Soc.*, **88**, 4537 (1966).
81. Dollimore, D., R. D. Gillard and E. D. McKenzie, *J. Chem. Soc.*, **1965**, 4479.
82. Dunlop, J. H., R. D. Gillard and G. Wilkinson, *J. Chem. Soc.*, **1964**, 3160.

83. Dunlop, J. H., and R. D. Gillard, *J. Chem. Soc.*, **1965**, 6531.
84. Dwyer, F. P., R. S. Nyholm and L. E. Rogers, *J. Proc. Roy. Soc. N. S. Wales*, **81**, 267 (1947).
85. Dwyer, F. P., and R. S. Nyholm, *J. Proc. Roy. Soc. N. S. Wales*, **75**, 122 (1941).
86. Dwyer, F. P., and R. S. Nyholm, *J. Proc. Roy. Soc. N. S. Wales*, **76**, 275 (1942).
87. Dwyer, F. P., and A. M. Sargeson, *J. Am. Chem. Soc.*, **75**, 984 (1953).
88. Dwyer, F. P., and F. L. Garvan, *J. Am. Chem. Soc.*, **82**, 4823 (1960).
89. Dwyer, F. P., and A. M. Sargeson, *J. Am. Chem. Soc.*, **81**, 2335 (1959).
90. Dwyer, F. P., and R. S. Nyholm, *J. Proc. Roy. Soc. N. S. Wales*, **75**, 122 (1941).
91. Dwyer, F. P., and R. S. Nyholm, *J. Proc. Roy. Soc. N. S. Wales*, **78**, 67 (1944).
92. Dwyer, F. P., and R. S. Nyholm, *J. Proc. Roy. Soc. N. S. Wales*, **78**, 266 (1944); **79**, 126 (1945).
93. Dwyer, F. P., and R. S. Nyholm, *J. Proc. Roy. Soc. N. S. Wales*, **75**, 140 (1941).
94. Englman, R., *Mol. Phys.*, **6**, 345 (1963).
95. Evans, D. F., D. Jones and G. Wilkinson, *J. Chem. Soc.*, **1964**, 3164.
95a. Evans, D., F. H. Jardine, J. Osborn and G. Wilkinson, *Nature*, **208**, 1203 (1965).
96. Ezerskaya, N. A., and V. N. Filimonova, *Russ. J. Inorg. Chem. Eng. Transl.*, **8**, 424 (1963).
97. Fay, R. C., and T. S. Piper, *J. Am. Chem. Soc.*, **85**, 500 (1963).
98. Fay, R. C., and T. S. Piper, *Inorg. Chem.*, **3**, 348 (1964).
99. Feldman, I., R. S. Nyholm and E. Watton, *J. Chem. Soc.*, **1965**, 4724.
99a. Fellenberg, L. R. von, *Ann.*, **50**, 63 (1840).
100. Fergusson, J. E., J. D. Karran and S. Seevaratnam, *J. Chem. Soc.*, **1965**, 2627.
101. Figgis, B. N., R. D. Gillard, R. S. Nyholm and G. Wilkinson, *J. Chem. Soc.*, **1964**, 5189.
102. Fischer, E. O., and K. Bittler, *Z. Naturforsch.*, **16B**, 225 (1961).
103. Fischer, E. O., and K. Bittler, *Z. Naturforsch.*, **16B**, 835 (1961).
104. Fischer, E. O., and U. Zahn, *Ber.*, **92**, 1624 (1959).
105. Fischer, E. O., and H. H. Lindner, *J. Organomet. Chem.*, **1**, 307 (1964).
105a. Fischer, E. O., and H. Wawersik, *J. Organomet. Chem.*, **5**, 559 (1966).
106. Fraenkel, O. von, *Monatsh.*, **35**, 119 (1914).
106a. Fritz, H. P., and J. Manchot, *J. Organomet. Chem.*, **2**, 8 (1964).
106b. Fritz, H. P., and K. E. Schwarzhans, *J. Organomet. Chem.*, **5**, 283 (1966).
106c. Fritz, H. P., and C. G. Kreiter, *J. Organomet. Chem.*, **4**, 198 (1965).
106d. Fritzman, E. K., and V. V. Krinitskii, *J. Appl. Chem. USSR Eng. Transl.*, **11**, 1610, 1618 (1938).
107. Forrester, J. S., and G. H. Ayres, *J. Phys. Chem.*, **63**, 1979 (1959).
108. Freymann, M., and J-P. Mathieu, *Bull. Soc. Chim. France*, **4**, 1297 (1937).
109. Garland, C. W., and J. R. Wilt, *J. Chem. Phys.*, **36**, 1094 (1962).
109a. Geller, S., *J. Am. Chem. Soc.*, **77**, 2641 (1955).
110. Gerloch, M., and R. Masom, *Proc. Roy. Soc. (London), Ser. A*, **279**, 170 (1964).

111. Ghosh, S. P., and A. I. P. Sinha, *J. Indian Chem. Soc.*, **40**, 249 (1963).
112. Gillard, R. D., J. A. Osborn and G. Wilkinson, *J. Chem. Soc.*, **1965**, 4107.
113. Gillard, R. D., and G. Wilkinson, *J. Chem. Soc.*, **1964**, 1368.
114. Gillard, R. D., and G. Wilkinson, *J. Chem. Soc.*, **1963**, 4271.
115. Gillard, R. D., *Spectrochim. Acta*, **20**, 1431 (1964).
116. Gillard, R. D., and G. Wilkinson, *J. Chem. Soc.*, **1964**, 870.
117. Gillard, R. D., and G. Wilkinson, *J. Chem. Soc.*, **1963**, 3594.
118. Gillard, R. D., and G. Wilkinson, *J. Chem. Soc.*, **1964**, 1224.
119. Gillard, R. D., J. A. Osborn and G. Wilkinson, *J. Chem. Soc.*, **1965**, 1951.
120. Gillard, R. D., and G. Wilkinson, *J. Chem. Soc.*, **1963**, 3193.
121. Gillard, R. D., *J. Inorg. Nucl. Chem.*, **27**, 1321 (1965).
122. Gillard, R. D., *J. Chem. Soc.*, **1963**, 2092.
123. Gillard, R. D., and G. Wilkinson, *J. Chem. Soc.*, **1964**, 1640.
124. Gillard, R. D., J. A. Osborn, P. B. Stockwell and G. Wilkinson, *Proc. Chem. Soc.*, **1964**, 284.
125. Gillard, R. D., and G. Wilkinson, *Inorg. Syn. IX*, in press.
126. Gillard, R. D., and R. Ugo, *J. Chem. Soc.*, **1966**, 549.
126a. Gillard, R. D., E. D. McKenzie and M. D. Ross, *J. Inorg. Nucl. Chem.*, **28**, 1429 (1966).
127. Ginzburg, S. I., and N. N. Chalisova, *Russ. J. Inorg. Chem. Eng. Transl.*, **10**, 440, 1312 (1965).
127a. Ginzburg, S. I., N. N. Chalisova and O. N. Estaf'eva, *Russ. J. Inorg. Chem.* (*Eng. Transl.*) **11**, 404, 738 (1966).
128. Goloubkine, G., *Bull. Soc. Chim. Belges*, **24**, 392 (1910).
129. Gray, H. B., and A. Wojcicki, *Proc. Chem. Soc.* (*London*), *Ser. A*, **1960**, 358.
130. Green, M. L. H., L. Pratt and G. Wilkinson, *J. Chem. Soc.*, **1959**, 3753.
131. Griffith, W. P., unpublished results.
132. Griffith, W. P., J. Lewis and G. Wilkinson, *J. Chem. Soc.*, **1959**, 1775.
133. Griffith, W. P., and G. Wilkinson, *J. Chem. Soc.*, **1959**, 2757.
134. Griffith, W. P., *J. Chem. Soc.*, **1966**, *Ser. A*, **1966**, 899.
135. Grinberg, A. A., L. V. Vrublevskaya, Kh. I. Gil'dengershel' and A. I. Stetsenko, *Russ. J. Inorg. Chem., Eng. Transl.*, **4**, 462 (1959).
135a. Grinberg, A. A. and Y. S. Varshavskii, *Proc. Acad. Sci. USSR Eng. transl.*, **163**, 692 (1965).
136. Grube, G., and H. Autenrieth, *Z. Elektrochem.*, **43**, 880 (1937).
137. Grube, G., and Bau-Tschang Gui, *Z. Elektrochem.*, **43**, 397 (1937).
138. Grube, G., and E. Kesting, *Z. Elektrochem.*, **39**, 948 (1933).
139. Grube, G., and H. Autenrieth, *Z. Elektrochem.*, **44**, 296 (1938).
140. Gutbier, A., and A. Huttlinger, *Z. Anorg. Allgem. Chem.*, **95**, 247 (1916).
141. Gutbier, A., and H. Bertsch, *Z. Anorg. Allgem. Chem.*, **129**, 67 (1923).
142. Gutbier, A., and A. Huttlinger, *Ber.*, **41**, 215 (1908).
143. Guthrie, A. N., and L. T. Bourland, *Phys. Rev.*, **37**, 303 (1931).
144. Hair, M. L., and P. L. Robinson, *J. Chem. Soc.*, **1960**, 3419.
144a. Handy, L. B., P. M. Treichel, L. F. Dahl and A. G. Hayter, *J. Am. Chem. Soc.*, **88**, 366 (1966).
145. Harris, C. M., and E. D. McKenzie, *J. Inorg. Nucl. Chem.*, **25**, 171 (1963).
146. Harrod, J. F., and A. J. Chalk, *J. Am. Chem. Soc.*, **86**, 1776 (1964).
146a. Harrod, J. F., and A. J. Chalk, *J. Am. Chem. Soc.*, **88**, 3491 (1966).

147. Harrod, J. F., and J. Halpern, *Can. J. Chem.*, **37**, 1933 (1959).
148. Hayter, R. G., *Inorg. Chem.*, **3**, 301 (1964).
149. Heck, R. F., *J. Am. Chem. Soc.*, **86**, 2796 (1964).
149a. Heil, B., and L. Marko, *J. Am. Chem. Soc.*, **99**, 1086 (1966).
150. Hepworth, M. A., P. L. Robinson, and G. J. Westland, *J. Chem. Soc.*, **1954**, 4269.
151. Hepworth, M. A., K. H. Jack, R. D. Peacock and G. J. Westland, *Acta Cryst.*, **10**, 63 (1957).
151a. Herberlin, F., J. D. Herberlin, J.-P. Mathieu and H. Poulet, *Spectrochim. Acta*, **22**, 1515 (1966).
151b. Herr, W., *Z. Naturforsch.*, **9A**, 180 (1954).
152. Hieber, W., and K. Heinicke, *Z. Naturforsch.*, **14B**, 819 (1959); Hieber, W., and H. Heusinger, *Angew. Chem.*, **68**, 679 (1956).
153. Hieber, W., and K. Heinicke, *Z. Anorg. Allgem. Chem.*, **316**, 321 (1962).
154. Hieber, W., and H. Lagally, *Z. Anorg. Allgem. Chem.*, **251**, 96 (1943).
154a. Hieber, W., and F. Volker, *Ber.*, **99**, 2614 (1966); **100**, 148 (1967).
155. Hieber, W., H. Heusinger and O. Vohler, *Ber.*, **90**, 2425 (1957).
156. Holloway, J. H., P. R. Rao and N. Bartlett, *Chem. Commun.*, **1965**, 306.
156a. Hopkins, P. D., and B. E. Douglas, *Inorg. Chem.*, **3**, 357 (1964).
157. Howarth, O. W., R. E. Richards and L. M. Venanzi, *J. Chem. Soc.*, **1964**, 3335.
157a. Hulliger, F., *Nature*, **204**, 644 (1964).
158. Hunt, J. P., and H. Taube, *J. Chem. Phys.*, **18**, 757 (1950).
159. Hunt, J. P., and R. A. Plane, *J. Am. Chem. Soc.*, **76**, 5960 (1954).
159a. Hunt, R. L., and G. Wilkinson, *Inorg. Chem.*, **4**, 1270 (1965).
160. Hurwitz, P., and K. Kustin, *Inorg. Chem.*, **3**, 823 (1964).
161. Ibers, J. A., and R. G. Snyder, *Acta Cryst.*, **15**, 923 (1962).
161a. Iguchi, M., *J. Chem. Soc. Japan*, **60**, 1287 (1939).
162. Jaeger, F. M., and W. Thomas, *Rec. Trav. Chim.*, **38**, 300 (1919).
163. Jaeger, F. M., and J. A. van Dijk, *Z. Anorg. Allgem. Chem.*, **227**, 321 (1936); *Proc. Acad Amst.* **37**, 280 (1934).
164. Jaeger, F. M., and H. B. Blumendd, *Z. Anorg. Allgem. Chem.*, **175**, 207 (1928).
165. Jaeger, F. M., and L. Bijkerk, *Z. Anorg. Allgem. Chem.*, **233**, 139 (1937).
166. James, B. R., and G. L. Rempel, *Can. J. Chem.*, **44**, 233 (1966).
166a. Jardine, F. H., J. A. Osborn, G. Wilkinson and J. F. Young, *Chem. Ind. (London)*, **1965**, 560.
166b. Johnson, B. F. G., and R. A. Walton, *J. Inorg. Nucl. Chem.*, **28**, 1901 (1966).
166c. Johnson, B. F. G., and R. A. Walton, *Spectrochim. Acta*, **22**, 1853 (1966).
166d. Johnson, B. F. G., J. Lewis, I. G. Williams and J. M. Wilson, *J. Chem. Soc., Ser. A.*, **1967**, 341.
167. Johnson, S. A., H. R. Hunt and H. M. Neumann, *Inorg. Chem.*, **2**, 960 (1963).
168. Johnson, S. A., and F. Basolo, *Inorg. Chem.*, **1**, 925 (1962).
169. Johnson, S. A., F. Basolo and R. G. Pearson, *J. Am. Chem. Soc.*, **85**, 1741 (1963).
170. Joly, A., and E. Leidie, *Compt. Rend.*, **127**, 103 (1898).

171. Jones, L. H., *J. Chem. Phys.*, **41**, 856 (1964).
172. Jorgensen, C. K., *Acta Chem. Scand.*, **12**, 1539 (1958).
173. Jorgensen, C. K., *Mol. Phys.*, **4**, 231 (1961).
174. Jorgensen, C. K., *Mol. Phys.*, **2**, 309 (1959).
175. Jorgensen, C. K., *J. Inorg. Nucl. Chem.*, **24**, 1571 (1962).
176. Jorgensen, C. K., *Mol. Phys.*, **5**, 485 (1962).
177. Jorgensen, C. K., *Acta Chem. Scand.*, **10**, 500 (1956).
178. Jorgensen, C. K., *Acta Chem. Scand.*, **11**, 151 (1957).
179. Jorgensen, S. M., *J. Prakt. Chem.*, **44**, 48 (1891).
180. Jorgensen, S. M., *J. Prakt. Chem.*, **27**, 434 (1883); *Z. Anorg. Allgem. Chem.*, **34**, 85 (1903).
181. Jorgensen, S. M., *J. Prakt. Chem.*, **34**, 394 (1886).
182. Juza, R., O. Hulsmann, K. Meisel and W. Biltz, *Z. Anorg. Allgem. Chem.*, **225**, 380 (1935).
182a. Kalal, J., S. Doszlop and F. Svec, *Coll. Czech. Chem. Commun.*, **31**, 3405 (1966).
182b. Karim, S. M., and R. Samuel, *Bull. Acad. Sci. Allahabad*, **3**, 166 (1933).
183. Kauffmann, G. B., and J. H. Tsai, *J. Less-Common Metals*, **4**, 519 (1962).
183a. Kauffmann, G. B., and J. H. Tsai, *Inorg. Syn.*, **8**, 217 (1966).
184. Keen, I. M., *Platinum Metals Rev.*, **8**, 143 (1964).
185. Kettle, S. F. A., *Nature*, **207**, 1384 (1965); *J. Chem. Soc., Ser. A*, **1967**, 314.
186. Khanolkar, D. D., *Current Sci.* (*India*), **30**, 52 (1961).
187. Kharasch, M. S., and H. S. Isbell, *J. Am. Chem. Soc.*, **53**, 2701 (1931).
188. King, R. B., *Inorg. Chem.*, **2**, 528 (1963).
188a. King, R. B., *Inorg. Chem.*, **1**, 82 (1966).
189. Krauss, F., and H. Umbach, *Z. Anorg. Allgem. Chem.*, **180**, 47 (1929).
190. Krauss, F., and H. Umbach, *Z. Anorg. Allgem. Chem.*, **182**, 414 (1929).
191. Krauss, F., and H. Umbach, *Z. Anorg. Allgem. Chem.*, **179**, 357 (1929).
191a. Krauzmann, A., *Compt. Rend. Ser.*, *B*, **262**, 765 (1966).
192. Krishnamurty, K. V., *Inorg. Chem.*, **1**, 422 (1962).
192a. Kristjanson, A. M., and M. Lederer, *J. Less-Common Metals*, **1**, 245 (1959).
193. Kruck, T., W. Lang and N. Derner, *Z. Naturforsch.*, **20B**, 705 (1965); Th. Kruck and W. Lang, *Angem. Chem.*, **4**, 870 (1965); **6**, 53 (1967).
193a. Kulasingam, G. C., and W. R. McWhinnie, *J. Chem. Soc.*, **1965**, 7145.
194. Lamb, A. B., *J. Am. Chem. Soc.*, **61**, 699 (1939).
195. LaPlaca, S. J., and J. A. Ibers, *J. Am. Chem. Soc.*, **85**, 3501 (1963); *Acta Cryst.*, **18**, 511 (1965).
196. Lawson, D. N., M. J. Mays and G. Wilkinson, *J. Chem. Soc.*, *Ser. A*, **1966**, 52.
196a. Lawson, D. N., J. A. Osborn and G. Wilkinson, unpublished results.
197. Lawson, D. N., and G. Wilkinson, *J. Chem. Soc.*, **1965**, 1900.
197a. Lawson, D. N., J. A. Osborn and G. Wilkinson, *J. Chem. Soc.*, *Ser. A*, **1966**, 1733.
198. Lebedinskii, V. V., and E. V. Shenderetskaya, *Russ. J. Inorg. Chem. Eng. Transl.*, **2** (8), 89 (1959).
198a. Lebedinskii, V. V., and E. V. Shenderetskaya, *Izvest. Inst. po Izuch. Plating Drugikh Blagorodnykh Metallov*, **30**, 99 (1955).
199. Lebedinskii, V. V., E. S. Schapiro and I. P. Kasaltina, *Izvest. Inst. po Izuch. Plating Drugikh Blagorodnykh metallov*, **12**, 101 (1935).

200. Lebedinskii, V. V., and V. S. Volkov, *Izvest. Inst. po Izuch. Plating Drugikh Blagorodnykh metallov*, **12**, 79 (1935).
201. Lebedinskii, W. W., *Izvest. Inst. po Izuch. Plating Drugikh Blagorodnykh metallov*, **12**, 67, 77 (1935).
202. Lebedinskii, W. W., *Izvest. Inst. po Izuch. Plating Drugikh Blagorodnykh metallov*, **11**, 10 (1933).
203. Lebedinskii, W. W., and S. F. Silin, *Izvest. Inst. po Izuch. Plating Drugikh Blagorodnykh metallov*, **14**, 38 (1937).
204. Lebedinskii, V. V., and I. A. Fedorov, *Izvest. Inst. po Izuch. Plating Drugikh Blagorodnykh metallov*, **22**, 258 (1948).
205. Lebedinskii, V. V., and I. A. Fedorov, *Izvest. Inst. po Izuch. Plating Drugikh Blagorodnykh metallov*, **12**, 87 (1935).
206. Lebedinskii, V. V., and J. A. Fedorov, *Izvest. Inst. po Izuch. Plating Drugikh Blagorodnykh metallov*, **21**, 157 (1948); **22**, 158 (1948).
206a. Lederer, M., *Russ. J. Inorg. Chem., Eng. Transl.*, **3** (8), 111 (1958).
207. Leidie, E., *Compt. Rend.*, **107**, 235 (1888); *Ann. Chim. Phys.*, **17**, 257 (1889).
208. Leidie, E., *Compt. Rend.*, **111**, 106 (1890); **127**, 103 (1898).
208a. Lewis, J., R. S. Nyholm and P. W. Smith, *J. Chem. Soc.*, **1961**, 4590.
208b. Lewis, J., R. S. Nyholm and G. A. Rodley, *J. Chem. Soc.*, **1965**, 1483.
208c. Lewis, J., R. S. Nyholm and G. K. N. Reddy, *Chem. Ind. (London)*, **1960**, 1386.
208d. Liu, C. F., and C. H. Liu, *Inorg. Chem.*, **3**, 678 (1964).
209. Lohr, L. L., and W. N. Lipscomb, *Inorg. Chem.*, **3**, 22 (1964).
210. Loo, van, G., and J. A. Page, *Talanta*, **12**, 227 (1965).
211. Lunde, G., *Z. Anorg. Allgem. Chem.*, **163**, 348 (1927).
212. McCaffery, A. J., S. F. Mason and R. E. Ballard, *J. Chem. Soc.*, **1965**, 2883.
213. McCleverty, J. A., and G. Wilkinson, *Inorg. Syn.*, **8**, 211 (1966).
214. McCleverty, J. A., and G. Wilkinson, *J. Chem. Soc.*, **1964**, 4200.
215. McCleverty, J., and G. Wilkinson, *Inorg. Syn.*, **8**, 214 (1966).
215a. McDonald, C. G., and J. S. Shannon, *Australian J. Chem.*, **19**, 1545 (1966).
216. McDonald, J. E., and J. W. Cobble, *J. Phys. Chem.*, **66**, 791 (1962).
216a McPartlin, M., and R. Mason, *Chem. Comm.*, **1967**, 16.
216b. McVey, S., and P. M. Maitlis, *Can. J. Chem.*, **44**, 2429 (1966).
216c. Mague, J. T., and G. Wilkinson, *J. Chem. Soc., Ser. A*, **1966**, 1736.
216d. Maher, J., *Chem. Comm.*, **1966**, 785.
217. Maitlis, P. M. and S. McVey, *J. Organomet. Chem.*, **4**, 254 (1965).
217a. Maki, A. H., N. Edelstein, A. Davison and R. H. Holm, *J. Am. Chem. Soc.*, **86**, 4580 (1964).
218. Malatesta, L., *Gazz. Chim. Ital.*, **68**, 195 (1938).
219. Malatesta, L., and F. Turner, *Gazz. Chim. Ital.*, **72**, 489 (1942).
220. Malatesta, L., and L. Vallarino, *J. Chem. Soc.*, **1956**, 1867.
221. Manchot, W., and Konig, *Ber.*, **60**, 2130 (1937).
222. Manchot, W., and H. Schmid, *Ber.*, **64**, 2672 (1931).
223. Mann, F. G., *Nature*, **130**, 368 (1932); **155**, 3149 (1933).
224. Mann, F. G., and W. J. Pope, *Proc. Roy. Soc. (London), Ser. A*, **107**, 91 (1925); *J. Chem. Soc.*, **1926**, 2675.

225. Martin, B., and G. M. Waind, *J. Chem. Soc.*, **1958**, 4284.
226. Martin, B., W. R. McWhinnie and G. M. Waind, *J. Inorg. Nucl. Chem.*, **23**, 207 (1961).
227. Martius, C. A., *Ann.*, **117**, 369 (1861).
227a. Mason, S. F., and B. J. Norman, *J. Chem. Soc.*, **1966**, 307.
228. Mathieu, J-P., *Compt. Rend.*, **204**, 682 (1937); *J. Phys. Radium*, **8**, 169 (1937).
229. Mathieu, J-P., and S. Cornevin, *J. Chim. Phys.*, **36**, 271 (1939).
230. Mathieu, J-P., *Compt. Rend.*, **198**, 1600 (1934); *J. Chim. Phys.*, **33**, 78 (1936).
231. Mathieu, J-P., J. Badoz, M. Billardon and J. P. Mathieu, *Compt. Rend.*, **251**, 1477 (1960).
232. Mathieu, J-P., *Compt. Rend.*, **253**, 2232 (1961).
232a. Mawby, R. J., and L. M. Venanzi, *Experientia*, Suppl. No. 9, 240 (1964).
233. Mays, J., and G. Wilkinson, *J. Chem. Soc.*, **1965**, 6629.
234. Meyer, M. J., and K. Hoehne, *Z. Anorg. Allgem. Chem.*, **231**, 372 (1937).
235. Meyer, J., and H. Kienitz, *Z. Anorg. Allgem. Chem.*, **242**, 281 (1939).
235a. Meyer, J., and M. Kawczyk, *Z. Anorg. Allgem. Chem.*, **228**, 296 (1939).
235b. Mills, O. S., and E. F. Paulus, *Chem. Comm.*, **1966**, 815.
236. Monacelli, F., F. Basolo and R. G. Pearson, *J. Inorg. Nucl. Chem.*, **24**, 1241 (1962).
237. Muetterties, E. L., and C. M. Wright, *J. Am. Chem. Soc.*, **87**, 4706 (1965).
238. Muraveiskaya, G. S., I. I. Chernyaev and V. F. Sorokina, *Russ. J. Inorg. Chem. Eng. Transl.*, **8**, 434 (1963).
239. Nazarova, L. A., I. I. Chernyaev and A. S. Morozova, *Russ. J. Inorg. Chem. Eng. Transl.*, **10**, 291 (1965).
240. Newman, G., and D. B. Powell, *Spectrochim. Acta*, **19**, 213 (1963).
241. Nicholson, J. K., and B. L. Shaw, *Proc. Chem. Soc. (London)*, **1963**, 282.
242. Nicholson, J. K., and B. L. Shaw, *Tetrahedron Letters*, **1965**, 3533.
243. Norman, J. H., H. G. Staley, and W. E. Bell, *J. Phys. Chem.*, **68**, 662 (1964).
244. Norman, J. H., and H. G. Staley, *quoted in J. G. Dillard and R. W. Kiser, J. Phys. Chem.*, **69**, 3893 (1965).
245. Nyholm, R. S., and K. Vrieze, *J. Chem. Soc.*, **1965**, 5331.
245a. Nyholm, R. S., *J. Chem. Soc.*, **1950**, 857.
245b. Nyholm, R. S., and A. G. Sharpe, *J. Chem. Soc.*, **1952**, 3579.
246. Odell, A. L., R. W. Olliff and F. B. Seaton, *J. Chem. Soc.*, **1965**, 2280.
246a. Ogilvie, F. B., and O. G. Holmes, *Can. J. Chem.*, **44**, 447 (1966).
247. Osborn, J. A., R. D. Gillard and G. Wilkinson, *J. Chem. Soc.*, **1964**, 3168.
248. Osborn, J. A., F. H. Jardine, J. F. Young and G. Wilkinson, *J. Chem. Soc., Ser. A*, **1966**, 1711.
249. Osborn, J. A., G. Wilkinson and J. F. Young, *Chem. Commun.*, **1965**, 17.
249a. Osborn, J. A., A. R. Powell and G. Wilkinson, *Chem. Commun.*, **1966**, 461.
249b. Osborn, J. A., and G. Wilkinson, *Inorg. Syn.*, *in press*.
250. Paiaro, G., A. Musco and F. Diano, *J. Organomet. Chem.*, **4**, 466 (1965).
251. Palmer, J. W., and F. Basolo, *J. Inorg. Nucl. Chem.*, **15**, 279 (1960).
252. Pantani, F., *J. Electroanal. Chim.*, **5**, 40 (1963).
253. Pantani, F., *Ric. Sci. Rend., Sez. A*, **4**, 41 (1964).
253a. Pantani, F., *Talanta*, **9**, 15 (1962).
254. Parshall, G., and F. N. Jones, *J. Am. Chem. Soc.*, **87**, 5356 (1965).

255. Pauling, L., *Proc. Nat. Acad. Sci. U.S.*, **15**, 712 (1929).
256. Peacock, R. D., and D. W. A. Sharp, *J. Chem. Soc.*, **1959**, 2762.
257. Peacock, R. D., *J. Chem. Soc.*, **1955**, 3291.
258. Pearson, R. G., *J. Am. Chem. Soc.*, **85**, 3533 (1963).
259. Peters, W., *Z. Anorg. Allgem. Chem.*, **77**, 137, 165 (1912); *Ber.*, **42**, 4829 (1909).
260. Phillips, R. F., and H. M. Powell, *Proc. Roy. Soc. (London), Ser. A*, **173**, 147 (1939).
261. Piccini, A., and L. Marino, *Z. Anorg. Allgem. Chem.*, **27**, 62 (1901).
262. Plumb, W., and G. M. Harris, *Inorg. Chem.*, **3**, 542 (1964).
263. Pnevmanticakis, G. A., E. C. Stathis and E. K. Fields, *J. Inorg. Nucl. Chem.*, **28**, 2059 (1966); **27**, 895 (1965).
263a. Poë, A. J., and K. Shaw, *Chem. Comm.*, **1967**, 52
264. Popov, G., *Cryst. Acad. Nauk. USSR*, **5**, 201 (1949).
265. Porai-Koshits, M. A., and A. S. Antsyshkina, *Proc. Acad. Sci. USSR, Chem. Sect. Eng. Transl.*, **146**, 902 (1962).
266. Porri, L., A. Lionetti, G. Allegra and A. Immirzi, *Chem. Commun.*, **1965**, 336.
266a. Porri, L., and A. Lionetti, *J. Organometal. Chem.*, **6**, 422 (1966).
266b. Porte, A. L., H. S. Gutowsky and G. M. Harris, *J. Chem. Phys.*, **34**, 66 (1961).
266c. Postollec, M., J-P. Mathieu and H. Poulet, *J. Chim. Phys.*, **60**, 1319 (1963).
267. Poulenc, P., *Ann. Chim.*, **4** (11), 567 (1935).
268. Poulenc, P., *Ann. Chim.*, **4** (11), 648 (1935).
269. Poulenc, P., *Compt. Rend.*, **191**, 54 (1930).
270. Powell, D. B., and N. Sheppard, *J. Chem. Soc.*, **1961**, 1112; **1959**, 791.
270a. Powell, J., and B. L. Shaw, *Chem. Commun.*, **1966**, 236, 323.
270b. Powell, P., and H. Nöth, *Chem. Commun.*, **1966**, 637.
270c. Prince, R. H., and K. A. Raspin, *Chem. Commun.*, **1966**, 156.
271. Puche, F., *Ann. Chim.*, **9**, 300 (1938).
272. Randall, E. W., and D. Shaw, *Mol. Phys.*, **10**, 41 (1965); **11**, 395 (1966).
273. Randall, J. J., and L. Katz, *Acta Cryst.*, **12**, 519 (1959).
274. Raziunas, V., G. Macur and S. Katz, *J. Chem. Phys.*, **43**, 1010 (1965).
274a. Reddy, G. K. W., and E. G. Leelamani, *Current Sci. (India)*, **34**, 146 (1965).
275. Reihlen, H., and W. Huhn, *Z. Anorg. Chem.*, **214**, 189 (1933).
276. Rinehart, R. E., and J. S. Lasky, *J. Am. Chem. Soc.*, **86**, 2516 (1964).
277. Rinehart, R. E., H. P. Smith, H. S. Witt and H. Romeyn, *J. Am. Chem. Soc.*, **83**, 4864 (1961).
278. Robb, W., and G. M. Harris, *J. Am. Chem. Soc.*, **87**, 4472 (1965).
278a. Robb, W., and M. M. de V. Steyn, *Inorg. Chem.*, **6**, 616 (1967).
279. Ruff, O., and E. Ascher, *Z. Anorg. Chem.*, **183**, 206 (1929).
280. Rund, J. V., F. Basolo and R. G. Pearson, *Inorg. Chem.*, **3**, 658 (1964).
281. Rusina, A., and A. A. Vlcek, *Nature*, **206**, 295 (1965).
281a. Ryan, D. E., *Analyst*, **75**, 557 (1950).
282. Sacco, A., and R. Ugo, *J. Chem. Soc.*, **1964**, 3274.
282a. Sacco, A., R. Ugo and A. Moles, *J. Chem. Soc., Ser. A*, **1966**, 1670.
283. Scheer, J. J., A. E. van Arkel and R. D. Heyding, *Can. J. Chem.*, **33**, 683 (1955).

283a. Scherzer, J., P. K. Phillips, L. B. Clapp and J. O. Edwards, *Inorg. Chem.*, **5**, 847 (1966).
284. Schmahl, N. O., and E. Minzl, *Z. Physik. Chem. (Frankfurt)*, **41**, 78 (1964).
285. Schmidt, G. B., *Z. Physik. Chem. (Frankfurt)*, **41**, 26 (1964).
286. Schmidt, G. B., W. Herr and K. Rossler, *Angew. Chem.*, **4**, 990 (1965).
287. Schmidtke, H. H., *Z. Physik. Chem. (Frankfurt)*, **40**, 96 (1964).
288. Schmidtke, H. H., *Z. Physik. Chem. (Frankfurt)*, **34**, 295 (1962).
289. Schmidtke, H. H., *Z. Physik. Chem. (Frankfurt)*, **45**, 305 (1965).
290. Schmidtke, H. H., *Z. Anorg. Allgem. Chem.*, **339**, 103 (1965).
290a. Schmidtke, H. H., *Z. Physik. Chem. (Frankfurt)*, **38**, 170 (1963).
291. Schrauzer, G. N., and K. C. Dewhirst, *J. Am. Chem. Soc.*, **86**, 3265 (1964).
292. Sen, D., and W. C. Fernelius, *J. Inorg. Nucl. Chem.*, **10**, 269 (1959).
293. Sharp, D. W. A., *Proc. Chem. Soc. (London)*, **1960**, 317.
294. Sharpe, A. G., *J. Chem. Soc.*, **1950**, 3444.
295. Shukla, S. K., *J. Chromatog.*, **1**, 457 (1958).
296. Shukla, S. K., and M. Lederer, *J. Less-Common Metals*, **1**, 202 (1954).
297. Shukla, S. K., *Ann. Chim.*, **6**, 1383 (1961).
298. Shukla, M., and M. Lederer, *J. Less-Common Metals*, **1**, 255 (1959).
299. Sidgwick, N. V., *Chemical Elements and their Compounds*, Oxford University Press, Oxford, 1949, pp. 1518 and 1529.
299a. P. Spacu, M. Brezeanu and D. Roman-Vacarescu, *Analete Univ. Bucharest, Ser. Stiint. Nat.*, **13**, 179 (1964); *Chem. Abstr.*, **64**, 12178 (1965).
299b. Steigman, J., *Phys. Rev.*, **59**, 498 (1941).
300. Stephenson, T. A., S. M. Morehouse, A. R. Powell, J. P. Heffer and G. Wilkinson, *J. Chem. Soc.*, **1965**, 3632.
300a. Swaminathan, K., and G. M. Harris, *J. Am. Chem. Soc.*, **88**, 4411 (1966).
300b. Syrokomskii, V. S., and N. N. Proshenkova, *J. Anal. Chem., USSR Eng. Transl.*, **2**, 247 (1947); cf. also *Analyst*, **73**, 361 (1948).
301. Takaki, G. T., and R. T. M. Fraser, *Proc. Chem. Soc. (London)*, **1964**, 116.
302. Tchugaev, L., *Bull. Soc. Chim. France*, **25**, 236 (1919).
303. Tchugaev, L., and W. Lebedinskii, *Z. Anorg. Allgem. Chem.*, **83**, 4 (1913).
304. Tchugaev, L., and E. Fritzmann, *Z. Anorg. Allgem. Chem.*, **172**, 221 (1928).
305. Terpstra, P., and J. ter Berg, *Proc. Acad. Sci. Amsterdam*, **40**, 602 (1937).
305a. Teyssie, P., and R. Dauby, *J. Polymer Sci., Ser. B*, **2**, 413 (1964).
306. Thomassen, L., *Z. Physik. Chem. (Frankfurt)*, **4**, 277 (1929).
306a. Torrible, E. G., *J. Inorg. Nucl. Chem.*, **28**, 907 (1966).
306b. Townsend, M. G., *J. Chem. Phys.*, **41**, 3149 (1964).
307. Troitskaye, A. D., and S. N. Sarkisijan, Fr. Khazansk, *Khim. Technol. Inst.* **33**, 28 (1964).
308. Tsuji, J., and K. Ohno, *Tetrahedron Letters*, **1965**, 3969; **1966**, 4713; *J. Am. Chem. Soc.*, **88**, 3452 (1966).
309. Ugo, R., F. Bonati and S. Cenini, *Rend. Ist. Lombardo Sci. Lettere A*, **98**, 627 (1964).
310. Ugo, R., and F. Bonati, *Rend. Ist. Lombardo Sci. Lettere A*, **98**, 548 (1964).
311. Vallarino, L., *J. Chem. Soc.*, **1957**, 2473.
312. Vallarino, L., *Inorg. Chem.*, **4**, 161 (1965).
313. Vallarino, L., *J. Inorg. Nucl. Chem.*, **8**, 288 (1958).

314. Vallarino, L., *Gazz. Chim. Ital.*, **89**, 1632 (1959).
315. Vallarino, L., *J. Chem. Soc.*, **1957**, 2287.
316. Vaska, L., and J. W. DiLuzio, *J. Am. Chem. Soc.*, **83**, 2784 (1961).
317. Vaska, L., *Inorg. Nucl. Chem. Letters*, **1**, 89 (1965); L. Vaska and R. E. Rhodes, *J. Am. Chem. Soc.*, **87**, 4970 (1965).
317a. Vaska, L., and S. S. Bath, *J. Am. Chem. Soc.*, **88**, 1333 (1966).
317b. Verkade, J. G., and T. S. Piper, *Inorg. Chem.*, **1**, 453 (1962).
317c. Volger, H. C., and K. Vrieze, *J. Organomet. Chem.*, **6**, 297 (1966).
318. Wagnerova, D. M., *Collection Czech. Chem. Commun.*, **26**, 2076 (1961).
319. Waller, J. F., J. Hu and B. E. Bryant, *J. Inorg. Nucl. Chem.*, **27**, 2371 (1965).
319a. Walton, R. A., *Can. J. Chem.*, **44**, 1480 (1966).
319b. Watkins, S. F., J. Obi and L. F. Dahl, *Inorg. Chem.*, *in press*.
320. Watt, G. W., and B. J. McCormick, *Inorg. Chem.*, **4**, 143 (1965).
321. Watt, G. W., J. K. Crum and J. T. Summers, *J. Am. Chem. Soc.*, **87**, 4641 (1965); G. W. Watt and J. K. Crum, *J. Am. Chem. Soc.*, **87**, 5366 (1965).
321a. Wei, C. H., and L. F. Dahl, *J. Am. Chem. Soc.*, **88**, 1821 (1966).
322. Weinstock, B., H. H. Claassen and C. L. Chernick, *J. Chem. Phys.*, **38**, 1470 (1963).
323. Weise, E., and W. Klemm, *Z. Anorg. Allgem. Chem.*, **272**, 211 (1953).
324. Wendlandt, W. W., and P. H. Franke, *J. Inorg. Nucl. Chem.*, **26**, 1885 (1964).
325. Werner, A., *Ber.*, **45**, 1230 (1912).
326. West, C. D., *Z. Krist.*, **91**, 181 (1935).
326a. Willis, J. A., *J. Am. Chem. Soc.*, **66**, 1067 (1944).
326b. Winkhaus, G., and H. Singer, *Ber.*, **99**, 3593, 3602 (1966).
327. Wohler, L., and W. Muller, *Z. Anorg. Allgem. Chem.*, **149**, 132 (1925).
328. Wohler, L., and K. F. A. Ewald, *Z. Anorg. Allgem. Chem.*, **201**, 145 (1931).
329. Wohler, L., and N. Jochum, *Z. Physik. Chem.* (*Frankfurt*), **167**, 169 (1935); L. Wohler and W. Muller, *Z. Anorg. Allgem. Chem.*, **149**, 125 (1925).
330. Wojcicki, A., and F. Basolo, *J. Am. Chem. Soc.*, **83**, 525 (1961).
330a. Wolf, L., E. Butter and H. Weinelt, *Z. Anorg. Allgem. Chem.*, **306**, 87 (1960).
331. Wolsey, W. C., C. A. Reynolds and J. Kleinberg, *Inorg. Chem.*, **2**, 463 (1963).
332. Yamasaki, K., and K. Suguera, *Naturwissenschaften*, **63**, 552 (1961).
333. Young, J. F., R. D. Gillard and G. Wilkinson, *J. Chem. Soc.*, **1964**, 5176.
334. Young, J. F., J. A. Osborn, F. H. Jardine and G. Wilkinson, *Chem. Commun.*, **1965**, 860.
334a. Zachariasen, W. H., *Acta Cryst.*, **20**, 334 (1966).
335. Zvonkova, A. V., *Zh. Fiz. Khim.*, **27**, 101 (1953).
336. Zvyagintsev, O. E., I. V. Prokov'eva and A. E. Bukanova, *Zh. Neorgan. Khim.*, **11**, 2070 (1966).

APPENDIX

NATURAL AND ARTIFICIAL ISOTOPES OF THE METALS

(Reproduced by permission from the tables by R. H. Heath, *Handbook of Chemistry and Physics*, Chemical Rubber Publishing Co., Cleveland, 1964.)

Z	Isotope	% Natural abundance	Atomic mass [a] (A)	Lifetime $t_{1/2}$	Modes of decay [b]	Decay energies (MeV)	Particle energies (MeV)	Particle intensities	Gamma energies (MeV) [b]	Gamma intensities [b]	Thermal neutron capture cross-sections (Barns) σ_c
Os			190·2								15
76	$^{181}_{76}Os$			23 min	EC				0·167		
									0·174		
	$^{182}_{76}Os$			22 h	EC				0·0276		
									0·0555		
									0·1802		
									0·510		
	$^{183m}_{76}Os$			10 h	IT	0·171	EC	54%	0·0673	6%	
					EC		IT	46%	0·1707	46%	
									1·036	6%	
									1·103	26%	
									1·1095	22%	
	$^{183}_{76}Os$			12 h	EC		EC		0·3818	87%	
									0·1144	92%	
									0·1679	17%	
									0·496	4%	
									0·2362	6%	
									$>10\gamma$'s		
	$^{184}_{76}Os$	0·018	183·9526								<200
	$^{185}_{76}Os$			94 days	EC	0·982	EC		0·646	80%	
									0·872	7·4%	
									0·879	7%	
									0·718	4%	

$^{186}_{76}Os$	1·59	185·9539								
$^{187}_{76}Os$	1·64	186·9560								
$^{188}_{76}Os$	13·3	187·9560								
$^{189m}_{76}Os$			5·7 h	IT	0·03			0·0304 (CE)	100% (100%)	
$^{189}_{76}Os$	16·1	188·9586								(<.02 + ?)
$^{190m}_{76}Os$			49·5 min	IT	1·698			0·039 0·1865 0·359 0·505 0·617	100% 100% 100% 100% 100%	
$^{190}_{76}Os$	26·4	189·9586								(32 + 8)
$^{191m}_{76}Os$			14 h	IT	0·0742	IT		0·07420	100%	
$^{191}_{76}Os$			15 days	β^-	0·314	β^- 0·143	99 + %	0·042D 0·129D (See ^{191m}Ir)		
$^{192}_{76}Os$	41·0	191·9612								1·6
$^{193}_{76}Os$			32 h	β^-	1·132	β^- 1·13 1·05 0·99 0·67	66% 12% 8% 8%	0·072 0·139 0·281 0·460 0·559 > 10γ's	14% 10% 2% 4% 2%	200
$^{194}_{76}Os$			~2 years	β^-				(See ^{194}Ir)		
$^{195}_{76}Os$			6 min	β^-		β^- 2·0				

Z	Isotope	% Natural abundance	Atomic mass[a] (A)	Lifetime $t_{1/2}$	Modes of decay[b]	Decay energies (MeV)	Particle energies (MeV)	Particle intensities	Gamma energies (MeV)[b]	Gamma intensities[b]	Thermal neutron capture cross-sections (Barns) σ_c
Ru			101·07								
44	$^{93}_{44}$Ru			50 sec			β^+		Ann. Rad.		
	$^{94}_{44}$Ru			57 min	EC				Ann. Rad.		
					β^+						
	$^{95}_{44}$Ru			99 min	EC	2·2	EC		0.145	1[c]	
					β^+		β^+ 1·2		0·340	4[c]	
									0·640	0·5[c]	
									1·053	1[c]	
									Ann. Rad.		
	$^{96}_{44}$Ru	5·51	95·9076								0·2
	$^{97}_{44}$Ru			2·9 days			EC		0·1091		
									0·2180	14[c]	
									0·325	1[c]	
									0·567		
	$^{98}_{44}$Ru	1·87	97·9055								
	$^{99}_{44}$Ru	12·72	98·9061								
	$^{100}_{44}$Ru	12·62	99·9030								
	$^{101}_{44}$Ru	17·07	100·9041								
	$^{102}_{44}$Ru	31·61	101·9037								1·4
	$^{103}_{44}$Ru			40 days	β^-	0·75	β^- 0·21	90%	0·055	4[c]	
							0·13		0·2956	$\approx$4[c]	
							0·71		0·35	$\approx$3[c]	
									0·497	1000[c]	
									0·560		
									0·6100	80[c]	

	$^{104}_{44}Ru$	18·58	103·9055								0·7
	$^{105}_{44}Ru$			4·45 h	β^-	1·91	β^- 1·88 1·15 1·08		0·130D 0·265 0·315 0·400 0·475 0·670 0·725 0·870 0·960	100%	
	$^{106}_{44}Ru$			1·0 years	β^-	0·04	β^- 0·04	100%	(See ^{106}Rh)		
	$^{107}_{44}Ru$			4·2 min	β^-	3·2	β^- 2·1–3·1		0·22		
	$^{108}_{44}Ru$			4·4 min	β^-	1·3	β^- 1·1–1·3		0·17		
Ir			192·2								460
77	$^{182}_{77}Ir$			15 min	EC β^+		EC β^+		Ann. Rad.		
	$^{183}_{77}Ir$			55 min	EC				0·24		
	$^{184}_{77}Ir$			3·2 h	EC β^+				0·13 0·27 0·29–4·3 Ann. Rad.		
	$^{185}_{77}Ir$			15 h	EC				0·0374 0·0599 0·0973 0·1008 0·1044 0·2544		

Z	Isotope	% Natural abundance	Atomic mass[a] (A)	Lifetime $t_{1/2}$	Modes of decay[b]	Decay energies (MeV)	Particle energies (MeV)	Particle intensities	Gamma energies (MeV)[b]	Gamma intensities[b]	Thermal neutron capture cross-sections (Barns) σ_c
	$^{186}_{77}Ir$			+5 h	EC	3·8			0·138	100	
					β^+				0·298	100	
									0·436	80	
									0·628		
									0·769		
									0·774		
									0·9230		
									Ann. Rad.		
	$^{187}_{77}Ir$			12 h	EC				0·025–0·99		
									$>10\gamma$'s		
	$^{188}_{77}Ir$			41 h	EC	2·8	EC	99+%	0·155		
					β^+		β^+ 1·8	0·6%	0·633		
									0·32–2·2		
									$>10\gamma$'s		
									Ann. Rad.		
	$^{189}_{77}Ir$			11 days	EC				0·0695		
									0·245		
									0·033–·276		
									$>10\gamma$'s		
	$^{190m}_{77}Ir$			3·2 h	EC		EC	88%	0·186	100%	
					β^+		β^+ 2·0	12%	0·361	100%	
									≈0·56	100%	
									0·62	100%	
									Ann. Rad.		

$^{190}_{77}Ir$			11 days	EC	2·1			0·1865	72%	
								0·359		
								0·371		
								0·404		
								≈0·52	27%	
								0·5575	28%	
								0·568		
								0·607	32%	
								0·80		
								1·33		
$^{191m}_{77}Ir$			4·9 sec	IT	0·042	IT		0·0416	100%	
								0·129	100%	
$^{191}_{77}Ir$	37·3	190·9609								(250 + 750)
$^{192m}_{77}Ir$			1·4 min	IT	0·048		99·9%	0·058	99·9%	
				β^-			0·1%	0·316	0·1%	
$^{192}_{77}Ir$			74 days	β^-	1·45	β^- 0·67	41%	0·3165		
				EC	1·15	0·53	38%	0·468		
						0·24	15%	0·6045		
						EC	5%	> 10γ's		
$^{193m}_{77}Ir$			12 days	IT	0·08			0·08019	100%	
$^{193}_{77}Ir$	62·7	192·9633								1·20
$^{194}_{77}Ir$			19 h	β^-	2·24	β^- 2·24	68%	0·294	5·5%	
						1·90	15%	0·328	29%	
						0·98	9%	0·645	6%	
						0·19–0·74		0·939	3%	
								0·6–2·04		
								> 10γ's		

Z	Isotope	% Natural abundance	Atomic mass[a] (A)	Lifetime $t_{1/2}$	Modes of decay[b]	Decay energies (MeV)	Particle energies (MeV)	Particle intensities	Gamma energies (MeV)	Gamma intensities	Thermal neutron capture cross-sections (Barns) σ_c
	$^{196}_{77}Ir$			2·3 h	β^-	1·1	β^- 1·1 0·6		0·070 0·42 0·66 0·88		
	$^{197}_{77}Ir$			7 min	β^-	2·0	β^- 2·0 1·5				
	$^{198}_{77}Ir$			50 sec	β^-	4·4	β^- 3·6		0·78		
Rh			102·905								150
45	$^{96}_{45}Rh$			~11 min							
	$^{97}_{45}Rh$			35 min	β^+				Ann. Rad.		
	$^{98}_{45}Rh$			8·7 min	β^+ EC	4·2	β^+ 2·5		0·650 Ann. Rad.		
	$^{99m}_{45}Rh$			4·7 h	EC β^+	2·11	EC β^+ 0·75		0·286 0·35 0·61 0·89 1·26 1·41 Ann. Rad.	 70% 20%	
	$^{99}_{45}Rh$			16 days	EC β^+	2·1	EC β^+ 1.03		0·350 0·089 Ann. Rad.		

$^{100}_{45}Rh$			21 h	EC	3·63	EC		0·54		
				β^+		β^+ 2·61		0·44		
								0·30–2·4		
								$>10\gamma$'s		
								Ann. Rad.		
$^{101m}_{45}Rh$			4·7 days	IT	0·158	EC	96%	0·158	4%	
						IT	4%	0·31	96%	
$^{101}_{45}Rh$			5 years		EC			0·195	100%	
								0·127	100%	
$^{102}_{45}Rh$			206 days	EC		EC	65%	0·48		
				β^-	1·15	β^- 1·15	20%	0·51		
				β^+	2·3	β^+ 1·30	10%	1·42–2·06		
						0·82		$>10\gamma$'s		
								Ann. Rad.		
$^{103m}_{45}Rh$			57 min	IT	0·040	IT		0·0400	100%	
									(CE 98%)	
$^{103}_{45}Rh$	100	102.9048								(12 + 138)
$^{104m}_{45}Rh$			4·4 min	IT	0·128	IT	99%	0·0514	100%, CE	800
				β^-		β^-	0·1%	0·0772	100%, CE	
								0·56–1·53		
$^{104}_{45}Rh$			42 sec	β^-	2·44	β^- 2·44	89%	0·555	2%	
						1·88	2%	1·24	0·1%	40
$^{105m}_{45}Rh$			40 sec	IT	0·130	IT		0·130	100%	
									(CE 75%)	
$^{105}_{45}Rh$			36 h	β^-	0·56	β^- 0·56	80%	0·0800		15,000
						0·24	30%	0·160		
								0·220	20%	
$^{105}_{45}Rh$								0·308		
								0·316	20%	
								0·415		
								0·550		

Z	Isotope	% Natural abundance	Atomic mass[a] (A)	Lifetime $t_{1/2}$	Modes of decay[b]	Decay energies (MeV)	Particle energies (MeV)	Particle intensities	Gamma energies (MeV)	Gamma intensities	Thermal neutron capture cross-sections (Barns) σ_c
	$^{106m}_{45}Rh$			2·2 h	β^-		β^- 0·79–		0·51		
							1.62		0·22–1·22		
									> 10γ's		
	$^{106}_{45}Rh$			30 sec	β^-	3·53	β^- 3·53	72%	0·51	20%	
									0·62	11%	
									0·7–3·4		
									> 10γ's		
	$^{107}_{45}Rh$			21·7 min	β^-	1·5	β^- 1·2		0·095		
							1·5		0·145		
									0·305	100[c]	
									0·388	18[c]	
									0·475	1·6[c]	
									0·575	3[c]	
									0·680		
	$^{108}_{45}Rh$			17 sec	β^-		β^- 4		0·43		
									0·62		
									0·51		
									1·52		
	$^{109m}_{45}Rh$			50 sec	IT	0.11			0·11	100%	
	$^{109}_{45}Rh$			30 sec	β^-		β^-		0·49–0·31		
	$^{110}_{45}Rh$			3.6 sec	β^-						

[a] Based on ^{12}C = 12·00000.
CE = intensity of conversion electrons in per cent decays
D = delayed gamma rays
Ann. Rad. = radiation (0·511 MeV) resulting from annihilation of positrons
[b] EC = orbital electron capture
IT = isomeric transition from upper to lower isomeric state.
[c] Relative intensities.

AUTHOR INDEX

This author index is designed to enable the reader to locate the author's name and work with the aid of the reference numbers appearing in the text. The page numbers are printed in normal type in ascending numerical order, followed by the reference numbers in brackets. The numbers in italics refer to the pages on which the references are actually listed.

SUBJECT INDEX

Principal page references are given in italics.

FORMULA INDEX

Only formulae from the main text are given here; those from the tables of complexes in the last four chapters are not listed separately here.

IRIDIUM

OSMIUM

RHODIUM

RUTHENIUM